Drug Discovery Targeting Metalloenzymes

Drug Discovery Targeting Metalloenzymes

Strategies and Applications

Edited by Guo-Bo Li

Volume 1

WILEY-VCH

Editor

Prof. Guo-Bo Li
Sichuan University
Chengdu, 610041
P.R. China

Cover Design: Wiley
Cover Image: Courtesy of Guo-Bo Li

Typesetting: Straive, Chennai, India
Printing and Binding: CPI Group (UK) Ltd, Croydon, CR0 4YY

Library of Congress Card No.: applied for

British Library Cataloguing-in-Publication Data A catalogue record for this book is available from the British Library.

Bibliographic information published by the Deutsche Nationalbibliothek
The Deutsche Nationalbibliothek lists this publication in the Deutsche Nationalbibliografie; detailed bibliographic data are available on the Internet at http://dnb.d-nb.de.

Print ISBN: 978-3-527-35639-3
ePDF ISBN: 978-3-527-84867-6
ePub ISBN: 978-3-527-84866-9
oBook ISBN: 978-3-52784-868-3

C9783527356393_170226

Contents

Preface

Metalloenzymes constitute an ubiquitous ensemble of enzymes that rely on metal ions for their bioactivity, structural integrity, signaling functions, and others. Remarkably, over one-third of all known enzymes are assigned as metalloenzymes. These enzymes have long been recognized for their significance across a wide range of research fields and societal applications. In synthetic biology, for example, functionally diverse artificial metalloenzymes have been developed, underscoring the potential to engineer novel biocatalytic transformations that are not found in nature. Given their critical roles in various biological processes and diseases, metalloenzymes have emerged as key targets for therapeutic intervention. Although several drugs and drug candidates targeting metalloenzymes have been identified, most disease associations and therapeutic potentials for metalloenzymes remain largely untapped, indicating a vast and largely unexplored frontier for drug discovery and development in this field.

Metalloenzymes are unique due to the presence of metal ion(s) with strong electron deficiencies, which makes drug design targeting metalloenzymes particularly challenging compared to other types of targets. This results in potentially more diverse mechanisms of drug action, while also presenting significant challenges in terms of drug selectivity. In recent years, a variety of approaches have emerged to enhance the efficiency of drug discovery targeting metalloenzymes, including chemo-/bio-informatics, bioinformatics, artificial intelligence technologies, proteomics, structural biology, and spectroscopy. Additionally, an increasing number of potential metalloenzyme drug targets have been identified, along with many successful drug discovery examples. To further advance the field of metalloenzyme drug discovery and attract more researchers to this area, I have leveraged my own research experience and knowledge to collaborate with experts in the field to compile this book, which aims to provide insights and drive progress in this exciting area of study.

This book is organized into three sectors: (i) computational and experimental strategies for metalloenzyme drug discovery (Chapters 1–5), (ii) approaches and cases for drug discovery targeting metalloenzyme families (Chapters 6–11), and (iii) approaches and cases for drug discovery targeting individual metalloenzymes (Chapters 12–18). The first sector begins with metalloenzyme informatics and state-of-the-art drug design techniques, which are important for advancing drug discovery targeting metalloenzymes. Given the critical role of metal ions in these enzymes, this section also includes metal-binding pharmacophores that interact with metal ions, particularly within metalloenzyme active sites, emphasizing the need for careful optimization to enhance both binding affinity and specificity. Quantum mechanical/molecular mechanical calculations have provided valuable insights into the complex catalytic mechanisms (reaction pathways) of metalloenzymes and play a critical role in the discovery of metalloenzyme inhibitors. Complementing this theoretical framework, the book also covers experimental strategies essential for studying metalloenzyme mechanisms, offering a well-rounded perspective that integrates both computational and laboratory approaches. Additionally, metallo-drugs, which primarily target metalloenzymes by interacting with or disrupting their metal ion centers through multifaceted interference, represent an emerging class of promising therapeutics. While challenges persist in developing selective metallo-drugs, recent successes highlight the potential of this approach in treating complex diseases, including cancer.

The second sector focuses on several key human metalloenzyme families that have emerged as important drug targets in recent years, including phosphodiesterases, histone deacetylases, and carbonic anhydrases. These families consist of multiple subtypes, each involved in distinct biological pathways and exhibiting varying tissue distributions, and are implicated in a wide range of diseases. As a result, drug discovery targeting these families spans a broad spectrum of therapeutic indications. While these families share common features that can guide cross-disciplinary approaches, there is also an urgent need for the development of subtype-specific drugs. Additionally, the sector explores bacterial metallo-β-lactamases and virus-associated metalloenzymes. Metallo-β-lactamases represent a large and expanding family of enzymes closely linked to antibiotic resistance, with drug development requiring careful consideration of bacterial membrane permeability. In contrast, several virus-related metal enzymes play crucial roles in virus replication, assembly, and host cell invasion, making them significant drug targets.

The third sector covers additional important metalloenzyme targets, which are involved in essential biological processes and often act as key regulators in disease progression, along with their drug discovery approaches and case studies. For example, autotaxin and ENPP1 play critical roles in regulating extracellular lipid signaling, and inhibiting these enzymes has shown promise for treating diseases such as cancer and fibrosis. In oxygen sensing, hypoxia-inducible factor prolyl hydroxylases are essential for the body's adaptive response to low oxygen levels, making them an attractive target for conditions like anemia and ischemia. Histone demethylases, such as KDM5B, regulate gene expression through epigenetic modifications, and inhibiting them could provide novel therapeutic strategies for cancer and other diseases driven by aberrant gene expression. LpxC, involved in bacterial outer membrane synthesis, holds promise for developing new antibiotics to combat antibiotic resistance in Gram-negative infections. Similarly, human glutaminyl cyclases, implicated in neurodegenerative diseases, and tryptophan/indoleamine 2,3-dioxygenase, which plays a key role in immune regulation, present exciting new opportunities for treating neurological disorders and immune-related diseases. These examples underscore the vast potential of targeting metalloenzymes in drug discovery, offering innovative therapeutic strategies across a wide range of diseases.

In addition to offering a comprehensive overview of current progress in strategies and cases, this book casts a forward-looking vision on the future of metalloenzyme drug discovery. The interplay between computational techniques and experimental strategies is set to fuel breakthroughs in drug discovery. There is also a need for new computational and experimental tools, including artificial intelligence models, with the ability to perform metalloenzyme profiling, to infer the relationships between metalloenzymes and diseases, and other issues in this field. The potential of targeting metalloenzymes for innovative drug discovery is vast, and this book offers a window into this rapidly evolving field.

Although my team and I have made some progress in the field of metalloenzyme drug discovery, the scope and depth of our work remain limited, and our understanding of key issues in this field still requires ongoing strengthening. I would like to express my sincere gratitude to the experts and teams whose invaluable contributions have shaped this book. Through their generous sharing of insights and experiences, this book has come to embody such rich and comprehensive content. A special thanks goes to my PhD supervisor, Professor Shengyong Yang, and my postdoctoral mentor, Professor Christopher J. Schofield; their guidance, inspiration, and mentorship have been instrumental in introducing me to the field of metalloenzyme drug discovery. I would also like to extend my thanks to Dr. Lifen Yang, Priyadarshini Natarajan, Sundhar Karuthudiyan, and the entire editorial team for their dedication and hard work in bringing this book to fruition. Finally, I am deeply grateful to my own team for their contributions to this work.

I hope that this book will serve as a valuable reference for researchers in the field. If there are any shortcomings or errors, we kindly ask you to point them out, and we will do our best to address them in future updates or incorporate them into our ongoing work. Additionally, I hope that this book will inspire a new generation of scientists to explore the untapped therapeutic potential of metalloenzymes. The path ahead is full of promise, and as our understanding of metalloenzyme mechanisms and their association with diseases deepens, so too will the opportunities to develop innovative and effective treatments for a wide range of diseases.

January, 2025 *Guo-Bo Li*

1

Metalloenzyme Informatics and Drug Design

Jun-Lin Yu, Xiao-Tian Huang, Dao-Xing Chen, Cong Zhou, Yao-Gen Wang, and Guo-Bo Li

Sichuan University, Department of Medicinal Chemistry, West China School of Pharmacy, No. 17, Section 3, Renmin South Road, Chengdu 610041, China

Sharp tools make good work.
—An ancient Chinese idiom, originally from The Analects of Confucius, Chapter Ling-Gong Wei.

1.1 Introduction

Metalloenzymes are attractive research targets in fields of chemistry, biology, and medicine [1]. Metalloenzymes constitute a ubiquitous ensemble of enzymes that contain one or more functionally essential metal ions at their active sites; over a third of all known enzymes fall into the category of metalloenzymes [2]. Metalloenzymes are widely present in the human body and play a crucial role in almost all life processes, including signal transduction, epigenetic regulation, immune modulation, and the synthesis and degradation of protein molecules [3, 4]. Their overexpression or abnormal activity is closely related to the occurrence and development of human diseases, making them an important class of drug targets for therapeutic intervention [5]. Although some small molecule inhibitors targeting metalloenzymes have been clinically used to treat diseases such as skin inflammation, asthma, cardiovascular conditions, and tumors [6–8], many metalloenzyme targets related to diseases have not been fully exploited, indicating that there is immense research potential in drug discovery targeting metalloenzymes.

Recent advancements in computational biology, bioinformatics, and artificial intelligence (AI) have profoundly transformed the landscape of drug discovery, enabling more efficient and targeted approaches, even with regard to the unique characteristics of metalloenzymes. As experimental data related to metalloenzymes

* J.-L.Y. and X.-T.H. are co-first authors

Drug Discovery Targeting Metalloenzymes: Strategies and Applications, First Edition. Edited by Guo-Bo Li.

and their ligands continue to accumulate, researchers have developed several specialized databases, such as MeDBA [1], MeLAD [9], and MetalPDB [10], which provide extensive information on the chemical, structural, and functional properties of metalloenzymes and their interactions with ligands. In parallel, a variety of bioinformatics tools have been developed to facilitate the mining, analysis, and expansion of metalloenzyme-related data. Tools like MeCOM [11], MeSiteIG [12], and MetalNet [13] are specifically designed to enhance researchers' ability to explore and leverage this growing body of information. Further advancing the field, computational tools tailored for metalloenzyme drug design have emerged, such as AncPhore [14], IFPanalysis [15], DiffPhore [16], and MetalProGNet [17]. These approaches are specifically aimed at supporting drug discovery targeting metalloenzymes by modeling metalloenzyme–ligand interactions and conducting virtual screening. These resources form a foundational toolkit that accelerates metalloenzyme-related research, particularly holding significant promise for advancing innovative drug discovery targeting metalloenzymes.

1.2 Metalloenzyme Informatics

1.2.1 Metal Site Database

Metalloenzymes are specific drug targets due to their metal ion-containing structural features and diverse biological activities. Metal ion coordination is fundamental to the functionality of metalloenzymes, as these metal ions directly or indirectly participate in catalytic processes. Understanding the intricate details of metal-binding sites is crucial for advancing research on the structural and functional characteristics of metalloenzymes.

MetalPDB, developed by Antonio's research group [10], is the pioneering database that provides information on metal-binding sites. This database introduces the concept of minimal functional sites (MFSs) to represent metal-binding sites in proteins and nucleic acids as the ensemble of atoms surrounding the metal ion or cofactor, including its endogenous and exogenous ligands (Figure 1.1). MFSs describe the local environment around the metal ions and their coordination geometry, without being affected by the larger context of the macromolecular structure. These sites are further categorized into equistructural and equivalent sites, allowing users to investigate similarities and variations in metal–macromolecule interactions and correlate these with functional information. Equivalent sites are metal-binding sites that share the same classification, have at least 50% sequence identity, are structurally superimposable within 3.5 Å, and contain the same metal elements in the same positions. Equistructural sites meet the first two criteria but do not require identical metal positioning; thus, all equivalent sites are equistructural, but not vice versa.

MetalPDB is updated monthly in an automated manner, ensuring that users can access the latest data. The 2018 update of MetalPDB introduced new features, including the ability to include proteins lacking metal ions in their structures but

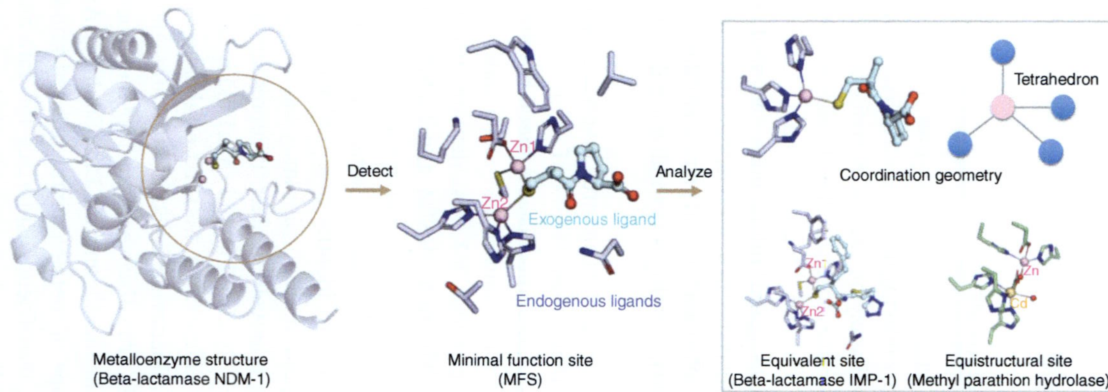

Figure 1.1 The overview of MetalPDB.

containing known MFSs in their sequences [18]. Users can query the database using a list of Protein Data Bank (PDB) identifiers and obtain functional annotations for MFSs, along with statistical analyses of the database content.

As a comprehensive and continually updated resource, MetalPDB plays a vital role in advancing research into metalloenzyme structures and functions. By facilitating the exploration of metal-binding sites and their biological roles, it has become an essential tool for understanding the structure–function relationships of metal–macromolecule interactions.

1.2.2 Metalloenzyme Databases

The expanding structural data on metalloenzymes, particularly metalloenzyme-ligand complex structures, are proving invaluable for drug discovery efforts targeting metalloenzymes. The Metalloenzyme-Ligand Association Database (MeLAD) [9] is the first dedicated resource focused specifically on metalloenzyme–ligand interactions. It provides curated structural data and detailed information on resolved metalloenzyme–ligand interactions, as well as their underlying interconnections. These relationships are represented through metal-binding pharmacophores (MBPs), metalloenzyme structural similarity (MeSIM), and ligand chemical similarity (LigSIM), creating a centralized tailored resource to advance metalloenzyme research.

MeLAD comprises 6086 complex structures involving 1416 unique metalloenzymes and 3564 ligands. Among these, 63.0% of these structures involve classical metal-binding interactions, 2.3% non-classical metal-binding interactions, 34.4% non-metal-binding interactions, and 0.3% metal-water-bridging interactions. Additionally, the database provides 263 monodentate, 191 bidentate, and 15 tridentate MBP chemotypes. Through MeSIM and LigSIM analyses, MeLAD has identified 3726 and 52,740 potential metalloenzyme–ligand associations, respectively, broadening the range of these associations. Furthermore, a metalloenzyme profiling module allows users to identify potential metalloenzyme–ligand associations for any given ligand through similarity-based searches. Although the data volume in MeLAD is relatively modest, it represents a pioneering effort in metalloenzyme informatics. By curating and interlinking detailed structural data on metalloenzyme–ligand interactions, MeLAD establishes a foundation for systematic exploration of metalloenzyme function, structure, and ligand associations, facilitating advancements in drug discovery targeting metalloenzyme.

Building upon MeLAD, the Metalloenzyme Data Bank and Analysis (MeDBA) [1] platform broadens the scope of metalloenzyme-focused knowledge and services, offering a comprehensive, user-friendly interface for data analysis. The MeDBA construction involves the following key steps: identifying metalloenzymes through structural examination and keyword queries; conducting human curation to filter out unexpected structures; categorizing them into three self-defined types – M-I, M-II, and M-III; and retrieving detailed information that encompasses systematic data, involved ligands, and metalloenzyme–ligand associations (Figure 1.2).

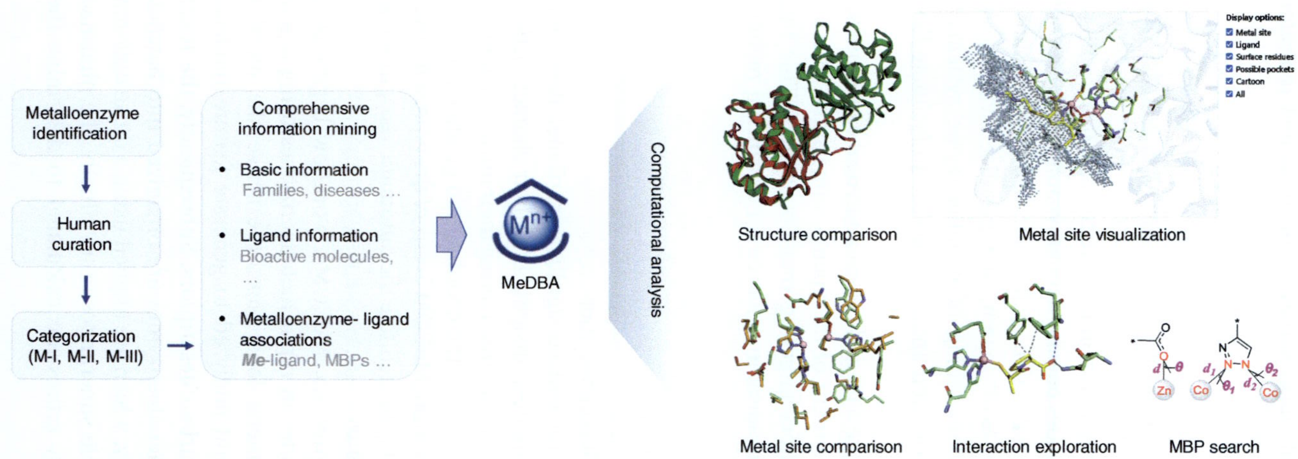

Figure 1.2 The development workflow of MeDBA.

Currently, MeDBA includes extensive data on 82,540 metalloenzymes (comprising 74,267 M-I enzymes, 7338 M-II enzymes, and 935 M-III enzymes), along with 440,631 ligands, 10,613 metalloenzyme-ligand complexes, 21,616 metal sites, and 1501 MBPs. The platform serves as an integrated repository of information on metalloenzymes, detailing protein families, associated diseases, metal active sites, and ligands – including bioactive molecules, substrates/products, drugs, drug candidates, and PROTACs – alongside their metalloenzyme–ligand associations. Additionally, it provides access to experimentally determined structures of metalloenzyme-ligand, metalloenzyme-protein, and metalloenzyme-DNA/RNA complexes, helping researchers connect structural insights with functional implications. Notably, MeDBA goes beyond data provision by offering advanced tools such as metal active site visualization, active site comparison, substructure searches, interaction exploration, MBP search, and metalloenzyme profiling (Figure 1.2), enabling a deeper understanding of metalloenzyme systems. Users can freely search, browse, download, and analyze this data to facilitate flexible and in-depth exploration.

By combining extensive data and robust analytical capabilities, MeDBA supports the discovery and refinement of therapeutic targets and offers valuable clues for designing novel inhibitors targeting metalloenzymes. This integrated approach makes MeDBA an indispensable resource for advancing metalloenzyme research and drug discovery.

1.2.3 Metal Site Analysis

1.2.3.1 3D Metal Site Superimposition

Given the increasingly recognized significance of metalloenzymes in various biological processes, gaining deep insights into their characteristics – especially their metal active sites – is crucial for uncovering their intricate catalytic mechanisms and structural complexities. Taking the coordination geometry and local context of the metal sites into consideration, MeCOM is one of the representative 3D superposition algorithms developed [11] to facilitate the automatic recognition and comparison of metalloenzyme active sites.

As illustrated in Figure 1.3, MeCOM's workflow begins by identifying metal ion-containing active sites in input metalloenzymes using a geometric algorithm focused on qualified metal ions. Next, the active site metal ions and surface residues are defined and analyzed to generate feature models characterized by pharmacophore or α-carbon descriptors. Subsequently, the feature models of the reference and query metalloenzymes are organized into batches of metal-centric quadruples, respectively, which are aligned using a quadruple-matching algorithm to search for all possible superimpositions. Finally, the pharmacophore/α-carbon feature-based similarity scores are calculated to determine the best superposition mode.

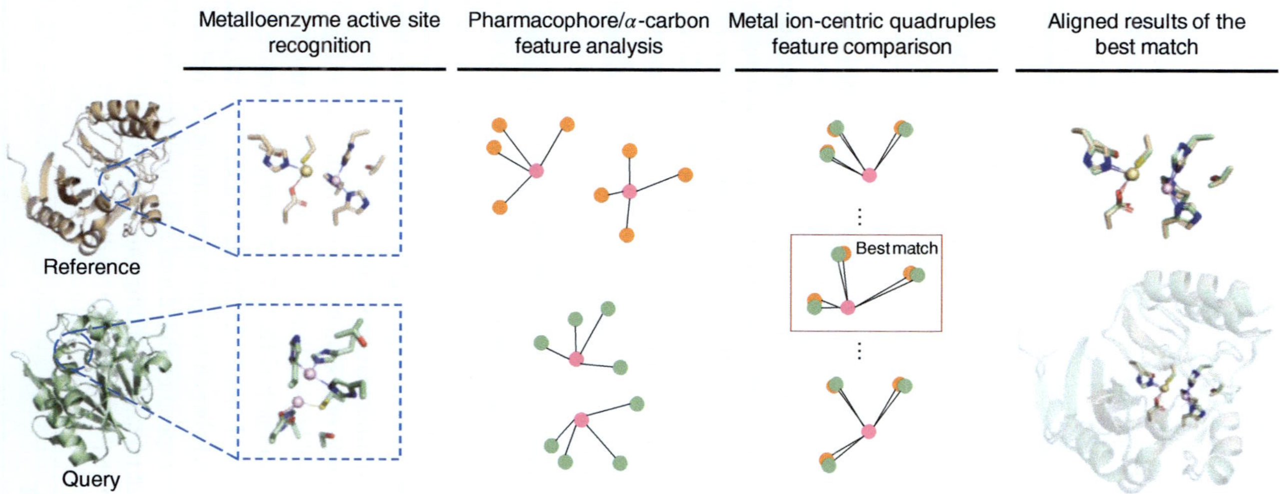

Figure 1.3 The workflow of MeCOM.

Instrumental Box 1.1

3D superposition algorithm is a structural alignment algorithm that identifies the optimal spatial alignment between two 3D structures, such as proteins or molecules. It achieves this by rotating and translating one structure onto the other to minimize the distance between corresponding atoms. This allows for the identification of structurally similar arrangements even when amino acid sequences differ. The resulting superposition is evaluated using a root-mean-square deviation (RMSD) score, providing a quantitative measure of similarity. 3D superposition has proven valuable in various applications, including comparing protein structures, elucidating evolutionary relationships, and understanding protein function and interactions. Additionally, 3D superposition can identify similar binding sites that would be useful for molecular selectivity study, especially for cross-family metalloenzymes.

Evaluated on an extensive dataset of over 4000 metalloenzyme-ligand complexes, MeCOM exhibits high predictive accuracy in identifying and comparing active sites, establishing it as a reliable tool for researchers. Its robust capabilities allow for the discernment of intricate structural differences among metalloenzymes, revealing potential functional similarities that may inform the design of specific inhibitors. MeCOM is written in C/C++ and can be run in Linux, Windows, and Mac. An additional PyMOL plug-in is provided for graphic display. This program is available for free academic use. Users can download MeCOM and its manual by visiting https://mecom.ddtmlab.org/.

1.2.3.2 Structural Alignment-Based Metal-Binding Site Identification

The identification of metal-binding sites is a crucial step in metal site engineering, as it facilitates the discovery of novel metalloenzymes and deepens our understanding of their catalytic mechanisms. The methods used for identifying metal-binding sites can be broadly categorized into sequence-based and structure-based approaches, which differ in the type of information utilized.

A representative example of a structure-based method is the metal ion-binding (MIB) predictor, developed by the Chih-Hao Lu research group [19]. MIB leverages a fragment transformation method [20] to compare the structure features of query proteins with a collection of metal-binding templates. By evaluating the sequence and structural similarities between the query proteins and templates, MIB identifies potential binding sites for specified metal ions and query proteins. MIB supports the prediction of 12 types of metal ion binding sites, including Ca^{2+}, Cu^{2+}, Fe^{3+}, Mg^{2+}, Mn^{2+}, Zn^{2+}, Cd^{2+}, Fe^{2+}, Ni^{2+}, Hg^{2+}, Co^{2+}, and Cu^{+}.

Instrumental Box 1.2

The fragment transformation method is a structural alignment algorithm that combines both structural and sequence information to identify local structural motifs in proteins. This method is used to detect specific structural patterns, such as the metal binding motif and the treble clef motif, which are important for protein function. By comparing the structural and sequence information of a query motif with target proteins, the algorithm clusters triplets of atoms based on orientation similarity and calculates alignment scores to assess the quality of the alignment. This method has been successfully applied to identify structural motifs like the metal binding motif and the treble clef motif in proteins.

A subsequent upgrade, MIB2 [21], introduces significant improvements to the similarity score function by incorporating the binding preferences of specific residue and atom types, which has been demonstrated to evidently increase the accuracy of its predictions. Additionally, MIB2 expands its coverage to include 18 metal ions, namely Ca^{2+}, Cu^{2+}, Fe^{3+}, Mg^{2+}, Mn^{2+}, Zn^{2+}, Cd^{2+}, Fe^{2+}, Ni^{2+}, Hg^{2+}, Co^{2+}, Cu^{+}, Au^{+}, Ba^{2+}, Pb^{2+}, Pt^{2+}, Sm^{3+}, and Sr^{2+}. In terms of input capabilities, MIB2 now supports the use of protein sequences as input, enabling users to predict protein structures through methods such as AlphaFold or homology modeling $(PS)^2$. This expanded feature set ensures that MIB2 can effectively handle cases where experimentally resolved protein structures are unavailable, thereby broadening its applicability in research and analysis.

Generally, MIB and MIB2 leverage the sequence and structural conservation of metal-binding sites by aligning prepared templates to the query structures to identify these sites. However, this reliance on existing templates can hinder the detection of metalloenzymes with novel or unique local structures that do not closely resemble those in the database. Consequently, MIB may overlook potential binding sites in proteins that exhibit significant structural variations or lack sufficient homologous templates. This limitation underscores the need for continued development of metal-binding site prediction methods that can effectively identify and characterize novel metalloenzymes, particularly those with distinct structural features.

1.2.3.3 Machine Learning-Based Metal Site Identification

In addition to traditional algorithms, machine learning (ML) methods are increasingly utilized for metal site identification. Among these, MetalNet stands out as a cutting-edge computational approach specifically designed for analyzing and predicting metal-binding sites using the sequence information [13].

As shown in Figure 1.4, the MetalNet approach begins by generating co-evolution contact maps through multiple sequence alignments (MSA), from which metal-binding co-evolved residue pairs are extracted, focusing exclusively on Cys/His/Glu/Asp residues. An ML model is then trained to classify these pairs, assessing their potential as metal-binding sites. Subsequently, a graph filtering technique is applied to identify high-order co-evolution networks, further improving the prediction accuracy.

MetalNet has been successfully applied to predict metalloproteins in the proteomes of four representative prokaryotic species, resulting in the identification of 4849 potential metalloproteins. Several previously unannotated metal-binding

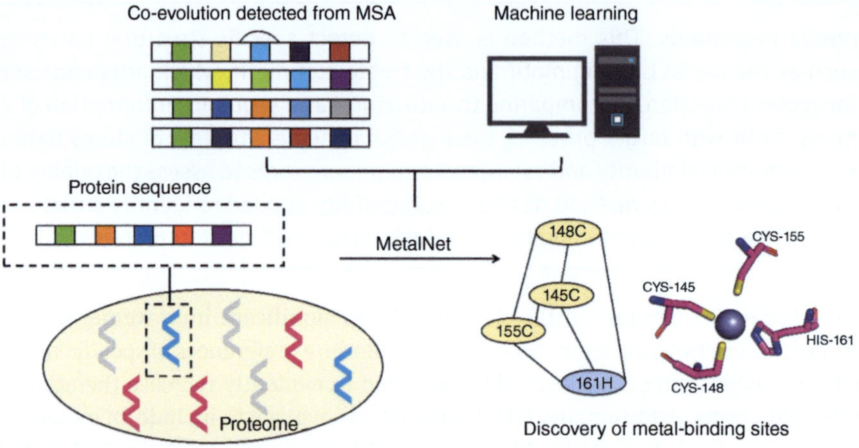

Figure 1.4 The workflow of MetalNet.

sites were biochemically and structurally validated, including the apo-citrate lyase phosphoribosyl-dephospho-CoA transferase [13] from *Escherichia coli*. Additionally, MetalNet accurately recapitulated all known zinc-binding sites from the human spliceosome complex. By effectively complementing structural determination efforts, MetalNet aids both experimental and computational approaches in studying metalloproteins.

Despite its reliance on MSA and the exclusion of residues other than CHED, MetalNet represents a significant advancement in predicting metal-binding sites. By leveraging co-evolutionary data and ML, it uncovers hidden metalloproteomes and enhances our understanding of metal biology.

1.2.3.4 Geometric Deep Learning Enabled Metal Site Identification

With the advancement of AI technologies, the field of metal-binding site prediction has undergone significant evolution. Beyond traditional ML methods, geometric deep learning approaches represent metal-binding sites as 3D grids or 3D graphs, allowing models to be trained with more expressive geometric information of the metal sites. This enables the effective generalization of predictions for novel or uncharacterized proteins.

Metal3D is a deep learning framework designed to accurately predict the location of metal ions, particularly zinc ions, within protein structures [22]. Utilizing a 3D convolutional neural network (3D-CNN), Metal3D analyzes the three-dimensional structural environment of proteins to predict per-residue metal density. The model is trained on a high-resolution dataset of 2085 crystal structures containing zinc ion positions, resulting in over 250,000 voxelized protein environments. During prediction, Metal3D voxelizes the space around each residue and calculates the zinc density for each one, generating a comprehensive zinc density map for the entire protein. The model achieves remarkable accuracy, with predicted metal ion locations within 0.70 ± 0.64 Å of experimental measurements. High-probability predictions yield nearly spherical distributions of zinc ions, indicating precise locations. In addition to zinc, Metal3D can be adapted to predict other metal ions by modifying its training dataset. This flexibility allows for broader applications in metalloprotein research and the development of new metal catalysts and drug targets.

Recently, Li's research group proposed a novel geometric deep learning-driven bifunctional tool [12], MeSiteIG, with capabilities for both metal-binding site identification and grafting, established based on the geometric conservation of metal-binding sites. By combining E3-equivariant graph neural networks (EGNN) and a 3D superposition algorithm (enhanced version of MeCOM), MeSiteIG can predict potential metal-binding and potential grafting sites in proteins without prior knowledge of coordinating residue types or side chain information, also providing grafting solutions.

MeSiteIG uses a four-step workflow to identify potential metal-binding or grafting sites and propose grafting solutions, as illustrated in Figure 1.5. Initially, the system retrieves all residue triplets within the input protein structure located on the protein surface or within internal pockets. These candidate triplets are subsequently evaluated using a trained EGNN, which efficiently assesses their likelihood of forming metal-binding sites and filters out ineligible candidates. To further enhance prediction accuracy, the retained triplets are compared against known metal-binding sites using 3D superposition, ensuring geometric consistency and structural reliability. Upon completing the analysis, MeSiteIG outputs the potential metal-binding sites identified within the input protein; or optionally find the potential grafting sites and proposed grafting solutions.

MeSiteIG serves as a versatile tool that seamlessly integrates geometric deep learning with 3D superposition analysis, excelling in the identification and rational design of metal-binding sites and grafting strategies. The tool not only facilitates the accurate prediction of potential metal-binding sites but also provides scientifically robust grafting solutions grounded in geometric conservation principles. With its innovative architecture and reduced dependency on prior knowledge, MeSiteIG significantly advances the efficiency and reliability of structural analysis. Moreover, its implementation has the potential to accelerate the development of artificial metalloenzymes, deepen our understanding of protein–metal interactions, and inspire novel applications across synthetic biology and structural biology.

1.2.3.5 Metalloprotein Structure Prediction

The study of protein folding is crucial for understanding the structural and functional roles of proteins, particularly those that interact with metal ions. The incorporation of metal ions into protein structures can significantly influence their folding pathways, stability, and overall functionality. Recent advancements in computational methods have enabled researchers to explore the complex interplay between protein folding and metal ion coordination, leading to innovative applications in metal site structure prediction.

AlphaFold3 (AF3) is recognized as the state-of-the-art protein folding algorithm capable of modeling various biomolecular complex systems, including protein–protein, protein-ligand, protein–nucleic acid, and especially protein–metal

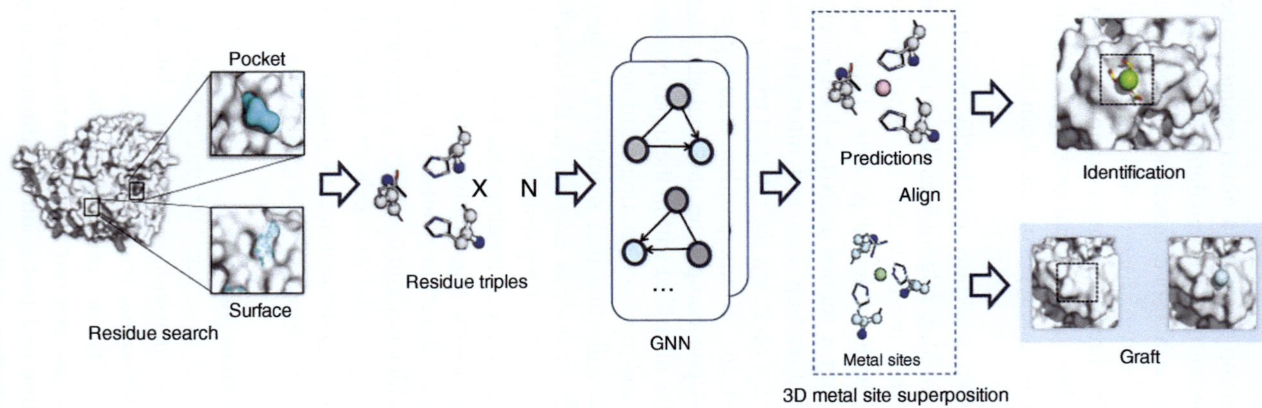

Figure 1.5 The workflow of MeSiteIG prediction method.

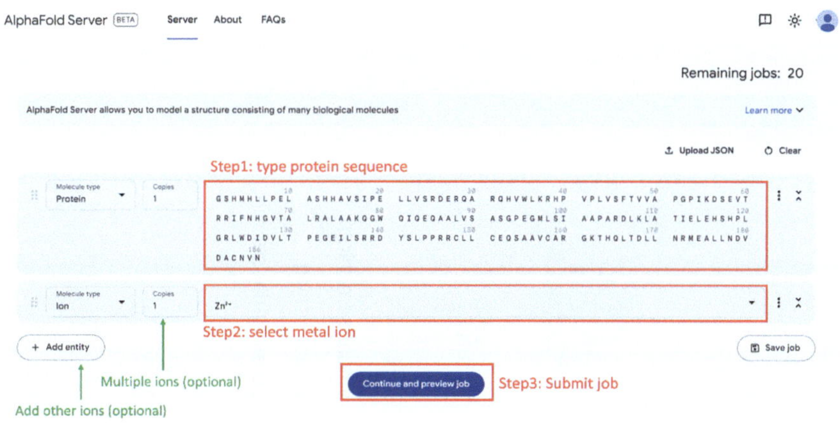

Figure 1.6 The usage of AlphaFold Server.

ion [23]. Compared to its predecessor, AlphaFold 2 (AF2), AF3 introduces a diffusion-based architecture that replaces the evoformer module with a pairformer module, enhancing data efficiency and predictive accuracy across a broader range of biomolecular interactions [24]. Notably, the adoption of a diffusion model allows AF3 to handle complex molecular interactions with greater precision by bypassing the complexities associated with torsion angles and backbone frames used in AF2. Instead, it directly predicts atomic coordinates, making it well-suited for modeling complex chemical entities like metal ions. AF3 can predict potential metal-binding sites in proteins by identifying amino acid residues that form coordination bonds with metal ions. This capability is particularly useful for studying the role of metal ions in protein function and structure.

Currently, the DeepMind team provides the source code for AF3 along with a web server for user access (https://alphafoldserver.com/). As shown in Figure 1.6, users can input protein sequences and select target metal ions to submit tasks for predictions. Unfortunately, the current website only supports the selection of metal ions such as Mg^{2+}, Zn^{2+}, Ca^{2+}, Na^{+}, Mn^{2+}, K+, Fe^{3+}, Cu^{2+}, and Co^{2+}. It is worth noting that this method can simultaneously predict the binding of multiple metal ions.

1.3 Computational Tools for Metalloenzyme Drug Design

1.3.1 Anchor Pharmacophore

Anchor pharmacophore refers to the most critical pharmacophore features in a drug molecule that are essential for its biological recognition and interaction with its target protein. These features play a pivotal role in ensuring a strong binding affinity between the ligand (drug molecule) and the target site. Anchor pharmacophore analysis allows researchers to focus on these key features, enabling efficient molecular fitting and virtual screening processes. In drug discovery, identifying anchor

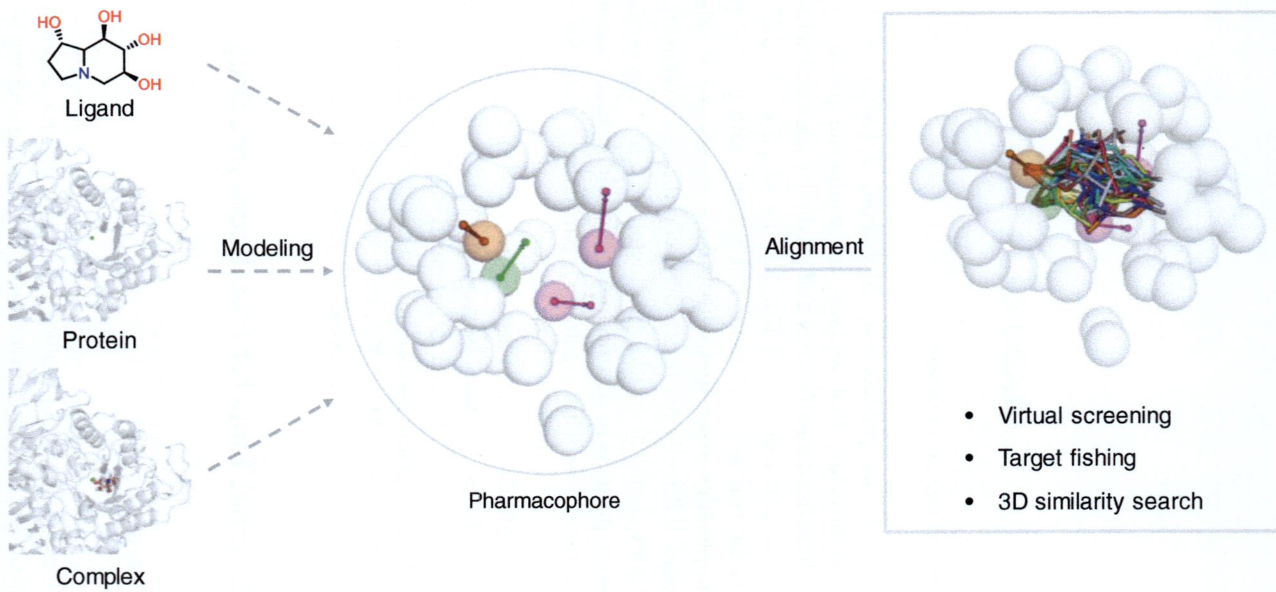

Figure 1.7 The functionality of AncPhore.

pharmacophores helps in recognizing the biologically conserved regions of target proteins, thereby leading to the development of more potent and selective inhibitors.

Adopting the concept of anchor pharmacophore, AncPhore serves as a versatile tool for pharmacophore-based drug discovery [14]. The main features of AncPhore include pharmacophore feature analysis, and anchor pharmacophore steered molecular fitting and its applications for virtual screening, target fishing, and 3D ligand similarity search (Figure 1.7). It has a large degree of flexibility to achieve different functions, such as: (i) pharmacophore feature recognition and model generation for a ligand structure, an apo-protein structure, or a protein-ligand complex structure; (ii) ligand conformation generation by torsion-driving systematic search (TDSS) [25] and genetic algorithms (GA) [26]; (iii) ligand superimposition and similarity calculation according to their pharmacophore features; (iv) ligand fitting with a pharmacophore model; and (v) high-throughput virtual screening in a single-model or multi-model manner. Especially, AncPhore incorporates features for modeling metal ion interactions, including metal coordination (MB), positively charged centers (PO), and cation-π interactions (CR).

Notably, AncPhore uses a "Largest-Overlapping-Volume-Winning" algorithm for molecular fitting, which optimizes the rotation and alignment of the ligand with the pharmacophore model. To match an input molecule with a reference pharmacophore model, AncPhore first analyzes the pharmacophore features of the ligand and generates combinations that meet the same pharmacophore types and distance criteria. The aligned poses corresponding to each matching combination are then calculated and evaluated with a pharmacophore fitness score APScore (Eq. 1.1). APScore takes the matching of pharmacophore features (V_{overlap}), the rate of matched pharmacophore pairs ($\frac{n}{N}$), clashing with the exclusion spheres ($V_{\text{overlapEX}}$) into consideration. It emphasizes the key interactions by increasing the weights assigned to anchor pharmacophore features. The matching pose with the highest APScore corresponds to the best superimposition against the pharmacophore model. Equation (1.1) The pharmacophore fitness score (APScore):

$$\text{APScore} = \frac{V_{\text{overlap}}}{V_{\text{ref}}} + k_1 \times \frac{n}{N} - k_2 \times \frac{\sum V^2_{\text{overlapEX}}}{V^2_{\text{refEX}}} \tag{1.1}$$

where V_{overlap} is the overlapping volume between the query and reference model, V_{ref} corresponds to the volume of the reference pharmacophore model, $\sum V^2_{\text{overlapEX}}$ is the sum of the squares of overlapping volumes with exclusion volumes, V^2_{refEX} corresponds to the square of exclusion volumes of the reference model, k_1/k_2 refer to the weighting factor with default values 0.2/5, n is defined as the number of matching pharmacophore pairs, and N is the number of reference pharmacophore features.

Instrumental Box 1.3

Anchor pharmacophore is a practical concept in target-centered drug discovery that focuses on identifying the most essential pharmacophore features responsible for strong interactions between a ligand and its target protein.

(Continued)

Instrumental Box 1.3 (Continued)

These anchor features are critical for achieving high-binding affinity and are often conserved in the active sites of protein families. As observed for clinically relevant metallo-β-lactamases, albeit with large sequence differences, they contain a specific conservative active-site region involving anchor pharmacophore features that specifically recognize the β-lactam antibacterials and the potent inhibitors [14]. By concentrating on these key interaction points, anchor pharmacophore approaches streamline virtual screening and molecular fitting, improving hit rates and lead discovery.

AncPhoreis particularly useful in the discovery of inhibitors for metalloenzymes like metallo-β-lactamases (MBLs). These enzymes, which play a role in antibiotic resistance, contain specific active-site regions where metal ions coordinate with ligands. The anchor pharmacophore approach identifies crucial interaction features, such as metal coordination, hydrogen bonds, and ionic interactions, which are necessary for the ligand to effectively inhibit the enzyme's activity. Through virtual screening using anchor pharmacophore models, researchers have successfully identified diverse inhibitors for metalloenzymes, some of which exhibit potent inhibition of clinically relevant MBLs like VIM-2 and NDM-1. This methodology improves the precision of drug discovery by targeting the essential features required for strong ligand–enzyme interactions.

1.3.2 Molecular Docking Combined with Interaction Fingerprint Analysis

Interaction fingerprint (IFP) is a method for the evaluation of target-specific binding features by examining critical protein–ligand interactions, such as electrostatic interactions. When combined with molecular docking simulations, IFP-based filtering becomes a powerful tool for identifying compounds that engage key interactions with catalytically or biologically significant residues of a target protein.

A notable example is IFPanalysis [15], which recognizes and calculates interaction similarities across eight types of protein–ligand interactions [27], including metal–ligand interactions, essential for analyzing metalloenzyme targets. IFPanalysis is designed to capture crucial interactions with catalytically import residues, whose importance can be further specified via customized weights. In an IFP model, interaction bit value of "1" signifies the presence of a specific type of interaction, while "0" indicates its absence. Given the reference and query IFP models, IFPscore is computed to quantify their similarity using (Eq. 1.2):

$$\text{IFPscore} = \frac{\frac{\sum C_i \times W_i}{\sum D_i \times W_i + \sum R_i \times W_i - \sum C_i \times W_i} + \frac{\sum C_i \times W_i}{\sum R_i \times W_i}}{2} \tag{1.2}$$

where D_i represents the sum of bits in the query IFP model, R_i is the sum of bits in the reference IFP model, C_i denotes the sum of the bits in common between the two models, and W_i is the corresponding weight for each interaction type.

Using IFPanalysis, Li et al. carried out a customized virtual screening protocol against Vistas-M library, combining molecular docking simulations with IFP filtration, to search for promising inhibitors of a representative class B1 metallo-β-lactamase VIM-2 [15]. A weighted reference IFP model for VIM-2 was established, including catalytical important residues Phe61, Tyr67, Aps119, Arg228, Asn233, and the two zinc ions. This virtual screening procedure includes: (i) input compound preparation; (ii) docking simulation using AutoDock Vina; (iii) scoring and filtration of docking poses with IFPanalysis; (iv) refined docking using GOLD with subsequent pose scoring *via* IFPanalysis; (v) human inspection to select hits for bioassays. This robust methodology yielded 15 active compounds out of 20 selected for experimental validation, demonstrating inhibitory activity against VIM-2. Crystallographic analyses confirmed that the screened compounds effectively mimic the substrate interactions within the enzyme's active site.

These findings underscore the utility of IFP-based filtration for improving the efficiency of virtual screening by focusing on compounds that facilitate specific key active-site features.

1.3.3 Metalloenzyme-Specific Scoring Function

Recent advances in scoring methods for metalloprotein–ligand interactions have seen the emergence of various approaches, including traditional molecular docking tools, physics-based free energy calculations, and novel AI models. Among these, AI-based models have demonstrated significant advantages, particularly in handling the complex interactions between metalloproteins and ligands.

One of the most prominent methods is MetalProGNet [17], a deep learning model that explicitly models the metal coordination interactions between metal ions, protein atoms, and ligand atoms using graph convolutional networks. As shown in Table 1.1, MetalProGNet exhibits exceptional performance in predicting binding energies, with a Pearson correlation coefficient (Rp) of 0.703 ± 0.010 and a root mean square error (RMSE) of 1.285 ± 0.020. This surpasses the performance of other models, such as RosENet (Rp = 0.600 ± 0.011, RMSE = 1.473 ± 0.019) and NNScore2.0 (Rp = 0.629 ± 0.002, RMSE = 1.391 ± 0.004), which demonstrate

Table 1.1 Scoring functions for metalloprotein-ligand binding affinity prediction.

Scoring functions	Rp	RMSE
MetalProGNet	0.703 ± 0.010	1.285 ± 0.020
RosENet	0.600 ± 0.011	1.473 ± 0.019
NNScore2.0	0.629 ± 0.002	1.391 ± 0.004
Glide SP	−0.051	—
Plants	−0.204	—
MM/GBSA (OPLS3e)	−0.207	—
MM/GBSA (OPLS_2005)	−0.280	—

Source: Adapted from Jiang, D et al., [17].

acceptable but relatively weaker performance. In contrast, traditional docking tools like Glide SP and PLANTS, as well as physics-based free energy calculation methods like MM/GBSA, perform considerably worse in this context. For instance, Glide SP yields an Rp of −0.051, PLANTS has an Rp of −0.204, and MM/GBSA (using OPLS3e and OPLS_2005 force fields) scores −0.207 and −0.280, respectively. These results indicate that traditional methods struggle to accurately predict binding affinities in metalloprotein systems, particularly in capturing the intricate metal–ligand interactions.

In conclusion, MetalProGNet's graph-based deep learning framework significantly improves the accuracy and interpretability of metalloprotein–ligand interaction predictions, outperforming both other ML methods and traditional scoring functions. Its superior performance positions it as a powerful tool for drug design targeting metalloenzymes. Conversely, traditional docking and free energy calculation methods show limitations when applied to these complex systems, underscoring the need for more advanced models like MetalProGNet in this field.

1.4 Metalloenzyme-Disease Association

Identifying diseases associated with metalloenzymes is critically important for understanding underlying biological mechanisms and developing targeted therapies. However, traditional experimental approaches for predicting the complex links between metalloenzymes and various diseases are often time-consuming, costly, and limited by the inherent complexity of biological systems. Against this backdrop, knowledge graphs (KGs) have emerged as a powerful tool in the biomedical domain. By systematically integrating and organizing diverse biomedical data, KGs can reveal intricate, previously hidden associations, offering valuable insights into disease mechanisms and guiding more informed, strategically focused hypotheses.

Recently developed by Li's team, TarKG [28] is a large-scale biomedical knowledge graph engineered to accelerate disease target discovery. It encompasses 1,143,313 entities and 33,280,467 relationships, spanning 15 entity types and 171 relationship types, with diseases, genes, and compounds at its core. Among these, TarKG has specifically enriched information on popular targets, including metalloenzymes. Although metalloenzyme entities account for only 1.09% of the gene entities in TarKG, they are involved in 13.19% of all gene-related relationships, highlighting their importance in biological research.

One illustrative case is glutamine cyclase (QC), a metalloenzyme that catalyzes the cyclization of N-terminal glutamine or glutamate residues. Both secretory QC (sQC) and Golgi-resident QC (gQC) isoforms have been implicated in cancer, inflammation, and neurodegenerative diseases [29]. As shown in Figure 1.8, the reasoning framework using ComplEx model identifies neoplasms as the highest-scoring disease category associated with sQC. Moreover, the diseases ranked fifth, eighth, and tenth are also tumor- or cancer-related. Notably, Alzheimer's disease and Parkinson's disease are ranked second and fourth, respectively, aligning with recent

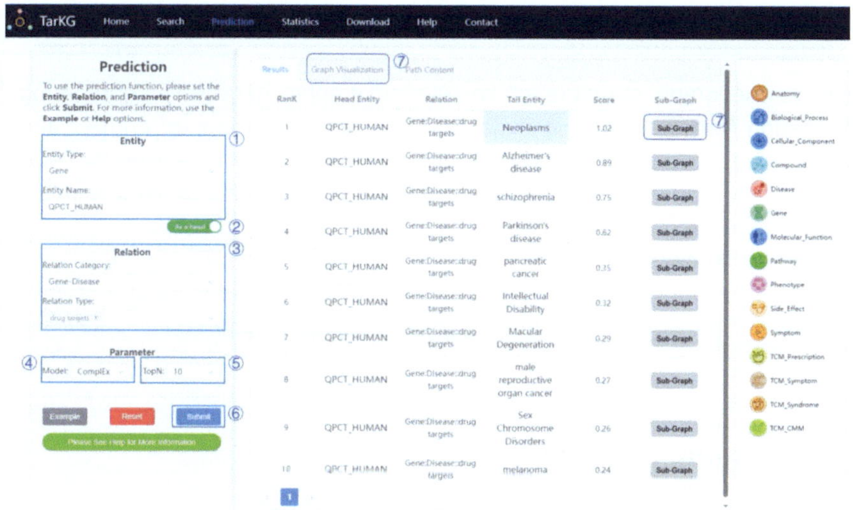

Figure 1.8 The workflow for predicting diseases potentially associated with sQC on ComplEx model using the TarKG web server.

research findings [30, 31]. This example underscores the powerful capability of knowledge graph reasoning to reveal previously unknown associations between metalloenzymes and various diseases.

Knowledge graph reasoning can further amplify the utility of KG-based resources, predicting previously unknown relationships within these expansive networks. This approach has already found broad application in areas such as drug repositioning, drug–protein interactions, and disease target discovery. To facilitate these analyses, TarKG has developed a user-friendly web server (https://tarkg.ddtmlab.org/) that integrates five mainstream knowledge graph reasoning models, enabling direct prediction of metalloenzyme-related diseases.

Instrumental Box 1.4

KG reasoning models embed existing entities and relationships as low-dimensional vectors and use specific scoring functions to predict unknown relationships within the knowledge graph. Current mainstream reasoning methods include distance-based, semantic-based, and graph neural network-based approaches. Distance-based models, such as TransE and TransR, predict relationships by calculating the distance between entity vectors. Semantic-based models, such as RESCAL and DisMult, predict relationships based on semantic similarity. Graph neural network-based models, such as R-GCN,

(Continued)

Instrumental Box 1.4 (Continued)

leverage the graph structure of knowledge graphs, iteratively aggregating information from neighboring nodes to learn representations of entities and relationships. Beyond these three categories, reinforcement learning has also been applied to knowledge graph reasoning, training agents to explore paths in the knowledge graph to discover new relationships.

Generally, knowledge graph reasoning has the potential to effectively identify and predict previously unknown connections between metal enzymes and diseases, providing valuable insights for drug development.

1.5 Concluding Remarks

The majority of metalloenzymes still lack effective drugs or viable drug candidates, and their roles in various diseases remain insufficiently explored. This creates a significant opportunity for drug discovery targeting metalloenzymes. While the resources and tools discussed in this chapter are valuable for advancing metalloenzyme-targeted drug development, the field still requires more practical computational methods and tools. For instance, it would be beneficial to extract common characteristics across different metalloenzyme families. There is also a need for tools that can predict the selectivity of metalloenzyme inhibitors, accurately predict the binding modes and affinities between metalloenzymes and ligands, and robustly infer the relationships between metalloenzymes and diseases. Additionally, there is the need to consider the impact of metal ion oxidation states on drug interactions. This chapter aims to inspire further exploration of metalloenzymes as a unique class of drug targets, promoting the development of specialized tools for metalloenzyme drug discovery and ultimately driving the progress of drug discovery targeting metalloenzymes.

Glossary

MetalPDB A database of metal sites in biological macromolecular structures.
MeLAD The Metalloenzyme-Ligand Association Database.
MeDBA The metalloenzyme data bank and analysis platform.
MeCOM The metalloenzyme active site comparison tool.
MIB/MIB2 Metal ion-binding site prediction and modeling tool.
MetalNet Architecture of CNN binary classification network, which can systematically predict metal-binding sites in proteomes.
Metal3D A general deep learning framework for accurate metal ion location prediction in proteins.
MeSiteIG The metal site identification and grafting tool.

AlphaFold2 An artificial intelligence model, which performs predictions of protein structure.

AlphaFold3 An artificial intelligence model, which performs predictions of various biomolecular complexes, including protein–ligand, protein–nucleic acid, and other small molecule interactions.

Anchor pharmacophore It refers to a set of critical features of ligand binding to target, which is related to the conservation of family targets, has biological significance (e.g., crucial for catalytic reactions or natural ligand binding), and contributes significantly to the affinity of ligand binding to target.

AncPhore An anchor pharmacophore-based tool.

TarKG The holistic biomedical knowledge graph tailored for target discovery.

IFPanalysis An interaction fingerprint analysis and similarity calculation tool.

MetalProGNet A structure-based deep graph model for metalloprotein–ligand interaction predictions.

RosENet A 3D-CNN framework for predicting absolute binding affinity using molecular mechanics energies.

NNScore 2.0 A neural-network receptor–ligand scoring function.

Glide SP An empirical scoring function, which refers to the binding affinity predictions of small molecules and proteins made by the Schrödinger company's molecular docking software, Glide, in SP mode.

PLANTS An empirical scoring function, which refers to the binding affinity predictions of small molecules and proteins made by docking software PLANTS.

MM/GBSA A computational method that combines molecular mechanics (MM) with the generalized born and surface area (GBSA) model to estimate the binding free energy of molecular complexes, such as drug–protein interactions, by accounting for both molecular mechanics and solvation effects.

MM/GBSA (OPLS3e) MM/GBSA calculated in the OPLS3e force field.

References

1. Yu, J.L., Wu, S., Zhou, C. et al. (2023). MeDBA: the metalloenzyme data bank and analysis platform. *Nucleic Acids Research* 51: D593–D602.
2. Ragsdale, S.W. (2006). Metals and their scaffolds to promote difficult enzymatic reactions. *Chemical Reviews* 106: 3317–3337.
3. Shakespear, M.R., Halili, M.A., Irvine, K.M. et al. (2011). Histone deacetylases as regulators of inflammation and immunity. *Trends in Immunology* 32: 335–343.
4. Shen, M., Pan, P., Li, Y. et al. (2015). Farnesyltransferase and geranylgeranyltransferase I: structures, mechanism, inhibitors and molecular modeling. *Drug Discovery Today* 20: 267–276.
5. Chen, A.Y., Adamek, R.N., Dick, B.L. et al. (2019). Targeting metalloenzymes for therapeutic intervention. *Chemical Reviews* 119: 1323–1455.
6. Boswell-Smith, V., Spina, D., and Page, C.P. (2006). Phosphodiesterase inhibitors. *British Journal of Pharmacology* 147: S252–S257.

7 Moretto, J., Pudlo, M., and Demougeot, C. (2021). Human-based evidence for the therapeutic potential of arginase inhibitors in cardiovascular diseases. *Drug Discovery Today* 26: 138–147.

8 Peng, T., Gong, J., Jin, Y. et al. (2018). Inhibitors of phosphodiesterase as cancer therapeutics. *European Journal of Medicinal Chemistry* 150: 742–756.

9 Li, G., Su, Y., Yan, Y.H. et al. (2020). MeLAD: an integrated resource for metalloenzyme-ligand associations. *Bioinformatics* 36: 904–909.

10 Andreini, C., Cavallaro, G., Lorenzini, S., and Rosato, A. (2013). MetalPDB: a database of metal sites in biological macromolecular structures. *Nucleic Acids Research* 41: D312–D319.

11 Li, G., Dai, Q.Q., and Li, G.B. (2022). MeCOM: a method for comparing three-dimensional metalloenzyme active sites. *Journal of Chemical Information and Modeling* 62: 730–739.

12 Yu, J.-L., Wang, Y.-G., Peng, J. et al. (2024). Geometric deep learning-enabled metal-binding site identification and grafting. *Fundamental Research.*

13 Cheng, Y., Wang, H., Xu, H. et al. (2023). Co-evolution-based prediction of metal-binding sites in proteomes by machine learning. *Nature Chemical Biology* 19: 548–555.

14 Dai, Q., Yan, Y., Ning, X. et al. (2021). AncPhore: a versatile tool for anchor pharmacophore steered drug discovery with applications in discovery of new inhibitors targeting metallo-β-lactamases and indoleamine/tryptophan 2,3-dioxygenases. *Acta Pharmaceutica Sinica B* 11: 1931–1946.

15 Li, G.-B., Abboud, M.I., Brem, J. et al. (2017). NMR-filtered virtual screening leads to non-metal chelating metallo-β-lactamase inhibitors. *Chemical Science* 8: 928–937.

16 Yu, J.L., Zhou, C., Ning, X.L. et al. Knowledge-guided diffusion model for 3D ligand-pharmacophore mapping. *Nature* 16: https://diffphore.ddtmlab.org/.

17 Jiang, D., Ye, Z., Hsieh, C.Y. et al. (2023). MetalProGNet: a structure-based deep graph model for metalloprotein-ligand interaction predictions. *Chemical Science* 14: 2054–2069.

18 Putignano, V., Rosato, A., Banci, L., and Andreini, C. (2018). MetalPDB in 2018: a database of metal sites in biological macromolecular structures. *Nucleic Acids Research* 46: D459–D464.

19 Lin, Y.F., Cheng, C.W., Shih, C.S. et al. (2016). MIB: metal ion-binding site prediction and docking server. *Journal of Chemical Information and Modeling* 56: 2287–2291.

20 Lu, C.H., Lin, Y.S., Chen, Y.C. et al. (2006). The fragment transformation method to detect the protein structural motifs. *Proteins* 63: 636–643.

21 Lu, C.H., Chen, C.C., Yu, C.S. et al. (2022). MIB2: metal ion-binding site prediction and modeling server. *Bioinformatics* 38: 4428–4429.

22 Dürr, S.L., Levy, A., and Rothlisberger, U. (2023). Metal3D: a general deep learning framework for accurate metal ion location prediction in proteins. *Nature Communications* 14: 2713.

23 Abramson, J., Adler, J., Dunger, J. et al. (2024). Accurate structure prediction of biomolecular interactions with AlphaFold 3. *Nature* 630: 493–500.

24 Jumper, J., Evans, R., Pritzel, A. et al. (2021). Highly accurate protein structure prediction with AlphaFold. *Nature* 596: 583–589.

25 O'Boyle, N.M., Vandermeersch, T., Flynn, C.J. et al. (2011). Confab - systematic generation of diverse low-energy conformers. *Journal of Cheminformatics* 3: 8.

26 Judson, R.S., Jaeger, E.P., Treasurywala, A.M., and Peterson, M.L. (1993). Conformational searching methods for small molecules. II. Genetic algorithm approach. *Journal of Computational Chemistry* 14: 1407–1414.

27 Li, G.-B., Yang, L.-L., Wang, W.-J. et al. (2013). ID-Score: a new empirical scoring function based on a comprehensive set of descriptors related to protein–ligand interactions. *Journal of Chemical Information and Modeling* 53: 592–600.

28 Zhou, C., Cai, C.-P., Huang, X.-T. et al. (2024). TarKG: a comprehensive biomedical knowledge graph for target discovery. *Bioinformatics* 40: btae598.

29 Zhang, Y., Wang, Y., Zhao, Z. et al. (2022). Glutaminyl cyclases, the potential targets of cancer and neurodegenerative diseases. *European Journal of Pharmacology* 931: 175178.

30 Vijayan, D.K. and Zhang, K.Y.J. (2019). Human glutaminyl cyclase: structure, function, inhibitors and involvement in Alzheimer's disease. *Pharmacological Research* 147: 104342.

31 Coimbra, J.R.M., Moreira, P.I., Santos, A.E., and Salvador, J.A.R. (2023). Therapeutic potential of glutaminyl cyclases: current status and emerging trends. *Drug Discovery Today* 28: 103644.

2

Metal-Binding Pharmacophores in Metalloenzyme Drug Discovery

Lilia M. Baldauf, Emily A. Podd, and Seth M. Cohen

University of California San Diego, Department of Chemistry and Biochemistry, 9500 Gilman Drive, La Jolla, CA, 92093-0358, USA

2.1 Introduction

The term "pharmacophore" describes a portion of a molecule that is recognized by a protein receptor site and contributes to observed bioactivity [1]. Pharmacophores can utilize a variety of intermolecular forces including hydrogen-bonding, hydrophobic interactions, π-π stacking, electrostatic charges, and others. A metal-binding pharmacophore (MBP) is a small molecule that can bind to the metal ion(s) in the active site of metalloenzymes by forming strong, but reversible metal–ligand bonds (also known as dative bonds or coordinate covalent bonds) [2, 3]. Before the term "metal-binding pharmacophores" and MBPs were widely used, these fragments were often called metal-binding groups (MBGs) or zinc-binding groups (ZBGs, based on their widespread use in the development of inhibitors for Zn(II)-dependent metalloenzymes) [4]. Nearly all metalloenzyme inhibitors rely on an MBP that forms bonds with the active site metal ions in their target enzymes. Figure 2.1 shows a series of FDA-approved metalloenzyme inhibitors, with the metal-donor atom(s) of MBPs highlighted.

The charge of the active site metal ion(s), number of metal ions present, surrounding residues, and coordinated water molecules can influence the interactions between the MBP and the active site. The identity of the metal ion can also impact the selectivity of the MBP. Hard-Soft Acid–Base (HSAB) theory is often used to describe trends in ligand metal-binding preferences, and hence selectivity, wherein the polarizability of both the Lewis acidic atom (the metal ion) and the Lewis basic atom (the ligand donor atom) determines the strength of the resulting coordination complex. "Hard" Lewis acids (high oxidation state metal ions such as Mg(II), Ti(IV), or Fe(III)) have a small ionic radius and high charge, and prefer to form more ionic metal–ligand bonds with "hard" Lewis bases (such as anionic oxygen donor atoms, and to a lesser extent, nitrogen atoms). "Soft" Lewis acids (low oxidation state metal ions such as Cu(I), Fe(II), or large 4d and 5d transition metals) have larger ionic radii and a lower cationic charge density, and prefer to

Drug Discovery Targeting Metalloenzymes: Strategies and Applications, First Edition. Edited by Guo-Bo Li.

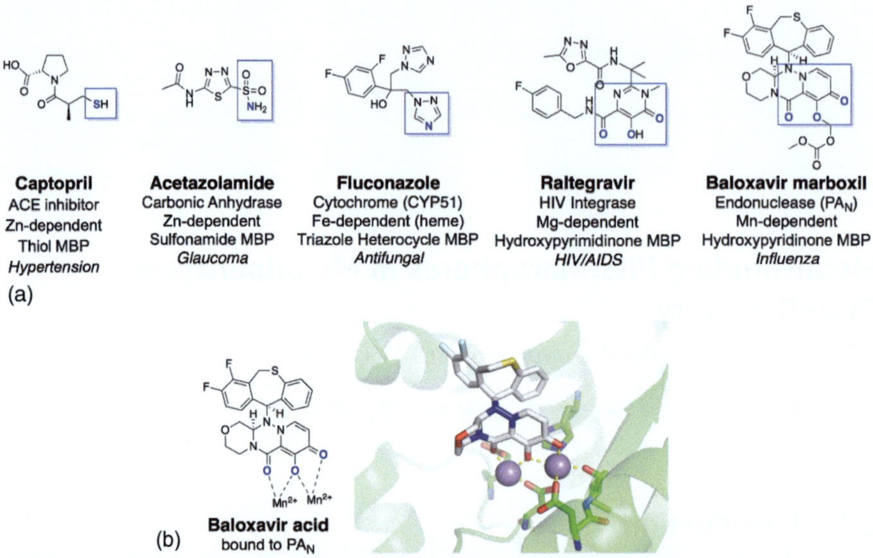

Figure 2.1 (a) Structure of five FDA-approved metalloenzyme inhibitors listing the inhibitor name, target metalloenzyme, active site metal ion, and indication. Baloxavir marboxil is a prodrug that is converted in vivo to baloxavir acid, the active form of the drug. Donor atoms (which bind the active site metal ions) on the metal-binding pharmacophores (MBPs) are highlighted in bold blue. (b) Illustration and X-ray structure of baloxavir acid bound to the dinuclear Mn(II) active site of the influenza PA_N endonuclease (PDB: 6FS6).

form metal–ligand bonds with "soft" bases (neutral ligands, aromatic nitrogen donors, sulfur donors) that form bonds that are more covalent in character. "Intermediate" acids and bases can display hard or soft characteristics depending on the molecular environment (oxidation state, nature of other donor ligands, etc.), which all influence the polarizability and ligand preferences of the metal ion. The polarizability (or lack thereof) of Lewis acids or bases influences which donor atoms might be preferred for bonding. For example, hard acid, oxophilic metal ions, such as Ca(II) and Mn(II), will prefer oxygen donors, and to a lesser extent, nitrogen donor atoms, whereas more intermediate Lewis acids, such as Zn(II), may be more broadly accepting of oxygen, nitrogen, and sulfur donor atoms. As such, the identity of the donor atoms in MBPs is very important, but it is not the only factor in determining the potential utility of an MBP for a given metalloenzyme active site. Other features (e.g. size, shape, hydrogen bond donors/acceptors) of a specific MBP can interact with the surrounding active site residues, nearby water molecules, or hydrophobic/hydrophilic pockets to also influence binding affinity and selectivity [2, 3, 5]. Furthermore, there may be more than one metal ion in the metalloenzyme active site, bridging water or hydroxyl groups between the metal ions, and other features of the metal coordination environment that influence MBP binding and selectivity [6, 7].

In addition to identifying and designing MBPs for optimal metalloenzyme inhibition, the physiochemical properties of MBPs must be considered as well. For example, carboxylic acids have shown effective inhibition of a broad range of metalloenzymes and are ubiquitous in drug design. However, carboxylic acid groups will be deprotonated at physiological pH, and the negative charge of the resulting carboxylate may limit permeability across membranes [8, 9]. This potential limitation can be addressed by the development of isosteres, which have been used to improve the drug-like characteristics of molecules. Isosteres are chemical functional groups that have similar structural and physical properties, but differ in chemical composition. Isosteres play an important role in medicinal chemistry by improving drug-like properties in molecules, such as solubility, permeability, and others [8, 10]. The use of isosteres with MBPs will be discussed later in this chapter.

One manner by which to identify and employ MBPs for metalloenzyme inhibitor discovery and development is employing them in fragment-based drug discovery (FBDD). The use of MBP libraries in FBDD has matured substantially in the last ~20 years. The creation of the first MBP libraries was described in 2011 and has since proved to be an effective approach for metalloenzyme hit identification [4, 11]. These MBP libraries have been successfully used in a relatively conventional hit to lead process utilizing fragment growth and merging approaches [6, 12–14]. MBP fragment libraries have been used in several studies not only to identify new metalloenzyme inhibitors, but also to integrate principles of bioinorganic chemistry with medicinal chemistry and drug discovery [15, 16].

2.2 MBP Databases and MBP Trends

2.2.1 MeDBA – A Database for Metalloenzymes and MBPs

There are currently several databases that are useful for examining MBP and metalloenzyme interactions. The Protein Data Bank (PDB) is a widely used, vast collection of protein and macromolecular crystal structures, cocrystals, and cryogenic electron microscopy (Cryo-EM) structures [17]. Another is the Braunschweig Enzyme Database (BRENDA), a comprehensive collection of biochemical and biological data on enzymes [18]. These databases are very useful as they present data on potential targets and their known inhibitors. For metalloenzymes specifically, the Metalloenzyme Data Bank and Analysis Platform (MeDBA) is a particularly powerful resource [19]. Originally published as the "Metalloenzyme-Ligand Associations database (MeLAD)" [20], the repository was recently reworked into a publicly accessible database specifically for metalloenzymes, ligands, and their interactions.

The MeDBA database currently contains information on 82,540 metalloenzyme crystal structures, of which 1634 are human metalloenzymes [19]. The "Metalloenzymes Statistics" component of MeDBA provides summaries of the metalloenzyme data available on MeDBA. MeDBA breaks down the available data by enzyme class, metal ion distribution, and disease association. Metalloenzymes in the MeDBA are further categorized into three subgroups: M-I, M-II, and M-III (Figure 2.2). M-I type metalloenzymes contain a metal ion(s) that is found in the active site and is directly involved in catalysis; an example is glutaminyl cyclase, a metalloenzyme with a tightly bound catalytic Zn(II) ion in the active site [21, 22]. M-II metalloenzymes

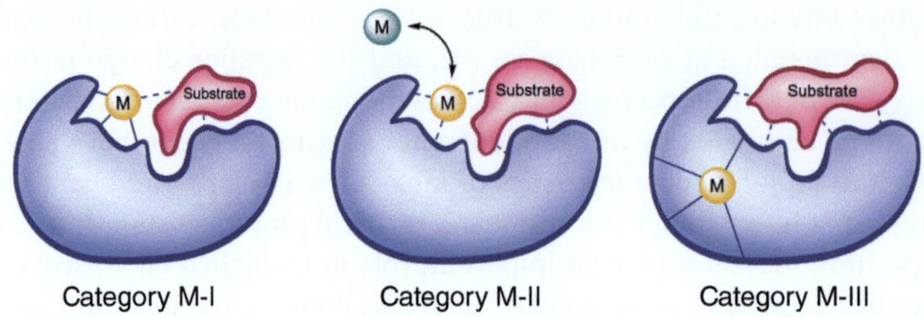

Figure 2.2 Representative illustration of the categories of metalloenzymes found in the MeDBA, listing the name of each category (M-I, M-II, M-III). The metalloenzyme is shown in blue, a bound substrate in pink, and generic metal ions are shown as orange and green spheres.

also have metal ion(s) in the active site that are involved in catalysis, but the metal ions are not tightly bound in the active site. An example of an M-II type metalloenzyme would be hypoxia-inducible factor-1α (HIF-1α), wherein the active site contains a Fe(II) ion that is involved in catalysis, but can be displaced by other metal ions relatively easily [23, 24]. Finally, M-III metalloenzymes do not use metal ions for catalysis and do not possess metal ions in the active site; instead, M-III metalloenzymes use metal ions as structural elements. For example, human furin is a calcium-dependent serine endoprotease that contains a Ca(II) cofactor for structural support, but is not part of the catalytic mechanism of the enzyme [25, 26].

MeDBA also allows for several types of searches, such as "Metalloenzyme Statistics" and "Ligand Statistics". These searches are quite powerful; for example, they can be used to identify FDA-approved drugs, as well as the clinical status of candidate inhibitors organized by metalloenzyme subgroup (M-I, II, or III) and by enzyme class. There are search functions for metalloenzyme-protein complexes (where the metalloenzyme is interacting with additional proteins) and metalloenzyme-RNA/DNA complexes (where the metalloenzyme has known interactions with RNA/DNA). Collectively, this makes the MeDBA a very useful tool for the study of metalloenzymes and their inhibitors.

Perhaps the most unique feature of MeDBA is the metal-binding pharmacophore search function ("MBP Search"), which identifies MBPs that have been reported to form complexes with metalloenzymes based on crystallographic data available in the PDB. Every MBP motif in the MBP Search function has a known cocrystal structure published with a metalloenzyme. Below is an analysis of the MBP data presently available using the MBP Search function of the MeDBA. Note, that although this analysis was performed in the Fall of 2024, at the time of the analysis the database contained data available through approximately April of 2022.

2.2.2 MeDBA Analysis of Metal Ions in Metalloenzymes of Interest

Of the complete 82,450 metalloenzymes in the MeDBA, 55% of these are Zn-dependent metalloenzymes. This is followed by Fe-dependent, Mn-dependent, Cu-dependent, and Mg-dependent metalloenzymes. Most of these entries are of the M-I type, with the exception of Mg-dependent metalloenzymes. The majority of

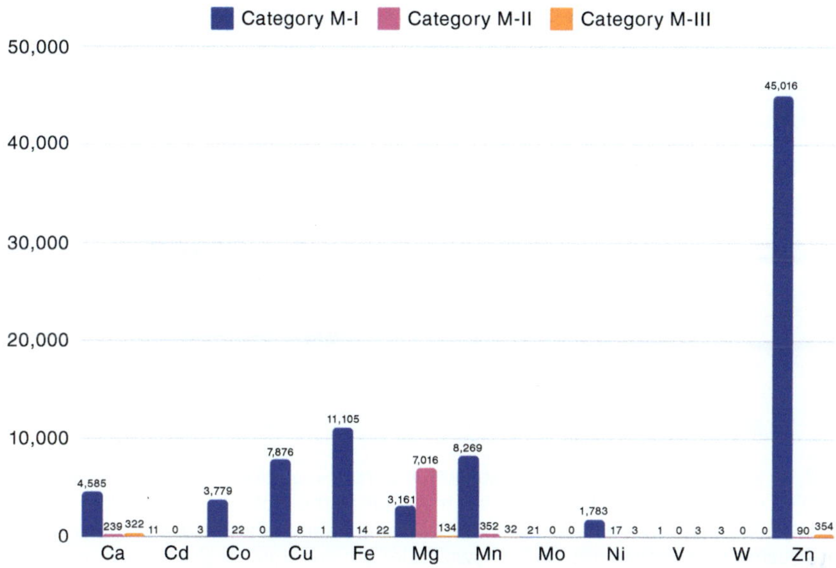

Figure 2.3 Bar graph showing the distribution of active site metal ion(s) in metalloenzymes found in the MeDBA. Number of entries for each metal ion and metalloenzyme category are listed above the bars. Metalloenzyme categories are colored M-I (blue), M-II (pink), and M-III (orange).

Mg-dependent metalloenzymes are of the M-II type, with only 44% of Mg-dependent metalloenzymes in the M-I category. A detailed breakdown of this data can be found on the MeDBA under "Metalloenzyme Statistics"; an example analysis is shown in Figure 2.3.

An analysis using the MeDBA shows differences between the overall distribution of metals found in all metalloenzymes in the database (Figure 2.3) versus the metal ions found in metalloenzymes that are structurally characterized with a bound MBP (Figure 2.4). Note, the MBP Search function of the MeDBA only contains data on MBPs cocrystallized with M-I type metalloenzymes, where the metal ion is found in the active site and directly involved in catalysis (Figure 2.2) [19]. Applying the MBP Search function, it is found that Zn-dependent metalloenzymes comprise ~50% of all metalloenzymes that have been structurally characterized with a bound MBP. Mn and Mg metalloenzymes are the next most common, making up ~15% and ~14% of bound structures, respectively. While Mg-dependent metalloenzymes make up only 4% of metalloenzymes in the total MeDBA database, they are overrepresented at ~14% of the MeDBA metalloenzyme structures with a bound MBP. By contrast, Cu-dependent metalloenzymes are far more prevalent in the MeDBA, making up 10% of all metalloenzymes in the MeDBA, but are highly underrepresented with bound MBPs, where they make up only 0.31% of structurally characterized MBP-metalloenzyme complexes. Finally, Fe-active sites make up ~10% of MBP-bound structures, with Ca at ~5%, and Ni, Co, Mo, Cd, Cu, and V collectively make up the remaining ~5% of active site metal ions bound by MBPs in the MeDBA.

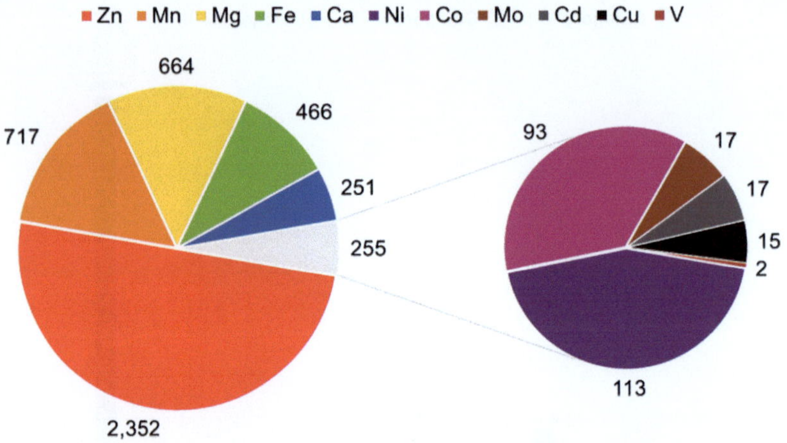

Figure 2.4 Pie charts displaying the distribution of MBP-metalloenzyme complexes in the MeDBA, organized by the identity of the metal ion in the metalloenzyme active site. Data analysis was performed using the MBP Search function in the MeDBA. Number of crystal structures for each metal ion is shown. Color scheme from largest number to smallest: zinc (red), manganese (orange), magnesium (yellow), iron (green), calcium (blue), nickel (purple), cobalt (pink), molybdenum (brown), cadmium (gray), copper (black), and vanadium (maroon).

2.2.3 MBP Trends Found in the MeDBA

When using the MBP Search function in MeDBA, each distinct MBP is listed as an individual entry, resulting in a total of 1501 distinct molecular compositions. For each MBP entry, the MeDBA will list all known cocrystal structures with metalloenzymes, for which there are a total of 4704 protein-bound crystal structures. The MBP Search function only contains MBPs that have a published cocrystal structure with a metalloenzyme target reported as of April 2022 or earlier. In addition, there are ~20 entries generated from this MBP search of the MeDBA that do not have an associated crystal structure with a metalloenzyme target.

Of the 1501 "distinct" MBP entries in the MBP Search function of the MeDBA, many contain the same MBP, but have a different overall molecular structure (i.e. are derivatives of the same core MBP scaffold). In the analysis reported here, MBP entries with common MBP core scaffolds have been grouped together to best identify the true number of unique MBP motifs in the MeDBA (based on the contents of the MeDBA as of December 24, 2024). This analysis found that of the 1501 MBPs listed in the MeDBA, there are ~269 unique MBP motifs. The number of ~269 is approximate because there may be ambiguities in assigning MBP scaffolds depending on what parameters are used to define a minimal MBP. In this analysis, the following parameters were used to classify and group MBP motifs from the MeDBA (Figure 2.5 provides pictorial representation of these rules):

A) Conventional organic nomenclature was used to identify and name molecules; however, only the portion of each MBP entry that was involved in metal binding was used for classification.

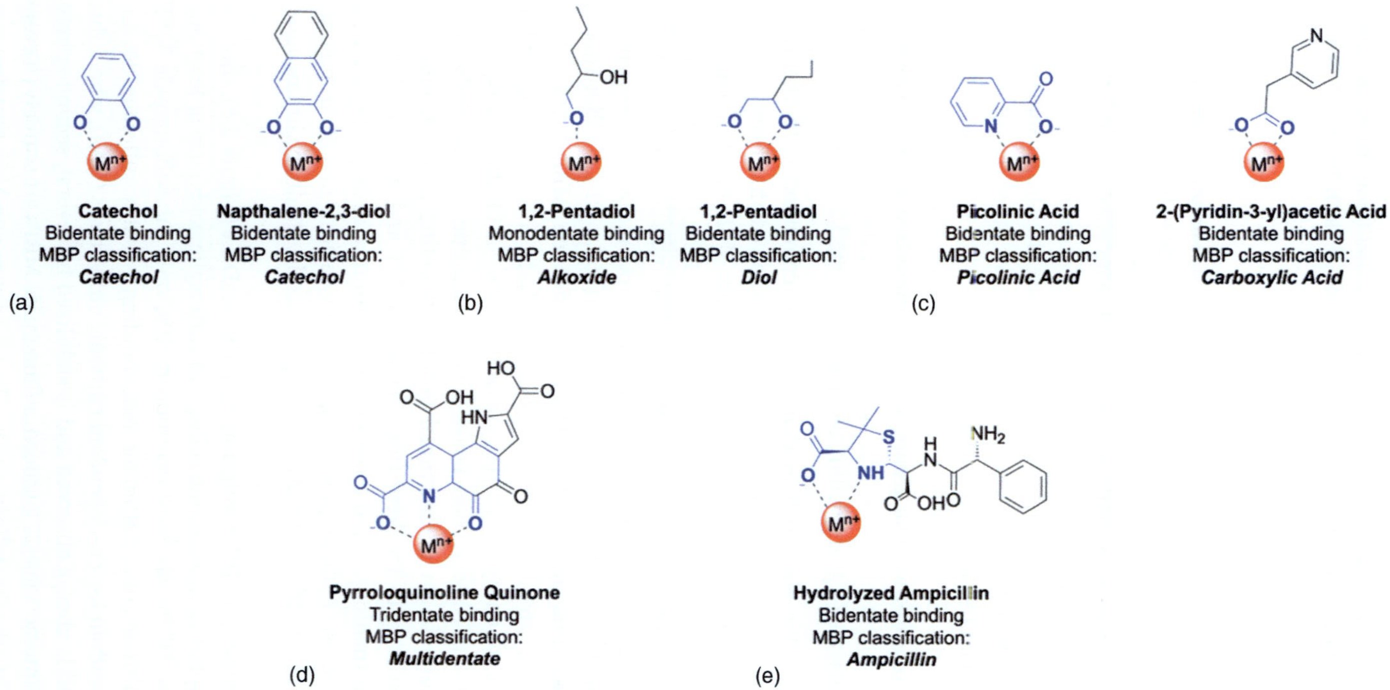

Figure 2.5 Illustration of parameters used to classify MBPs using the MBP Search function analysis in MeDBA. (a) Catechol and napthalene-2,3-diol bound to a generic metal ion, both classified as catechol MBPs. (b) 1,2-Pentadiol bound to a generic metal ion. Monodentate binding results in an alkoxide MBP classification; bidentate binding results in a diol MBP classification. (c) Picolinic acid and 2-(pyridin-3-yl)acetic acid, both which contain heterocycle groups, but are classified as a picolinic acid (heterocyclic MBP) and carboxylic acid (non-heterocycle MBP), respectively based on their mode of metal coordination. (d) Pyrroloquinoline Quinone binding tridentate to a generic metal ion, classified as a multidentate MBP. (e) Hydrolyzed ampicillin binding to a generic metal ion through nitrogen and oxygen donor atoms, classified as the compound name ampicillin. Color scheme: MBPs are highlighted in blue with donor atoms in bold blue (and anionic charges shown), and generic metal ions are red spheres.

B) Further classification of the MBPs was based on the mode of binding to metal ions in their metalloenzyme targets. For example, when considering a diol, if only one hydroxyl group was bound to the active site metal ion (monodentate), then it was classified as an alkoxide MBP. However, if both hydroxyl groups chelate to the metal ion (bidentate), it was classified as a diol MBP. For MBPs that are classified into two groups, such as amino aldehyde, this refers to chelation by both an amine and an aldehyde group.

C) If an entry in the MeDBA contained a heterocycle, it was only classified as a heterocyclic MBP if an endocyclic or exocyclic heteroatom of the ring was bound to a metal ion in the reported metalloenzyme structures.

D) A category of "multidentate" MBP was used to classify entries in the MeDBA that utilize three or more donor atoms and bound to two or more metal ions in the reported structures (e.g., tridentate or tetradentate chelators). Some entries classified as multidentate MBPs are composed of two or more classes of MBPs, but are contained on the same molecular scaffold.

E) Finally, some entries in the MeDBA are complete drug-like molecules, where one or more complex functional groups, including heterocycles, are involved in metal binding. In these cases, the MBP was classified by the conventional name of the entire molecule (e.g. ampicillin, cephalosporin, etc.).

As noted above, using the MBP Search function, combined with the rules stated above (Figure 2.5), an analysis of the MeDBA showed that from the 1501 individual molecular entries, there were ~269 distinct MBP motifs. Figure 2.6 shows the output of this analysis in a graphical format. Of the 1501 unique entries in the MBP Search function, consisting of 4704 MBP-metalloenzyme cocrystal structures, the most common MBPs are (numbers in parantheses represent the number of associated crystal structures): phosphates (956, ~21%), sulfonamides (694, ~15%), hydroxamic acids (533, ~11%), multidentate MBPs (315, ~7%), carboxylic acids (292, ~6%), thiols (180, ~4%), catechols (149, ~3%), phosphoramidites (128, 3%), alpha-hydroxycarboxylic acids (123, ~3%), diols (104, ~2%), and boronates (80, ~2%, see section below). The remaining 23% of MBPs classified make up a diverse set of functional groups, including many heterocyclic motifs that are too long to list here (for a complete list and analysis data see Supplementary Information); some representative examples include (Figure 2.6): hydroxypyridinethiones, hydroxyquinolines, picolinic acids, uracil, tropolone, imidazoline, hydantoin, picolinamide, hydroxyimidazole, hydroxychromenone, and many others.

Of the six most common MBP motifs found in the MeDBA (Figure 2.6), three of these groups (phosphates, hydroxamic acids, and carboxylic acids) use at least one oxygen donor atom. Of the six most common motifs, only the sulfonamide MBP uses exclusively a nitrogen donor atom for metal binding. Notably, sulfonamides are a privileged MBP scaffold for Zn-dependent carbonic anhydrases (CAs), where this Zn-N bonding motif is always observed and is stabilized by several, second-sphere hydrogen-bonding interactions [27]. Indeed, sulfonamide MBPs are scarcely (if ever) used for inhibitors of other metalloenzymes. The other common MBP that does not use an oxygen donor atom is the thiol group, which predictably binds metal ions

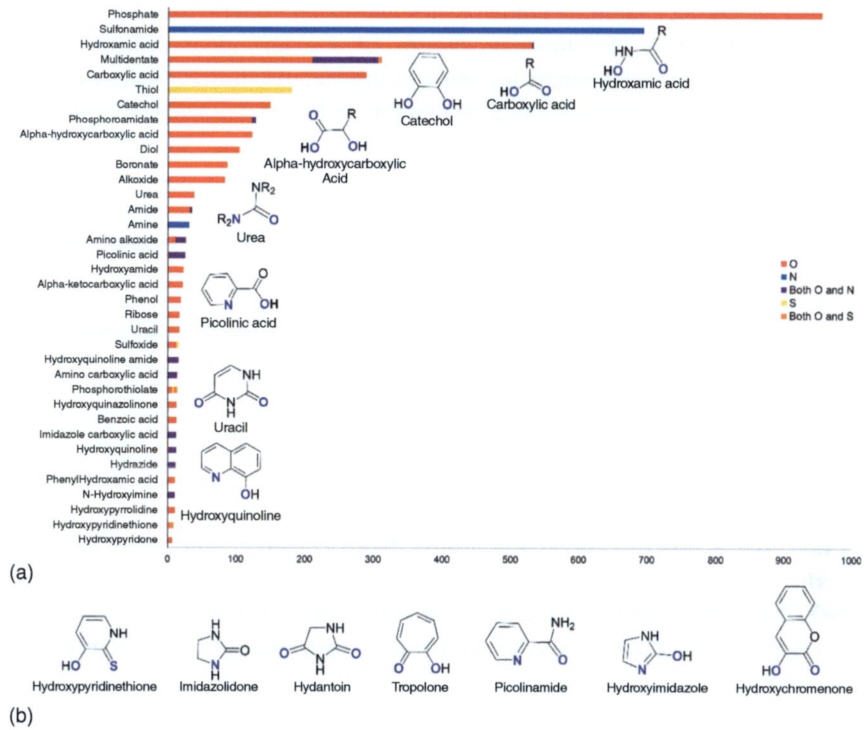

Figure 2.6 (a) Bar graph detailing showing the distribution of MBP categories in the MeDBA, with an emphasis on the most common MBPs. The data in the bar graph is color-coded based on the nature of the donor atoms: oxygen (red), nitrogen (blue), sulfur (yellow), both oxygen and nitrogen (purple), and both oxygen and sulfur (orange). (b) Other representative MBPs found from an analysis of the MeDBA. All MBP structure illustrations show the donor atom(s) highlighted in bold blue.

using sulfur donor atoms. Examining all the categorized MBPs shows that oxygen remains the most common donor atom, making up ~70% of MBP donor atoms identified in the MeDBA (Figure 2.6). The second most abundant donor atom is nitrogen, comprising ~17% of MBP donor atoms, followed by MBPs with both oxygen and nitrogen chelator atoms (~7%), and sulfur donor atoms at ~2% of metal-donor atoms in MBP motifs (Figure 2.6). MBPs with both nitrogen and sulfur donor atoms, those with nitrogen, sulfur, and oxygen atoms, and those using any other donor atoms collectively make up <1% of the donor atoms in this MBP analysis.

The analysis presented here reveals some basic trends in the use of MBPs in metalloenzyme inhibition. First, phosphate, carboxylate, sulfonamide, and hydroxamates remain the most prevalent and well-characterized (and most widely utilized) MBPs in the MeDBA. The overrepresentation of these MBPs, while not unwarranted or unexpected due to their historical dominance [2, 28], reveals an opportunity for innovation in metalloenzyme inhibitor development by utilizing novel MBPs [4, 16]. The use of isosteres may be one potential avenue to discover novel MBPs and is discussed in greater detail later in this chapter. This analysis also suggests that Cu-dependent metalloenzymes may be an underexploited target class for inhibitor discovery. As shown in Figure 2.4, Cu-dependent metalloenzymes make up ~10% of all metalloenzymes found in the MeDBA; however, there are only seven MBPs reported bound to Cu-dependent, type M-I metalloenzymes, and only one of these seven reported MBP structures is with a validated therapeutic target (tyrosinase) [29]. This suggests a substantial opportunity for lead development against Cu-dependent metalloenzymes. Overall, the MeDBA is a useful tool for MBP analysis and metalloenzyme inhibitor development that can be used to highlight opportunities for future research directions.

2.3 Recent Advancements in MBP Development

2.3.1 Overview

In this section, some recent trends in MBPs and implementation in inhibitor development are presented. First, the emergence of boron-based MBPs is discussed as a new and distinctive functional group class that has found utility in metalloenzyme inhibitor development, particularly with metallo-β-lactamases (MBLs). Second, the recent use of a simple nitrogen heterocycle MBP is examined as a case study on the nuances of MBP chemistry and the importance of interactions beyond metal binding.

2.3.2 Emergent Boron-Based MBPs

Boron-containing compounds in medicinal chemistry have been on the rise for over two decades [30]. The utility of boron-containing compounds is attributed to the energetically accessible empty *p*-orbital that makes these functional groups highly Lewis acidic. In particular, boronic acid has gained notoriety as a valuable pharmacophore, with five FDA-approved drugs that contain boronic acid (boronates when bound to metal ions) or cyclic boronate (borole) motifs: bortezomib (Veclade) in 2003 (multiple myeloma) [31], tavaborole (Kerydin) in 2014 (multiple myeloma) [32], ixazomib citrate (Sarclisa) in 2015 (antifungal) [33], crisaborole (Eucrisa) in 2016 (eczema) [34], and vaborbactam (Vabomere), a β-lactamase inhibitor combined with meropenem in 2017 (antibacterial) [35] (Figure 2.7).

Boronates, particularly boroles (cyclic boronates), gained prominence in 2009 as a selective phosphodiesterase-4 (PDE4) inhibitor for the treatment of psoriasis and eczema [36]. PDE4 is a metalloenzyme that contains an unusual dinuclear active site with one Zn(II) ion and one Mg(II) ion. Structures of PDE4 show the binding of the borole-based prodrug **AN2898**, an analogue to crisaborole (**AN2728**), to the Zn(II) and Mg(II) ions in a chelating and bridging manner [34] (Figure 2.8). Of particular note, the boronate MBP has a unique mechanism of inhibition against the dinuclear PDE4 metalloenzyme: the boronate moiety undergoes a nucleophilic attack by a hydroxyl group that bridges the two active site metal ions, converting the central boron atom from a trigonal planar sp^2 geometry to a tetrahedral sp^3 geometry with the addition of a third hydroxyl group. After the nucleophilic attack occurs, the now tetrahedral orthoboronate moiety chelates to both the Zn(II) and Mg(II)

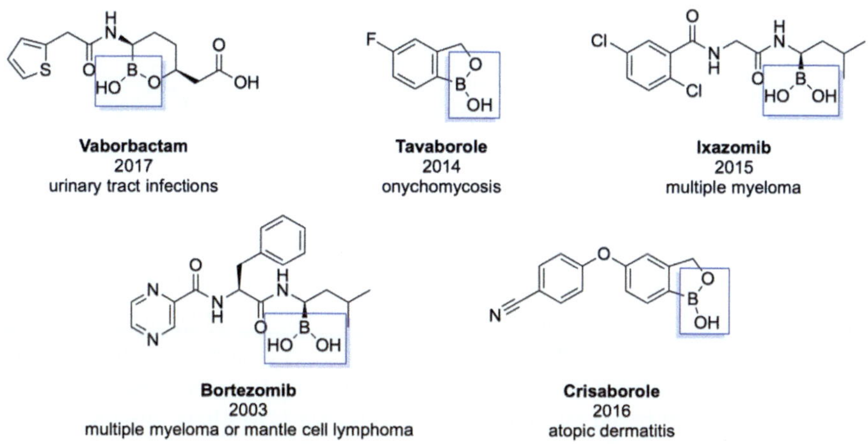

Figure 2.7 Structures of five FDA-approved drugs listing the name, year of approval, and indication. The boronate MBP on each molecule is highlighted in a blue box.

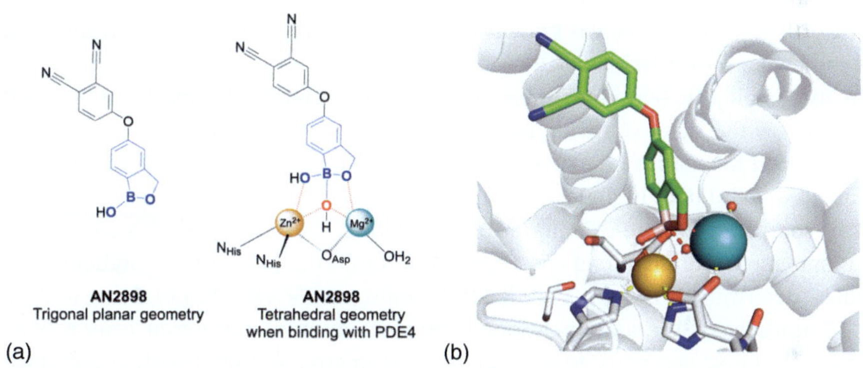

Figure 2.8 (a) Illustration of **AN2898**, a crisaborole analogue, in its inactive form and in its active form bound to PDE4. The oxygen atoms of the boronate MBP (in bold blue) are coordinated to the Zn(II) (orange sphere) and Mg(II) (teal) ions. The bridging hydroxyl group between metal ions and bound to **AN2898** in its active form is highlighted in bold red. (b) Crystal structure of **AN2898** (highlighted in green) complexed in active site of PDE4 (PDB: 3O0J). Color scheme: Mg(II) ion (teal sphere), Zn(II) ion (orange sphere), water molecules (red spheres), nitrogen (blue), oxygen (red), boron (pink), carbon (gray), ligand carbon (green). Ligand–metal interactions are drawn as red dashed lines, metal-amino acid residue interactions are drawn as yellow dashed lines (or black in the illustration).

ions in a tridentate, bridging fashion (Figure 2.8). This phenomenon has been well documented and occurs both in cyclic and acyclic boronate molecules [7, 37–40].

In recent years, interest in boronate MBPs for MBL inhibition has grown tremendously [37]. Lactam-based antibiotics are commonly used to treat bacterial infections [41]. Examples of common antibiotics include penicillins, carbapenems, cephalosporins, and monobactams (Figure 2.9). However, the overuse and misuse of these drugs have caused several antibiotic-resistant bacterial strains to emerge [42, 43]. One such mechanism for the degradation of lactam-based antibiotics is MBLs, which catalyze the hydrolysis of lactam rings in antibiotics [43].

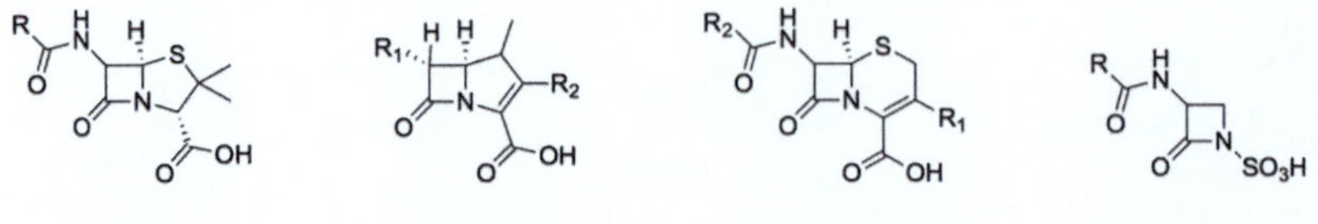

Figure 2.9 Illustration of chemical structures of common antibiotics containing lactam rings.

There are three clinically relevant families of MBLs: the New Delhi MBLs (NDM), Imipenemases (IMPs), and Verona integron-encoded MBLs (VIM), all of which are dinuclear metalloenzymes containing two Zn(II) ions. A strategy to mitigate growing antibiotic resistance has been to inhibit MBL activity to re-establish antibacterial activity of lactam-based antibiotics [44, 45]. Borole MBPs have shown efficacy against multiple classes of MBLs [46]. The affinity of boroles toward the dinuclear active site of MBLs is attributed to the previously discussed orthoborate tetrahedral intermediate formed (Figure 2.8), as it mimics the structure of MBL-hydrolyzed penicillins and cephalosporins [47, 48]. Furthermore, the sp^3 tetrahedral geometry of the orthoboronate moiety is known to be a bioisostere for phosphates, a common but somewhat indiscriminate MBP [49].

In 2019, a bicyclic boronate inhibitor (**VNRX-5133**, taniborbactam) was reported as broadly active against a wide range of MBLs (Figure 2.10) [44]. Activity assays of **VNRX-5133** against a panel of clinically relevant MBLs revealed that the compound exhibited high levels of activity against multiple classes of MBLs when compared to pre-existing MBL inhibitors, indicating **VNRX-5133** as a new and more potent broad-spectrum MBL inhibitor [47, 50]. Crystallographic studies determined that a **VNRX-5133** analogue (**VNRX-5133-D1**) bound to VIM-2 underwent the aforementioned transformation at the boron center, from a trigonal planar geometry to a tetrahedral geometry, as found with compounds such as **AN2898**, and served as model for **VNRX-5133** binding to MBL active sites (Figure 2.8). However, the complexation of **VNRX-5133** to another MBL, namely NDM-1, showed a second form of **VNRX-5133**. Specifically, a tricyclic form of the compound had formed and was also bound to the Zn(II) ions in the active site (Figure 2.10) [50]. In the NDM-1-bound structure, **VNRX-5133** was found in both the bicyclic (60% occupancy) and tricyclic form (40% occupancy). The tricyclic form of **VNRX-5133** still showed the conversion of the boron atom from trigonal pyramidal to tetrahedral geometry upon attack of a water/hydroxyl nucleophile; however, the tricyclic boron center was now also bound by an adjacent amide oxygen atom creating the third ring component (hence the tricyclic classification). The newly formed quasi-oxazole ring distorts out of plane to accommodate the tetrahedral geometry around the boron atom, and all boron-bound oxygen atoms collectively act as donor atoms to the Zn(II) ions, retaining the favorable geometry for MBL inhibition. This unusual outcome is not entirely without precedent, as other cyclic boronates containing neighboring amide groups have been observed to undergo similar intramolecular cyclization reactions [51–53]. The elucidation of both the bicyclic and tricyclic forms of **VNRX-5133** provides insight into the

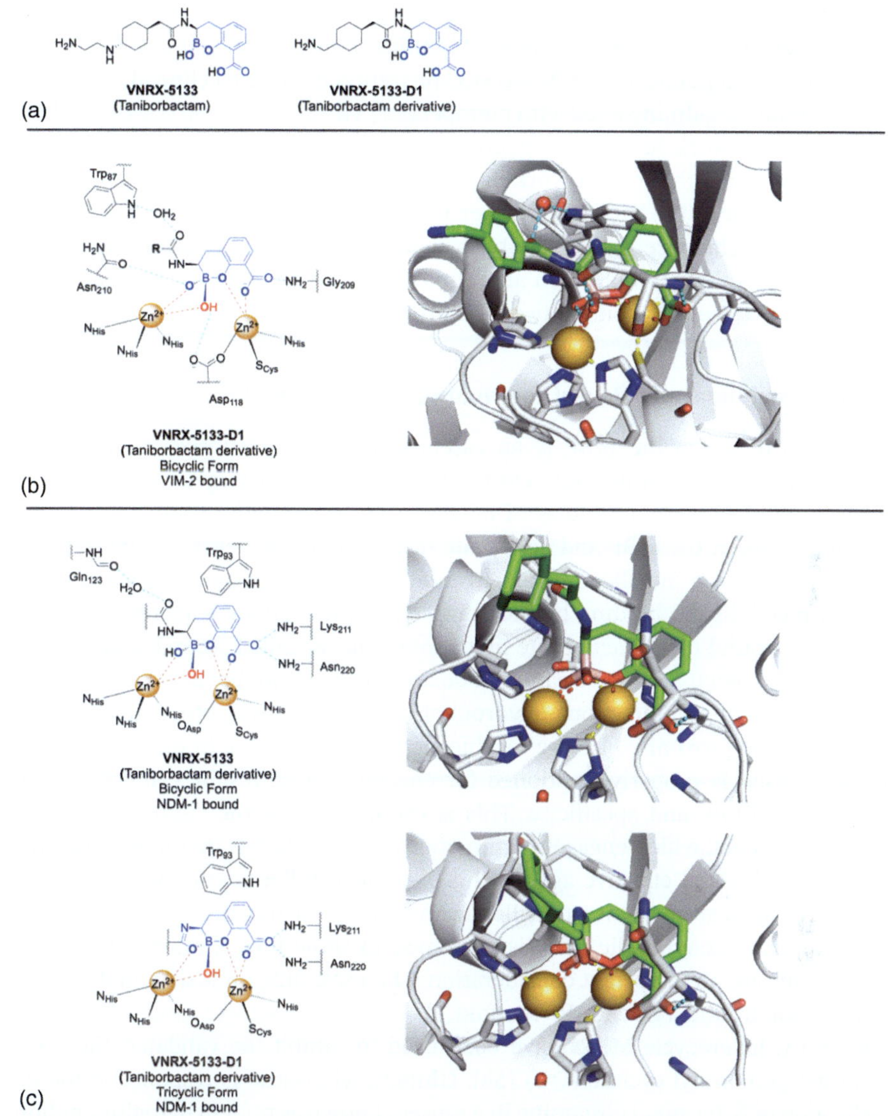

Figure 2.10 (a) Structure of **VNRX-5133** (taniborbactam) and a derivative **VNRX-5133-D1** with MBPs highlighted in blue and donor atoms in bold blue. (b) Interaction diagram and cocrystal structure of **VNRX-5133-D1** bound to VIM-2 (PDB: 5FQC). (c) Interaction diagram and cocrystal structure of **VNRX-5133** (taniborbactam) in its bicyclic and tricyclic forms bound to NDM-1 (PDB: 6RMF). Donor atoms are highlighted in bold blue, and bridging hydroxyl group is highlighted in red. The protein backbone is shown in gray, carbon (green), nitrogen (blue), oxygen (red), boron (pink), zinc (orange spheres). Note that the ethylamino atoms of **VNRX-5133** lacked observable electron density and were not modeled in the structure.

mechanism of inhibition, and how the chemistry of boron-based MBPs can provide new, interesting, and adaptable modes of binding to metalloenzymes.

Since its initial publication, **VNRX-5133** has entered Phase III clinical trials as an MBL inhibitor co-administered with meropenem [54, 55]. Burns and coworkers have continued their work on developing prodrug borole-based MBL inhibitors, although it should be noted that recent work has focused on modifying substituents on the cyclic backbone of the molecule, rather than altering properties of the boronate MBP [56, 57]. This recent work establishes boroles as a novel class of MBPs, with the unique reactivity of the boron atom upon coordination to the metal active site contributing to the high suitability of this MBP for MBL inhibition.

2.3.3 Benzimidazoles Reveal the Nuances of MBP Design

As described above, the MBP is an essential part of metalloenzyme inhibitors for providing both affinity and selectivity for the desired target. Generally, this has been pursued with a mindset of maximizing the strength of the metal–ligand bonding between the MBP and active site metal ion(s). However, the interactions of the MBP with a metalloenzyme active site can be more nuanced and expand beyond metal–ligand binding by including other interactions with residues close to, but not bound to, the active site metal ions. The so-called second coordination sphere of the metal active site can include amino acids suitably poised for making hydrogen-bonding interactions, hydrophobic contacts, and other interactions. Because of the proximity of these residues to the metal ion(s), in many cases only the MBP itself is properly positioned for engaging these residues and providing additional affinity and specificity. This is exemplified by the sulfonamide MBP inhibitors of CAs, which engage in numerous hydrogen bonds that make this MBP highly selective and effective against this class of metalloenzyme (and essentially ineffective against any other metalloenzymes) [27]. In this section, the use of a very simplistic heterocyclic MBP is examined to show how these second-sphere interactions are an important consideration when selecting an MBP and designing an inhibitor around a given MBP scaffold.

Recently, heterocycle MBPs have been used to inhibit the validated therapeutic target glutaminyl cyclase (QC) [58]. Glutaminyl cyclase is responsible for the cyclization of N-terminal glutamine in a process known as protein pyroglutamation, a posttranslational modification that enhances the protein stability and bioactive conformation [21, 22]. Excessive or aberrant protein pyroglutamation modifications have been linked to several human diseases, including Alzheimer's disease and Parkinson's disease [59–62]. In humans, QC has two isoforms: secretory glutaminyl cyclase (sQC) and Golgi resident glutaminyl cyclase (gQC) [63, 64]. Both isoforms have similar secondary and tertiary structures and have a highly conserved active site, containing a single Zn(II) ion bound by Asp_{159}, Glu_{202}, and His_{330} residues. The active site also contains an important catalytic triad, composed of three residues that are also involved in catalysis (Glu_{201}-Asp_{248}-Asp_{305}) [62, 65]. During protein pyroglutamation, the Zn(II) ion stabilizes the γ-amido of the substrate, facilitating nucleophilic attack by the α-amino group and subsequent cyclization.

In designing an inhibitor of a mononuclear Zn(II)-dependent metalloenzyme, such as QC, an obvious selection would be a bidentate, chelating MBP, such as the widely used hydroxamic acid [2, 28]. However, in 2003, it was found that compounds with simple monodentate heterocyclic imidazole MBPs were effective inhibitors of both sQC and gQC [65]. This discovery led to a plethora of imidazole and other heterocycle-based inhibitors of sQC and gQC, almost all of which are substrate-competitive inhibitors and involve monodentate coordination to the active site Zn(II) ion [66–71]. One of the more significant candidates (presently in clinical trials) is the compound designated as **PQ912** (IC_{50} = 0.036 μM sQC, 0.01 μM gQC), which contains a benzimidazole MBP [68]. Li and coworkers obtained the first crystal structure of **PQ912** in the active site of sQC [72], which showed that one of the endocyclic nitrogen atoms of the benzimidazole ring weakly coordinates to the Zn(II) ion at an extremely long distance of ~2.6 Å, and in a very distorted (and somewhat suspect) coordination geometry (Figure 2.11). The other heterocyclic nitrogen atom of the benzimidazole MBP (which is not metal coordinating) plays an important role by hydrogen bonding to the Asp_{248} residue of the catalytic triad. Additionally, the fused ring system of the benzimidazole group is engaged in face-to-face and edge-to-face aromatic interactions with the indole rings of nearby Trp_{207} and Trp_{329} residues (Figure 2.11). This highlights an important feature of these benzimidazole MBPs, in that they can engage in multiple interactions with the protein active site: metal-binding, hydrogen-bonding, and aromatic/hydrophobic interactions. These all contribute to the binding of **PQ912** to sQC and raise the question of which of these interactions (or what balance of these various interactions) is most important for strong inhibition of sQC.

Subsequently, synthetic derivatives of **PQ912** have been studied to further develop the structure–activity relationship (SAR) around this class of inhibitors. **PQ912-D1**, which contains a hydroxyindolin-2-one substituent, was found to have IC_{50} values of 4.04 and 3.22 μM against sQC and gQC, respectively [72]. Although far less active than **PQ912** (IC_{50} = 0.036 μM), **PQ912-D1** provided useful insight via its cocrystal structure with sQC. **PQ912-D1** binds to sQC and shows a distance between the nitrogen atom of the benzimidazole and the Zn(II) ion of 1.9 Å (Figure 2.11), substantially shorter than that found with the more potent **PQ912** (nitrogen-to-Zn(II) distance of 2.6 Å), while the indolin-2-one moiety forms face-to-face and edge-to-face aromatic interactions with Trp_{207} and Trp_{329}. This again suggests that the role of the MBP is more than just metal binding, as in this case a shorter metal–ligand bond does not correlate with improved inhibitory activity. This implies that a more nuanced view of the MBP, its interactions with all elements of the metalloenzyme active site must be considered (and can be exploited) to maximize the efficacy of an inhibitor.

Several additional SAR studies on derivatives of **PQ912** are reported in the same study that are not detailed here [72]. These SAR studies focused on synthetic analogues of the aromatic acyl groups, resulting in a cocrystal structure of another derivative, **PQ912-D2**, obtained with sQC (Figure 2.11). Consistent with the other structures of **PQ912** and **PQ912-D1**, **PQ912-D2** coordinates to the Zn(II) ion with a Zn–N distance of 2.0 Å, as well as being engaged in hydrogen bonding with the catalytic triad residue Asp_{248}, and hydrophobic interactions with the neighboring

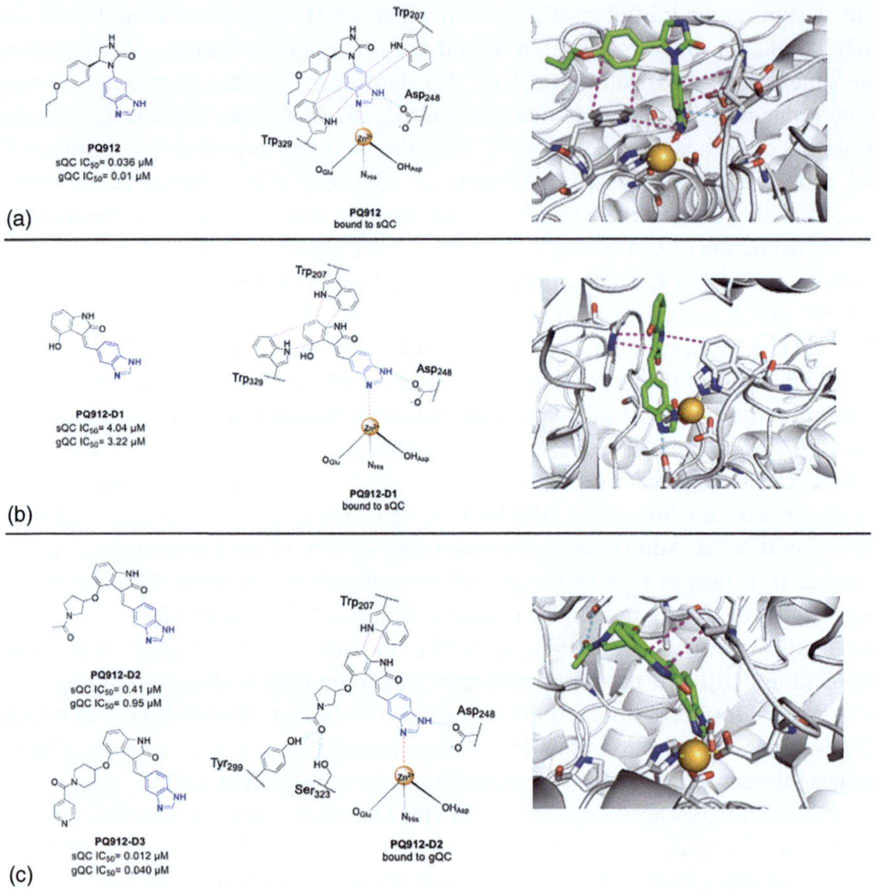

Figure 2.11 (a) Illustration, interaction diagram, and X-ray structure of **PQ912** cocrystallized with sQC (PDB: 8XGB). (b) Illustration, interaction diagram, and X-ray structure of **PQ912-D1** cocrystallized with sQC (PDB: 8XGT). (c) Illustration and chemical diagram of **PQ912-D2** and **PQ912-D3**, interaction diagram of **PQ912-D2**, and X-ray structure of **PQ912-D2** cocrystallized with gQC (PDB: 8XGY). MBPs are highlighted in blue with donor atoms in bold blue. Atom colors: carbon (green inhibitor, gray protein backbone), nitrogen (blue), oxygen (red), zinc (orange spheres). Metal–ligand bonds are shown as red dashed lines and aromatic interactions as magenta hashed lines.

Trp_{207}. Furthermore, the acyl group of **PQ912-D2** engages in additional hydrogen bonding with Ser_{323} and Tyr_{299} residues in the nearby shallow groove of loops 10 and 11, respectively. Although **PQ912-D2** does not have better activity than **PQ912**, it provides insight into the potent activity of another derivative, **PQ912-D3** (sQC IC_{50} = 0.012 μM, gQC IC_{50} = 0.040 μM) (Figure 2.11). No cocrystal structure of **PQ912-D3** and sQC or gQC was published, but the high structural similarities between **PQ912-D2** and **PQ912-D3** provide a potential explanation for the excellent activity of **PQ912-D3**: the hydrogen-bonding and hydrophobic interactions established by the indolin-2-one and the acyl groups of **PQ912-D3** are likely similar to those seen in the cocrystal structure of **PQ912-D2** and sQC, but the additional pyridine substituent may provide supplemental aromatic interactions and hydrogen-bonding opportunities. This, combined with the results seen from **PQ912-D1**, show that in MBP design, prioritizing metal–ligand interactions over other intermolecular interactions does not guarantee improvements in activity. Rather, by taking a holistic view of the interactions of the MBP with the metal and neighboring residues, prioritizing different MBP interactions with the target (not only the metal–ligand bond strength), can result in favorable changes in target affinity and selectivity.

2.4 Metal-Binding Isosteres (MBIs)

2.4.1 Background

Isosteres (including classical, non-classical, and bioisosteres) play an important role in medicinal chemistry and lead development by improving the drug-like properties of a molecule such as solubility, permeability, PK, or by reducing toxicity [8–10, 73]. In a sense, the development of new MBPs can be considered a type of isostere development, by identifying alternatives to the widely used hydroxamic acid and carboxylic acid MBPs. However, many MBPs have not been optimized for drug-like properties. For example, carboxylic acid MBPs, or other MBPs that contain carboxylic acid groups, may present problems with pharmacokinetics, absorption, distribution, metabolism, and excretion (ADME) properties; indeed, carboxylic acids have been replaced in drug development campaigns by isosteres to address such issues [8, 9]. Ballatore and coworkers described the structure–property relationship (SPR) of 35 phenylpropionic acid derivatives [8]. In this elegant study, the carboxylic acid moiety of phenylpropionic acid was replaced with a series of established isosteres, including hydroxamic acid, phosphonic acid, sulfonic acid, squaric acid, sulfonamide, tetrazole, isoxazole, and others (Figure 2.12). The 35 phenylpropionic acid derivatives were evaluated for aqueous solubility, $\log D_{7.4}$, pK_a, and other physiochemical properties. This study showed that a wide range of physiochemical characteristics could be obtained over this diverse cohort of isosteres, and provided a benchmark study for comparing and selecting isosteres in drug development. In this section, the emergence of metal-binding isosteres (MBIs) is discussed with a focus on studies from the research literature; it should be noted that there are many efforts not described here in the patent literature that are not presented. Although the reports in the patent literature are not explicitly described as MBIs, they nonetheless fit the definition of MBIs in the context of the discussion presented here.

2.4.2 Picolinic Acid MBIs

Relatively recent reports have attempted to deliberately combine the concept of the MBP and isosteres to generate a new class of fragments termed metal-binding isosteres (MBIs) [16]. MBIs have the potential benefit of not only improving the

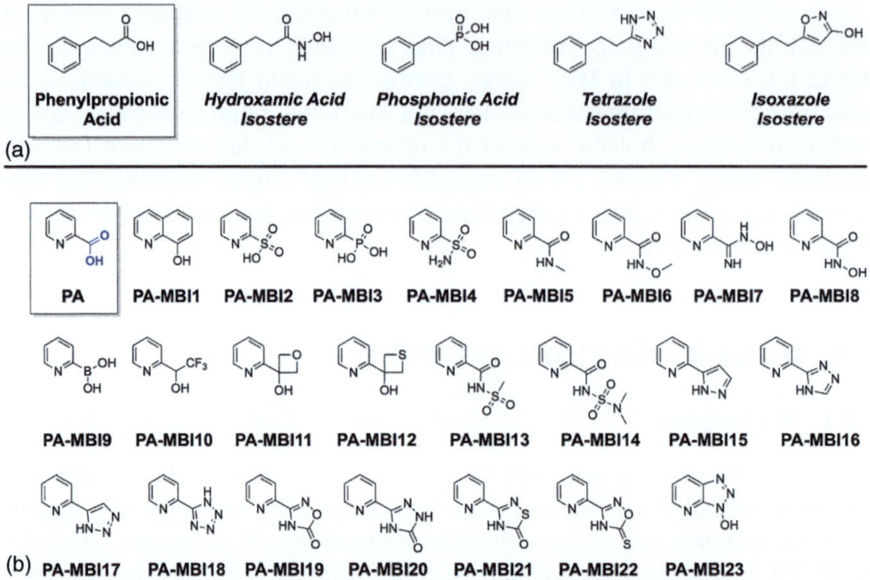

Figure 2.12 (a) Representative examples of phenylpropionic acid (in box) isosteres (*Source:* Adapted from [9]). (b) Series of 23 metal-binding isosteres (MBIs) (*Source:* with Adapted from [16]). The carboxylic group of PA is highlighted in blue as the site of isostere replacement.

drug-like properties of MBPs, but also may have the benefit of constituting new chemical matter, enhancing the chemical diversity of metal-binding fragments, and providing a source of scaffolds with a broad, tunable range of favorable physiochemical properties (e.g. solubility, permeability, pK_a, etc.). In 2018, a study that paralleled the effort with phenylpropionic acid isosteres reported a set of 23 MBIs derived from picolinic acid (PA, Figure 2.12) [16].

As with conventional isosteres, it was found that the picolinic acid isosteres (Figure 2.12) possessed a range of physiochemical characteristics, depending on the nature of the isosteric replacement. For example, the pK_a value of PA is <1.5, while the pK_a values of **PA-MBI5** and **PA-MBI15** were determined to be >12.5, and the pK_a values of **PA-MBI17** and **PA-MBI20** were determined to be 7.88 and 8.02, respectively. Similarly, the log$D_{7.4}$ value for PA is <−2, while the log$D_{7.4}$ value for compounds **PA-MBI5**, **PA-MBI15**, **PA-MBI17**, and **PA-MBI20** were determined to be −0.66, 1.29, 0.84, and 0.02, respectively [16]. Collectively, these data show that MBIs can span a broad, tunable range of physiochemical properties, like conventional isosteres [9]. Also of significance, many of these MBIs were new compositions of matter, creating opportunities for inhibitor development using novel, unexplored chemical, and intellectual property space.

Unlike conventional isosteres, MBIs have an additional requirement, which is they must maintain the ability to bind to metal ions, specifically those found bound in the active site of metalloenzymes. As a proxy for metalloenzyme binding, bioinorganic model compounds provide a rapid and facile method for verifying metal binding by MBIs (and MBPs). To verify metal binding by PA MBIs, a model

[$(Tp^{Ph,Me})Zn(\textbf{MBI})$] [$(Tp^{Ph,Me})Zn(\textbf{PA-MBI4})$] [$(Tp^{Ph,Me})Zn(\textbf{PA-MBI11})$]

[$(Tp^{Ph,Me})Zn(\textbf{PA-MBI19})$] [$(Tp^{Ph,Me})Zn(\textbf{PA-MBI22})(H_2O)$]

Figure 2.13 Using X-ray crystallography, [$(Tp^{Ph,Me})Zn(\textbf{MBI})$] complexes (illustration at left) reveal the binding mode of new MBIs. Single-crystal X-ray structures (SCXRD) of [$(Tp^{Ph,Me})Zn(\textbf{MBI})$] complexes of (left-to-right): [$(Tp^{Ph,Me})Zn(\textbf{PA-MBI4})$], [$(Tp^{Ph,Me})Zn(\textbf{PA-MBI11})$], [$(Tp^{Ph,Me})Zn(\textbf{PA-MBI19})$], and [$(Tp^{Ph,Me})Zn(\textbf{PA-MBI22})(H_2O)$]. ORTEPs shown at 50% probability ellipsoids with hydrogen atoms and $Tp^{Ph,Me}$ phenyl rings removed for clarity. Colors: boron (pink), carbon (gray), nitrogen (blue), oxygen (red), sulfur (yellow), zinc (green). A red arrow in [$(Tp^{Ph,Me})Zn(\textbf{PA-MBI22})(H_2O)$] highlights the partial ligand dissociation induced by this MBI.

compound composed of Zn(II) and the hydrotris(3,5-methylphenylpyrazolyl)borate ($Tp^{Ph,Me}$) ligand was used as a model of the generic $Zn(His)_3$ active site found in many metalloenzyme targets [74, 75]. Combining this Zn(II) complex with MBIs resulted in a series of [$(Tp^{Ph,Me})Zn(\textbf{MBI})$] model complexes that enabled characterization of the binding mode of several MBIs. Figure 2.13 shows the structure of four PA MBIs (**PA-MBI4**, **PA-MBI11**, **PA-MBI519**, **PA-MBI22**), all of which bind in a bidentate fashion to the Zn(II) ion. Interestingly, MBIs **PA-MBI22** (and **PA-MBI20**, structure not shown) result in dissociation of one of the pyrazole "arms" of the $Tp^{Ph,Me}$ ligand (Figure 2.13). Partial ligand dissociation (not to be confused with metal stripping or removal) has been observed on rare occasions in metalloenzyme inhibitors [64], but has not been widely studied or exploited and may represent a relatively unexplored, advantageous mechanism for metalloenzyme inhibition.

Having used [$(Tp^{Ph,Me})Zn(\textbf{MBI})$] model complexes to demonstrate and characterize metal binding, a final test for MBIs was to evaluate metalloenzyme inhibition. To be useful as fragments for metalloenzyme inhibitor development, it is necessary that MBIs retain the ability to inhibit relevant metalloenzymes, without inducing undesired or unexpected off-target activity. Indeed, the same study, showed that the majority of MBIs (Figure 2.12, **PA-MBI1–23**) showed equal or better inhibitory activity than PA against a dinuclear Mn(II)-dependent viral metalloenzyme of interest, while almost none showed emergent off-target activity against mononuclear, Zn (II)-dependent carbonic anhydrase [16].

2.4.3 Additional MBIs

Several other studies have described additional MBIs derived from a variety of MBPs. For example, in addition to isosteres of the carboxylic acid moiety of the PA MBP, another study prepared MBIs that varied both the pyridine ring and carboxylic acid moieties of PA; a similar study reported a series of salicylic acid (SA) MBIs that had isostere substitutions at both the phenol ring and carboxylic acid substituent (Figure 2.14). As reported in the PA study, the physicochemical properties, metal-binding ability, and inhibitory activity of these MBIs were evaluated using appropriate solution analytical methods (i.e. potentiometric titrations, partitioning measurements), model complexes, and metalloenzyme assays, respectively [16]. Beyond these systems, isosteres of wholly distinct MBPs, such as 8-hydroxyquinoline (8HQ) and 1,2-hydroxypyridinethione (HPT) MBIs have been described (Figure 2.14) [76, 77].

MBIs have also been investigated to address other physiochemical liabilities such as the reactivity of thiols. As noted above, although thiols are among the most common MBPs in the MeDBA, free thiols have a known propensity for redox reactivity and reactivity with other biomolecules (particularly with biomolecules

Figure 2.14 Parent MBPs (in box, PA = picolinic acid, SA = salicylic acid, 8HQ = 8-hydroxyquinoline, HPT = 1,2-hydroxypyridinethione) and six representative MBIs based on each MBP (*Source:* [76, 77]). The donor atoms in the parent MBPs are highlighted in bold blue.

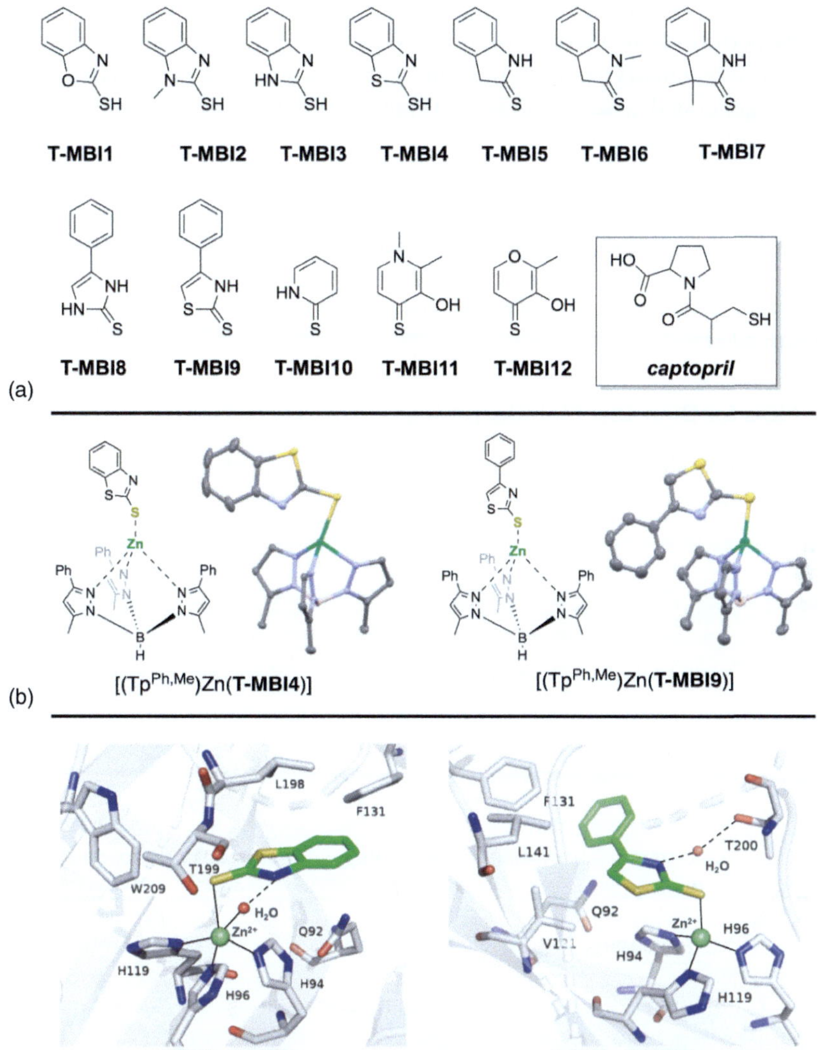

Figure 2.15 (a) Twelve MBIs (**T-MBI1–12**) were synthesized as thiol isomers; captopril was selected as a control compound (in box), as a representative free thiol drug. (b) SCXRD structures of model complexes [(Tp^{Ph,Me})Zn(**T-MBI4**)] and [(Tp^{Ph,Me})Zn(**T-MBI9**)] reveal the binding modes of the MBIs (chemical and SCXRD structures shown; phenyl groups removed from SCXRD for clarity). (c) Macromolecular X-ray structures of **T-MBI4** and **T-MBI9** complexed with Zn (II)-dependent carbonic anhydrase II (hCAII; PDB: 8FAL, 8FAU) are consistent with the binding modes observed in the model compounds. Key interactions are highlighted, including bound waters. Colors: carbon (gray; green for ligand), nitrogen (blue), oxygen (red), sulfur (yellow), zinc (green sphere) (*Source:* [78] / Royal Society of Chemistry).

that also possess free thiols, e.g. glutathione). In the context of this liability, a study was performed to identify thiol isosteres that could still bind metal ions and serve as metalloenzyme inhibitors, but with reduced off-target reactivity [78]. This study generated a series of MBIs (Figure 2.15) that were tested for their reactivity with various thiols. Several of these compounds (**T-MBI1**, **T-MBI2**, **T-MBI3**, **T-MBI4**, **T-MBI6**, and **T-MBI8**) were found to have low reactivity when compared to free-thiol-containing compounds such as l-cysteine methyl ester or the known CA inhibitor captopril (Figure 2.15). In addition, these compounds were found to form complexes with a [$(Tp^{Ph,Me})Zn(MBI)$] model complex, which was further recapitulated upon binding and cocrystallization with Zn (II)-dependent CA (Figure 2.15).

2.4.4 MBIs for Dinuclear Metalloenzymes

A recent report shows that a relatively wide variety of hydroxypyridinones (HOPO) heterocycle MBIs can bind to a dinuclear metalloenzyme [79].

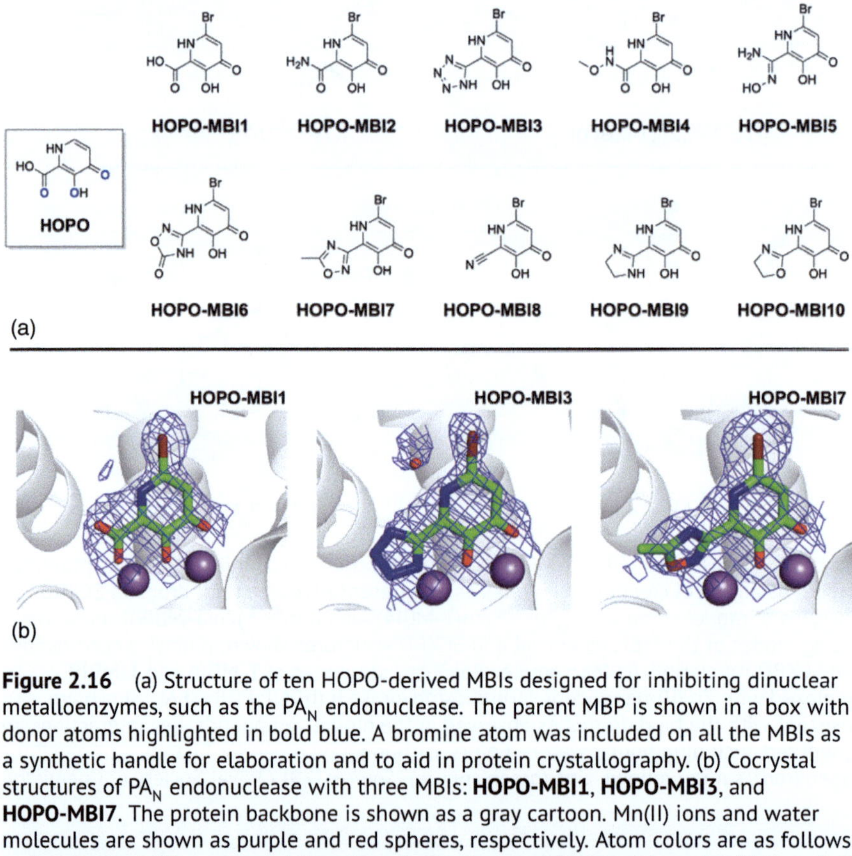

Figure 2.16 (a) Structure of ten HOPO-derived MBIs designed for inhibiting dinuclear metalloenzymes, such as the PA_N endonuclease. The parent MBP is shown in a box with the donor atoms highlighted in bold blue. A bromine atom was included on all the MBIs as a synthetic handle for elaboration and to aid in protein crystallography. (b) Cocrystal structures of PA_N endonuclease with three MBIs: **HOPO-MBI1**, **HOPO-MBI3**, and **HOPO-MBI7**. The protein backbone is shown as a gray cartoon. Mn(II) ions and water molecules are shown as purple and red spheres, respectively. Atom colors are as follows: carbon (green MBI, gray protein), oxygen (red), nitrogen (blue), and bromine (dark red). The electron density of each MBI and the Mn(II) ions is displayed as a blue mesh (*Source:* [79] / American Chemical Society).

A carboxylate-substituted HOPO heterocycle was previously reported to be an excellent lead MBP for inhibition of the influenza virus polymerase acidic N-terminal domain (PA_N) endonuclease, a validated antiviral target [6, 80]. A series of MBIs, where the carboxylate group was replaced with various isosteres were examined for their inhibitory activity and binding to PA_N (Figure 2.16). Most of the MBIs were potent inhibitors (based on measured IC_{50} values) and yielded cocrystal structures of the MBIs complexed with the dinuclear metal active site of PA_N [79]. This study unambiguously shows the ability of MBIs to bind to the active site of a target metalloenzyme, thereby providing novel starting scaffolds for inhibitor development. Taken together, these studies validate the unification of MBPs and isostere chemistry to create MBIs, which may serve as a valuable and novel strategy for developing next-generation metalloenzyme inhibitors.

Glossary

Fragment-Based Drug Discovery (FBDD) An approach in drug discovery based on the creation or use of a molecular fragment library (composing of hundreds or thousands of low molecular weight fragment compounds) and screening these fragments against a target enzyme. After screening fragment molecules, "hits" are validated through other biophysical methods.

Hard-Soft Acid–Base (HSAB) Theory A theory that (i) classifies atoms as "hard" or "soft" based on the polarizability of an atom, and (ii) predicts the likelihood of two or more atoms forming bonds based on these classifications. Hard acids tend to bond with hard bases; soft acids tend to bond with soft bases.

Isostere Chemical functional groups that have similar structural and physical properties, but differ in chemical composition. Isosteres are used in drug development to maintain favorable chemical or electrostatic interactions with a target, while altering physiochemical and pharmacokinetic characteristics to achieve better drug-like properties.

Metal-Binding Pharmacophore (MBP) A small molecule used for binding metal ions in metalloenzymes by forming strong, but reversible metal–ligand bonds (a.k.a., dative bonds, covalent coordinative bonds).

References

1 J. Dinić T, Efferth, A.T, Garcia-Sosa et al. (2020), Repurposing old drugs to fight multidrug resistant cancers. *Drug Resistance Updates* 52, 100713.

2 Chen, A.Y., Adamek, R.N., Dick, B.L. et al. (2019). Targeting metalloenzymes for therapeutic intervention. *Chemical Reviews* 119: 1323–1455.

3 Cohen, S.M. (2017). A bioinorganic approach to fragment-based drug discovery targeting metalloenzymes. *Accounts of Chemical Research* 50: 2007–2016.

4 Jacobsen, J.A., Fullagar, J.L., Miller, M.T. et al. (2011). Identifying chelators for metalloprotein inhibitors using a fragment-based approach. *Journal of Medicinal Chemistry* 54: 591–602.

5 A. Bonardi A. Nocentini, Bua. S et al., Sulfonamide inhibitors of human carbonic anhydrases designed through a three-tails approach: improving ligand/isoform matching and selectivity of action. *Journal of Medicinal Chemistry* 63, 7422–7444 (2020).

6 Credille, C.V., Dick, B.L., Morrison, C.N. et al. (2018). Structure–activity relationships in metal-binding pharmacophores for influenza endonuclease. *Journal of Medicinal Chemistry* 61: 10206–10217.

7 Fernandes, G.F.S., Denny, W.A., and Dos Santos, J.L. (2019). Boron in drug design: recent advances in the development of new therapeutic agents. *European Journal of Medicinal Chemistry* 179: 791–804.

8 Ballatore, C., Huryn, D.M., and A. B. (2013). Smith Iii, carboxylic acid (bio)isosteres in drug design. *ChemMedChem* 8: 385–395.

9 Lassalas, P., Gay, B., Lasfargeas, C. et al. (2016). Structure property relationships of carboxylic acid isosteres. *Journal of Medicinal Chemistry* 59: 3183–3203.

10 Silverman, R.B. and Holladay, M.W. (2014). *The Organic Chemistry of Drug Design and Drug Action*. San Diego: Academic Press.

11 Agrawal, A., Johnson, S.L., Jacobsen, J.A. et al. (2010). Chelator fragment libraries for targeting metalloproteinases. *ChemMedChem* 5: 195–199.

12 Garner, A.L., Fullagar, J.L., Day, J.A. et al. (2013). Development of a high-throughput screen and its use in the discovery of Streptococcus pneumoniae immunoglobulin A1 protease inhibitors. *Journal of the American Chemical Society* 135: 10014–10017.

13 Perez, C., Barkley-Levenson, A.M., Dick, B.L. et al. (2019). Metal-binding pharmacophore library yields the discovery of a glyoxalase 1 inhibitor. *Journal of Medicinal Chemistry* 62: 1609–1625.

14 Perez, C., Li, J., Parlati, F. et al. (2017). Discovery of an inhibitor of the proteasome subunit Rpn11. *Journal of Medicinal Chemistry* 60: 1343–1361.

15 Day, J.A. and Cohen, S.M. (2013). Investigating the selectivity of metalloenzyme inhibitors. *Journal of Medicinal Chemistry* 56: 7997–8007.

16 Dick, B.L. and Cohen, S.M. (2018). Metal-binding isosteres as new scaffolds for metalloenzyme inhibitors. *Inorganic Chemistry* 57: 9538–9543.

17 Berman, H.M. (2000). The protein data bank. *Nucleic Acids Research* 28: 235–242.

18 Chang, A., Jeske, L., Ulbrich, S. et al. (2021). BRENDA, the ELIXIR core data resource in 2021: new developments and updates. *Nucleic Acids Research* 49: D498–D508.

19 Yu, J.-L., Wu, S., Zhou, C. et al. (2023). MeDBA: the metalloenzyme data bank and analysis platform. *Nucleic Acids Research* 51: D593–D602.

20 Li, G., Su, Y., Yan, Y.H. et al. (2020). MeLAD: an integrated resource for metalloenzyme-ligand associations. *Bioinformatics* 36: 904–909.

21 Shih, Y.-P., Chou, C.-C., Chen, Y.-L. et al. (2014). Linked production of pyroglutamate-modified proteins via self-cleavage of fusion tags with TEV protease and autonomous N-terminal cyclization with glutaminyl cyclase *in vivo*. *PLoS One* 9: e94812.

22 Wu, V.W., Dana, C.M., Iavarone, A.T. et al. (2017). Identification of glutaminyl cyclase genes involved in pyroglutamate modification of fungal lignocellulolytic enzymes. *MBio* 8: 10–128.

23 Elkins, J.M., Hewitson, K.S., McNeill, L.A. et al. (2003). Structure of factor-inhibiting hypoxia-inducible factor (HIF) reveals mechanism of oxidative modification of HIF-1α. *Journal of Biological Chemistry* 278: 1802–1806.

24 Koivunen, P., Hirsilä, M., Günzler, V. et al. (2004). Catalytic properties of the asparaginyl hydroxylase (FIH) in the oxygen sensing pathway are distinct from those of Its prolyl 4-hydroxylases. *Journal of Biological Chemistry* 279: 9899–9904.

25 Anderson, E.D., Molloy, S.S., Jean, F. et al. (2002). The ordered and compartment-specific autoproteolytic removal of the furin intramolecular chaperone is required for enzyme activation. *Journal of Biological Chemistry* 277: 12879–12890.

26 Molloy, S.S., Bresnahan, P.A., Leppla, S.H. et al. (1992). Human furin is a calcium-dependent serine endoprotease that recognizes the sequence Arg-X-X-Arg and efficiently cleaves anthrax toxin protective antigen. *Journal of Biological Chemistry* 267: 16396–16402.

27 Supuran, C.T. (2019). *Carbonic Anhydrases: Biochemistry and Pharmacology of an Evergreen Pharmaceutical Target* (ed. C.T. Supuran and A. Nocentini). Elsevier.

28 Whittaker, M., Floyd, C.D., Brown, P., and Gearing, A.J.H. (1999). Design and therapeutic application of matrix metalloproteinase inhibitors. *Chemical Reviews* 99: 2735–2776.

29 Goldfeder, M., Kanteev, M., Isaschar-Ovdat, S. et al. (2014). Determination of tyrosinase substrate-binding modes reveals mechanistic differences between type-3 copper proteins. *Nature Communications* 5: 4505.

30 Messner, K., Vuong, B., and Tranmer, G.K. (2022). The boron advantage: the evolution and diversification of boron's applications in medicinal chemistsry. *Pharmaceuticals* 15: 264.

31 Kane, R.C., Bross, P.F., Farrell, A.T., and Pazdur, R. (2003). Velcade(R): U.S. FDA approval for the treatment of multiple myeloma progressing on prior therapy. *The Oncologist* 8: 508–513.

32 Sharma, N. and Sharma, D. (2015). An upcoming drug for onychomycosis: tavaborole. *The Journal of Pharmacy and Pharmacology* 6: 236–239.

33 Hušák, M., Jegorov, A., Rohlíček, J. et al. (2018). Determining the crystal structures of peptide analogs of boronic acid in the absence of single crystals: intricate motifs of ixazomib citrate revealed by XRPD guided by ss-NMR. *Crystal Growth & Design* 18: 3616–3625.

34 Freund, Y.R., Akama, T., Alley, M.R. et al. (2012). Boron-based phosphodiesterase inhibitors show novel binding of boron to PDE4 bimetal center. *FEBS Letters* 586: 3410–3414.

35 Burgos, R.M., Biagi, M.J., Rodvold, K.A., and Danziger, L.H. (2018). Pharmacokinetic evaluation of meropenem and vaborbactam for the treatment of urinary tract infection. *Expert Opinion on Drug Metabolism & Toxicology* 14: 1007–1021.

36 Akama, T., Basker, S.J., Zhang, Y.K. et al. (2009). Discovery and structure–activity study of a novel benzoxaborole anti-inflammatory agent (AN2728) for the potential topical treatment of psoriasis and atopic dermatitis. *Bioorganic & Medicinal Chemistry Letters* 19: 2129–2132.

37 Cahill, S.T., Cain, R., Wang, D.Y. et al. (2017). Cyclic boronates inhibit all classes of beta-lactamases. *Antimicrobial Agents and Chemotherapy* 61: 10–128.

38 Cendron, L., Quotadamo, A., Maso, L. et al. (2019). X-ray crystallography deciphers the activity of broad-spectrum boronic acid β-lactamase inhibitors. *ACS Medicinal Chemistry Letters* 10: 650–655.

39 Parkova, A., Lucic, A., Krajnc, A. et al. (2020). Broad spectrum beta-lactamase inhibition by a thioether substituted bicyclic boronate. *ACS Infectious Diseases* 6: 1398–1404.

40 Santucci, M., Spyrakis, F., Cross, S. et al. (2017). Computational and biological profile of boronic acids for the detection of bacterial serine- and metallo-β-lactamases. *Scientific Reports* 7: 1–5.

41 Elander, R.P. (2003). Industrial production of beta-lactam antibiotics. *Applied Microbiology and Biotechnology* 61: 385–392.

42 Catherine, L.T., Philip, H., Eilis, C.B. et al. (2019). β-lactamases and β-lactamase inhibitors in the 21st century. *Journal of Molecular Biology* 431: 3472–3500.

43 Munita, J.M. and Arias, C.A. (2016). Mechanisms of antibiotic resistance. *Microbiology Spectrum* 4: https://doi.org/10.1128/microbiolspec.VMBF-0016-2015.

44 Liu, B., Trout, R.E., Chu, G.H. et al. (2020). Discovery of taniborbactam (VNRX-5133): a broad-spectrum serine- and metallo-β-lactamase inhibitor for carbapenem-resistant bacterial infections. *Journal of Medicinal Chemistry* 63: 2789–2801.

45 Zhang, H., Yang, K., Cheng, Z. et al. (2021). Spectroscopic and biochemical characterization of metallo-β-lactamase IMP-1 with dicarboxylic, sulfonyl, and thiol inhibitors. *Bioorganic & Medicinal Chemistry* 40: 116183.

46 Bush, K. (2015). A resurgence of β-lactamase inhibitor combinations effective against multidrug-resistant gram-negative pathogens. *International Journal of Antimicrobial Agents* 46: 483–493.

47 Brem, J., Cain, R., Cahill, S. et al. (2016). Structural basis of metallo-β-lactamase, serine-β-lactamase and penicillin-binding protein inhibition by cyclic boronates. *Nature Communications* 7: 12406.

48 Meini, M.-R., Llarrull, L.I., and Vila, A.J. (2015). Overcoming differences: the catalytic mechanism of metallo-β-lactamases. *FEBS Letters* 589: 3419–3432.

49 Xiao, Y.-C., Yu, J.-L., Dai, Q.-Q. et al. (2021). Targeting metalloenzymes by boron-containing metal-binding pharmacophores. *Journal of Medicinal Chemistry* 64: 17706–17727.

50 Krajnc, A., Brem, J., Hinchliffe, P. et al. (2019). Bicyclic boronate VNRX-5133 inhibits metallo- and serine-β-lactamases. *Journal of Medicinal Chemistry* 62: 8544–8556.

51 Inglis, S.R., Woon, E.C.Y., Thompson, A.L., and Schofield, C.J. (2010). Observations on the deprotection of pinanediol and pinacol boronate esters via fluorinated intermediates. *Journal of Organic Chemistry* 75: 468–471.

52 Matteson, D.S., Michnick, T.J., Willett, R.D., and Patterson, C.D. (1989). [(1R)-1-acetamido-3-(methylthio)propyl]boronic acid and the x-ray structure of its ethylene glycol ester. *Organometallics* 8: 726–729.

53 Snow, R.J., Bachovchin, W.W., Barton, R.W. et al. (1994). Studies on proline boronic acid dipeptide inhibitors of dipeptidyl peptidase IV: identification of a cyclic species containing a B—N bond. *Journal of the American Chemical Society* 116: 10860.

54 Dowell, J.A., Marbury, T.C., Smith, W.B., and Henkel, T. (2022). Safety and pharmacokinetics of taniborbactam (VNRX-5133) with cefepime in subjects with various degrees of renal impairment. *Antimicrobial Agents and Chemotherapy* 66: e0025322.

55 McGovern, P.C., Wagenlehner, F., Gasink, L. et al. (2022). 731. CERTAIN-1: a phase 3 study of cefepime-taniborbactam efficacy and safety in the treatment of complicated urinary tract infections (cUTI), including acute pyelonephritis (AP). *Open Forum Infectious Diseases* 9: ofac492-022.

56 Trout, R.E., Zulli, A., Mesaros, E. et al. (2021). Discovery of VNRX-7145 (VNRX-5236 Etzadroxil): an orally bioavailable β-lactamase inhibitor for enterobacterales expressing ambler class A, C, and D enzymes. *Journal of Medicinal Chemistry* 64: 10155–10166.

57 Yan, Y.H., Li, G., and Li, G.B. (2020). Principles and current strategies targeting metallo-β-lactamase mediated antibacterial resistance. *Medicinal Research Reviews* 40: 1558–1592.

58 Ichikawa, S., Flaxman, H.A., Xu, W. et al. (2022). The E3 ligase adapter cereblon targets the C-terminal cyclic imide degron. *Nature* 610: 775–782.

59 Bayer, T.A. (2022). Pyroglutamate Aβ cascade as drug target in Alzheimer's disease. *Molecular Psychiatry* 27: 1880–1885.

60 Coimbra, J.R.M., Moreira, P.I., Santos, A.E., and Salvador, J.A.R. (2023). Therapeutic potential of glutaminyl cyclases: current status and emerging trends. *Drug Discovery Today* 28: 103644.

61 Hartlage-Rübsamen, M., Bluhm, A., Moceri, S. et al. (2021). A glutaminyl cyclase-catalyzed α-synuclein modification identified in human synucleinopathies. *Acta Neuropathologica* 142: 399–421.

62 Vijayan, D.K. and Zhang, K.Y.J. (2019). Human glutaminyl cyclase: structure, function, inhibitors and involvement in Alzheimer's disease. *Pharmacological Research* 147: 104342.

63 Busby, W.H., Quackenbush, G.E., Humm, J. et al. (1987). An enzyme(s) that converts glutaminyl-peptides into pyroglutamyl-peptides. presence in pituitary, brain, adrenal medulla, and lymphocytes. *Journal of Biological Chemistry* 262: 8532–8536.

64 Cynis, H., Rahfeld, J.-U., Stephan, A. et al. (2008). Isolation of an isoenzyme of human glutaminyl cyclase: retention in the Golgi complex suggests involvement in the protein maturation machinery. *Journal of Molecular Biology* 379: 966–980.

65 Schilling, S., Niestroj, A.J., Rahfeld, J.U. et al. (2003). Identification of human glutaminyl cyclase as a metalloenzyme - potent inhibition by imidazole derivatives and heterocyclic chelators. *Journal of Biological Chemistry* 278: 49773.

66 Buchholz, M., Heiser, U., Schilling, S. et al. (2006). The first potent inhibitors for human glutaminyl cyclase: synthesis and structure–activity relationship. *Journal of Medicinal Chemistry* 49: 664–677.

67 Dileep, K.V., Sakai, N., Ihara, K. et al. (2021). Piperidine-4-carboxamide as a new scaffold for designing secretory glutaminyl cyclase inhibitors. *International Journal of Biological Macromolecules* 170: 415–423.

68 Hoffmann, T., Meyer, A., Heiser, U. et al. (2017). Glutaminyl cyclase inhibitor PQ912 improves cognition in mouse models of Alzheimer's disease-studies on relation to effective target occupancy. *Journal of Pharmacology and Experimental Therapeutics* 362: 119–130.

69 Jimenez-Sanchez, M., Lam, W., Hannus, M. et al. (2015). siRNA screen identifies QPCT as a druggable target for Huntington's disease. *Nature Chemical Biology* 11: 347–354.

70 Ramsbeck, D., Buchholz, M., Koch, B. et al. (2013). Structure–activity relationships of benzimidazole-based glutaminyl cyclase inhibitors featuring a heteroaryl scaffold. *Journal of Medicinal Chemistry* 56: 6613–6625.

71 Vijverberg, E.G.B., Axelsen, T.M., Bihlet, A.R. et al. (2021). Rationale and study design of a randomized, placebo-controlled, double-blind phase 2b trial to evaluate efficacy, safety, and tolerability of an oral glutaminyl cyclase inhibitor varoglutamstat (PQ912) in study participants with MCI and mild AD-VIVIAD. *Alzheimer's Research & Therapy* 13: 1–142.

72 Mou, J., Ning, X.L., Wang, X.Y. et al. (2024). X-ray structure-guided discovery of a potent benzimidazole glutaminyl cyclase inhibitor that shows activity in a Parkinson's Disease mouse model. *Journal of Medicinal Chemistry* 67: 8730–8756.

73 Meanwell, N.A. (2011). Synopsis of some recent tactical application of bioisosteres in drug design. *Journal of Medicinal Chemistry* 54: 2529–2591.

74 Parkin, G. (2000). The bioinorganic chemistry of zinc: synthetic analogues of zinc enzymes that feature tripodal ligands. *Chemical Communications* https://doi.org/10.1039/b004816j, 1971–1985.

75 Seo, H., Prosser, K.E., Kalaj, M. et al. (2021). Evaluating metal–ligand interactions of metal-binding isosteres using model complexes. *Inorganic Chemistry* 60: 17161–17172.

76 Adamek, R.N., Suire, C.N., Stokes, R.W. et al. (2021). Hydroxypyridinethione inhibitors of human insulin-degrading enzyme. *ChemMedChem* 16: 1775–1787.

77 Seo, H., Jackl, M.K., Kalaj, M., and Cohen, S.M. (2022). Developing metal-binding isosteres of 8-hydroxyquinoline as metalloenzyme inhibitor scaffolds. *Inorganic Chemistry* 61: 7631–7641.

78 Seo, H., Kohlbrand, A.J., Stokes, R.W. et al. (2023). Masking thiol reactivity with thioamide, thiourea, and thiocarbamate-based MBPs. *Chemical Communications* 59: 2283–2286.
79 Stokes, R.W., Kohlbrand, A.J., Seo, H. et al. (2023). Carboxylic acid isostere derivatives of hydroxypyridinones as core scaffolds for influenza endonuclease inhibitors. *ACS Medicinal Chemistry Letters* 14: 75–82.
80 Credille, C.V., Chen, Y., and Cohen, S.M. (2016). Fragment-based identification of influenza endonuclease inhibitors. *Journal of Medicinal Chemistry* 59: 6444–6454.

Supplementary Material

Summary: This document provides graphical representations of the complete MBP analysis performed using the MeDBA database and MBP Search function. Please note a small number of MBPs are designated as "non-metal binding" MBPs. Based on the cocrystal structures of these MBPs with a metalloenzyme, the donor atoms of the MBP are too far to form a bond with the active site metal ion(s). Because the MeDBA classifies these as MBPs, they remain included in this analysis. Of the 4704 MBP cocrystal structures in the MeDBA, 12 are non-metal binding. Of the 269 MBP groups identified in this analysis of the MeDBA, 10 have at least one non-metal binding structure: nitrobenzoic acid, thioether, urea (3 structures), oxadiazole (2 structures), hydroxyimine, phosphorothiolate, sulfate, and thioamide. Among the MBP groups that have a non-metal binding cocrystal structure, the thioamide MBP (MBP0989) has only one cocrystal structure entry and it is nonmetal binding.

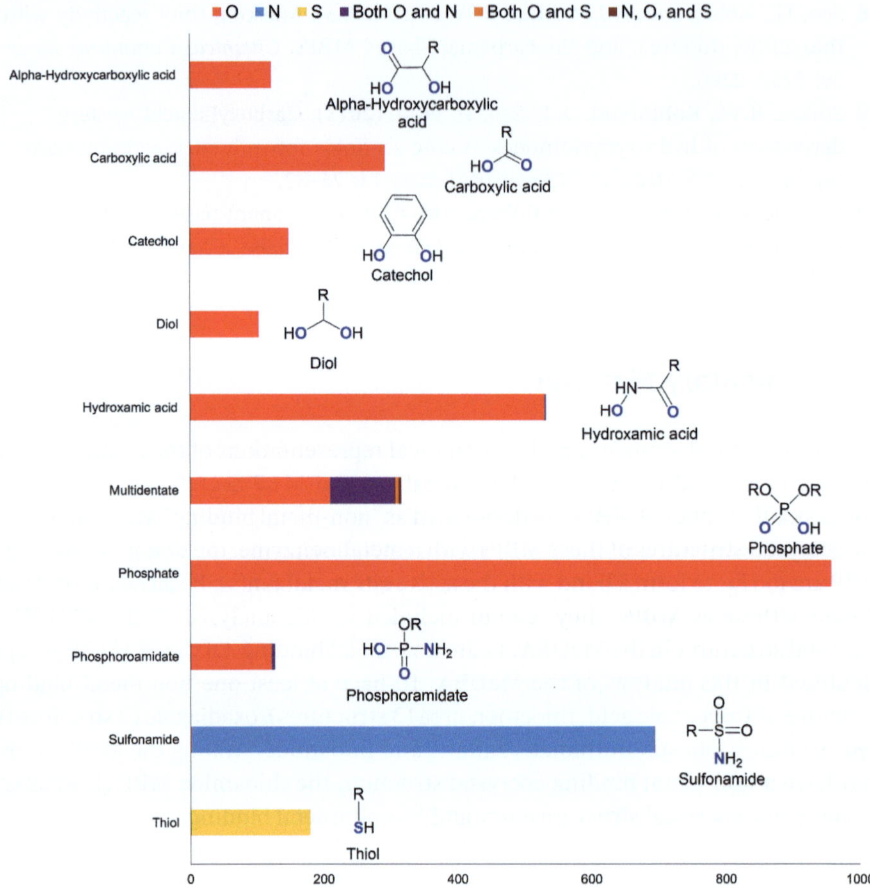

Figure S1. Bar graph detailing the distribution of MBP categories in the MeDBA, with an emphasis on the 10 most common MBPs. The data in the bar graph is color-coded based on the nature of the MBP donor atoms: oxygen (red), nitrogen (blue), sulfur (yellow), both oxygen and nitrogen (purple), both oxygen and sulfur (orange), and N, O, and S (tridentate) (brown). MBP donor atom(s) highlighted in bold blue.

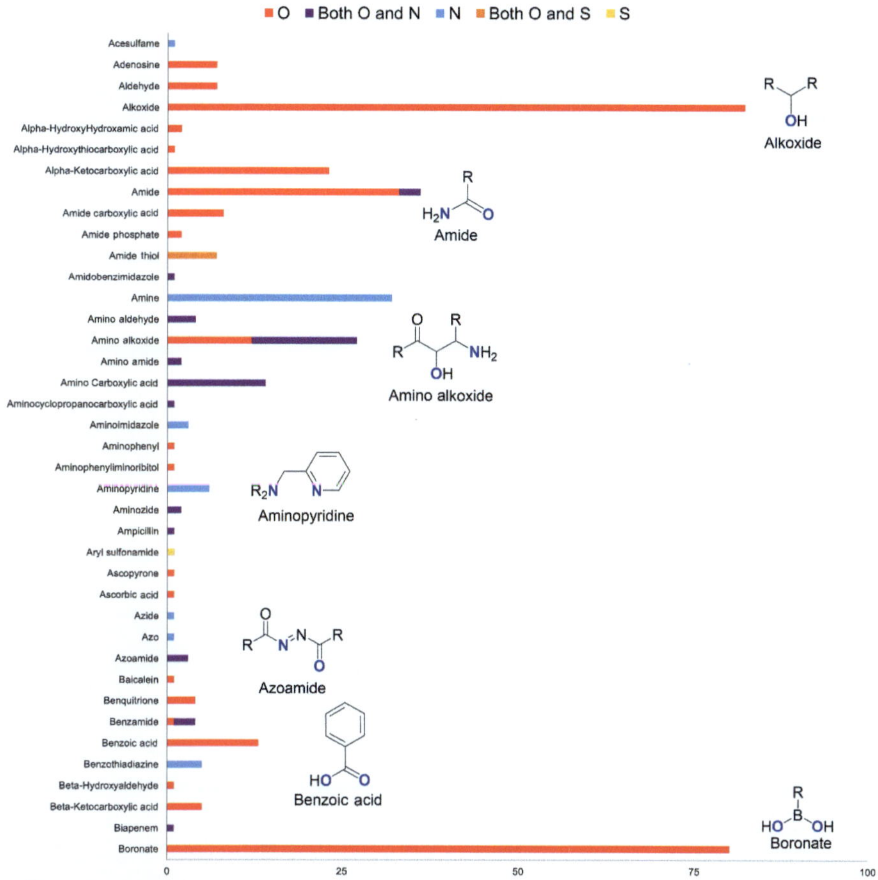

Figure S2. Bar graph detailing the distribution of MBP categories in the MeDBA, with MBPs listed alphabetically beginning with the letters A through B (excluding MBPs that were among the 10 most common). The data in the bar graph is color-coded based on the nature of the donor atoms: oxygen (red), both oxygen and nitrogen (purple), nitrogen (blue), both oxygen and sulfur (orange), and sulfur (yellow). MBP donor atom(s) highlighted in bold blue.

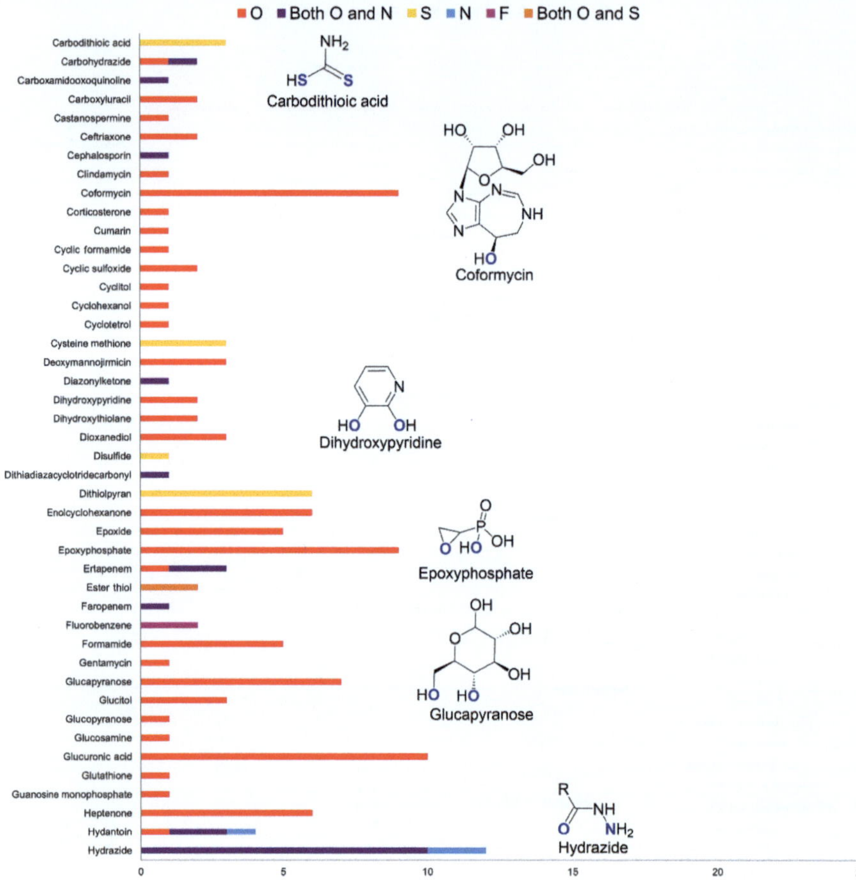

Figure S3. Bar graph detailing the distribution of MBP categories in the MeDBA, with MBPs listed alphabetically beginning with the letters C through H (excluding MBPs that were among the 10 most common). The data in the bar graph is color-coded based on the nature of the donor atoms: oxygen (red), both oxygen and nitrogen (purple), nitrogen (blue), sulfur (yellow), fluorine (pink), and both oxygen and sulfur (orange). MBP donor atom(s) highlighted in bold blue.

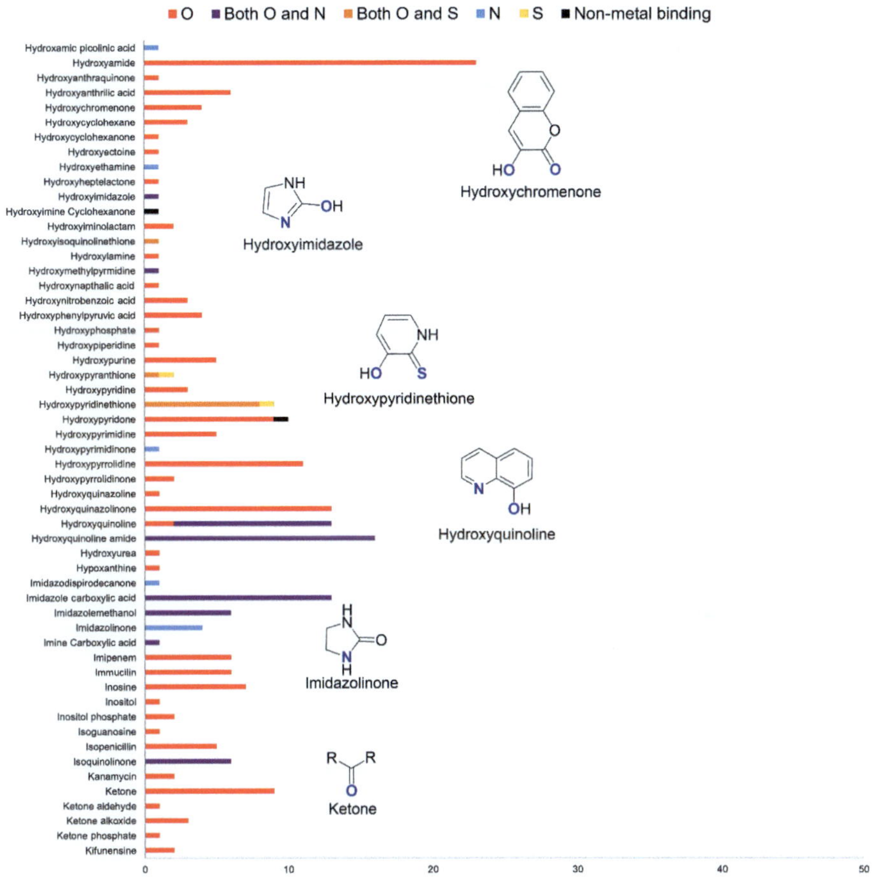

Figure S4. Bar graph detailing the distribution of MBP categories in the MeDBA, with MBPs listed alphabetically beginning with the letters H through K (excluding MBPs that were among the 10 most common). The data in the bar graph is color-coded based on the nature of the donor atoms: oxygen (red), both oxygen and nitrogen (purple), both oxygen and sulfur (orange), nitrogen (blue), sulfur (yellow), and non-metal binding (black). MBP donor atom(s) highlighted in bold blue.

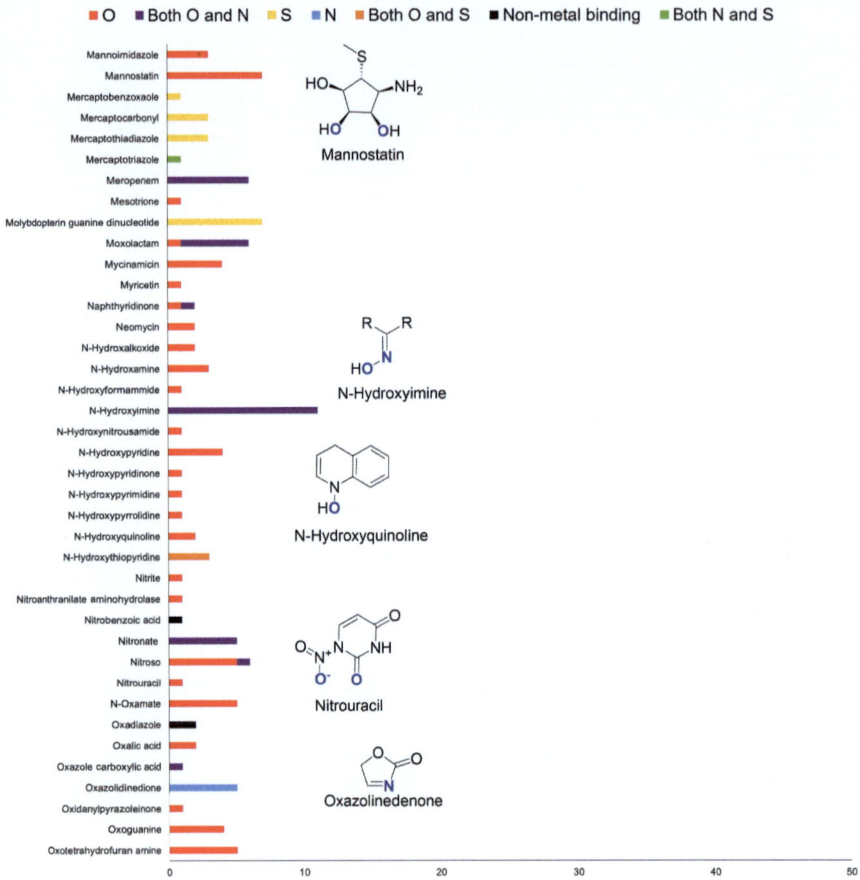

Figure S5. Bar graph detailing the distribution of MBP categories in the MeDBA, with MBPs listed alphabetically beginning with the letters M through O (excluding MBPs that were among the 10 most common). The data in the bar graph is color-coded based on the nature of the donor atoms: oxygen (red), both oxygen and nitrogen (purple), sulfur (yellow), nitrogen (blue), both oxygen and sulfur (orange), non-metal binding (black), and both nitrogen and sulfur (green). MBP donor atom(s) highlighted in bold blue.

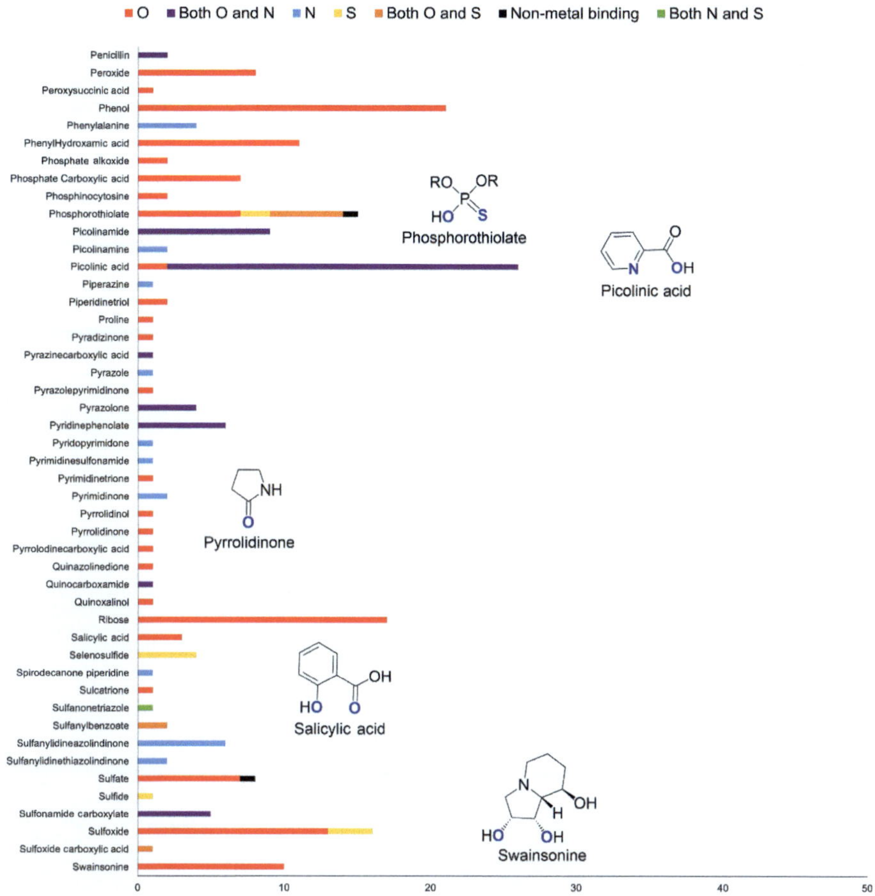

Figure S6. Bar graph detailing the distribution of MBP categories in the MeDBA, with MBPs listed alphabetically beginning with the letters P through S (excluding MBPs that were among the 10 most common). The data in the bar graph is color-coded based on the nature of the donor atoms: oxygen (red), nitrogen (blue), sulfur (yellow), both oxygen and nitrogen (purple), and both oxygen and sulfur (orange). MBP donor atom(s) highlighted in bold blue.

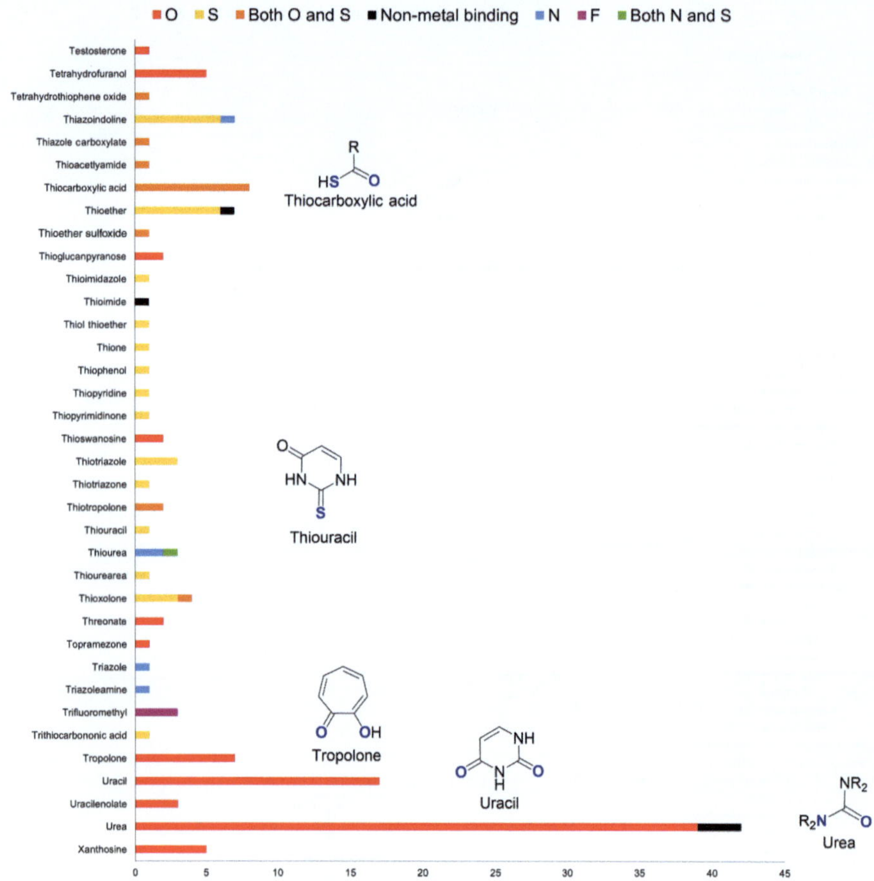

Figure S7. Bar graph detailing the distribution of MBP categories in the MeDBA, with MBPs listed alphabetically beginning with the letters T through X (excluding MBPs that were among the 10 most common). The data in the bar graph is color-coded based on the nature of the donor atoms: oxygen (red), sulfur (yellow), both oxygen and sulfur (orange), nitrogen (blue), non-metal binding (black), fluorine (pink), and both nitrogen and sulfur (green). MBP donor atom(s) highlighted in bold blue.

3

Modeling Metalloenzyme Catalytic Mechanisms by QM/MM Calculations

Zhe Li and Ruibo Wu

Sun Yat-sen University, School of Pharmaceutical Sciences, No. 132 Waihuan East Road, Guangzhou 510006, P.R. China

Section I

3.1 Introduction

Metalloenzymes, a subclass of enzymes that contain metal ions in their active sites, play a pivotal role in catalyzing a wide range of biochemical reactions [1–3]. These enzymes are essential for numerous biological processes, and understanding their catalytic mechanisms is crucial for both fundamental research and practical applications [4–8], such as drug discovery and biocatalysis. The advent of computational chemistry has revolutionized the study of metalloenzymes, providing researchers with powerful tools to investigate their structure, function, and reaction mechanisms at an unprecedented level of detail [9–12].

In the mid-twentieth century, the focus of biochemistry shifted from determining the structural characteristics of biomolecules to unraveling the underlying mechanisms and processes that govern their behavior. This paradigm shift prompted the application of two pivotal approaches in the field of computational chemistry: quantum mechanics (QM) and molecular mechanics (MM). QM methods, based on the principles of quantum theory, provided valuable insights into the electronic structure of molecules, allowing researchers to study chemical reactivity and bonding. However, the computational cost and limitations of QM methods restricted their application to small molecules, making it challenging to directly investigate chemical phenomena within larger biomolecular systems. On the other hand, MM methods relied on classical physics and empirical force fields to

Drug Discovery Targeting Metalloenzymes: Strategies and Applications, First Edition. Edited by Guo-Bo Li.

describe the interactions between atoms and molecules. While MM simulations were computationally efficient and could handle large biomolecular systems, they were incapable of studying chemical reactivity and electronic properties, which are crucial aspects of enzymatic catalysis.

The breakthrough in bridging the gap between QM and MM approaches came with the pioneering work [13–18] of Martin Karplus, Michael Levitt, and Arieh Warshel. They introduced the concept of hybrid quantum mechanics/molecular mechanics (QM/MM) models, which combined the accuracy of QM calculations for specific regions of interest with the efficiency of MM simulations for the remaining system. In QM/MM simulations, the region where the chemical process occurs, typically the active site of the metalloenzyme, is treated using quantum chemistry theory. This allows for an accurate description of the electronic structure, bonding, and reactivity of the metal center and its immediate surroundings. The rest of the enzyme, along with the solvent environment, is described using an MM force field, which captures the overall structure and dynamics of the system. This multiscale approach allowed researchers to study chemical reactivity in large biomolecular systems, such as metalloenzymes, with unprecedented accuracy and computational feasibility.

QM/MM simulations provide atomic-level insights into the reaction mechanisms and the influence of individual amino acid residues in metalloenzymes. They can reveal detailed information about the electronic structure of the metal center, the nature of the substrate binding, and the role of the protein environment in modulating the catalytic activity and selectivity. Moreover, QM/MM simulations can provide information that is difficult to measure experimentally, such as the structure and energetics of reaction intermediates [19–21], fluorescence lifetimes [22, 23], quantum yields [24], and spectra [25, 26]. In recent years, QM/MM simulations have been widely used to gain a deeper understanding of metalloenzyme catalytic mechanisms. These studies have provided valuable insights into the role of metal ions in catalysis, the influence of the protein environment on the reaction pathway, and the nature of the substrate–enzyme interactions. QM/MM simulations have been applied to a diverse range of metalloenzymes, including cytochrome P450 enzymes [27, 28], hydrogenases [29–31], nitrogenases [32–34], and multicopper oxidases [35, 36], among others.

An illustrative representation of a QM/MM system is given in Figure 3.1. The significance of QM/MM methods in the study of complex chemical systems was recognized by the scientific community when Martin Karplus, Michael Levitt, and Arieh Warshel were awarded the Nobel Prize in Chemistry in 2013 “for the development of multiscale models for complex chemical systems.” In this chapter, the basic theory of QM/MM will be introduced, followed by its applications in the study of various kinds of metalloenzymes. Hopefully, this content can provide insight into the rational design of novel metalloenzymes with enhanced catalytic properties using the QM/MM method, as well as in the development of small-molecule inhibitors for therapeutic applications.

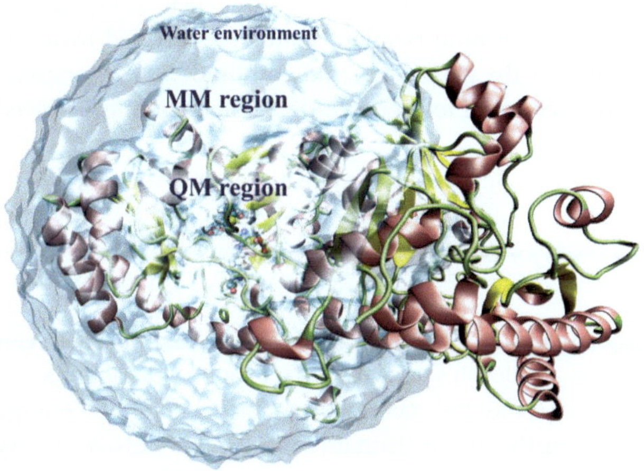

Figure 3.1 A representative QM/MM system, including the QM region and the MM region.

3.2 The QM/MM Method

3.2.1 The MM and QM Energy Expression

MM [37, 38] is currently a widely used computational method to study the structure, dynamics, and energetics of molecules, especially biomolecular systems. It is based on the principles of classical mechanics, with the potential energy expression described by empirical MM force fields. MM force fields are parameterized to reproduce experimental data and are designed to approximate the interactions between atoms in a molecule. The fundamental premise of the MM approach is to approximately define the potential energy of a system by considering the interactions between individual atoms or groups of atoms. These interactions were usually categorized into two main types: bonded interactions and non-bonded interactions.

$$E_{\text{total}} = E_{\text{bonded}} + E_{\text{nonbonded}}$$

Bonded interactions include covalent bonds, bond stretching, angle bending, and torsional rotation. The energy associated with these interactions is described by mathematical functions that approximate the potential energy as a function of the relevant geometric parameters, which is also named as force field. Different force fields have different energy expressions and parameters, especially for the non-bonded energy terms, but they are basically similar. Here, we take the Amber force field [39, 40] as an example.

$$\begin{aligned} E_{\text{bonded}} &= E_{\text{bond}} + E_{\text{angle}} + E_{\text{dihedral}} + E_{\text{improper}} \\ &= \Sigma\, k^2_{b(r-r_0)} + \Sigma\, k^2_{\theta(\theta-\theta_0)} + \Sigma\, k_{\varphi[1+\cos(n\varphi-\delta)]} + \Sigma\, k^2_{\omega(\omega-\omega_0)} \end{aligned}$$

where bond stretching, angle bending, and improper dihedral interactions are approximated by harmonic potential energy functions, where the energy increases as the bond/angle/dihedral deviates from their equilibrium values. The potential energy associated with the rotation around covalent bonds is described by a torsional function, which accounts for the periodicity and amplitude of the torsional motion and includes terms for each set of four consecutive bonded atoms involved in a torsional angle.

Non-bonded interactions include electrostatic interactions and van der Waals interactions.

$$E_{\text{nonbonded}} = \Sigma\, 4\varepsilon \left[\left(\frac{\sigma}{r} \right)^{12} - \left(\frac{\sigma}{r} \right)^{6} \right] + \Sigma \frac{q_i q_j}{4\pi\varepsilon_0 r_{ij}}$$

where the potential energy associated with electrostatic interactions between charged atoms is described by Coulomb's law. Van der Waals interactions are described by the Lennard-Jones potential energy function, where the energy decreases as the distance between the atoms decreases, and it is repulsive at very short distances. In addition to these components, some force fields may include additional terms to account for specific effects, such as hydrogen bonding or metal–ligand interactions.

The energy expression in MM calculations is typically a sum of all these components, representing the total potential energy of the system. It is important to note that MM calculations fundamentally rely on empirical parameters tailored to individual atoms, whereas they neglect the electron behavior and consequently exclude quantum mechanical effects. While MM methods have proven to be powerful and computationally efficient for studying large molecular systems, they have inherent limitations [41, 42] in accurately describing certain types of chemical phenomena, such as bond breaking and forming, as well as the complex electron configuration associated with metal ions.

In contrast, QM theory provides a more accurate and fundamental description of matter at the atomic and molecular levels [3, 43–45]. The basic principle of QM is that particles, such as electrons, exhibit both wave-like and particle-like properties. This wave-particle duality is described by the Schrödinger equation, which is the foundation of QM theory. The Schrödinger equation comes in two forms: the time-dependent Schrödinger equation, which describes the time evolution of a quantum system's wave function, and the time-independent Schrödinger equation, which describes the stationary states of a quantum system, i.e. the states with well-defined energy.

The time-dependent form is given by

$$i\hbar\, \partial\Psi(r,t)/\partial t = \widehat{\mathrm{H}}\Psi(r,t)$$

where i is the imaginary unit, $\hbar$ is the reduced Planck's constant ($h/2\pi$), $\Psi(r, t)$ is the wave function, r represents the position coordinates, t represents time, and $\widehat{\mathrm{H}}$ is the Hamiltonian operator, which corresponds to the total energy of the system.

While the time-independent form is obtained from the time-dependent form by applying the separation of variables technique, assuming that the potential energy is time-independent, and is given by

$$\widehat{\mathrm{H}}\Psi(r) = E\Psi(r),$$

where $\hat{H}$ is the Hamiltonian operator, $\Psi(r)$ is the time-independent wave function, also known as the energy eigenstate or eigenfunction, and E is the energy eigenvalue, which represents the energy of the stationary state.

The wave function contains all the information about the quantum state of the system, and its modulus squared, $|\Psi|^2$, represents the probability density of finding a particle at a specific position r. By solving the Schrödinger equation for a given system, one can obtain the allowed energy levels and the corresponding wave functions, which provide a complete description of the system's quantum behavior. The solution of the Schrödinger equation typically involves the use of various computational methods, such as the Hartree-Fock (HF) method [46] or density functional theory (DFT) [45]. These methods aim to either approximate the many-electron wave function or the electron density, through an iterative process of solving a set of coupled equations until self-consistency is achieved. Although these methods have been successful in many application cases by describing the electronic structure of molecules, they usually come with a significant computational cost. The computational complexity of HF and post-HF methods scales as N^4 to N^7, where N is the number of basis functions used to represent the molecular orbitals [47]. For DFT methods, the scaling is typically N^4 to N^6, depending on the specific approximations employed [48]. The limitation in computational cost has led to the development of various strategies to reduce the computational burden, such as the use of localized basis sets, pseudopotentials, and linear-scaling methods. However, despite these advancements, the application of full QM methods to large systems, such as proteins, remains challenging and often requires significant computational resources. In the realm of computational chemistry, the semi-empirical QM methodologies, with computational costs typically from N^2 to N^3, exhibit the capability to tackle vast systems encompassing thousands of atoms [49–51]. However, their application is often hindered by a deficiency in accuracy, particularly when dealing with intricate metal enzyme systems. This limitation underscores the need for continued refinement and optimization of these approaches to ensure reliable predictions in such complex scenarios.

To overcome these limitations, QM/MM hybrid methods have been developed. The QM region typically includes the active site or the region of interest where the chemical process occurs, while the MM region includes the rest of the system. This strategic partitioning in QM/MM calculations enables a more accurate treatment of the electronic structure and chemical reactions in the QM region, while simultaneously leveraging the computational efficiency of MM methods in the larger MM region.

3.2.2 The Energy of a QM/MM System

3.2.2.1 Subtractive Coupling Scheme

There are typically two ways to calculate the energy of the QM/MM combined system, the "subtractive coupling scheme" [52, 53] and the "additive coupling scheme" [54]. In the subtractive QM/MM coupling scheme, the MM energy of the entire system is calculated using empirical force fields. The electronic energy and properties of the QM region are calculated by the QM method. To avoid double-counting interactions between the QM and MM regions, the MM energy of the QM region is subtracted from the sum of the QM energy of the QM region and the MM energy of the entire system. The subtractive scheme can be represented by the following equation:

$$E(\text{QM/MM}) = E(\text{QM, QM region}) + E(\text{MM, entire system}) \\ - E(\text{MM, QM region})$$

where E(QM/MM) is the total energy of the QM/MM system, E(QM, QM region) is the QM energy of the QM region, E(MM, entire system) is the MM energy of the entire system, and E(MM, QM region) is the MM energy of the QM region. The subtractive scheme is schematically illustrated in Figure 3.2.

One of the most widely used subtractive QM/MM methods is the ONIOM (Our own N-layered Integrated molecular Orbital and molecular Mechanics) method, which is implemented in the Gaussian software package. The ONIOM method allows for the division of the system into two or even three layers, each treated at a different level of theory. In the two-layer ONIOM scheme, the system is divided into a high-level (HL) layer, which is treated with a more accurate QM method, and a low-level (LL) layer, which is treated with a less computationally expensive method, such as a lower-level QM method or an MM method. The total energy of the system is then calculated as:

$$E(\text{ONIOM}) = E(\text{HL, model}) + E(\text{LL, real}) - E(\text{LL, model})$$

where E(HL, model) is the energy of the model system (usually the QM region) calculated at the high level of theory, E(LL, real) is the energy of the entire system calculated at the low level of theory, and E(LL, model) is the energy of the model system calculated at the low level of theory.

The three-layer ONIOM scheme extends this concept by introducing an intermediate layer, which is treated at a level of theory between the high and low levels. This allows for a more gradual transition between the QM and MM regions and can be useful for systems with a large QM region or with significant long-range interactions.

$$E(\text{ONIOM}) = E(\text{HL, model}) + E(\text{ML, intermediate}) - E(\text{ML, model}) \\ + E(\text{LL, real}) - E(\text{LL, intermediate})$$

where E(HL, model) is the energy of the model system (usually the QM region) calculated at the high level of theory, E(ML, intermediate) is the energy of the intermediate system (which includes both the QM region and a portion of the MM region) calculated at the medium level of theory, E(ML, model) is the energy of the model system calculated at the medium level of theory, E(LL, real) is the energy of the entire

Figure 3.2 The subtractive scheme for QM/MM energy calculation.

system calculated at the low level of theory, and E(LL, intermediate) is the energy of the intermediate system calculated at the low level of theory.

The subtractive scheme is relatively simple and straightforward to implement. It allows the use of standard MM force fields without any modifications. In this scheme, the QM region is embedded in the MM environment, and the electrostatic interactions between the two regions are treated using point charges, dipoles, or higher-order multipoles (also known as Mechanical Embedding, ME) [55]. The MM region provides a static external potential that influences the electronic structure of the QM region, while the QM region contributes to the total energy of the system through its electronic energy and the electrostatic interaction energy with the MM point charges. By treating the QM–MM interactions classically, the ME scheme avoids the need for a self-consistent optimization of the electronic structure in the presence of the MM environment. This makes ME particularly suitable for large systems. However, this scheme has its limitations. The QM and MM regions are not directly coupled in the subtractive scheme, which can lead to potential inconsistencies in the description of the QM/MM boundary. This can be particularly problematic when there are covalent bonds crossing the boundary. The use of fixed point charges to represent the MM region may not accurately capture the polarization effects induced by the QM region. This can lead to an underestimation of the electrostatic interactions and may affect the accuracy of the calculated properties, especially for systems with significant charge transfer or polarization between the QM and MM regions.

Considering that the topic focuses on metalloenzymes, it is worth mentioning another limitation specific to this application. The subtractive coupling scheme with ME requires the construction of a force field for the metal coordination structure, which can be highly challenging. Metal coordination structures often exhibit complex electronic configurations and unique chemical properties, making it difficult to develop accurate force field parameters. Traditional force fields are typically parameterized for organic molecules and biological macromolecules and may not adequately describe the properties of metal coordination bonds, such as bond lengths, coordination geometries, and ligand field effects. Furthermore, the charge distribution and polarization effects around metal ions may not be fully compatible with classical force field models, leading to inaccurate descriptions of charge transfer and polarization phenomena.

3.2.2.2 Additive Coupling Scheme

The additive coupling scheme was developed to address the limitations of the subtractive coupling scheme and to provide a more accurate and consistent treatment of the QM/MM boundary. In this scheme, the total energy is obtained by explicitly adding the QM energy of the QM region, the MM energy of the MM region, and the interaction energy between the QM and MM regions.

$$E(\text{QM/MM}) = E(\text{QM, QM region}) + E(\text{MM, MM region}) \\ + E(\text{QM} - \text{MM interaction})$$

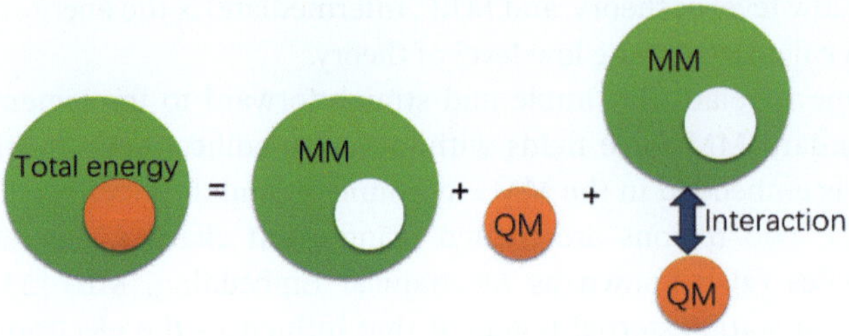

Figure 3.3 The additive scheme for QM/MM energy calculation.

where *E*(QM/MM) is the total energy of the QM/MM system, *E*(QM, QM region) is the QM energy of the QM region, *E*(MM, MM region) is the MM energy of the MM region, and *E*(QM–MM interaction) is the interaction energy between the QM and MM regions. The additive scheme is also shown in Figure 3.3 to be more illustrative.

In this scheme, the most complicated part is the calculation of QM–MM interaction term, *E*(QM–MM interaction). This term can be further decomposed into different components, such as electrostatic, van der Waals, and bonded interactions, depending on the specific implementation of the additive scheme. The van der Waals interactions between the QM and MM regions are usually described using empirical potential functions, such as the Lennard-Jones potential. These interactions account for the dispersion and repulsion forces between the QM and MM atoms. The electrostatic and bonded interactions are more complicated.

For the electrostatic interaction, electrostatic embedding (EE) [55] is an important scheme for additive QM/MM coupling, which directly provides a more reliable description of the electrostatic interactions between the QM and MM regions compared to the ME scheme. In the EE scheme, the MM region is represented by a set of point charges that polarize the QM region. The electrostatic potential of the MM charges is included in the QM Hamiltonian, allowing the QM electrons to respond to the MM environment. Although the polarization effect extending from QM to MM region and the charge transfer are not considered, the polarization imparted by the protein onto the QM region is incorporated through a self-consistent optimization of the QM electronic structure in the presence of the MM point charges.

The key advantage of the EE scheme is its ability to account for the mutual polarization between the QM and MM regions. By including the MM electrostatic potential in the QM Hamiltonian, the EE scheme allows the QM region to adapt its electronic structure in response to the MM environment. This leads to a more accurate description of the electrostatic interactions and can be particularly important for metal enzyme systems with significant charge transfer or polarization effects.

The inclusion of the MM electrostatic potential in the QM Hamiltonian also has implications for the calculation of QM properties. In the EE scheme, the QM energy and properties are computed in the presence of the MM point charges, which can lead to improved accuracy compared to the ME scheme. However, this also means that the QM calculations in the EE scheme are more computationally demanding, as the QM electronic structure needs to be optimized self-consistently with the MM environment.

The implementation of the EE scheme requires a careful treatment of the QM–MM boundary. To avoid over-polarization of the QM region by the nearby MM point charges, various boundary schemes have been developed. These include the use of link atoms, boundary atom charges, and frozen localized orbitals. The choice of the boundary scheme depends on the nature of the system and the specific QM and MM methods employed.

Beyond the EE scheme, the recent development of polarization embedding (PE) [55] extends the EE approach by explicitly including the polarization effects of the MM region in response to the QM charge density. In the PE scheme, the MM region is represented by a set of polarizable sites, typically point dipoles or higher-order multipoles, in addition to the point charges used in the EE scheme.

The key idea behind the PE scheme is to capture the mutual polarization between the QM and MM regions. In contrast to the EE scheme, where the MM region only polarizes the QM region through the fixed point charges, the PE scheme allows the MM region to respond to the changes in the QM charge density. This is achieved by introducing a self-consistent polarization of the MM sites in the presence of the QM electrostatic potential.

In the PE scheme, the total energy of the system is expressed as the sum of the QM energy, the MM energy, and the QM–MM interaction energy. The QM–MM interaction energy includes the electrostatic interactions between the QM charge density and the MM point charges, as well as the polarization energy arising from the interaction between the QM charge density and the induced dipoles (or higher-order multipoles) of the MM sites.

The self-consistent treatment of the mutual polarization in the PE scheme involves an iterative procedure. In each iteration, the QM charge density is calculated in the presence of the MM point charges and induced dipoles, and the MM-induced dipoles are updated based on the new QM charge density. This process is repeated until convergence is reached, ensuring that the QM and MM regions are mutually polarized in a consistent manner.

By explicitly including the polarization effects stemming from the MM region, the PE scheme provides a heightened accuracy in delineating electrostatic interactions and the reciprocal polarization between the QM and MM regions. This enhanced capability is crucial for systems characterized by prominent polarization effects, particularly those residing in highly polar or charged environments. The PE scheme allows the charge of the MM region to adaptively respond to the charge density of the QM part, thereby meticulously capturing the dynamic feature of the MM polarization. This is in contrast to the EE scheme, where the MM region is represented by fixed point charges that do not adapt to the changes in the QM region. The PE scheme is naturally compatible with polarizable MM force fields, which include explicit polarization terms. This ensures a consistent treatment of the polarization effects across the QM and MM regions and can improve the accuracy of the QM/MM results.

3.2.3 Bonded Interactions Crossing the QM/MM Boundary

If covalent bonds traverse the QM/MM boundary, their treatment becomes a critical aspect of QM/MM methods, as it requires a tailored approach to maintain the integrity of the system and avoid artifacts [56–59]. Splitting such a covalent bond makes it necessary to "cap" the QM region to satisfy the valence fulfillment of the QM atoms and prevent the spurious effects stemming from dangling bonds. To handle these bonded interactions, various sophisticated approaches are employed, including the link atoms, boundary atoms, or frozen orbitals.

3.2.3.1 Link Atom Approach

In the link atom approach [60], a fictitious atom, called a link atom, is introduced at the QM/MM boundary to cap the dangling valence of the QM atom that forms a covalent bond with an MM atom. The link atom is usually a hydrogen atom or a parameterized atom that mimics the properties of the MM atom it replaces. The link atom is included in the QM calculation and is treated as part of the QM region. The bond between the QM atom and the link atom is described using the QM method, while the interactions between the link atom and the MM atoms are treated classically using the MM force field. The link atom approach is relatively simple to implement and has been widely used in QM/MM simulations, which can be easily integrated with various QM methods and MM force fields. The choice of the link atom type (hydrogen or parameterized atom) provides flexibility in adapting to different systems. However, the introduction of the link atom can lead to over-polarization of the QM region, as the link atom's charge is not fully balanced by the MM environment. This can result in artificial charge transfer between the QM and MM regions. Besides, the link atom introduces additional degrees of freedom that are not present in the original system. This can lead to unphysical interactions and may require careful positioning of the link atom to minimize artifacts.

3.2.3.2 Boundary Atom Approach

The boundary atom approach [61], also known as the capping bond approach or the pseudobond approach, is an alternative method to the link atom approach for treating covalent bonds. In the boundary atom approach, instead of introducing a fictitious link atom, the covalent bond crossing the QM/MM boundary is capped by a special boundary atom. The boundary atom is a parameterized atom that represents the MM atom involved in the covalent bond. The bond between the QM atom and the boundary atom is treated using a special potential function that mimics the properties of the original covalent bond. The boundary atom is included in the QM calculation and is treated as part of the QM region, while its interactions with the MM environment are described classically using the MM force field. The parameterization of the boundary atom and the special potential function need to be optimized to accurately represent the properties of the original covalent bond and the MM atom. The boundary atom approach avoids the introduction of artificial degrees of freedom associated with the link atom, as the boundary atom directly represents the MM atom involved in the covalent bond. The boundary atom's charge is more accurately balanced by the MM environment, reducing the over-polarization effect compared to the link atom approach. The boundary atom is explicitly included in the QM calculation, providing a more consistent treatment of the QM/MM boundary.

3.2.3.3 Generalized Hybrid Orbital (GHO) Method

In the generalized hybrid orbital (GHO) method [62, 63], the covalent bond crossing the QM/MM boundary is described using a set of hybrid orbitals that are optimized to represent the electronic structure of the QM/MM boundary region accurately. The hybrid orbitals are constructed by combining the atomic orbitals of the QM and MM atoms involved in the covalent bond. The GHO method introduces a set of auxiliary orbitals, called the GHO orbitals, which are placed at the QM/MM boundary. These GHO orbitals are optimized to minimize the energy and maintain the correct electronic structure of the QM/MM boundary region. The interactions between the GHO orbitals and the QM and MM regions are described using specialized potential functions. The GHO method provides a more accurate and consistent description of the electronic structure at the QM/MM boundary compared to the link atom and boundary atom approaches. The GHO method minimizes the artifacts associated with the link atom approach, such as over-polarization and artificial charge transfer. The GHO orbitals are optimized to accurately represent the real electronic structure of the QM/MM boundary region, thereby fostering the transferability across different systems. While this approach, along with the inclusion and optimization of the additional auxiliary orbitals in the QM calculation, may increase the computational cost compared to simpler approaches like the link atom method, the enhanced reliability and reduced artifacts make it particularly valuable for systems where accurate treatment of the boundary region is crucial. The GHO method requires the parameterization of the specialized potential functions, which describe the interactions between the GHO orbitals and the QM and MM regions. Rigorous calibration and validation of these parameters are essential to ensure reliability and predictive ability.

3.2.3.4 Further Development of Covalent Bonds Treatment Methods

Apart from the approaches described above, there are other approaches for treating the covalent bonds that cross the QM/MM boundary. For example, the adapted frozen orbitals (AFOs) method [64, 65] is developed from the GHO method. In this method, a set of localized orbitals called the AFOs is introduced at the QM/MM boundary to represent the electronic structure of the covalent bonds crossing the boundary. These orbitals are constructed by performing a localization procedure on the molecular orbitals of the QM region, focusing on the orbitals involved in the covalent bonds at the QM/MM interface. The AFOs are then optimized to minimize the energy and maintain the correct electronic structure of the QM/MM boundary region. The AFO approach employs specialized potential functions akin to the GHO method to delineate interactions between the frozen orbitals and QM as well as MM regions. Notably, the AFO method potentially offers reduced computational cost in comparison to GHO, as extra auxiliary orbitals are not incorporated.

Other approaches include the effective fragment potential (EFP) approach [66], PE approach [67, 68], frozen density embedding (FDE) method [69, 70], etc. However, due to the limited scope of this chapter, these techniques will not be discussed in detail.

3.2.4 Currently Widely Used QM/MM Packages

Several widely used software packages primarily designed for MM simulations of biomolecules also include QM/MM capabilities. These packages offer a comprehensive set of tools for modeling and analyzing complex biological systems, such as proteins, nucleic acids, and lipid membranes. The representative packages include AMBER (Assisted Model Building with Energy Refinement) [71], CHARMM (Chemistry at Harvard Macromolecular Mechanics) [72], BOSS (Biochemical and Organic Simulation System) [73], etc. For AMBER, its main components include LEaP for input file preparation, Sander for energy minimization, molecular dynamics (MD), and QM/MM simulations, pmemd (Particle Mesh Ewald Molecular Dynamics) for parallel MD simulations, and AmberTools for analyzing simulation results. As for CHARMM, it provides a comprehensive set of tools for modeling and analyzing biological systems, including the CHARMM GUI for setting up simulations, the CHARMM program for energy minimization, MD, and QM/MM simulations, and CHARMM tools for analyzing simulation results. BOSS includes well-established force fields like OPLS (optimized potentials for liquid simulations) [74] and OPLS-AA (optimized potentials for liquid simulations - all atom) [75], which are known for their efficiency and accuracy in handling small to medium-sized biomolecular systems.

Some of the quantum chemistry packages also include QM/MM capabilities, allowing for the treatment of larger and more complex systems. Gaussian is one of the most widely used quantum chemistry packages, offering a comprehensive suite of tools for electronic structure calculations. It includes the ONIOM method for QM/MM calculations, which allows for the division of the system into two or three layers, each treated at a different level of theory. Gaussian supports a wide range of QM methods, from semi-empirical to high-level *ab initio* methods, and can interface with various MM force fields. The package is known for its user-friendly interface, extensive documentation, and regular updates. However, Gaussian's MM capabilities are somewhat limited compared to dedicated MM packages. ADF (Amsterdam Density Functional) is a powerful quantum chemistry package [76] based on DFT. It includes a QM/MM module that is particularly well-suited for studying transition metal complexes and can handle large QM regions efficiently. ADF supports a range of MM force fields and includes a flexible scripting language for setting up QM/MM calculations. Q-Chem is a comprehensive quantum chemistry package that includes a QM/MM module. It supports a wide range of QM methods, from semi-empirical to high-level *ab initio* methods, and can interface with various MM force fields. Q-Chem [77] is known for its efficient algorithms and support for graphics processing units (GPUs), making it well-suited for large-scale QM/MM simulations. The package also includes a variety of analysis tools, such as natural bond orbital (NBO) analysis and electron density difference maps, which can provide valuable insights into the electronic structure and reactivity of the system.

In addition to the quantum chemistry packages discussed earlier, there are several other notable software packages that use/provide interfaces to connect QM and MM packages. For example, ChemShell is a modular computational chemistry package designed for QM/MM simulations of large and complex systems [78–80]. It provides a flexible and efficient framework for combining different QM and MM software packages, allowing users to choose the best combination of methods for their specific problem. ChemShell supports a wide range of QM packages, including Gaussian, GAMESS, ORCA, and NWChem, as well as several MM packages, such as DL_POLY, GULP (general utility lattice program), and AMBER. CP2K [81] is a quantum chemistry and solid-state physics software package that includes a QM/MM module. It is designed for large-scale atomistic simulations and can handle systems with thousands of atoms. CP2K supports a variety of QM methods, including DFT, HF, and post-HF methods, as well as several MM force fields. Q-C hem/Tinker interface allows users to combine the accuracy of Q-Chem's QM methods with the efficiency and flexibility of Tinker's MM methods. This combination is particularly well-suited for studying systems where polarization effects are important, such as in the modeling of enzymes, ion channels, and other biomolecular systems.

3.2.5 Computational Cost

We compared standard MM MD and QM/MM MD on different systems. Table 3.1 presents a comparison of computational speed between MM MD and QM/MM MD on different systems. As shown, MM MD simulations are orders of magnitude faster due to the computationally intensive nature of QM calculations in QM/MM MD simulations. In practice, researchers can also opt for QM/MM scans or optimizations followed by single-point energy calculations instead of QM/MM MD simulations to achieve a better balance between computational cost and accuracy. This approach yields reaction energy profiles rather than free energy profiles.

Table 3.1 Comparison of normal MM MD and QM/MM MD on different systems.

		MM MD		QM/MM MD			
System	**Atomic number**	**CPU model**	**Speed (ns/day)**	**Atomic number of QM**	**Basis function**	**Calculation level (method)**	**Speed (ps/day)**
AChE	67243	Tesla K80	13.42	49	384	B3LYP/6-31G[a)]	3.57
BjKS	40989	Tesla K80	20.80	68	462	M06-2X/6-31G[a)]	2.11
SaSS	87230	Tesla K80	10.97	79	548	M06-2X/6-31G[a)]	1.57
AoCAS	99804	Tesla K80	9.98	106	732	M06-2X/6-31G[a)]	0.77
SdS	46444	Tesla P100	63.01				
CYP76AH1	58511	Tesla P100	60.62				
		Tesla V100	108.06				

a) QChem-Amber Package: M06-2X/6-31G[a)]//f99SB, PBC condition with pseudo-atom for boundary MM-MD(50 ns) + Opt+FEP(500 ps) + Umbrella Sampling(20 ps), timestep = 1 fs; by 24cores@one node (CPU: E5-2692 v2@2.20GHz).

To address the computational cost of QM/MM MD simulations, especially for systems containing transition metals, efforts have been made to develop more efficient semi-empirical DFT methods. The self-consistent-charge-density-functional tight-binding (SCC-DFTB) method [82–84] was developed as a computationally efficient approximation to DFT. Similarly, Stefan Grimme has introduced the extended tight-binding (xTB) method [85], which is also designed to be computationally efficient while maintaining reasonable accuracy. These semi-empirical DFT methods can significantly reduce the computational cost of QM/MM MD simulations, making them more feasible for studying metalloenzymes and other systems containing transition metals. By carefully balancing the level of theory and computational cost, researchers can obtain valuable insights into the catalytic mechanisms and dynamics of these complex systems.

Notably, semi-empirical DFT methods enhanced computational efficiency, while may compromise on accuracy compared to higher-level QM methods [78, 86–91]. Therefore, it is essential to validate their outcomes against experimental data or higher-level QM calculations whenever possible. The following sections will focus on the practical applications of QM/MM methods in understanding the structure, function, and catalytic mechanisms of metalloenzymes.

References

1 Vilbert, A.C., Liu, Y., Dai, H., and Lu, Y. (2021). Recent advances in tuning redox properties of electron transfer centers in metalloenzymes catalyzing oxygen reduction reaction and H_2 oxidation important for fuel cells design. *Current Opinion in Electrochemistry* 30: 100780.

2 Sharma, K.K., Singh, D., Mohite, S.V. et al. (2023). Metal manipulators and regulators in human pathogens: A comprehensive review on microbial redox copper metalloenzymes "multicopper oxidases and superoxide dismutases". *International Journal of Biological Macromolecules* 233: 123534.

3 De Visser, S.P., Lin, Y.-T., Ali, H.S. et al. (2021). Negative catalysis/non-Bell-Evans-Polanyi reactivity by metalloenzymes: examples from mononuclear heme and non-heme iron oxygenases. *Coordination Chemistry Reviews* 439: 213914.

4 Guo, B., Chou, F., Huang, L. et al. (2022). Recent insights into oxidative metabolism of quercetin: catabolic profiles, degradation pathways, catalyzing metalloenzymes and molecular mechanisms. *Critical Reviews in Food Science and Nutrition* 64: 1312–1339.

5 Doboszewska, U., Wlaź, P., Nowak, G., and Młyniec, K. (2020). Targeting zinc metalloenzymes in coronavirus disease 2019. *British Journal of Pharmacology* 177: 4887–4898.

6 Palermo, G., Spinello, A., Saha, A., and Magistrato, A. (2021). Frontiers of metal-coordinating drug design. *Expert Opinion on Drug Discovery* 16: 497–511.

7 Mafy, N.N., Hudson, D.B., and Que, E.L. (2024). Control of metalloenzyme activity using photopharmacophores. *Coordination Chemistry Reviews* 499: 215485.

8 Chen, A.Y., Adamek, R.N., Dick, B.L. et al. (2019). Targeting metalloenzymes for therapeutic intervention. *Chemical Reviews* 119: 1323–1455.

9 Banerjee, R. and Lipscomb, J.D. (2021). Small-molecule tunnels in metalloenzymes viewed as extensions of the active site. *Accounts of Chemical Research* 54: 2185–2195.

10 Castro, C.B., Ferreira, M.P., and Marques Netto, C.G.C. (2021). Metalloenzyme mechanisms correlated to their turnover number and metal lability. *Current Research in Chemical Biology* 1: 100004.

11 Nguyen, R.C., Stagliano, C., and Liu, A. (2023). Structural insights into the half-of-sites reactivity in homodimeric and homotetrameric metalloenzymes. *Current Opinion in Chemical Biology* 75: 102332.

12 Masferrer-Rius, E. and Klein Gebbink, R.J.M. (2023). Non-noble metal aromatic oxidation catalysis: from metalloenzymes to synthetic complexes. *Catalysts* 13 (4): 773.

13 Kamerlin, S.C.L., Florián, J., and Warshel, A. (2008). Associative versus dissociative mechanisms of phosphate monoester hydrolysis: on the interpretation of activation entropies. *Chemphyschem: A European Journal of Chemical Physics and Physical Chemistry* 9: 1767–1773.

14 Frushicheva, M.P. and Warshel, A. (2012). Towards quantitative computer-aided studies of enzymatic enantioselectivity: the case of Candida antarctica lipase A. *Chembiochem: A European Journal of Chemical Biology* 13: 215–223.

15 Guo, H., Cui, Q., Lipscomb, W.N., and Karplus, M. (2003). Understanding the role of active-site residues in chorismate mutase catalysis from molecular-dynamics simulations. *Angewandte Chemie (International Ed. in English)* 42: 1508–1511.

16 Dobson, C.M., Šali, A., and Karplus, M. (1998). Protein folding: a perspective from theory and experiment. *Angewandte Chemie (International Ed. in English)* 37: 868–893.

17 Senn, H.M. and Thiel, W. (2009). QM/MM methods for biomolecular systems. *Angewandte Chemie (International Ed. in English)* 48: 1198–1229.

18 Warshel, A. and Levitt, M. (1976). Theoretical studies of enzymic reactions: dielectric, electrostatic and steric stabilization of the carbonium ion in the reaction of lysozyme. *Journal of Molecular Biology* 103: 227–249.

19 Berta, D., Buigues, P.J., Badaoui, M., and Rosta, E. (2020). Cations in motion: QM/MM studies of the dynamic and electrostatic roles of H^+ and Mg^{2+} ions in enzyme reactions. *Current Opinion in Structural Biology* 61: 198–206.

20 Zhang, F., Zeng, T., and Wu, R. (2023). QM/MM modeling aided enzyme engineering in natural products biosynthesis. *Journal of Chemical Information and Modeling* 63: 5018–5034.

21 Patel, D., Huma, Z.E., and Duncan, D. (2024). Reversible covalent inhibition–desired covalent adduct formation by mass action. *ACS Chemical Biology* 19: 824–838.

22 do Casal, M.T., Veys, K., Bousquet, M.H.E. et al. (2023). First-principles calculations of excited-state decay rate constants in organic fluorophores. *The Journal of Physical Chemistry A* 127: 10033–10053.

23 Osella, S. and Knippenberg, S. (2024). Photophysics in biomembranes: computational insight into the interaction between lipid bilayers and chromophores. *Accounts of Chemical Research* 57: 2245–2254.

24 Díaz Mirón, G. and González Lebrero, M.C. (2020). Fluorescence quantum yields in complex environments from QM-MM TDDFT simulations: the case of indole in different solvents. *The Journal of Physical Chemistry A* 124: 9503–9512.

25 Kar, R.K., Miller, A.-F., and Mroginski, M.-A. (2022). Understanding flavin electronic structure and spectra. *WIREs Computational Molecular Science* 12: e1541.

26 Zobel, J.P. and González, L. (2021). The quest to simulate excited-state dynamics of transition metal complexes. *JACS Au* 1: 1116–1140.

27 Guallar, V. and Friesner, R.A. (2004). Cytochrome P450CAM enzymatic catalysis cycle: a quantum mechanics/molecular mechanics study. *Journal of the American Chemical Society* 126: 8501–8508.

28 Lonsdale, R., Houghton, K.T., Żurek, J. et al. (2013). Quantum mechanics/molecular mechanics modeling of regioselectivity of drug metabolism in cytochrome P450 2C9. *Journal of the American Chemical Society* 135: 8001–8015.

29 Vidal-Limón, A.M., Tafoya, P., Santini, B.L. et al. (2017). Electron transfer pathways analysis of oxygen tolerant [NiFe]-hydrogenases for hydrogen production: A quantum mechanics/molecular mechanics – statistical coupled analysis. *International Journal of Hydrogen Energy* 42: 20494–20502.

30 Trohalaki, S. and Pachter, R. (2010). Mechanism of hydrogen production in [Fe–Fe]-hydrogenases: A quantum mechanics/molecular mechanics study. *International Journal of Hydrogen Energy* 35: 5318–5331.

31 Hedegård, E.D., Kongsted, J., and Ryde, U. (2015). Multiscale modeling of the active site of [Fe] hydrogenase: the H_2 binding site in open and closed protein conformations. *Angewandte Chemie International Edition* 54: 6246–6250.

32 Thorhallsson, A.T., Benediktsson, B., and Bjornsson, R. (2019). A model for dinitrogen binding in the E 4 state of nitrogenase. *Chemical Science* 10: 11110–11124.

33 Cao, L., Caldararu, O., and Ryde, U. (2018). Protonation and reduction of the FeMo cluster in nitrogenase studied by quantum mechanics/molecular mechanics (QM/MM) calculations. *Journal of Chemical Theory and Computation* 14: 6653–6678.

34 Jiang, H., Lundgren, K.J.M., and Ryde, U. (2023). Protonation of homocitrate and the E1 state of Fe-nitrogenase studied by QM/MM calculations. *Inorganic Chemistry* 62: 19433–19445.

35 Siegbahn, P.E.M. (2020). Theoretical study of O_2 reduction and water oxidation in multicopper oxidases. *The Journal of Physical Chemistry A* 124: 5849–5855.

36 Li, J., Farrokhnia, M., Rulíšek, L., and Ryde, U. (2015). Catalytic cycle of multicopper oxidases studied by combined quantum- and molecular-mechanical free-energy perturbation methods. *The Journal of Physical Chemistry B* 119: 8268–8284.

37 Ramachandran, K.I., Deepa, G., and Krishnan, N. (2008). *Computational Chemistry and Molecular Modeling*. Springer.

38 Allinger, N.L. (2011). Understanding molecular structure from molecular mechanics. *Journal of Computer-Aided Molecular Design* 25: 295–316.

39 He, X., Man, V.H., Yang, W. et al. (2020). A fast and high-quality charge model for the next generation general AMBER force field. *The Journal of Chemical Physics* 153: 114502.

40 Maier, J.A., Martinez, C., Kasavajhala, K. et al. (2015). ff14SB: improving the accuracy of protein side chain and backbone parameters from ff99SB. *Journal of Chemical Theory and Computation* 11: 3696–3713.

41 Pokorná, P., Kruse, H., Krepl, M., and Šponer, J. (2018). QM/MM calculations on protein–RNA complexes: understanding limitations of classical MD simulations and search for reliable cost-effective QM methods. *Journal of Chemical Theory and Computation* 14: 5419–5433.

42 van Gunsteren, W.F. and Oostenbrink, C. (2024). Methods for classical-mechanical molecular simulation in chemistry: achievements, limitations, perspectives. *Journal of Chemical Information and Modeling* 16: 6281–6304.

43 Møller, C. and Plesset, M.S. (1934). Note on an approximation treatment for many-electron systems. *Physical Review* 46: 618–622.

44 Slater, J.C. (1930). Note on Hartree's method. *Physical Review* 35: 210–211.

45 Kreibich, T. and Gross, E.K.U. (2001). Multicomponent density-functional theory for electrons and nuclei. *Physical Review Letters* 86: 2984–2987.

46 Fock, V. (1930). Näherungsmethode zur Lösung des quantenmechanischen Mehrkörperproblems. *Zeitschrift für Physik* 61: 126–148.

47 He, X. and Merz, K.M. Jr. (2010). Divide and conquer Hartree–Fock calculations on proteins. *Journal of Chemical Theory and Computation* 6: 405–411.

48 Whitfield, J.D., Schuch, N., and Verstraete, F. (2014). The computational complexity of density functional theory. In: *Many-Electron Approaches in Physics, Chemistry and Mathematics: A Multidisciplinary View* (ed. V. Bach and L. Delle Site), 245–260. Springer International Publishing.

49 Billeter, S.R., Turner, A.J., and Thiel, W. (2000). Linear scaling geometry optimisation and transition state search in hybrid delocalised internal coordinates. *Physical Chemistry Chemical Physics* 2: 2177–2186.

50 Lee, T., York, D.M., and Yang, W. (1996). Linear-scaling semiempirical quantum calculations for macromolecules. *The Journal of Chemical Physics* 105: 2744–2750.

51 Christensen, A.S., Kubař, T., Cui, Q., and Elstner, M. (2016). Semiempirical quantum mechanical methods for noncovalent interactions for chemical and biochemical applications. *Chemical Reviews* 116: 5301–5337.

52 Maseras, F. and Morokuma, K. (1995). IMOMM: a new integrated ab initio + molecular mechanics geometry optimization scheme of equilibrium structures and transition states. *Journal of Computational Chemistry* 16: 1170–1179.

53 Svensson, M., Humbel, S., Froese, R.D.J. et al. (1996). ONIOM: a multilayered integrated MO + MM method for geometry optimizations and single point energy predictions. A test for Diels–Alder reactions and $Pt(P(t\text{-}Bu)_3)_2 + H_2$ oxidative addition. *The Journal of Physical Chemistry* 100: 19357–19363.

54 Field, M.J., Bash, P.A., and Karplus, M. (1990). A combined quantum mechanical and molecular mechanical potential for molecular dynamics simulations. *Journal of Computational Chemistry* 11: 700–733.

55 Bakowies, D. and Thiel, W. (1996). Hybrid models for combined quantum mechanical and molecular mechanical approaches. *The Journal of Physical Chemistry* 100: 10580–10594.

56 Friesner, R.A. and Guallar, V. (2005). Ab initio quantum chemical and mixed quantum mechanics/molecular mechanics (QM/MM) methods for studying enzymatic catalysis. *Annual Review of Physical Chemistry* 56: 389–427.

57 Warshel, A. (2003). Computer simulations of enzyme catalysis: methods, progress, and insights. *Annual Review of Biophysics and Biomolecular Structure* 32: 425–443.

58 Lin, H. and Truhlar, D.G. (2007). QM/MM: what have we learned, where are we, and where do we go from here? *Theoretical Chemistry Accounts* 117: 185–199.

59 Vidossich, P. and Magistrato, A. (2014). QM/MM molecular dynamics studies of metal binding proteins. *Biomolecules* 4: 616–645.

60 Zlobin, A., Belyaeva, J., and Golovin, A. (2023). Challenges in protein QM/MM simulations with intra-backbone link atoms. *Journal of Chemical Information and Modeling* 63: 546–560.

61 Zhang, Y., Lee, T.-S., and Yang, W. (1999). A pseudobond approach to combining quantum mechanical and molecular mechanical methods. *The Journal of Chemical Physics* 110: 46–54.

62 Gao, J., Amara, P., Alhambra, C., and Field, M.J. (1998). A generalized hybrid orbital (GHO) method for the treatment of boundary atoms in combined QM/MM calculations. *The Journal of Physical Chemistry A* 102: 4714–4721.

63 Pu, J., Gao, J., and Truhlar, D.G. (2004). Generalized hybrid orbital (GHO) method for combining ab initio Hartree–Fock wave functions with molecular mechanics. *The Journal of Physical Chemistry A* 108: 632–650.

64 Fedorov, D.G., Jensen, J.H., Deka, R.C., and Kitaura, K. (2008). Covalent bond fragmentation suitable to describe solids in the fragment molecular orbital method. *The Journal of Physical Chemistry A* 112: 11808–11816.

65 Fedorov, D.G., Avramov, P.V., Jensen, J.H., and Kitaura, K. (2009). Analytic gradient for the adaptive frozen orbital bond detachment in the fragment molecular orbital method. *Chemical Physics Letters* 477: 169–175.

66 Gordon, M.S., Freitag, M.A., Bandyopadhyay, P. et al. (2001). The effective fragment potential method: A QM-based MM approach to modeling environmental effects in chemistry. *The Journal of Physical Chemistry A* 105: 293–307.

67 Olsen, J.M., Aidas, K., and Kongsted, J. (2010). Excited states in solution through polarizable embedding. *Journal of Chemical Theory and Computation* 6: 3721–3734.

68 Olsen, J.M.H. and Kongsted, J. (2011). Molecular properties through polarizable embedding. In: *Advances in Quantum Chemistry*, vol. 61 (ed. J.R. Sabin and E. Brändas), 107–143. Academic Press.

69 Wesolowski, T.A. and Warshel, A. (1993). Frozen density functional approach for ab initio calculations of solvated molecules. *The Journal of Physical Chemistry* 97: 8050–8053.

70 Wesolowski, T.A., Shedge, S., and Zhou, X. (2015). Frozen-density embedding strategy for multilevel simulations of electronic structure. *Chemical Reviews* 115: 5891–5928.

71 Case, D.A., Aktulga, H.M., Belfon, K. et al. (2023). AmberTools. *Journal of Chemical Information and Modeling* 63: 6183–6191.

72 Brooks, B.R., Brooks, C.L., MacKerell, A.D. et al. (2009). CHARMM: the biomolecular simulation program. *Journal of Computational Chemistry* 30: 1545–1614.

73 Jorgensen, W.L. and Tirado–Rives, J. (2005). Molecular modeling of organic and biomolecular systems using BOSS and MCPRO. *Journal of Computational Chemistry* 26: 1689–1700.

74 Jorgensen, W.L., Maxwell, D.S., and Tirado-Rives, J. (1996). Development and testing of the OPLS all-atom force field on conformational energetics and properties of organic liquids. *Journal of the American Chemical Society* 118: 11225–11236.

75 Robertson, M.J., Qian, Y., Robinson, M.C. et al. (2019). Development and Testing of the OPLS-AA/M Force Field for RNA. *Journal of Chemical Theory and Computation* 15: 2734–2742.

76 te Velde, G., Bickelhaupt, F.M., Baerends, E.J. et al. (2001). Chemistry with ADF. *Journal of Computational Chemistry* 22: 931–967.

77 Shao, Y., Gan, Z., Epifanovsky, E. et al. (2015). Advances in molecular quantum chemistry contained in the Q-Chem 4 program package. *Molecular Physics* 113: 184–215.

78 Lu, Y., Sen, K., Yong, C. et al. (2023). Multiscale QM/MM modelling of catalytic systems with ChemShell. *Physical Chemistry Chemical Physics* 25: 21816–21835.

79 Lu, Y., Farrow, M.R., Fayon, P. et al. (2019). Open-source, python-based redevelopment of the ChemShell multiscale QM/MM environment. *Journal of Chemical Theory and Computation* 15: 1317–1328.

80 Kästner, J., Carr, J.M., Keal, T.W. et al. (2009). DL-FIND: an open-source geometry optimizer for atomistic simulations. *The Journal of Physical Chemistry A* 113: 11856–11865.

81 Kühne, T.D., Iannuzzi, M., Del Ben, M. et al. (2020). CP2K: an electronic structure and molecular dynamics software package - Quickstep: efficient and accurate electronic structure calculations. *The Journal of Chemical Physics* 152: 194103.

82 Frauenheim, T., Seifert, G., Elsterner, M. et al. (2000). A self-consistent charge density-functional based tight-binding method for predictive materials simulations in physics, chemistry and biology. *Physica Status Solidi (B)* 217: 41–62.

83 Kullgren, J., Wolf, M.J., Hermansson, K. et al. (2017). Self-consistent-charge density-functional tight-binding (SCC-DFTB) parameters for ceria in 0D to 3D. *The Journal of Physical Chemistry C* 121: 4593–4607.

84 Elstner, M., Porezag, D., Jungnickel, G. et al. (1998). Self-consistent-charge density-functional tight-binding method for simulations of complex materials properties. *Physical Review B* 58: 7260–7268.

85 Bannwarth, C., Ehlert, S., and Grimme, S. (2019). GFN2-xTB—an accurate and broadly parametrized self-consistent tight-binding quantum chemical method with multipole electrostatics and density-dependent dispersion contributions. *Journal of Chemical Theory and Computation* 15: 1652–1671.

86 Elstner, M. (2006). The SCC-DFTB method and its application to biological systems. *Theoretical Chemistry Accounts* 116: 316–325.

87 Elstner, M., Frauenheim, T., and Suhai, S. (2003). An approximate DFT method for QM/MM simulations of biological structures and processes. *Journal of Molecular Structure: THEOCHEM* 632: 29–41.

88 Titmuss, S.J., Cummins, P.L., Rendell, A.P. et al. (2002). Comparison of linear-scaling semiempirical methods and combined quantum mechanical/molecular mechanical methods for enzymic reactions. II. An energy decomposition analysis. *Journal of Computational Chemistry* 23: 1314–1322.

89 Tzeliou, C.E., Mermigki, M.A., and Tzeli, D. (2022). Review on the QM/MM methodologies and their application to metalloproteins. *Molecules* 27 (9): 2660.

90 Kulkarni, P.U., Shah, H., and Vyas, V.K. (2022). Hybrid quantum mechanics/molecular mechanics (QM/MM) simulation: a tool for structure-based drug design and discovery. *Mini Reviews in Medicinal Chemistry* 22: 1096–1107.

91 Adrian Bramley, G., Tomos Beynon, O., Viktorovich Stishenko, P., and James Logsdail, A. (2023). The application of QM/MM simulations in heterogeneous catalysis. *Physical Chemistry Chemical Physics* 25: 6562–6585.

Section II

3.3 Application of the QM/MM Methods in Metalloenzymes

3.3.1 Heme Enzymes

Heme enzymes are a remarkable class of proteins that contain an iron-porphyrin complex (heme) as a prosthetic group. The unique electronic structure and chemical bonding of the heme cofactor endow these enzymes with the capability to achieve a

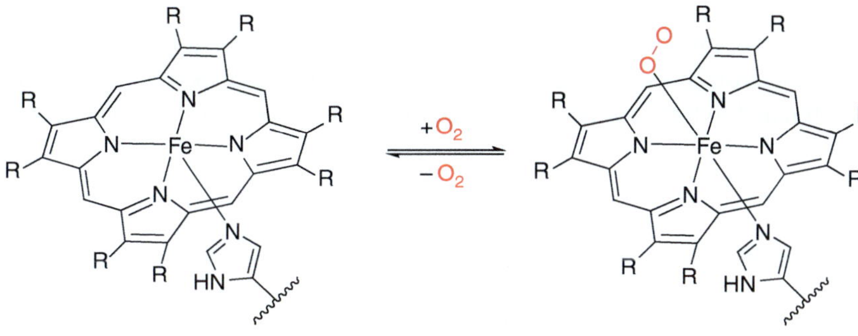

Figure 3.4 The role of heme in binding and releasing O_2.

wide range of critical biological functions, particularly in the management of oxygen (O_2), as shown in Figure 3.4 [1, 2]. The iron atom in heme can access multiple oxidation and spin states, allowing it to participate in diverse redox reactions and O_2 binding, transport, and storage. The porphyrin macrocycle provides a stable coordination environment for iron while also allowing fine-tuning of its electronic properties through interactions with the protein scaffold [3].

3.3.1.1 Cytochrome P450 Enzymes

Cytochrome P^{450} (CYP) enzymes are a family of heme enzymes involved in the metabolism of drugs, xenobiotics, and endogenous compounds [4, 5]. QM/MM studies have been widely used to elucidate the role of the active site residues, the heme group, and the substrate binding in the catalytic process [6–8]. These studies have provided insights into the regio- and stereoselectivity of cytochrome P^{450} enzymes and have aided in the rational design of improved biocatalysts.

The cytochrome P^{450} enzymes follow a general catalytic cycle that involves several key intermediates and transitions (as shown in Figure 3.5) [9, 10]. The cycle begins with the resting state (1), where the ferric heme is coordinated to a proximal cysteine residue and a water molecule. Substrate binding displaces the water ligand, forming a pentacoordinated ferric-porphyrin complex (2) and changing the spin state from low-spin to high-spin. This change facilitates the first electron transfer from a

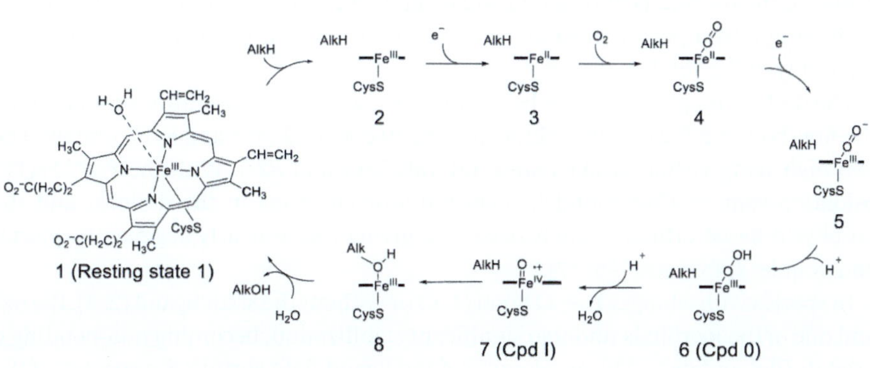

Figure 3.5 Catalytic mechanism of CYP enzymes.

reductase protein, yielding a high-spin ferrous complex (3). Molecular oxygen binds to the ferrous complex, forming an oxy-ferrous complex (4) with a singlet spin state. A second electron transfer generates the ferric-peroxo anion species (5), which is then protonated to form the ferric-hydroperoxide species (6), known as Compound 0 (Cpd 0). Another protonation event leads to the splitting of a water molecule and the formation of the high-valent iron-oxo species (7), called Compound I (Cpd I).

Cpd I is the active species that monooxygenates the substrate, e.g. converting an alkane to an alcohol (8). The product then exits the active site, allowing water molecules to re-enter and regenerate the resting state (1) [11].

The catalytic cycle requires a protonation machinery, believed to involve an acid-alcohol pair (e.g. Asp^{251} and Thr^{252} in CYP^{101}) and water molecules [12]. The control of water access to the active site is crucial for efficient catalysis, as too much water can lead to uncoupling products. Substrate binding and interactions between the cysteinate ligand and nearby residues also play a role in regulating the enzyme's activity.

The oxidation state formalism is a useful tool for understanding the electronic structure of the species in the P^{450} catalytic cycle [13]. In this formalism, the porphyrin ligand has an oxidation number of 2-, the cysteine ligand is 1-, and any molecular ligand with an electronic octet (like water) is counted as zero. The oxidation number of iron is determined by the number of electrons it needs to achieve a stable electronic configuration.

The resting state (1) and the pentacoordinated complex (2) have an iron oxidation state of Fe(III). After accepting one electron from the reductase, the pentacoordinate complex (3) becomes Fe(II). The oxy-ferrous complex (4) can be formally written as Fe(II)-O_2, but its bonding features are more appropriately represented by Fe(III)-O_2^-. The reduced complex (5) is a ferric-peroxy species, Fe(III)-O_2^{2-}. Compound 0 (6) is a ferric-hydroperoxide, Fe(III)-OOH, while Compound I (7) has a formal oxidation state of the entire heme as 5+, with Fe(IV) and a porphyrin π-cation-radical $Por^{\bullet+}$ [14, 15]. The product complex (8) is a neutral Fe(III) species.

The orbital labels and ground state configurations are shown for species 1–3, 6, and 7. Each species has five d-type orbitals, which differ depending on the interaction of the d-orbitals with the ligand orbitals. In Compound I (7), there is also a high-lying mixed porphyrin-thiolate orbital (a2u), which is sensitive to the donor capability of the thiolate ligand.

The d-block is split into three-below-two sets, with the lowest three orbitals being the non-bonding $\delta(dx^2 - y^2)$ orbital and the two π Fe-O (πxz and πyz) orbitals. The two high-lying virtual orbitals are σ orbitals (σxy and σz^2). With the $Por^{\bullet+}$Fe(IV) oxidation state in Compound I, there are four electrons in the d-block, and the porphyrin-based orbital is singly occupied, giving rise to nearly degenerate quartet and doublet spin states [16, 17].

In species with a longer Fe—O bond (1, 6) or without the sixth ligand (2, 3), the σz^2 and one of the π orbitals undergo significant stabilization, becoming non-bonding d orbitals (dz^2 and dxz). This weakening of the ligand field shrinks the spacing of the d-orbitals, leading to low-lying high-spin states as ground states.

3.3.1.2 Peroxidases

Peroxidases are a diverse class of heme enzymes that catalyze the oxidation of various substrates using hydrogen peroxide (H_2O_2) or other peroxides as the electron acceptor [18]. These enzymes play crucial roles in a wide range of biological processes, including the detoxification of reactive oxygen species [19], lignin degradation [20], and the synthesis of hormones and other signaling molecules [21]. The most well-studied peroxidases include horseradish peroxidase (HRP), cytochrome c peroxidase (CcP), and lignin peroxidase (LiP).

The catalytic cycle of peroxidases involves the formation of several distinct intermediates, each with unique spectroscopic and reactivity properties [22]. The resting state of the enzyme, known as the ferric (Fe(III)) state, reacts with H_2O_2 to form an oxo-ferryl (Fe(IV) = O) porphyrin π-cation radical intermediate, known as Compound I. Compound I then oxidizes the substrate by two sequential one-electron transfer steps, forming Compound II (Fe(IV) = O) and subsequently returning to the resting state [23]. The catalytic efficiency and substrate specificity of peroxidases are greatly influenced by the protein environment surrounding the heme cofactor, which modulates the electronic structure and reactivity of the heme center [24].

The catalytic cycle, as shown in Figure 3.6, begins with the resting state of the enzyme (1), which contains a ferric heme (Fe(III)). Binding of H_2O_2 to the ferric heme results in the formation of an iron(III)-peroxide complex (2) (analogous to Compound 0 of P450). The reaction of the ferric heme with H_2O_2 leads to the formation of the first reactive intermediate, known as Compound I (3a). Compound

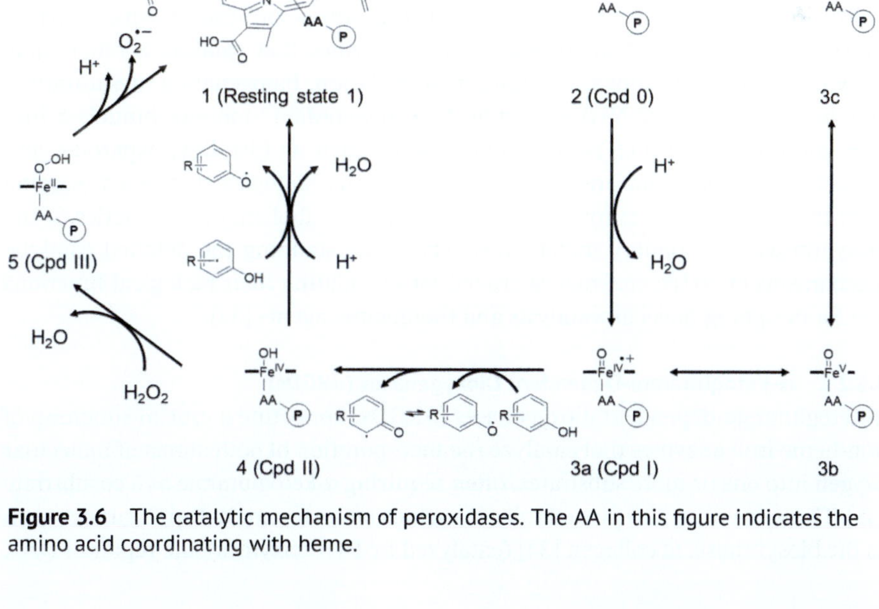

Figure 3.6 The catalytic mechanism of peroxidases. The AA in this figure indicates the amino acid coordinating with heme.

I also exists in different mesomeric forms: (3b) oxo-iron(V) complex, (3c) oxo-radical ferryl complex. QM/MM studies have provided valuable insights into the electronic structure of Compound I, which is best described as an oxo-ferryl porphyrin π-cation radical ($Fe(IV) = O^{\bullet +}$) [25]. The high-valent iron center and the porphyrin radical confer a high degree of reactivity to Compound I, enabling it to oxidize a wide range of substrates.

QM/MM calculations have also shed light on the role of the distal histidine residue in the formation and stabilization of Compound I [26, 27]. The distal histidine acts as an acid–base catalyst, facilitating the heterolytic cleavage of the O—O bond in H_2O_2 and the subsequent proton transfer to the distal oxygen atom. This process is crucial for the efficient formation of Compound I and the prevention of side reactions, such as the formation of inactive ferric-superoxide species.

Upon formation, Compound I facilitates substrate oxidation through a single-electron transfer process, generating a substrate radical (refer to Figure 6.6 using phenolic substrate as an example) and Compound II (4) (Fe(IV)-OH). QM/MM investigations have illuminated key factors influencing Compound's reactivity toward different substrates, such as the redox potential of the substrate, the accessibility of the active site, and the nature of the substrate binding interactions [28]. Compound II then oxidizes a second substrate molecule through another single-electron transfer, regenerating the ferric resting state and completing the catalytic cycle. Beyond the primary catalytic pathway, peroxidases can also undergo side reactions, for instance, forming Compound III, a ferrous-superoxide species ($Fe(II)\text{-}O_2^{\bullet -}$), under certain conditions [29]. However, Compound III is an inactive form of the catalytic activity.

3.3.2 Non-Heme Iron Enzymes

While iron is commonly found in heme cofactors, a significant number of enzymes utilize iron in non-heme environments. These non-heme iron enzymes (NHFe) constitute a diverse and important class of enzymes that catalyze a remarkable array of oxidation reactions, including hydroxylation, halogenation, desaturation, and dioxygenation [30]. NHFe enzymes typically contain mono- or binuclear iron sites coordinated by (O,N)-containing ligands, such as histidine, aspartate, and glutamate residues, and are involved in numerous biological processes, ranging from the synthesis of neurotransmitters and the metabolism of xenobiotics to the biosynthesis of secondary metabolites [31]. Understanding the detailed catalytic mechanisms of NHFe enzymes is crucial for elucidating their biological functions and for designing novel biocatalysts and therapeutic agents [32].

3.3.2.1 α-Ketoglutarate-Dependent Dioxygenases (αKGDs)

α-Ketoglutarate-dependent dioxygenases (αKGDs) constitute a crucial subgroup of non-heme iron enzymes that catalyze the incorporation of both atoms of molecular oxygen into one or more substrates, often requiring α-ketoglutarate as a cosubstrate [33]. These enzymes play pivotal roles in various biotechnological applications, such as the biosynthesis of collagen [34] (catalyzed by P4H enzymes), the repair of DNA or RNA (mediated by AlkB repair enzymes) [35], and the synthesis of antibiotics like fosfomycin [36] and viomycin [37]. Despite the diversity of their substrates and biological functions, αKGDs share a common catalytic mechanism, which involves the formation of a highly reactive Fe(IV)-oxo complex responsible for the oxidation of unactivated C-H bonds within the substrate. Structurally, αKGDs are characterized by a conserved double-stranded β-helix (DSBH or cupin) fold that houses a distinctive iron-binding motif (His^1-X-Asp/Glu-Xn-His^2) [38]. The iron center is further coordinated by α-ketoglutarate, which plays a crucial role in the activation of molecular oxygen during the catalytic cycle [39].

The proposed reaction mechanism of αKGDs involves several key steps, as illustrated in Figure 3.7 [40]. The catalytic cycle begins with the Fe(II) center in its initial state (I), followed by the binding of α-ketoglutarate (αKG) to the metal ion in a bidentate configuration (II). The cofactor αKG coordinates to the Fe(II) through its C2 keto oxygen and C1 carboxylate moieties. Subsequently, an O_2 molecule binds to the Fe(II) center (III or IV), setting the stage for the catalytic reaction [39].

The consensus mechanism of αKGDs (Figure 3.7) proceeds via the oxidative decarboxylation of the cosubstrate αKG, leading to the formation of a highly reactive Fe(IV)-oxo complex (V) [41, 42]. This irreversible decarboxylation step is a hallmark of the αKGD catalytic cycle and is essential for the activation of the Fe(II) center and the generation of the potent oxidizing species. The Fe(IV)-oxo intermediate then acts as the initiator for the hydroxylation of the primary substrate.

The hydrogen atom transfer (HAT) is a critical step in the catalytic cycle of αKGDs.

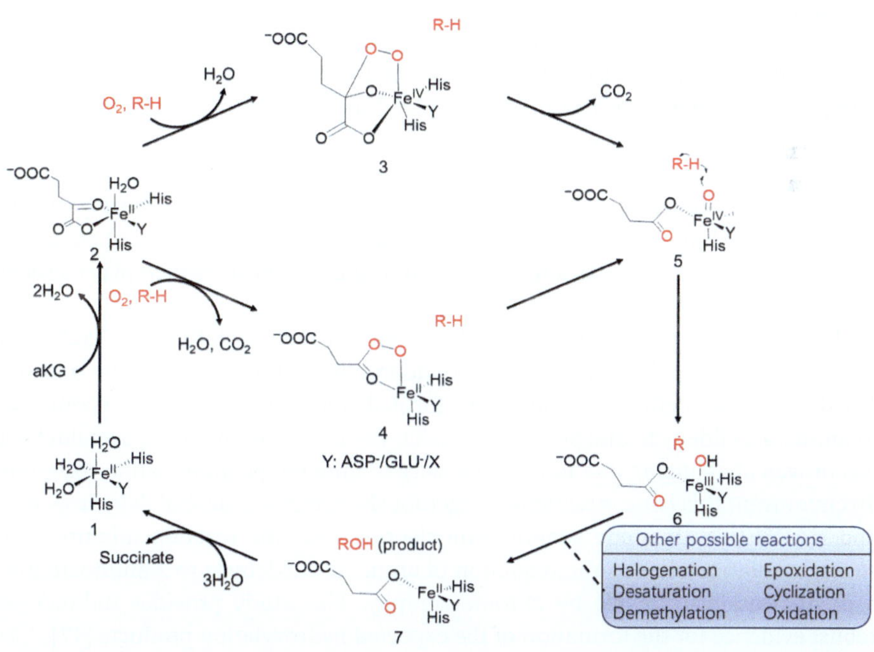

Figure 3.7 Proposed reaction mechanism of Fe(II)/α-ketoglutarate-dependent dioxygenases.

In the case of taurine/α-ketoglutarate dioxygenase (TauD), an extensively studied member of the αKGD family, catalyzes the formation of amino acetaldehyde and sulfite from taurine in bacteria such as *Escherichia coli*, the HAT involves the abstraction of a hydrogen atom from the singlet ($S = 0$) taurine moiety by the oxygen of an iron-oxo complex, initially residing in a quintet ($S = 2$) state. DFT calculations have provided a clearer understanding on the electronic structure of the Fe(IV)-oxo intermediate and the underlying factors that govern its unusual $S = 2$ ground state. These studies have shown that the quintet ground state can be rationalized by considering the splitting of the d-orbitals in a trigonal bipyramidal ligand field. In this geometry, the d-orbitals split into a high-energy a1 orbital and two sets of lower-lying e orbitals, with the latter accommodating four unpaired electrons, resulting in the experimentally observed $S = 2$ ground state [43].

The HAT process in TauD is proven to occur via a concerted mechanism, where the hydrogen atom is abstracted along with its electron from the taurine substrate by the Fe(IV)-oxo species, leading to the formation of an Fe(III)-OH intermediate and a substrate radical. After the HAT, the remaining taurine radical exists in a doublet state ($S = 1/2$), coupled antiferromagnetically to the Fe(III)-OH species in a sextet state ($S = 5/2$). These formal spin states have been confirmed by analyzing the spin densities projected on individual atoms in QM/MM snapshots. The taurine spin density changes from 0 to −1, corresponding to a spin-down $S = 1/2$ state after the HAT, while the spin density on the iron-oxo complex is mostly centered on the iron atom in the product Fe(III)-OH state. The smaller spin density observed on the ligands can be attributed to the partially covalent bonding between the iron and its ligands [43].

Interestingly, gas-phase studies have suggested that the HAT process may be divided into two distinct steps [44, 45]: (a) the formation of a "preparatory stage," interpreted as a highly electrophilic Fe(III)-oxyl species, and (b) the actual hydrogen transfer. However, QM/MM simulations of the HAT process in TauD have provided evidence for a concerted mechanism, where the hydrogen atom and its electron are abstracted simultaneously by the Fe(IV)-oxo species to form the Fe(III)-OH intermediate. Moreover, these studies have highlighted the significant enhancement of the HAT reaction by quantum mechanical tunneling effects, which play a crucial role in facilitating the hydrogen transfer process [46].

The final products of the taurine hydroxylation reaction catalyzed by TauD have been indirectly identified through chromatographic techniques [47]. The unstable 1-hydroxy-2-aminoethanesulfonic acid, formed upon hydroxylation, decomposes to amino acetaldehyde and sulfite. However, the detection of amino acetaldehyde has proven challenging due to its propensity to undergo polymerization reactions. To circumvent this issue, researchers ingeniously integrated alcohol dehydrogenase and NADH (nicotinamide adenine dinucleotide) into the reaction mixture. This strategic addition enables the reduction of amino acetaldehyde to 2-aminoethanol, a product easily traceable by chromatography. This study provides indirect yet robust evidence for the formation of the expected hydroxylation products [47].

3.3.2.2 Pterin-Dependent Hydroxylases

Pterin-dependent hydroxylases are a class of mononuclear non-heme iron enzymes that catalyze the hydroxylation of aromatic amino acids and other substrates using molecular oxygen and a pterin cofactor [48], such as tetrahydrobiopterin (BH4) or tetrahydrofolate (THF) [49, 50]. These enzymes play crucial roles in various biological processes, including the synthesis of neurotransmitters, the degradation of amino acids, and the biosynthesis of antibiotics. The most well-studied examples of pterin-dependent hydroxylases include phenylalanine hydroxylase (PAH) [51], tyrosine hydroxylase (TH), and tryptophan hydroxylase (TPH) [52]. PAH catalyzes the hydroxylation of phenylalanine to tyrosine, which is the rate-limiting step in the catabolism of phenylalanine and the biosynthesis of tyrosine [53]. TH and TPH play pivotal roles in the biosynthesis of dopamine and serotonin [54], respectively, by catalyzing the hydroxylation of tyrosine and tryptophan, thereby contributing to the production of these essential neurotransmitters.

Pterin-dependent hydroxylases share a common structural fold, which consists of an N-terminal regulatory domain, a catalytic domain, and a C-terminal tetramerization domain. The catalytic domain contains a non-heme iron center that is coordinated by two histidine residues and a glutamate residue [55, 56], forming a His-His-Glu triad [38]. This iron center is the site of oxygen activation and substrate hydroxylation. The pterin cofactor, which is essential for the catalytic activity of these enzymes, is bound in a pocket adjacent to the iron center. The role of the pterin cofactor is to provide electrons for the reduction of the iron center and the activation of molecular oxygen. The oxidation state of the pterin cofactor cycles between the tetrahydro and dihydro forms during the catalytic cycle [54].

Despite the biological importance of pterin-dependent hydroxylases and the availability of high-resolution crystal structures, the detailed catalytic mechanism of these enzymes has remained elusive. The hydroxylation reaction is a complex multistep process that involves the activation of molecular oxygen, the formation of reactive iron-oxo intermediates, and the transfer of an oxygen atom to the substrate [57, 58].

The catalytic cycle (as shown in Figure 3.8) begins with the enzyme in its resting state, where the non-heme iron center is in the ferrous (Fe(II)) state and is coordinated by the 2-His-1-carboxylate facial triad [58]. The pterin cofactor, in its tetrahydro form (e.g. tetrahydrobiopterin, BH4), is bound in a pocket adjacent to the iron center. The substrate (e.g. phenylalanine, tyrosine, or tryptophan) binds to the active site, displacing a water molecule and forming a ternary complex with the enzyme and the pterin cofactor [50, 59]. The next step involves the binding and activation of molecular oxygen by the iron center, which involves the transfer of an electron from the pterin cofactor to the iron center, forming a ferric-superoxo (Fe(III)-O2$^{\bullet-}$) intermediate. The pterin cofactor is thus oxidized to its dihydro form (e.g. dihydrobiopterin, BH2). The ferric-superoxo intermediate then undergoes a second electron transfer from the pterin cofactor, coupled with a proton transfer from the active site, leading to the formation of a high-valent iron-oxo (Fe(IV) = O) intermediate, also known as the ferryl species [60]. The ferryl intermediate is the key oxidant in the hydroxylation reaction, and its formation is considered to be the rate-limiting step in the catalytic cycle. The ferryl intermediate then attacks the aromatic ring of the substrate, leading to the formation of a hydroxylated product and a ferric-hydroxo (Fe(III)-OH) species. The hydroxylated product then

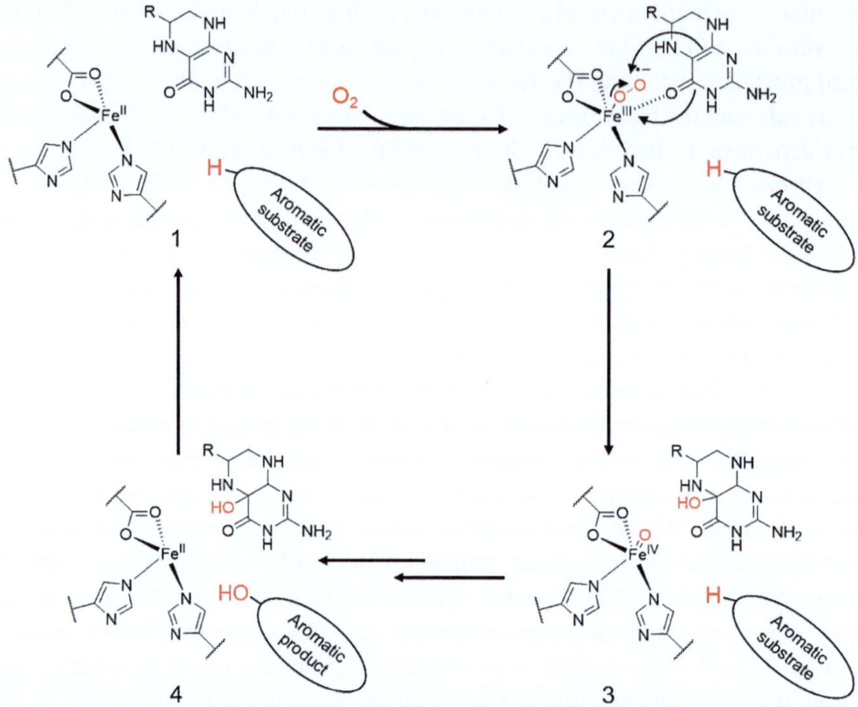

Figure 3.8 The catalytic mechanism of pterin-dependent hydroxylases.

dissociates from the active site, regenerating the ferrous enzyme and completing the catalytic cycle [61–64].

3.3.3 Copper Enzymes

Copper enzymes, a class of proteins that contain copper ions as essential cofactors, have garnered significant attention due to their crucial roles in various biological processes. The unique redox properties of copper enable these enzymes to perform a wide range of functions, particularly in redox reactions and electron transfer processes. Copper primarily exists in two oxidation states, Cu(I) and Cu(II), and can adopt different coordination environments within the protein scaffold. This versatility allows copper enzymes to participate in catalytic cycles involving the oxidation and reduction of diverse substrates, making them indispensable for many biochemical pathways [65, 66].

3.3.3.1 Copper-Dependent Lytic Polysaccharide Monooxygenases (LPMOs)

Lytic polysaccharide monooxygenases (LPMOs) play a crucial role in the degradation of recalcitrant polysaccharides, such as cellulose, chitin, and starch. These enzymes have attracted significant attention due to their potential applications in the production of biofuels and other value-added products from biomass. LPMOs distinguish themselves from other copper enzymes by uniquely harnessing a single

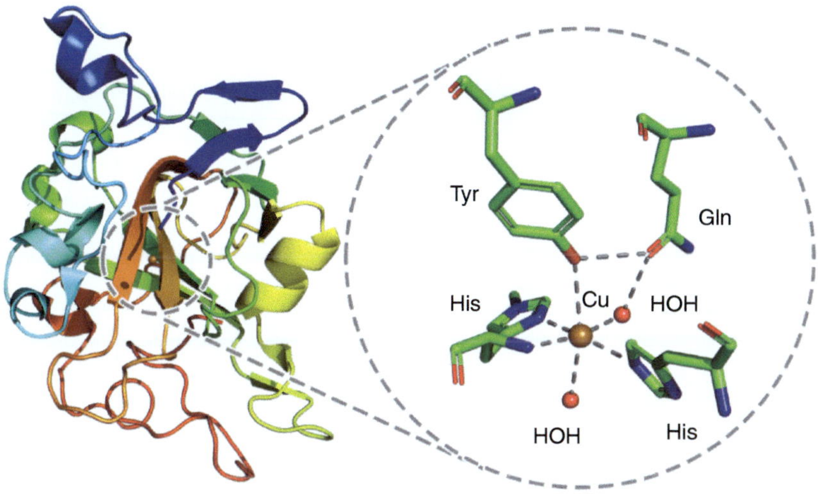

Figure 3.9 The active site of LPMOs (PDB ID: 2YET).

copper ion in their active site to activate molecular oxygen, enabling oxidative cleavage of glycosidic bonds [67, 68]. This mechanism contrasts sharply with the most copper-dependent oxygenases, which commonly utilize a binuclear copper center, or a mononuclear copper center aided by an organic cofactor like tyrosine or cysteine.

The active site of LPMOs (Figure 3.9) consists of a mononuclear copper center coordinated by two conserved histidine residues (the so-called histidine brace) and a terminal amine group from the N-terminus of the protein [69, 70]. This unique coordination geometry is thought to be essential for the enzyme's catalytic activity and selectivity. LPMOs are classified into several families based on their sequence similarity and substrate specificity. The most well-studied LPMO families are the auxiliary activity family 9 (AA9) [67] and 10 (AA10) [71], specializing in cellulose and chitin degradation, respectively. Recent discoveries have unveiled additional families, AA11 [72], AA13 [73], and AA14 [74], each with different substrate preferences, including starch and xylan.

The discovery of LPMOs has revolutionized our understanding of the enzymatic degradation of polysaccharides. Previously, it was thought that the degradation of recalcitrant polysaccharides, such as cellulose, was primarily carried out by hydrolytic enzymes, such as cellulases. However, the identification of LPMOs has revealed that oxidative cleavage plays a significant role in the depolymerization of these substrates, making them more accessible to hydrolytic enzymes [71].

The catalytic cycle of LPMOs (Figure 3.10) begins with the enzyme in its resting state, where the copper ion is in the Cu(I) oxidation state and is coordinated by the histidine brace and the terminal amine group [75]. The binding of the polysaccharide substrate, such as cellulose or chitin, to the enzyme's active site is accompanied by the displacement of a water molecule from the copper coordination sphere, creating an open coordination site for the binding of molecular oxygen.

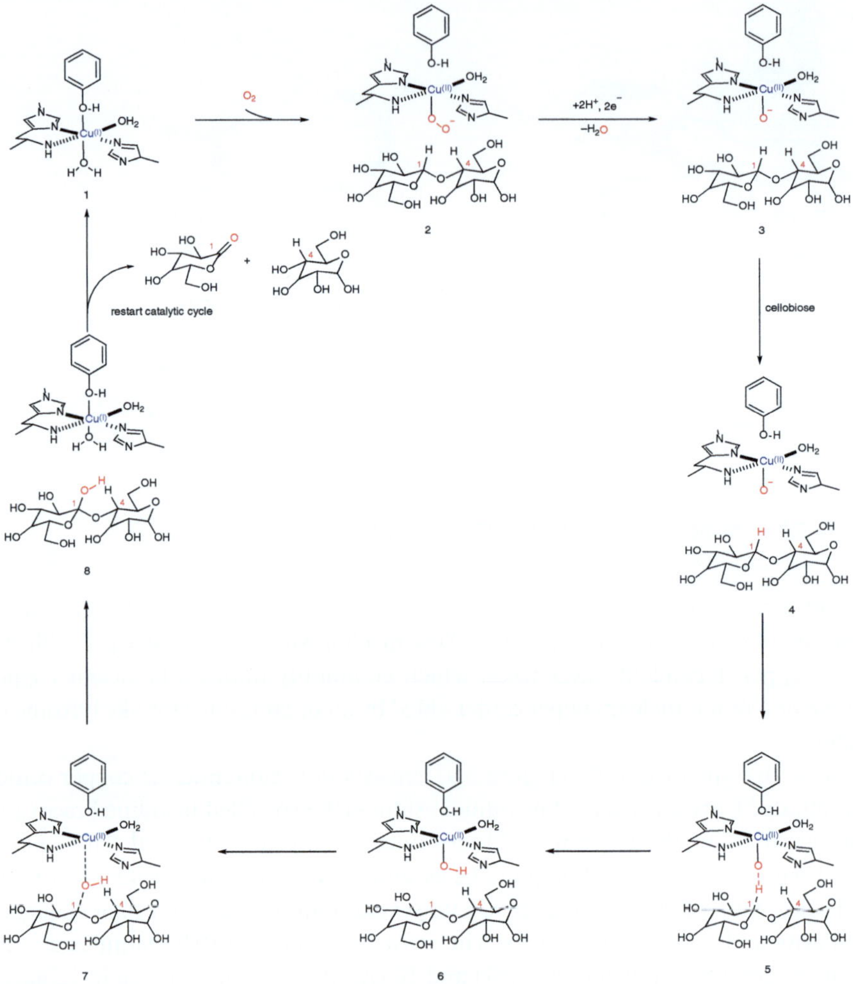

Figure 3.10 The catalytic mechanism of LPMOs.

The binding of O_2 to the copper ion results in the formation of a Cu(II)-superoxide intermediate, which has been characterized spectroscopically and computationally [76]. The formation of this intermediate is thought to be facilitated by the unique coordination environment provided by the histidine brace, which stabilizes the Cu(II) oxidation state and promotes the transfer of an electron from the copper ion to the bound oxygen.

The Cu(II)-superoxide intermediate then undergoes a one-electron reduction, coupled with the transfer of a proton from a nearby conserved residue (usually a glutamate or an aspartate), leading to the formation of a Cu(II)-hydroperoxide species [77].

The Cu(II)-hydroperoxide intermediate is believed to be the key species responsible for the oxidative cleavage of the glycosidic bond [78, 79]. Two main pathways have been proposed for this reaction: the "oxygen rebound" mechanism and the "substrate-assisted" mechanism.

In the oxygen rebound mechanism [80], the Cu(II)-hydroperoxide intermediate undergoes a homolytic cleavage of the O—O bond, generating a highly reactive Cu(III)-oxyl radical species and a hydroxide ion. The Cu(III)-oxyl radical then abstracts a hydrogen atom from the C1 or C4 position of the glycosidic bond, leading to the formation of a substrate radical intermediate. This intermediate then rebounds with the hydroxide ion, resulting in the hydroxylation of the substrate and the cleavage of the glycosidic bond.

In the substrate-assisted mechanism [81], the Cu(II)-hydroperoxide intermediate performs a direct attack on the C1 or C4 position of the glycosidic bond, leading to the formation of a cyclic peroxide intermediate. This intermediate then decomposes, resulting in the cleavage of the glycosidic bond and the formation of a lactone or ketone product.

Kim et al. [80] studied the above possible pathways for the oxidative cleavage of the glycosidic bond through DFT calculations. Results indicated that Cu-oxyl, oxygen-rebound mechanism showed a significantly lower energy barrier. Thus, the catalytic mechanism depicted in Figure 3.10 follows the oxygen rebound pathway.

3.3.3.2 Lysyl Oxidase (LOX) Enzymes

Lysyl oxidase (LOX) enzymes are key players in the remodeling of the extracellular matrix (ECM) [82] and stabilization of connective tissue in various organisms [83], including humans. This enzyme family comprises five known members: LOX, LOXL1, LOXL2, LOXL3, and LOXL4, each possessing unique yet overlapping biological functions [84, 85]. LOXL2 is particularly significant for its role in cross-linking collagen and elastin within the ECM [86]. LOXL2 catalyzes the oxidative deamination of lysine and hydroxylysine residues, forming aldehydes that lead to the cross-linking of collagen and elastin in the ECM. This cross-linking process is crucial for maintaining tissue stability and elasticity. Understanding the structure and catalytic mechanism of LOXL2 is of great importance, as it can provide insights into its function and potential therapeutic targets for diseases related to ECM dysfunction, such as fibrosis and cancer [83, 85].

The structure of LOXL2 consists of two main domains: the N-terminal domain, which contains four scavenger receptor cysteine-rich (SRCR) domains, and the C-terminal catalytic domain. The SRCR domains are involved in substrate recognition and binding, enhancing the enzyme's substrate specificity. The catalytic domain houses the active site, which includes a critical copper ion essential for the enzyme's catalytic activity. This copper ion is coordinated by specific histidine residues and plays a vital role in the redox reactions catalyzed by LOXL2 [87].

LOXL2's catalytic process involves two main steps: the formation of LTQ (lysine tyrosylquinone) and the subsequent catalytic reaction of LTQ with lysine [88]. Key residues, including histidine and lysine, coordinate the copper ion and stabilize reaction intermediates (Figure 3.11) [89, 90]. Posttranslational modifications like tyrosine cross-linking may also influence the enzyme's function. The binding of specific lipids and ligands modulates LOXL2's activity and stability, while interactions

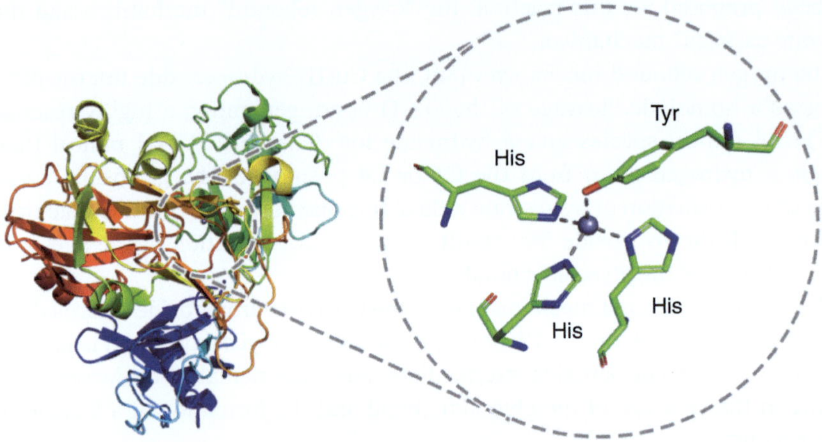

Figure 3.11 The active site of LOX enzymes (PDB ID: 5ZE3).

with ECM components hint at regulatory functions. Integrating structural analysis with QM/MM computation provides a comprehensive understanding of LOXL2's catalytic mechanism, emphasizing the critical role of its metal center and the sequential substrate oxidation to product formation. This knowledge can guide future therapeutic targeting of LOXL2 in diseases related to ECM dysfunction. Dong et al. [88] studied the reaction mechanism of LOXL2 with QM/MM simulations, and the reaction pathway can be summarized as follows.

As shown in Figure 3.12, in the first main step of LTQ Formation, the dioxygen binds to copper ion. Initially, O_2 enters the active site of LOXL2. Studies show that before O_2 binding, the copper ion is in the Cu^+ state with a tyrosine radical. After O_2 binding, it forms a Cu^{2+}-superoxide-tyrosine radical. DPQ (dopaquinone) is an intermediate. After O_2 binds to the copper ion, the superoxide group attacks the C-5 position of Tyr^{689}, forming a Cu-peroxide species (Int1), accompanied by electron transfer. Subsequently, a proton transfers from C-5 to a water molecule, forming Int2. The cleavage of the O—O bond then generates DPQ radical (DPQr) and Cu^{2+}—$O^\bullet$. In forming LTQ, the Nε atom of Lys^{653} attacks the C-2 position of DPQr. Cu^{2+}—$O^\bullet$ abstracts a hydrogen atom from DPQr or Lys^{653}, with the latter being more favorable. Lys^{653}'s ε-amino group then attacks Tyr^{689}'s C-2, forming Int4 and releasing significant energy. The Cu^{2+}—OH further obtains a hydrogen atom from C-2 position, forming Int5. Finally, a proton transfers from Lys^{653} to His^{652}, producing the reduced LTQ (rLTQ), which is oxidized by a second O_2 to form LTQ, preparing for the oxidative deamination of lysine [88].

In the subsequent catalytic reaction of LTQ with lysine, the Schiff base was first formed (Figure 3.13). The Nε atom of lysine attacks the C-5 atom on LTQ, forming $Int1_O$. Proton transfer from Nε to O-5, facilitated by a water molecule, forms the more stable $Int2_O$. Cleavage of the C-5 and O-5 bond produces the Schiff base $Int3_O$. Proton transfer from the Cε of lysine to His^{303} forms the more stable $Int4_O$. After that, the aldehyde product was formed. The Schiff base $Int4_O$ reacts with water to form the aldehyde. The oxygen atom of water attacks the Cε of lysine, forming $Int5_O$, with

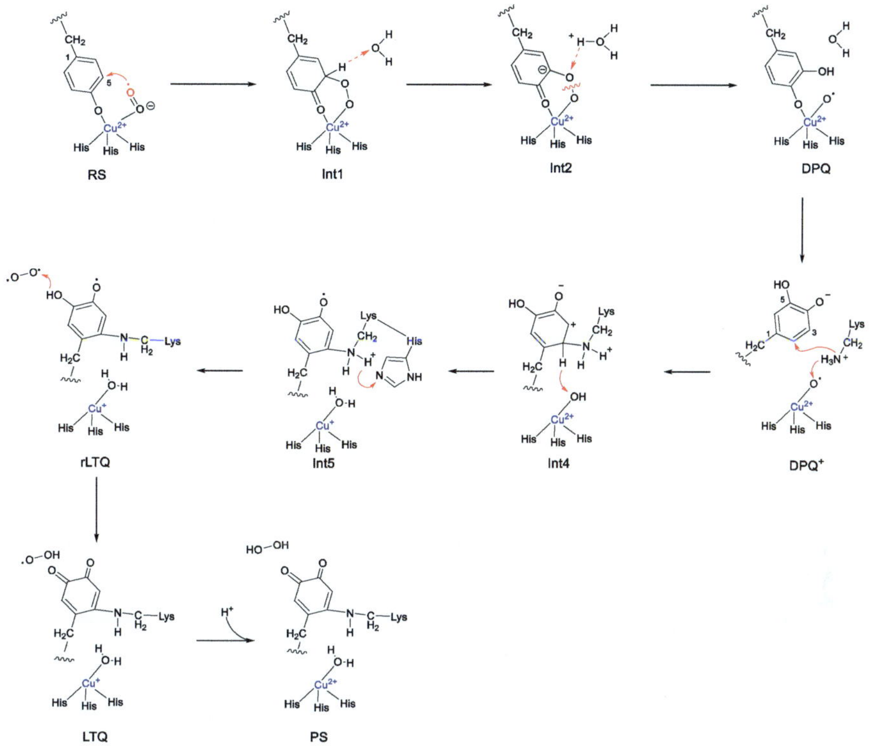

Figure 3.12 The first stage of the catalytic mechanism of LOXL2, the LTQ Formation.

two proton transfers occurring. Proton transfer from O-4 to Nε forms $Int6_O$. Cleavage of the C—N bond produces the aldehyde $Int7_O$. Copper ion acts as a redox catalyst but is not essential for the reaction. After releasing the aldehyde product, LTQ is regenerated. In the model ($Int8_O$), triplet O_2 enters, abstracting a hydrogen from O-4 to form the $HOO^•$ radical ($Int9_O$) and oxidizing the copper ion to Cu^{2+}. Subsequently, $HOO^•$ abstracts a hydrogen from N-5 to produce H_2O_2. Finally, $Int10_O$ reacts with water to regenerate LTQ [88].

3.3.3.3 Tyrosinase

Tyrosinase, a binuclear copper enzyme, is a prominent member of the copper enzyme family and plays a crucial role in melanin biosynthesis [91]. This enzyme catalyzes the hydroxylation of monophenols (e.g. tyrosine) to o-diphenols (e.g. L-DOPA) and the subsequent oxidation of o-diphenols to o-quinones, which ultimately polymerize to form melanin. The catalytic process involves the activation of molecular oxygen and electron transfer, facilitated by the enzyme's binuclear copper center [92]. The copper ions are coordinated by histidine residues and are essential for the enzyme's catalytic activity. Dysfunction or deficiency of tyrosinase can lead to several human diseases, such as albinism and melanoma [93, 94]. Mutations in the gene encoding tyrosinase result in severe pigmentary disorders like albinism. Additionally, alterations in tyrosinase activity are associated with

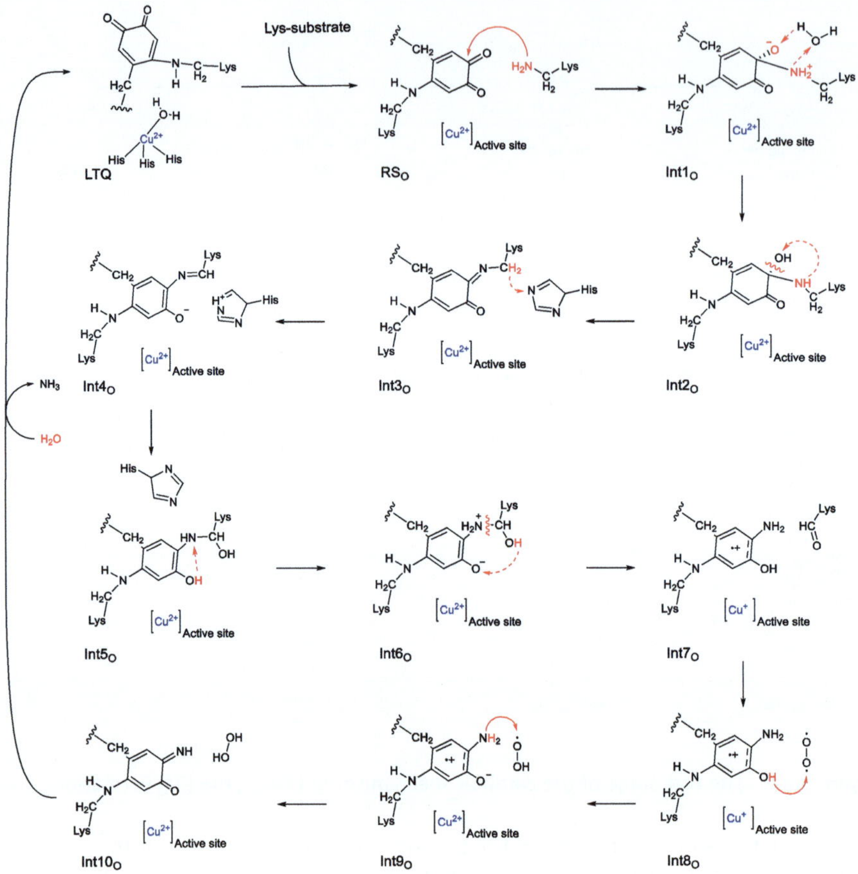

Figure 3.13 The second stage of the catalytic mechanism of LOXL2.

melanoma pathogenesis, where excessive tyrosinase activity may promote tumor progression [95].

Tyrosinase is a type III copper protein with its catalytic center located within a four-helix bundle, which contains a binuclear copper center (CuA and CuB), also known as the active site of tyrosinase [92]. These copper ions are crucial for the enzyme's catalytic activity, enabling it to bind and activate molecular oxygen. During catalysis, the binuclear copper site exists in three forms: oxidized (Eoxy), reduced (Emet), and deoxy (Edeoxy). Each copper ion is coordinated by three histidine residues, forming a highly conserved coordination environment essential for the enzyme's function. The overall protein structure provides a stable framework that supports the copper center, facilitating substrate binding and product release. The protein scaffold also helps fine-tune the electronic properties of the copper ions, optimizing their reactivity.

The structure and function of this enzyme highlight its crucial role in cellular processes. Notably, one significant biochemical pathway it participates in is melanin production through the monophenol cycle. Tyrosinase is the key enzyme in this pathway, and its catalytic mechanism involves redox changes of the dinuclear copper center, binding of water molecules, and proton transfer [91, 92].

In the resting oxy-Ty state, the active site contains a μ-η2:η2-peroxide dicopper(II) core that is H-bonded to two conserved water molecules. The monophenol substrate binds to the active site pocket of oxy-Ty fully protonated, without coordinating with the Cu centers. It displaces the active site water molecules and forms a single H-bond between its -OH group and the μ-η2:η2-peroxide. This forms the ternary Ty/O_2/monophenol intermediate. The O—O bond of the μ-η2:η2-peroxide then cleaves to accept the proton (H^+) and an electron (e^-) from the monophenol substrate, forming a μ-oxo-μ-hydroxo dicopper(II) core. The non-protonated μ-oxo attacks the ortho-carbon of the bound monophenolate substrate, while the substrate phenolate oxygen coordinates to CuA. This concerted step forms the new C—O bond on the aromatic ring and the O—CuA bond, yielding the o-diphenol product coordinated to the dicopper(II) core. The o-diphenol product then dissociates, regenerating the met-Ty state which can be reduced by catechols to the deoxy-Ty state. O_2 binding to deoxy-Ty reforms oxy-Ty to complete the catalytic cycle [96].

As shown in Figure 3.14, in the initial step, tyrosinase in its resting state contains a dinuclear Cu(II) center coordinated with water molecules or hydroxide ions [96]. The substrate, typically L-tyrosine or L-DOPA, binds to the active site, displacing these water molecules or hydroxide ions. This binding positions the substrate in the active site, preparing it for subsequent reactions.

In the next step, molecular oxygen binds to the copper center, forming a μ-η2:η2-peroxide dicopper(II) intermediate. This process involves the rapid and exergonic binding of oxygen to deoxy-tyrosinase, forming oxy-tyrosinase (oxy-Ty). Characteristic absorption bands at 345 and 650 nm indicate the presence of the μ-η2:η2-peroxide dicopper(II) active site [97].

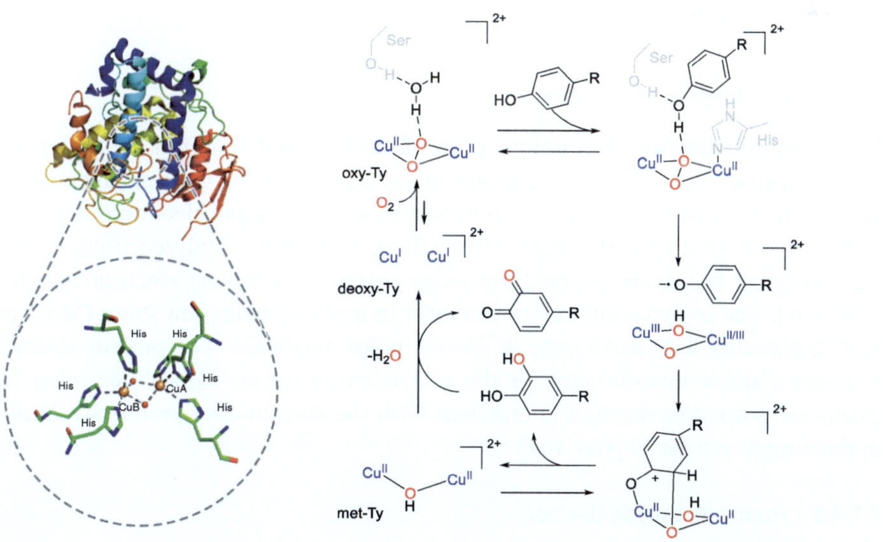

Figure 3.14 The binding site and catalytic mechanism of Tyrosinase (PDB ID: 2AHK).

After that, the peroxide intermediate facilitates the hydroxylation of the substrate, converting L-tyrosine into L-DOPA. Direct ortho-hydroxylation of the protonated substrate requires high energy barriers, so the substrate must first be deprotonated. The substrate proton is transferred along with the cleavage of the O—O bond, forming a μ-oxo-μ-hydroxo dicopper intermediate (2O), which is thermodynamically stable. This step involves the interaction between the substrate proton and the Cu_2O_2 core [98].

L-DOPA undergoes oxidation, accompanied by electron transfer, to yield the highly reactive DOPAquinone. Calculations show that the protonated substrate, uncoordinated to CuA and forming hydrogen bonds with the μ-η2:η2-peroxide, best aligns with the observed spectral data and thermodynamic stability [99, 100].

Finally, the oxidation products (e.g. DOPAquinone) are released from the enzyme's active site, and the enzyme returns to its resting state. The copper center re-coordinates with water molecules or hydroxide ions, preparing the enzyme for the next catalytic cycle. This step ensures that tyrosinase can continuously catalyze the reaction [96].

Research integrating experimental data with QM/MM calculations supports the key steps in the tyrosinase monooxygenation mechanism [101, 102]. The cleavage of the μ-η2:η2-peroxide O—O bond and subsequent proton transfer form a stable μ-oxo-μ-hydroxo dicopper intermediate (2O). The hydrogen bond between the substrate hydroxyl group and the μ-η2:η2-peroxide in the 1P structure stabilizes both the reactant state and the resulting 2O intermediate, making proton transfer and O—O bond cleavage more efficient. In the 2O intermediate, the non-protonated μ-oxo attacks the ortho-carbon of the substrate while the phenolate coordinates to CuA, completing the hydroxylation of the substrate. These findings clarify the steps of O—O bond cleavage, substrate deprotonation, and ortho-hydroxylation in the tyrosinase catalysis mechanism, providing a comprehensive understanding of the enzyme's function.

3.3.4 Molybdenum Enzymes

Molybdenum enzymes are a unique class of proteins that contain a molybdenum cofactor (MoCo) as a prosthetic group [103]. This cofactor typically includes a molybdenum atom coordinated by molybdopterin. The unique electronic structure and chemical bonding of the MoCo enable these enzymes to catalyze various essential biological functions, particularly redox reactions involving electron transfer [104, 105]. The molybdenum atom can exist in multiple oxidation states (Mo^{4+} to Mo^{6+}), allowing it to participate in diverse redox processes. The protein scaffold provides a stable environment for the molybdenum center while fine-tuning its electronic properties through interactions with the surrounding protein structure, optimizing its reactivity [106, 107].

3.3.4.1 Human Aldehyde Oxidase

Human aldehyde oxidase (AO) is an important molybdenum enzyme involved in the metabolism of a wide range of endogenous and exogenous aldehydes and

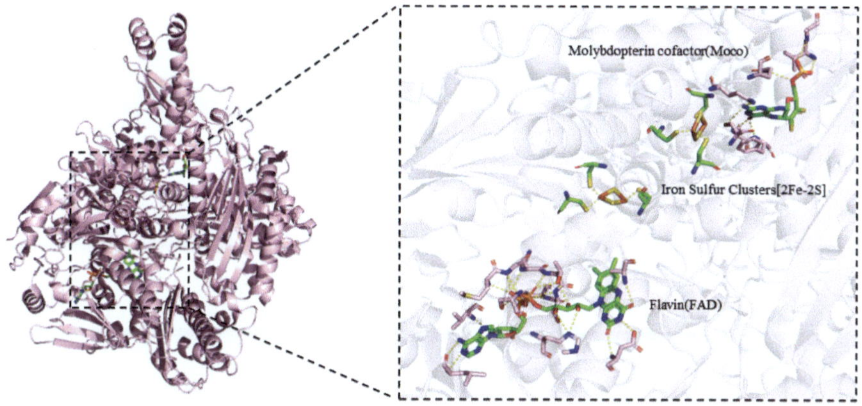

Figure 3.15 The structure of the catalytic site of AO (PDB ID: 4UHW).

nitrogen-containing compounds [108]. This enzyme catalyzes the oxidation of aldehydes to carboxylic acids, playing a crucial role in drug metabolism and detoxification [108, 109]. AO is of significant biomedical importance, as its dysfunction or abnormal activity is associated with various diseases [110]. For example, elevated AO activity can lead to accelerated drug metabolism, thereby reducing drug efficacy or increasing toxicity [109]. Additionally, abnormal expression of AO in certain tumor cells is linked to the development and progression of cancer [111].

As shown in Figure 3.15, AO has a complex structure consisting of multiple functional domains, including the MoCo domain, flavin adenine dinucleotide domain (FAD), and iron–sulfur cluster domain (FeS) [112]. These domains work together to enable AO to efficiently catalyze the oxidation of various substrates. The MoCo domain is the active center of AO, containing a molybdenum atom coordinated by molybdopterin. The molybdenum atom can cycle through different oxidation states (Mo^{4+} to Mo^{6+}), directly participating in the oxidation reaction of substrates [113]. The FAD domain contains an FAD molecule, which plays a crucial role in the redox reaction chain by accepting and transferring electrons [114]. The FeS domain contains two iron–sulfur clusters ([2Fe-2S]), which assist in the electron transfer process, ensuring that electrons are smoothly transferred from the substrate to the final electron acceptor [112].

During the catalytic process, the substrate first binds to the active site, where the hydroxyl group of the MoCo transfers a proton to a key residue (such as Glu), activating the hydroxyl group for nucleophilic attack. Subsequently, a series of redox reactions occur, oxidizing the substrate to the corresponding carboxylic acid. Electrons are transferred through the iron–sulfur clusters and FAD, ultimately completing the catalytic cycle [113].

The catalytic mechanism of human AO (as shown in Figure 3.16) follows a cycle involving redox changes of the molybdenum ion, water molecule binding and proton transfer, and electron transfer. After the substrate binding (1 to 2), lysine^{893} transfers a proton to the aldehyde substrate's nitrogen atom, increasing its carbon's electrophilicity (3). The aldehyde substrate then enters the active

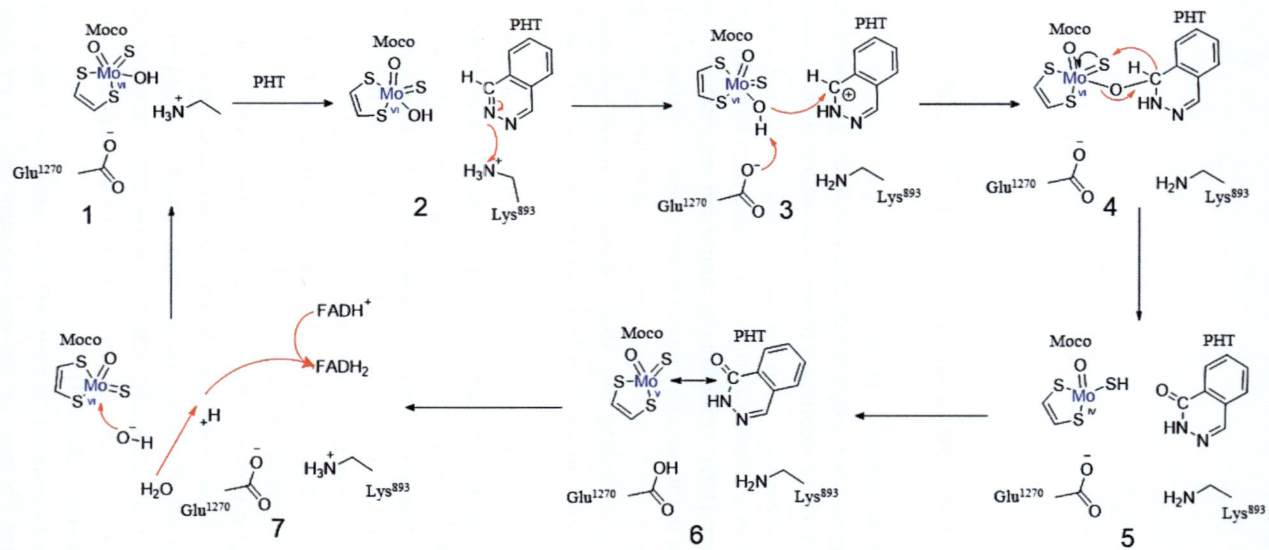

Figure 3.16 The catalytic mechanism of AO.

site, where it is nucleophilically attacked by the hydroxyl group coordinated to the MoCo, forming a tetrahedral intermediate (4). Next, a hydride is transferred from the intermediate to the sulfur atom coordinated with the molybdenum ion, reducing it from Mo(VI) to Mo(IV) (5). Subsequently, the intermediate is further oxidized, forming a carboxylic acid product, while electrons are transferred to the [2Fe-2S] clusters and ultimately to FAD, reducing it to FADH2 and reoxidizing the molybdenum ion to Mo(VI) (6 to 7). Finally, a water molecule enters the active site, coordinates with the molybdenum ion, and loses a proton, completing the catalytic cycle and preparing AO for another round of catalysis (7 to 1) [115–117].

3.3.4.2 Xanthine Oxidase

Xanthine oxidase (XO) is an enzyme involved in purine metabolism, catalyzing the oxidation of hypoxanthine to xanthine and xanthine to uric acid [118, 119]. Dysfunction or overactivity of this enzyme can lead to various diseases, the most prominent being gout and hyperuricemia [120]. Hyperuricemia is caused by elevated levels of uric acid in the blood, which is the final product of the XO-catalyzed reaction. Excess uric acid can form urate crystals in the joints, leading to gouty arthritis. QM/MM methods have been used to investigate the catalytic mechanism of XO, particularly focusing on the MoCo, active site residues, and substrate binding [121–123]. These studies have elucidated how the molybdenum center cycles through different oxidation states to facilitate electron transfer and the overall redox reaction. Through these studies, our understanding of the enzyme's function has been enhanced, providing valuable insights for the development of potential therapeutic inhibitors.

XO has a molecular weight of approximately 270,000 and contains two molecules of FAD, two molybdenum atoms, and eight iron atoms [124]. It is composed of two symmetrical structural units. In the enzyme, molybdenum exists in the form of a molybdopterin cofactor, which is the active site. The iron atoms are part of the [2Fe-2S] iron–sulfur clusters, participating in electron transfer reactions. XO and human AO share structural characteristics, notably containing MoCo domains, FAD domains, and iron–sulfur cluster domains [125]. XO primarily exists as a homodimer, with the MoCo domain serving a crucial role in catalysis [126]. The key structural features of XO are highly similar to those of AO as described in the previous section.

The process by which xanthine oxidase catalyzes the conversion of xanthine to uric acid involves redox changes of the molybdenum ion, binding and transfer of protons by water molecules, and electron transfer via [2Fe-2S] clusters and FAD. Initially, xanthine (XAN) enters the active site, where it undergoes nucleophilic attack by the hydroxyl group coordinated to the MoCo and Glu^{1261} (1), forming the URT (an anionic form of uric acid) molecule (2). A hydride is then transferred from the intermediate to the sulfur atom coordinated with the molybdenum ion, reducing its valence state from Mo(VI) to Mo(IV). Subsequently, Arg^{880} protonates the URT molecule (3), prompting the release of the uric acid (URC) molecule from the active site into the solvent, while FAD is reduced to $FADH_2$, oxidizing the molybdenum ion back from Mo(IV) to Mo(VI). Finally, a water molecule enters the active site, coordinates with the molybdenum ion, and loses a proton (4), completing the catalytic cycle [127–129].

Ribeiro et al. [127] studied the full catalytic cycle of XO with QM/MM methods, and the key steps can be summarized as follows (Figure 3.17).

In the initial stage of the oxidation of XAN to its anionic form (URC), Glu^{1261} abstracts a proton from the hydroxyl group coordinated to the Mo(VI) ion, enhancing the nucleophilicity of the hydroxyl oxygen atom. This allows the hydroxyl oxygen to nucleophilically attack the C11 carbon atom of the XAN molecule, forming a tetrahedral intermediate. Glu^{802} stabilizes the negative charge through hydrogen bonding. This step requires a Gibbs free energy of 16.6 kcal/mol and is an endergonic reaction with 11.7 kcal/mol.

In the second stage, a hydride is transferred from the C11 carbon atom to the sulfur atom (SO) coordinated with MoCo, reducing the Mo ion from Mo(VI) to Mo(IV). This reduction results in the cleavage of the bond between the Mo ion and the oxygen atom, releasing the URT molecule into the active site. Computational results indicate that the reaction follows a hydrogen-one electron-coupled transfer mechanism. The activation Gibbs free energy for this stage is 5.2 kcal/mol, and it is a thermodynamically favorable reaction ($\Delta G_R = -20.1$/kcal mol).

In the third stage, URT is protonated before being released as URC. Computational results indicate that URT can be protonated by either Arg^{880} or Glu^{1261} residues, with activation-free energies of 4.6 kcal/mol and 1.8 kcal/mol, respectively. The proton transfer from Arg^{880} to the N_8 atom of URT via a water molecule is highly exergonic ($\Delta G_R = -26.6$ kcal/mol), ensuring the irreversibility of the reaction. Ultimately, URC is ready to be released from the active site.

In the fourth step, after URC is released, the molybdenum ion is oxidized from Mo(IV) to Mo(VI). Two electrons are transferred through two [2Fe-2S] clusters to the FAD cofactor, reducing FAD to $FADH_2$. Subsequently, MoCo reacts with a water molecule. As MoCo is oxidized again to Mo(VI), a water molecule enters the active site through a water channel and binds to the Mo ion. Simulations indicate that deprotonation of Glu^{1261} first allows water molecule binding to the Mo ion, completing the catalytic cycle and preparing XO for another round of catalysis.

3.3.5 Zinc Enzymes

Zinc is vital for protein structure and for organizing protein domains which interact with biomolecules including proteins, DNA, RNA, and lipids [130]. Functional and/or structural organization of zinc enzymes critically depends on the zinc binding sites [131]. Besides catalytic functions (catalytic zincs) and structural functions (structural zincs), Zn^{2+} functions as a signal ion in cellular control and information transfer. The donors of Zn^{2+} in proteins typically are the side chain nitrogen of histidine, oxygen of aspartate/glutamate and solvent water, and sulfur of cysteine. Because of its flexibility, in proteins, the prevailing coordination numbers of Zn^{2+} are four and five with distorted tetrahedral or trigonal bipyramidal geometries, although coordination numbers of three and six have been observed too. The zinc–ligand distances play a fundamental role in metal discrimination of zinc proteins. The higher

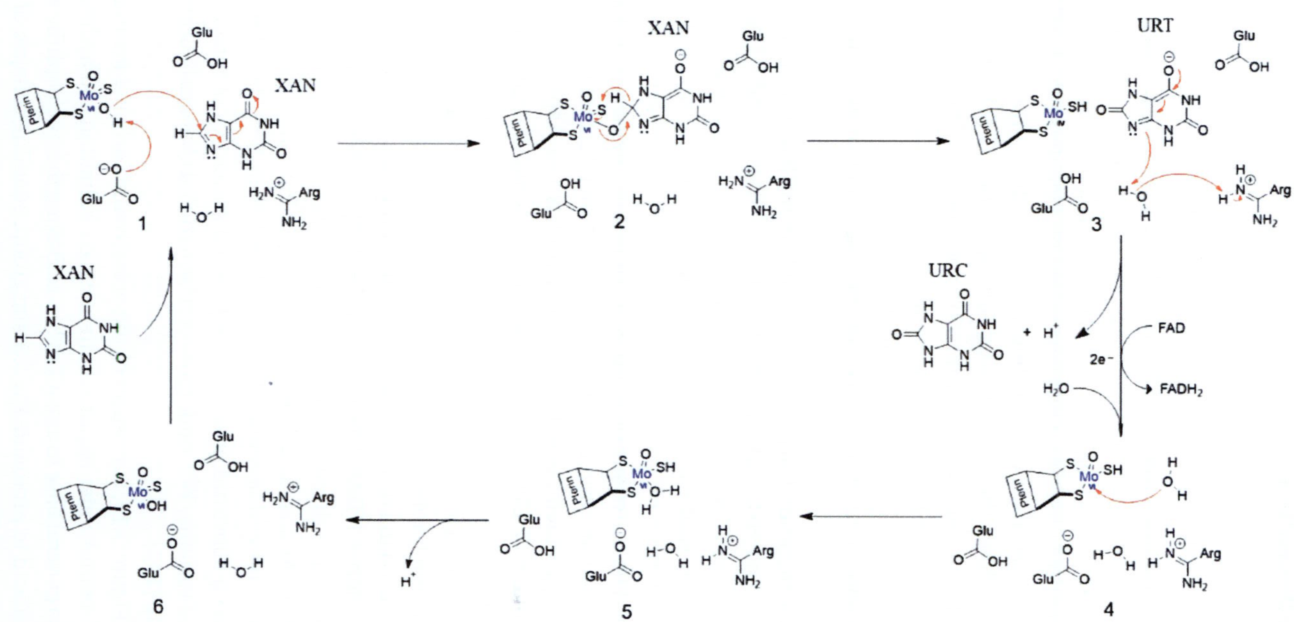

Figure 3.17 The catalytic mechanism of XO.

the metal coordination number, the longer the metal–ligand distances to minimize electronic repulsion among the ligands [132].

3.3.5.1 Histone Deacetylases

Histone deacetylases (HDACs) are a family of zinc metalloproteins present in eukaryotic cells that catalyze the removal of acetyl groups from lysine residues on histone proteins. This deacetylation process is crucial for various cellular functions, including apoptosis, proliferation, and senescence [133, 134], making HDACs significant targets in pharmaceutical development. Currently, two HDAC inhibitors are approved as anticancer agents, with additional candidates in clinical trials for neurodegenerative diseases Overexpression of zinc-dependent HDACs has been linked to various diseases, and their inhibitors show promise as anticancer agents. Notably, in 2006, the Federal Drug Administration (FDA) approved SAHA (vorinostat), an HDAC inhibitor that directly coordinates with the catalytic zinc ion, as an anticancer drug [135]. Understanding the catalytic mechanisms of zinc-dependent HDACs is therefore of both fundamental and medical importance, aiding in the development of new, mechanism-based, and subtype-specific HDAC inhibitors [136].

Based on phylogenetic analysis, the HDAC family is divided into four classes [137]: Class I (HDAC1–3 and HDAC8), Class II (HDAC4–7, HDAC9, and HDAC10), Class III (sirtuins 1–7), and Class IV (HDAC11). Class I HDACs, particularly HDAC8, have been extensively studied for their anticancer properties. X-ray crystallographic studies of HDAC8 have provided crucial insights into the biochemical functions of the entire family. The active site of HDAC8, as shown in Figure 3.18, is located in a narrow pocket within the protein and contains a Zn^{2+} metal cofactor, coordinated in a square pyramidal geometry with the side chains of His-180, Asp-178, and Asp-267. All known inhibitors of Class I, II, and IV HDACs contain a zinc-binding group (ZBG), a linker group that mimics the lysine side chain, and a cap group that interacts with the protein surface [138]. The properties of the ZBG are closely related to the efficacy of the inhibitors.

The catalytic mechanism of HDACs was first proposed based on the crystal structure of a bacterial HDAC-like protein [134, 139]. Further refinements to this mechanism were made through structural and enzymological studies of HDAC8. In the precatalytic Michaelis complex, the acetyllysine carbonyl coordinates to the catalytic Zn^{2+} ion and accepts a hydrogen bond from Y^{306}. This interaction is supported by metal-substitution studies and crystal structures of intact substrates bound to HDAC8 variants. Y^{306} undergoes conformational changes to accommodate substrate binding [140].

As shown in Figure 3.19, activation of the acetyllysine carbonyl for nucleophilic attack by a Zn^{2+}-bound water requires both metal coordination and hydrogen bonding. H^{143} acts as a general base to assist Zn^{2+} in activating the nucleophilic water, and then as a general acid to protonate the leaving group, enabling collapse of the tetrahedral intermediate. H^{142} serves as an electrostatic catalyst, remaining protonated throughout the catalytic cycle. Both histidines help orient the Zn^{2+}-bound water for attack. The acetate product may depart through a "backdoor" tunnel [141].

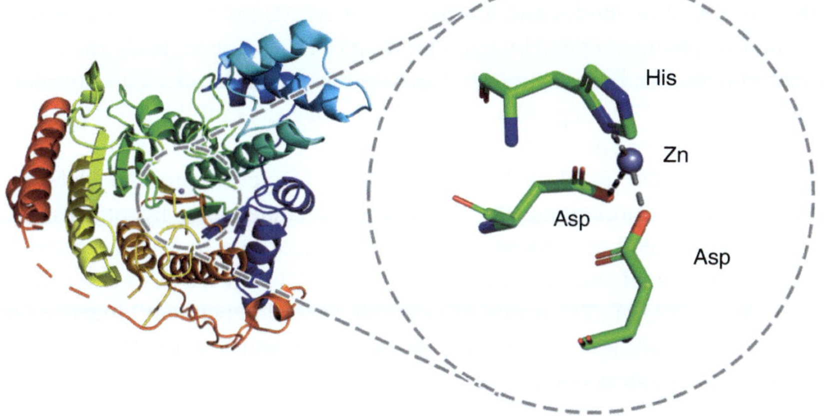

Figure 3.18 The structure of the catalytic site of HDAC (PDB ID: 6FU1).

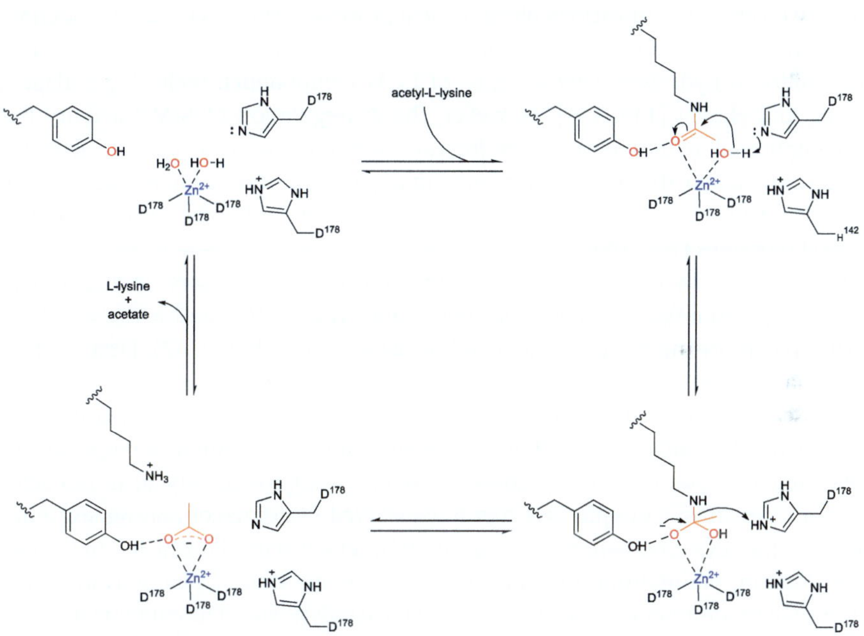

Figure 3.19 The catalytic mechanism of HDAC.

Structures of HDAC complexes with reactive substrate analogues, such as the cyclic tetrapeptides Trapoxin A and HC Toxin, have provided snapshots of the tetrahedral intermediate and its flanking transition states. These inhibitors contain an α,β-epoxyketone moiety that undergoes nucleophilic attack to yield a stable gem-diolate, mimicking the oxyanion intermediate. Crystal structures of HDAC4, HDAC6, and HDAC10 with α-trifluoromethylketones also reveal the binding of gem-diolate forms [140].

One of the key applications of QM/MM methods in HDAC inhibitor design is the study of the binding modes and interactions of HDAC inhibitors. For example, the inhibition mechanism of SAHA upon binding to HDAC, specifically the protonation mechanism, has been a subject of debate for over a decade. The prevalent "Class-dependent" or "Tyr-dependent" hypothesis suggests that the deprotonation of SAHA is primarily regulated by the conserved Tyr^{308} in class I HDAC, while it is replaced by His^{843} in class IIa HDAC [142]. However, through elaborate QM(DFT)/MM MD simulations, the researchers excluded this hypothesis and proposed a novel "Metal-dependent" mechanism. According to this mechanism, the remote second metal site (K^+ in most HDAC and Ca^{2+} in HDAC2) determines the protonation of SAHA. This proof-of-principle "Metal-dependent" mechanism opens up new possibilities for utilizing the second metal site in the design of isoform-selective inhibitors [142].

3.3.5.2 Matrix Metalloproteinases

Matrix metalloproteinases (MMPs) are a family of zinc-dependent endopeptidases that play pivotal roles in various physiological processes, such as tissue remodeling, cell migration, and cell–cell communication. These enzymes are characterized by their ability to hydrolyze a wide range of ECM components, including collagen, gelatin, and elastin [143, 144]. However, the dysregulation of MMP activity has been implicated in numerous pathological conditions, such as cancer, arthritis, and cardiovascular diseases. As a result, understanding the catalytic mechanism of MMPs at the molecular level is of utmost importance for the development of targeted therapies [145, 146].

The MMP family can be categorized into several main classes, including collagenases, gelatinases, stromelysins, membrane-type MMPs, and a more diverse subgroup comprising matrylysins, metalloelastase, and others [147]. Despite their functional diversity, all MMPs exhibit significant sequence homology and, in most cases, a shared multidomain architecture. This structure typically consists of an N-terminal prodomain, a catalytic domain, and a C-terminal hemopexin-like (HPX) domain [148–150]. The prodomain, which is approximately 80 amino acids in length, features a unique and highly conserved cysteine-containing sequence known as the "cysteine switch." This Bn-motif interacts with the zinc ion in the catalytic domain, maintaining the enzyme in its inactive state. Upon activation, the N-terminal prodomain is removed, exposing the catalytic site. The catalytic domain, spanning around 170 residues, is responsible for the hydrolytic activity of MMPs. It is characterized by a twisted five-stranded β-sheet, three α-helices, and several connecting loops, which together form the substrate-binding cleft and the catalytic center [151].

The catalytic domain of MMPs harbors the active site, which features a conserved zinc-binding motif with the sequence HEXXHXXGXXH. This motif is responsible for coordinating the catalytic zinc ion through three histidine residues (Figure 3.20). Additionally, the active site contains a conserved glutamate residue that has been shown, through mutagenesis experiments, to be essential for catalysis [152, 153].

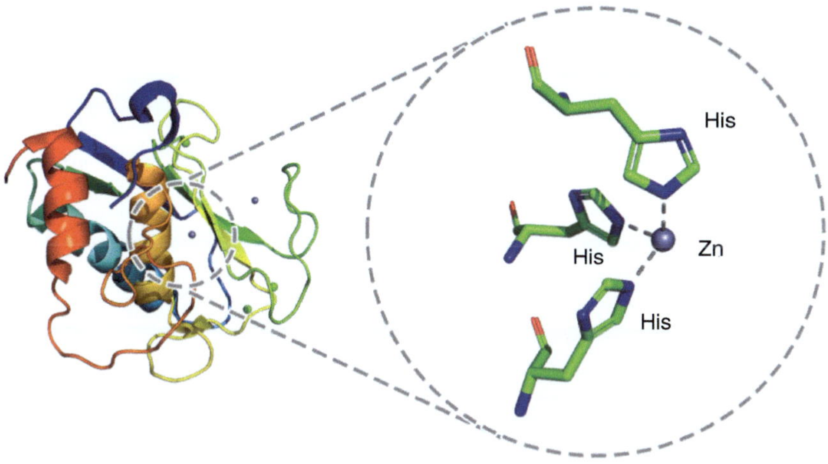

Figure 3.20 The structure of the catalytic site of MMPs (PDB ID: 2D1N).

Apart from the catalytic zinc, the catalytic domain of all MMPs also accommodates a second zinc ion, known as the structural zinc, as well as one to three calcium ions, which are believed to play a structural role [150]. The structural zinc is consistently liganded in a tetrahedral coordination sphere, formed by three histidine residues and one of the oxygen atoms from an aspartic acid side chain. The calcium ions, on the other hand, are coordinated in an octahedral manner by protein residues and water molecules [151].

MMP-1, a prominent member of the 24 human MMPs family, is the ubiquitous interstitial collagenase crucial in various physiological and pathological processes, notably tumor cell migration and invasion. Structurally, MMP-1 comprises an N-terminal catalytic (CAT) domain and a C-terminal HPX-like domain, interconnected by a 17-residue linker [148, 154]. The CAT domain, containing both catalytic and structural zinc(II) centers [155, 156], is responsible for the enzymatic activity of MMP-1. Conversely, the HPX domain orients the CAT domain optimally, facilitating the binding and subsequent hydrolysis of collagen triple-helical peptides (THPs) [157, 158].

The catalytic mechanism of MMP-1-mediated collagenolysis involves several key steps (Figure 3.21). Initially, the scissile bond carbonyl oxygen coordinates with the catalytic zinc(II) ion. A conserved second coordination sphere (SCS) glutamate residue then polarizes a zinc-bound water molecule (wat1), generating a nucleophilic hydroxide anion. This hydroxide anion performs a water-mediated nucleophilic attack on the scissile bond carbonyl, forming a tetrahedral intermediate. Subsequently, a rearrangement of the hydrogen bonding network around the glutamate residue facilitates access to the cleavage site. The glutamate acts as an efficient proton shuttle, transferring the proton abstracted from wat1 to the scissile amide group, thereby facilitating the cleavage of the scissile C—N bond. Finally, the product is released, completing the catalytic cycle [159].

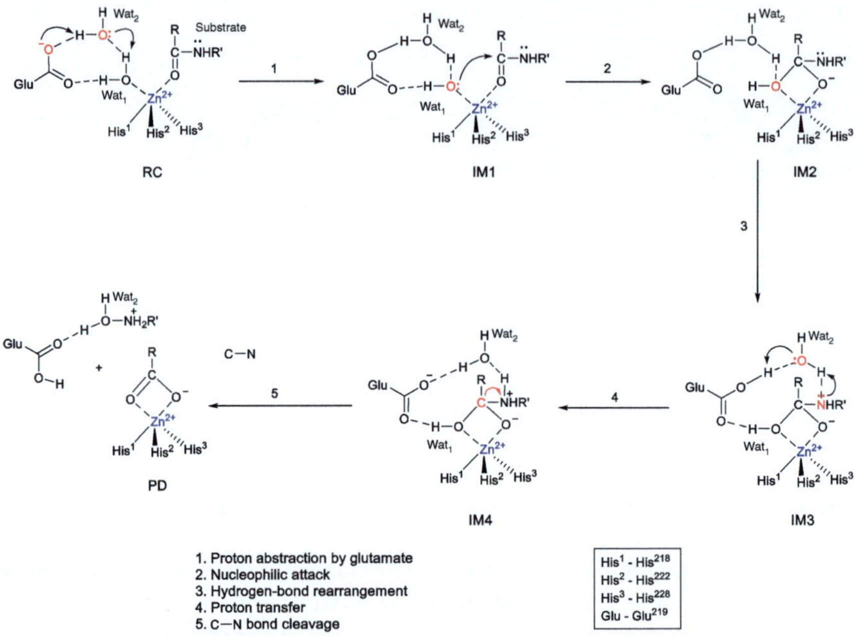

Figure 3.21 The catalytic mechanism of MMPs.

3.4 Summary

The application of QM/MM methods to study metalloenzyme catalytic mechanisms has significantly advanced our understanding of these complex biological systems. This chapter has explored the fundamental principles of QM/MM calculations and their application to various classes of metalloenzymes, including heme enzymes, non-heme iron enzymes, copper enzymes, molybdenum enzymes, and zinc enzymes. These studies revealed that when metal ions directly participate in the chemical reaction catalyzed by an enzyme, they can play several common roles. These roles are crucial for the catalytic mechanism and can significantly enhance the efficiency and specificity of the enzymatic reaction. Metal ions can act as electrophilic catalysts by withdrawing electron density from the substrate, making it more susceptible to nucleophilic attack. Metal ions can also function as nucleophilic catalysts by coordinating to and activating a water molecule or hydroxide ion, which then acts as a nucleophile in the reaction. The metal ion helps to lower the pKa of the coordinated water, making it a more effective nucleophile. Metal ions can stabilize high-energy transition states or reaction intermediates by providing a favorable electrostatic environment or by directly coordinating to them. Metal ions can bind to and activate substrates by altering their electronic structure or geometry, making them more reactive. Collectively, these studies demonstrate the prowess of QM/MM methods in unraveling the intricate facets of metalloenzyme catalysis. By providing atomic-level insights into reaction mechanisms, electronic structures, and the protein environment effects, QM/MM calculations have emerged as an indispensable tool in enzymology. Understanding the precise roles of metal ions in the enzymatic catalysis is crucial for elucidating structure–function relationships, designing enzyme inhibitors, or activators.

References

1 Dailey, H.A. (1997). Enzymes of heme biosynthesis. *JBIC Journal of Biological Inorganic Chemistry* 2: 411–417.

2 Layer, G., Reichelt, J., Jahn, D., and Heinz, D.W. (2010). Structure and function of enzymes in heme biosynthesis. *Protein Science* 19: 1137–1161.

3 Poulos, T.L. (2014). Heme enzyme structure and function. *Chemical Reviews* 114: 3919–3962.

4 Guengerich, F.P. (1995). Human cytochrome P450 enzymes. In: *Cytochrome P450: Structure, Mechanism, and Biochemistry* (ed. P.R.O. de Montellano), 473–535. US: Springer.

5 Bernhardt, R. (2006). Cytochromes P450 as versatile biocatalysts. *Journal of Biotechnology* 124: 128–145.

6 Meunier, B., De Visser, S.P., and Shaik, S. (2004). Mechanism of oxidation reactions catalyzed by cytochrome P450 enzymes. *Chemical Reviews* 104: 3947–3980.

7 Dubey, K.D., Wang, B., and Shaik, S. (2016). Molecular dynamics and QM/MM calculations predict the substrate-induced gating of cytochrome P450 BM3 and the regio- and stereoselectivity of fatty acid hydroxylation. *Journal of the American Chemical Society* 138: 837–845.

8 Su, H., Ma, G., and Liu, Y. (2018). Theoretical insights into the mechanism and stereoselectivity of olefin cyclopropanation catalyzed by two engineered cytochrome P450 enzymes. *Inorganic Chemistry* 57: 11738–11745.

9 Shaik, S., Cohen, S., Wang, Y. et al. (2010). P450 enzymes: their structure, reactivity, and selectivity—modeled by QM/MM calculations. *Chemical Reviews* 110: 949–1017.

10 Mak, P.J. and Denisov, I.G. (2018). Spectroscopic studies of the cytochrome P450 reaction mechanisms. *Biochimica Et Biophysica Acta (BBA) - Proteins and Proteomics* 1866: 178–204.

11 Shaik, S., Chen, H., Usharani, D., and Thiel, W. (2014). QM/MM studies of structure and reactivity of cytochrome P450 enzymes: methodology and selected applications. In: *Drug Metabolism Prediction* (ed. J. Kirchmair), 133–178. Wiley.

12 Kumar, D., Hirao, H., De Visser, S.P. et al. (2005). New features in the catalytic cycle of cytochrome P450 during the formation of compound I from compound 0. *The Journal of Physical Chemistry B* 109: 19946–19951.

13 Shaik, S., Lai, W., Chen, H., and Wang, Y. (2010). The valence bond way: reactivity patterns of cytochrome P450 enzymes and synthetic analogs. *Accounts of Chemical Research* 43: 1154–1165.

14 Liu, S., Xia, S., Yue, D. et al. (2022). The bonding nature of Fe–CO complexes in heme proteins. *Inorganic Chemistry* 61: 17494–17504.

15 Ortiz de Montellano, P.R. (2015). Substrate oxidation by cytochrome P450 enzymes. In: *Cytochrome P450: Structure, Mechanism, and Biochemistry* (ed. P.R. Ortiz de Montellano), 111–176. Springer International Publishing.

16 Kumar, D., Karamzadeh, B., Sastry, G.N., and De Visser, S.P. (2010). What factors influence the rate constant of substrate epoxidation by compound I of cytochrome P450 and analogous iron(IV)-oxo oxidants? *Journal of the American Chemical Society* 132: 7656–7667.

17 Hrycay, E.G. and Bandiera, S.M. (2012). The monooxygenase, peroxidase, and peroxygenase properties of cytochrome P450. *Archives of Biochemistry and Biophysics* 522: 71–89.

18 Zámocký, M. and Obinger, C. (2010). Molecular phylogeny of heme peroxidases. In: *Biocatalysis Based on Heme Peroxidases: Peroxidases as Potential Industrial Biocatalysts* (ed. E. Torres and M. Ayala), 7–35. Springer.

19 Auf Dem Keller, U., Kümin, A., Braun, S., and Werner, S. (2006). Reactive oxygen species and their detoxification in healing skin wounds. *Journal of Investigative Dermatology Symposium Proceedings* 11: 106–111.

20 Falade, A.O., Nwodo, U.U., Iweriebor, B.C. et al. (2017). Lignin peroxidase functionalities and prospective applications. *MicrobiologyOpen* 6: e00394.

21 Deme, D., Virion, A., Michot, J.L., and Pommier, J. (1985). Thyroid hormone synthesis and thyroglobulin iodination related to the peroxidase localization of oxidizing equivalents: studies with cytochrome c peroxidase and horseradish peroxidase. *Archives of Biochemistry and Biophysics* 236: 559–566.

22 Vlasova, I.I. (2018). Peroxidase activity of human hemoproteins: keeping the fire under control. *Molecules* 23: 2561.

23 Huang, X. and Groves, J.T. (2018). Oxygen activation and radical transformations in heme proteins and metalloporphyrins. *Chemical Reviews* 118: 2491–2553.

24 de Oliveira, F.K., Santos, L.O., and Buffon, J.G. (2021). Mechanism of action, sources, and application of peroxidases. *Food Research International* 143: 110266.

25 Ullrich, R. and Hofrichter, M. (2007). Enzymatic hydroxylation of aromatic compounds. *Cellular and Molecular Life Sciences* 64: 271–293.

26 Beckerson, P., Svistunenko, D., and Reeder, B. (2015). Effect of the distal histidine on the peroxidatic activity of monomeric cytoglobin. *F1000Research* 4: 87.

27 Nye, D.B., Preimesberger, M.R., Majumdar, A., and Lecomte, J.T.J. (2018). Histidine-lysine axial ligand switching in a hemoglobin: a role for heme propionates. *Biochemistry* 57: 631–644.

28 Abbruzzetti, S., Barker, A.J., Villar, I. et al. (2021). Unusually fast bis -histidyl coordination in a plant hemoglobin. *International Journal of Molecular Sciences* 22: 2740.

29 D'Annibale, A. (2012). Effect of additives on enzyme-catalyzed polymerization of phenols and aromatic amines. *Frontiers in Bioscience* S4: 1249–1265.

30 Kovaleva, E.G. and Lipscomb, J.D. (2008). Versatility of biological non-heme Fe(II) centers in oxygen activation reactions. *Nature Chemical Biology* 4: 186–193.

31 Solomon, E.I., Goudarzi, S., and Sutherlin, K.D. (2016). O_2 activation by non-heme iron enzymes. *Biochemistry* 55: 6363–6374.

32 Rokob, T.A., Chalupský, J., Bím, D. et al. (2016). Mono- and binuclear non-heme iron chemistry from a theoretical perspective. *JBIC Journal of Biological Inorganic Chemistry* 21: 619–644.

33 Islam, M.S., Leissing, T.M., Chowdhury, R. et al. (2018). 2-Oxoglutarate-dependent oxygenases. *Annual Review of Biochemistry* 87: 585–620.

34 Okuyama, K., Kawaguchi, T., Shimura, M. et al. (2013). Crystal structure of the collagen model peptide $(\text{Pro-Pro-Gly})_4$-Hyp-Asp-Gly-$(\text{Pro-Pro-Gly})_4$ at 1.0 Å resolution. *Biopolymers* 99: 436–447.

35 Reynolds, D., Cliffe, L., and Sabatini, R. (2015). 2-Oxoglutarate-dependent hydroxylases involved in DNA base J (β-D-glucopyranosyloxymethyluracil) synthesis. In: *2-Oxoglutarate-Dependent Oxygenases* (ed. C. Schofield and R. Hausinger), 309–323. The Royal Society of Chemistry.

36 Higgins, L.J., Yan, F., Liu, P. et al. (2005). Structural insight into antibiotic fosfomycin biosynthesis by a mononuclear iron enzyme. *Nature* 437: 838–844.

37 Yin, X. and Zabriskie, T.M. (2004). VioC is a non-heme iron, alpha-ketoglutarate-dependent oxygenase that catalyzes the formation of 3S-hydroxy-L-arginine during viomycin biosynthesis. *Chembiochem: A European Journal of Chemical Biology* 5: 1274–1277.

38 Koehntop, K.D., Emerson, J.P., and Que, L. (2005). The 2-His-1-carboxylate facial triad: A versatile platform for dioxygen activation by mononuclear non-heme iron(II) enzymes. *JBIC Journal of Biological Inorganic Chemistry* 10: 87–93.

39 Papadopoulou, A., Meyer, F., and Buller, R.M. (2023). Engineering Fe(II)/α-ketoglutarate-dependent halogenases and desaturases. *Biochemistry* 62: 229–240.

40 Wang, Z., Qiu, W., Pang, S. et al. (2022). Aqueous iron(IV)-oxo complex: an emerging powerful reactive oxidant formed by iron(II)-based advanced oxidation processes for oxidative water treatment. *Environmental Science & Technology* 56: 1492–1509.

41 Blomberg, M.R.A., Borowski, T., Himo, F. et al. (2014). Quantum chemical studies of mechanisms for metalloenzymes. *Chemical Reviews* 114: 3601–3658.

42 Borowski, T., Bassan, A., and Siegbahn, P.E.M. (2004). Mechanism of dioxygen activation in 2-oxoglutarate-dependent enzymes: A hybrid DFT study. *Chemistry (Weinheim an Der Bergstrasse, Germany)* 10: 1031–1041.

43 Álvarez-Barcia, S. and Kästner, J. (2017). Atom tunneling in the hydroxylation process of taurine/α-ketoglutarate dioxygenase identified by quantum mechanics/molecular mechanics simulations. *The Journal of Physical Chemistry B* 121: 5347–5354.

44 Ye, S. and Neese, F. (2009). Quantum chemical studies of C—H activation reactions by high-valent nonheme iron centers. *Current Opinion in Chemical Biology* 13: 89–98.

45 Ye, S. and Neese, F. (2011). Nonheme oxo-iron(IV) intermediates form an oxyl radical upon approaching the C—H bond activation transition state. *Proceedings of the National Academy of Sciences* 108: 1228–1233.

46 Godfrey, E., Porro, C.S., and de Visser, S.P. (2008). Comparative quantum mechanics/molecular mechanics (QM/MM) and density functional theory calculations on the oxo-iron species of taurine/alpha-ketoglutarate dioxygenase. *The Journal of Physical Chemistry. A* 112: 2464–2468.

47 Eichhorn, E., van der Ploeg, J.R., Kertesz, M.A., and Leisinger, T. (1997). Characterization of alpha-ketoglutarate-dependent taurine dioxygenase from *Escherichia coli*. *The Journal of Biological Chemistry* 272: 23031–23036.

48 Fitzpatrick, P.F. (1999). Tetrahydropterin-dependent amino acid hydroxylases. *Annual Review of Biochemistry* 68: 355–381.

49 Fitzpatrick, P.F. (2000). The aromatic amino acid hydroxylases. *Advances in Enzymology and Related Areas of Molecular Biology* 74: 235–294.

50 Fitzpatrick, P.F. (2003). Mechanism of aromatic amino acid hydroxylation. *Biochemistry* 42: 14083–14091.

51 Zhang, S., Hinck, A.P., and Fitzpatrick, P.F. (2015). The amino acid specificity for activation of phenylalanine hydroxylase matches the specificity for stabilization of regulatory domain dimers. *Biochemistry* 54: 5167–5174.

52 Wang, L., Erlandsen, H., Haavik, J. et al. (2002). Three-dimensional structure of human tryptophan hydroxylase and its implications for the biosynthesis of the neurotransmitters serotonin and melatonin. *Biochemistry* 41: 12569–12574.

53 Colette Daubner, S., McGinnis, J.T., Gardner, M. et al. (2006). A flexible loop in tyrosine hydroxylase controls coupling of amino acid hydroxylation to tetrahydropterin oxidation. *Journal of Molecular Biology* 359: 299–307.

54 Toone, E.J. (2011). Advances in enzymology and related areas of molecular biology. Preface. *Advances in Enzymology and Related Areas of Molecular Biology* 78: ix–xi.

55 Erlandsen, H., Kim, J.Y., Patch, M.G. et al. (2002). Structural comparison of bacterial and human iron-dependent phenylalanine hydroxylases: similar fold, different stability and reaction rates. *Journal of Molecular Biology* 320: 645–661.

56 Andersen, O.A., Stokka, A.J., Flatmark, T., and Hough, E. (2003). 2.0 Å resolution crystal structures of the ternary complexes of human phenylalanine hydroxylase catalytic domain with tetrahydrobiopterin and 3-(2-Thienyl)-l-alanine or l-norleucine: substrate specificity and molecular motions related to substrate binding. *Journal of Molecular Biology* 333: 747–757.

57 Pavon, J.A. and Fitzpatrick, P.F. (2005). Intrinsic isotope effects on benzylic hydroxylation by the aromatic amino acid hydroxylases: evidence for hydrogen tunneling, coupled motion, and similar reactivities. *Journal of the American Chemical Society* 127: 16414–16415.

58 Hegg, E.L. and Jr, L.Q. (1997). The 2-His-1-carboxylate facial triad—an emerging structural motif in mononuclear non-heme iron(II) enzymes. *European Journal of Biochemistry* 250: 625–629.

59 Pavon, J.A. and Fitzpatrick, P.F. (2006). Insights into the catalytic mechanisms of phenylalanine and tryptophan hydroxylase from kinetic isotope effects on aromatic hydroxylation. *Biochemistry* 45: 11030–11037.

60 Subedi, B.P. and Fitzpatrick, P.F. (2016). Kinetic mechanism and intrinsic rate constants for the reaction of a bacterial phenylalanine hydroxylase. *Biochemistry* 55: 6848–6857.

61 Iyer, S.R., Tidemand, K.D., Babicz, J.T. et al. (2021). Direct coordination of pterin to FeII enables neurotransmitter biosynthesis in the pterin-dependent hydroxylases. *Proceedings of the National Academy of Sciences* 118: e2022379118.

62 Frantom, P.A. and Fitzpatrick, P.F. (2003). Uncoupled forms of tyrosine hydroxylase unmask kinetic isotope effects on chemical steps. *Journal of the American Chemical Society* 125: 16190–16191.

63 Moran, G.R., Derecskei-Kovacs, A., Hillas, P.J., and Fitzpatrick, P.F. (2000). On the catalytic mechanism of tryptophan hydroxylase. *Journal of the American Chemical Society* 122: 4535–4541.

64 Lazarus, R.A., DeBrosse, C.W., and Benkovic, S.J. (1982). Structural determination of quinonoid dihydropterins. *Journal of the American Chemical Society* 104: 6871–6872.

65 Festa, R.A. and Thiele, D.J. (2011). Copper: an essential metal in biology. *Current Biology* 21: R877–R883.

66 Mustafa, S.K. and AlSharif, M.A. (2018). Copper (Cu) an essential redox-active transition metal in living system—a review article. *American Journal of Analytical Chemistry* 9 (1): 15–26.

67 Quinlan, R.J., Sweeney, M.D., Lo Leggio, L. et al. (2011). Insights into the oxidative degradation of cellulose by a copper metalloenzyme that exploits biomass components. *Proceedings of the National Academy of Sciences* 108: 15079–15084.

68 Phillips, C.M., Beeson, W.T., Cate, J.H., and Marletta, M.A. (2011). Cellobiose dehydrogenase and a copper-dependent polysaccharide monooxygenase potentiate cellulose degradation by *Neurospora crassa*. *ACS Chemical Biology* 6: 1399–1406.

69 Beeson, W.T., Phillips, C.M., Cate, J.H.D., and Marletta, M.A. (2012). Oxidative cleavage of cellulose by fungal copper-dependent polysaccharide monooxygenases. *Journal of the American Chemical Society* 134: 890–892.

70 Sabbadin, F., Hemsworth, G.R., Ciano, L. et al. (2018). An ancient family of lytic polysaccharide monooxygenases with roles in arthropod development and biomass digestion. *Nature Communications* 9: 756.

71 Vaaje-Kolstad, G., Westereng, B., Horn, S.J. et al. (2010). An oxidative enzyme boosting the enzymatic conversion of recalcitrant polysaccharides. *Science* 330: 219–222.

72 Hemsworth, G.R., Henrissat, B., Davies, G.J., and Walton, P.H. (2014). Discovery and characterization of a new family of lytic polysaccharide monooxygenases. *Nature Chemical Biology* 10: 122–126.

73 Lo Leggio, L., Simmons, T.J., Poulsen, J.-C.N. et al. (2015). Structure and boosting activity of a starch-degrading lytic polysaccharide monooxygenase. *Nature Communications* 6: 5961.

74 Couturier, M., Ladevèze, S., Sulzenbacher, G. et al. (2018). Lytic xylan oxidases from wood-decay fungi unlock biomass degradation. *Nature Chemical Biology* 14: 306–310.

75 Forsberg, Z., Røhr, Å.K., Mekasha, S. et al. (2014). Comparative study of two chitin-active and two cellulose-active AA10-type lytic polysaccharide monooxygenases. *Biochemistry* 53: 1647–1656.

76 Gregory, R.C., Hemsworth, G.R., Turkenburg, J.P. et al. (2016). Activity, stability and 3-D structure of the Cu(ii) form of a chitin-active lytic polysaccharide monooxygenase from *Bacillus amyloliquefaciens*. *Dalton Transactions* 45: 16904–16912.

77 Bissaro, B., Várnai, A., Røhr, Å.K., and Eijsink, V.G.H. (2018). Oxidoreductases and reactive oxygen species in conversion of lignocellulosic biomass. *Microbiology and Molecular Biology Reviews* 82: e00029-18.

78 Hedegård, E.D. and Ryde, U. (2018). Molecular mechanism of lytic polysaccharide monooxygenases. *Chemical Science* 9: 3866–3880.

79 Wang, B., Johnston, E.M., Li, P. et al. (2018). QM/MM studies into the H_2O_2-dependent activity of lytic polysaccharide Mmonooxygenases: Evidence for the formation of a caged hydroxyl radical intermediate. *ACS Catalysis* 8: 1346–1351.

80 Kim, S., Ståhlberg, J., Sandgren, M. et al. (2014). Quantum mechanical calculations suggest that lytic polysaccharide monooxygenases use a copper-oxyl, oxygen-rebound mechanism. *Proceedings of the National Academy of Sciences* 111: 149–154.

81 Bissaro, B., Streit, B., Isaksen, I. et al. (2020). Molecular mechanism of the chitinolytic peroxygenase reaction. *Proceedings of the National Academy of Sciences* 117: 1504–1513.

82 Kagan, H.M. and Li, W. (2003). Lysyl oxidase: properties, specificity, and biological roles inside and outside of the cell. *Journal of Cellular Biochemistry* 88: 660–672.

83 Trackman, P.C. (2016). Lysyl oxidase isoforms and potential therapeutic opportunities for fibrosis and cancer. *Expert Opinion on Therapeutic Targets* 20: 935–945.

84 Lucero, H.A. and Kagan, H.M. (2006). Lysyl oxidase: an oxidative enzyme and effector of cell function. *Cellular and Molecular Life Sciences* 63: 2304–2316.

85 Liburkin-Dan, T., Toledano, S., and Neufeld, G. (2022). Lysyl oxidase family enzymes and their role in tumor progression. *International Journal of Molecular Sciences* 23: 6249.

86 Peinado, H., La Cruz, M.D.C.I.-d., Olmeda, D. et al. (2005). A molecular role for lysyl oxidase-like 2 enzyme in Snail regulation and tumor progression. *The EMBO Journal* 24: 3446–3458.

87 Zhang, X., Wang, Q., Wu, J. et al. (2018). Crystal structure of human lysyl oxidase-like 2 (hLOXL2) in a precursor state. *Proceedings of the National Academy of Sciences* 115: 3828–3833.

88 Dong, G., Lin, L.-R., Xu, L.-Y., and Li, E.-M. (2020). Reaction mechanism of lysyl oxidase-like 2 (LOXL2) studied by computational methods. *Journal of Inorganic Biochemistry* 211: 111204.

89 Wang, S.X., Mure, M., Medzihradszky, K.F. et al. (1996). A crosslinked cofactor in lysyl oxidase: redox function for amino acid side chains. *Science* 273: 1078–1084.

90 Xu, L., Go, E.P., Finney, J. et al. (2013). Post-translational modifications of recombinant human lysyl oxidase-like 2 ($rhLOXL_2$) secreted from Drosophila S_2 cells*. *Journal of Biological Chemistry* 288: 5357–5363.

91 Solomon, E.I., Heppner, D.E., Johnston, E.M. et al. (2014). Copper active sites in biology. *Chemical Reviews* 114: 3659–3853.

92 Matoba, Y., Kumagai, T., Yamamoto, A. et al. (2006). Crystallographic evidence that the dinuclear copper center of tyrosinase is flexible during catalysis. *Journal of Biological Chemistry* 281: 8981–8990.

93 Ray, K., Chaki, M., and Sengupta, M. (2007). Tyrosinase and ocular diseases: Some novel thoughts on the molecular basis of oculocutaneous albinism type 1. *Progress in Retinal and Eye Research* 26: 323–358.

94 Peng, H., Wang, T., Li, G. et al. (2022). Dual-locked near-infrared fluorescent probes for precise detection of melanoma via hydrogen peroxide–tyrosinase cascade activation. *Analytical Chemistry* 94: 1070–1075.

95 Buitrago, E., Hardré, R., Haudecoeur, R. et al. (2016). Are human tyrosinase and related proteins suitable targets for melanoma therapy? *Current Topics in Medicinal Chemistry* 16: 3033–3047.

96 Kipouros, I., Stańczak, A., Ginsbach, J.W. et al. (2022). Elucidation of the tyrosinase/O_2/monophenol ternary intermediate that dictates the monooxygenation mechanism in melanin biosynthesis. *Proceedings of the National Academy of Sciences* 119: e2205619119.

97 Baldwin, M.J., Ross, P.K., Pate, J.E. et al. (1991). Spectroscopic and theoretical studies of an end-on peroxide-bridged coupled binuclear copper(II) model complex of relevance to the active sites in hemocyanin and tyrosinase. *Journal of the American Chemical Society* 113: 8671–8679.

98 Halfen, J.A., Mahapatra, S., Wilkinson, E.C. et al. (1996). Reversible cleavage and formation of the dioxygen O—O bond within a dicopper complex. *Science (New York, N.Y.)* 271: 1397–1400.

99 Pidcock, E., Obias, H.V., Zhang, C.X. et al. (1998). Investigation of the reactive oxygen intermediate in an arene hydroxylation reaction performed by Xylyl-bridged binuclear copper complexes. *Journal of the American Chemical Society* 120: 7841–7847.

100 Mirica, L.M., Vance, M., Rudd, D.J. et al. (2005). Tyrosinase reactivity in a model complex: an alternative hydroxylation mechanism. *Science* 308: 1890–1892.

101 Siegbahn, P.E.M. and Borowski, T. (2011). Comparison of QM-only and QM/MM models for the mechanism of tyrosinase. *Faraday Discussions* 148: 109–117.

102 Kipouros, I., Stańczak, A., Culka, M. et al. (2022). Evidence for H-bonding interactions to the μ-η2:η2-peroxide of oxy-tyrosinase that activate its coupled binuclear copper active site. *Chemical Communications* 58: 3913–3916.

103 Mendel, R.R. (2013). The molybdenum cofactor. *Journal of Biological Chemistry* 288: 13165–13172.

104 Romão, M.J., Archer, M., Moura, I. et al. (1995). Crystal structure of the xanthine oxidase-related aldehyde oxido-reductase from *D. gigas*. *Science* 270: 1170–1176.

105 Tiedemann, K., Iobbi-Nivol, C., and Leimkühler, S. (2022). The role of the nucleotides in the insertion of the bis-molybdopterin guanine dinucleotide cofactor into apo-molybdoenzymes. *Molecules* 27: 2993.

106 Schwarz, G. and Mendel, R.R. (2006). Molybdenum cofactor biosynthesis and molybdenum enzymes. *Annual Review of Plant Biology* 57: 623–647.

107 Metz, S. and Thiel, W. (2011). Theoretical studies on the reactivity of molybdenum enzymes. *Coordination Chemistry Reviews* 255: 1085–1103.

108 Pryde, D.C., Dalvie, D., Hu, Q. et al. (2010). Aldehyde oxidase: an enzyme of emerging importance in drug discovery. *Journal of Medicinal Chemistry* 53: 8441–8460.

109 Garattini, E. and Terao, M. (2012). The role of aldehyde oxidase in drug metabolism. *Expert Opinion on Drug Metabolism & Toxicology* 8: 487–503.

110 Jones, P., Atack, J.R., Braun, M.P. et al. (2006). Pharmacokinetics and metabolism studies on (3-tert-butyl-7-5-methylisoxazol-3-yl)-2-(1-methyl-1H-1,2,4-triazol-5-ylmethoxy) pyrazolo[1,5-d][1,2,4]triazine, a functionally selective $GABA_A$ α5 inverse agonist for cognitive dysfunction. *Bioorganic & Medicinal Chemistry Letters* 16: 872–875.

111 Beedham, C. (1985). Molybdenum hydroxylases as drug-metabolizing enzymes. *Drug Metabolism Reviews* 16: 119–156.

112 Coelho, C., Foti, A., Hartmann, T. et al. (2015). Structural insights into xenobiotic and inhibitor binding to human aldehyde oxidase. *Nature Chemical Biology* 11: 779–783.

113 Montefiori, M., Jørgensen, F.S., and Olsen, L. (2017). Aldehyde oxidase: reaction mechanism and prediction of site of metabolism. *ACS Omega* 2: 4237–4244.

114 Garattini, E., Fratelli, M., and Terao, M. (2008). Mammalian aldehyde oxidases: genetics, evolution and biochemistry. *Cellular and Molecular Life Sciences* 65: 1019–1048.

115 Ferreira, P., Cerqueira, N.M.F.S.A., Fernandes, P.A. et al. (2020). Catalytic mechanism of human aldehyde oxidase. *ACS Catalysis* 10: 9276–9286.

116 Hille, R., Hall, J., and Basu, P. (2014). The mononuclear molybdenum enzymes. *Chemical Reviews* 114: 3963–4038.

117 Cerqueira, N.M.F.S.A., Gonzalez, P.J., Fernandes, P.A. et al. (2015). Periplasmic nitrate reductase and formate dehydrogenase: similar molecular architectures with very different enzymatic activities. *Accounts of Chemical Research* 48: 2875–2884.

118 Richert, D.A. and Westerfeld, W.W. (1951). A bioassay procedure for the dietary factor related to xanthine oxidase. *The Journal of Biological Chemistry* 192: 49–56.

119 Morgan, E., Stewart, C., and Hopkins, F.G. (1922). On the anaerobic and aerobic oxidation of xanthin and hypoxanthin by tissues and by milk. *Proceedings of the Royal Society of London. Series B, Containing Papers of a Biological Character* 94: 109–131.

120 Becker, M.A., Schumacher, H.R., Wortmann, R.L. et al. (2005). Febuxostat compared with allopurinol in patients with hyperuricemia and gout. *New England Journal of Medicine* 353: 2450–2461.

121 Fernandes, H.S., Ramos, M.J., and Cerqueira, N.M.F.S.A. (2018). Catalytic mechanism of the serine hydroxymethyltransferase: a computational ONIOM QM/MM study. *ACS Catalysis* 8: 10096–10110.

122 Bai, J., Yan, L., and Liu, Y. (2019). Catalytic mechanism of the PrhA (V150L/A232S) double mutant involved in the fungal meroterpenoid biosynthetic pathway: a QM/MM study. *Physical Chemistry Chemical Physics* 21: 25658–25668.

123 Sudhakara, S., Ramakrishnan, C., Gromiha, M.M., and Chadha, A. (2020). New insights into the stereospecific reduction by an (S) specific carbonyl reductase from Candida parapsilosis ATCC 7330: experimental and QM/MM studies. *Catalysis Science & Technology* 10: 5925–5934.

124 Kumar, R., Joshi, G., Kler, H. et al. (2018). Toward an understanding of structural insights of xanthine and aldehyde oxidases: an overview of their inhibitors and role in various diseases. *Medicinal Research Reviews* 38: 1073–1125.

125 De Renzo, E.C., Kaleita, E., Heytler, P.G. et al. (1953). Identification of the xanthine oxidase factor as molybdenum. *Archives of Biochemistry and Biophysics* 45: 247–253.

126 Kostić, D.A., Dimitrijević, D.S., Stojanović, G.S. et al. (2015). Xanthine oxidase: isolation, assays of activity, and inhibition. *Journal of Chemistry* 2015: 1–8.

127 Ribeiro, P.M.G., Fernandes, H.S., Maia, L.B. et al. (2021). The complete catalytic mechanism of xanthine oxidase: a computational study. *Inorganic Chemistry Frontiers* 8: 405–416.

128 Dong, G. and Ryde, U. (2018). Reaction mechanism of formate dehydrogenase studied by computational methods. *JBIC Journal of Biological Inorganic Chemistry* 23: 1243–1254.

129 Caldararu, O., Feldt, M., Cioloboc, D. et al. (2018). QM/MM study of the reaction mechanism of sulfite oxidase. *Scientific Reports* 8: 4684.

130 Maret, W. (2012). New perspectives of zinc coordination environments in proteins. *Journal of Inorganic Biochemistry* 111: 110–116.

131 Maret, W. and Li, Y. (2009). Coordination dynamics of zinc in proteins. *Chemical Reviews* 109: 4682–4707.

132 Alberts, I.L., Nadassy, K., and Wodak, S.J. (1998). Analysis of zinc binding sites in protein crystal structures. *Protein Science* 7: 1700–1716.

133 Kouzarides, T. (2007). Chromatin modifications and their function. *Cell* 128: 693–705.

134 Smith, B.C. and Denu, J.M. (2009). Chemical mechanisms of histone lysine and arginine modifications. *Biochimica et Biophysica Acta* 1789: 45–57.

135 Sternson, S.M., Wong, J.C., Grozinger, C.M., and Schreiber, S.L. (2001). Synthesis of 7200 small molecules based on a substructural analysis of the histone deacetylase inhibitors trichostatin and trapoxin. *Organic Letters* 3: 4239–4242.

136 Bradner, J.E., West, N., Grachan, M.L. et al. (2010). Chemical phylogenetics of histone deacetylases. *Nature Chemical Biology* 6: 238–243.

137 Gregoretti, I., Lee, Y.-M., and Goodson, H.V. (2004). Molecular evolution of the histone deacetylase family: functional implications of phylogenetic analysis. *Journal of Molecular Biology* 338: 17–31.

138 Nielsen, T.K., Hildmann, C., Dickmanns, A. et al. (2005). Crystal structure of a bacterial class 2 histone deacetylase homologue. *Journal of Molecular Biology* 354: 107–120.

139 Anzellotti, A.I. and Farrell, N.P. (2008). Zinc metalloproteins as medicinal targets. *Chemical Society Reviews* 37: 1629–1651.

140 Vannini, A., Volpari, C., Gallinari, P. et al. (2007). Substrate binding to histone deacetylases as shown by the crystal structure of the HDAC8-substrate complex. *EMBO Reports* 8: 879–884.

141 Wu, R., Wang, S., Zhou, N. et al. (2010). A proton-shuttle reaction mechanism for histone deacetylase 8 and the catalytic role of metal ions. *Journal of the American Chemical Society* 132: 9471–9479.

142 Zhou, J., Wu, R., and Luo, H.-B. (2015). Inhibition mechanism of SAHA in HDAC: a revisit. *Physical Chemistry Chemical Physics* 17: 29483–29488.

143 Hey, S. and Linder, S. (2024). Matrix metalloproteinases at a glance. *Journal of Cell Science* 137: jcs261898.

144 McCawley, L.J. and Matrisian, L.M. (2001). Matrix metalloproteinases: they're not just for matrix anymore! *Current Opinion in Cell Biology* 13: 534–540.

145 Werb, Z. (1997). ECM and cell surface proteolysis: regulating cellular ecology. *Cell* 91: 439–442.

146 Sternlicht, M.D. and Werb, Z. (2001). How matrix metalloproteinases regulate cell behavior. *Annual Review of Cell and Developmental Biology* 17: 463–516.

147 Bode, W., Fernandez-Catalan, C., Tschesche, H. et al. (1999). Structural properties of matrix metalloproteinases. *Cellular and Molecular Life Sciences: CMLS* 55: 639–652.

148 Nagase, H. and Woessner, J.F. (1999). Matrix metalloproteinases. *The Journal of Biological Chemistry* 274: 21491–21494.

149 Bertini, I., Calderone, V., Cosenza, M. et al. (2005). Conformational variability of matrix metalloproteinases: beyond a single 3D structure. *Proceedings of the National Academy of Sciences* 102: 5334–5339.

150 Maskos, K. (2005). Crystal structures of MMPs in complex with physiological and pharmacological inhibitors. *Biochimie* 87: 249–263.

151 Díaz, N., Suárez, D., and Sordo, T.L. (2006). Quantum chemical study on the coordination environment of the catalytic zinc ion in matrix metalloproteinases. *The Journal of Physical Chemistry B* 110: 24222–24230.

152 Johnson, L.L., Pavlovsky, A.G., Johnson, A.R. et al. (2000). A rationalization of the acidic pH dependence for stromelysin-1 (matrix metalloproteinase-3) catalysis and inhibition*. *Journal of Biological Chemistry* 275: 11026–11033.

153 Arza, B., De Maeyer, M., Félez, J. et al. (2001). Critical role of glutamic acid 202 in the enzymatic activity of stromelysin-1 (MMP-3). *European Journal of Biochemistry* 268: 826–831.

154 Pardo, A. and Selman, M. (2005). MMP-1: The elder of the family. *The International Journal of Biochemistry & Cell Biology* 37: 283–288.

155 Murphy, G. and Nagase, H. (2008). Progress in matrix metalloproteinase research. *Molecular Aspects of Medicine* 29: 290–308.

156 Whittaker, M., Floyd, C.D., Brown, P., and Gearing, A.J.H. (1999). Design and therapeutic application of matrix metalloproteinase inhibitors. *Chemical Reviews* 99: 2735–2776.

157 Arnold, L.H., Butt, L.E., Prior, S.H. et al. (2011). The interface between catalytic and hemopexin domains in matrix metalloproteinase-1 conceals a collagen binding exosite. *Journal of Biological Chemistry* 286: 45073–45082.

158 Lauer-Fields, J.L., Chalmers, M.J., Busby, S.A. et al. (2009). Identification of specific hemopexin-like domain residues that facilitate matrix metalloproteinase collagenolytic activity*. *Journal of Biological Chemistry* 284: 24017–24024.

159 Varghese, A., Waheed, S.O., Gorantla, K. et al. (2023). Catalytic mechanism of collagen hydrolysis by zinc(II)-dependent matrix metalloproteinase-1. *The Journal of Physical Chemistry B* 127: 9697–9709.

4

Experimental Strategies in Metalloenzyme Mechanism Study and Drug Discovery

Si-Qi Wei, Zi-Yang Chen*, and Guo-Bo Li*

Wuhou District people's South Road, three 17, Sichuan University, West China School of Pharmacy, Department of Medicinal Chemistry, Chengdu 610041, Sichuan, P.R. China

4.1 Introduction

Metalloenzymes are catalytically active proteases widely found in living organisms, consisting of one or more metal ions tightly bound to proteins. They play a crucial role in diverse biological processes and constitute approximately one-third of the entire proteome [1]. The intrinsic metal ions are indispensable for various biological processes, including catalysis, regulation, and structural stabilization [2]. Compared to non-metalloenzymes, the catalytic activity of metalloenzymes consistently depends on metal ions. Metal ions facilitate catalytic reactions by providing the necessary charge, stabilizing reaction intermediates, or regulating catalytic activity. Metalloenzymes encompass all six enzyme classification types, including oxidoreductases, hydrolases, transferases, polymerases, isomerases, and ligases [3].

Due to the unique nature of metal-ion-containing active sites in metalloenzymes, characterized by electron deficiency, inhibitors of metalloenzymes typically interact with metal ions at these active sites through mechanisms such as metal ion deprivation, replacement, or cysteine modification [4]. During the catalytic process, metal ions often coordinate with substrates, and this coordination can vary between intermediates at different stages. During the catalytic process, metal ions often coordinate with substrates, and this coordination can vary between intermediates at different stages. Detecting metal ion coordination is also crucial for understanding the interaction mechanisms of drug molecules with metalloenzymes.

This chapter provides an overview of the experimental techniques used to study the catalytic mechanisms of metalloenzymes, emphasizing their advantages and unique features. It also covers methods for detecting metalloenzyme inhibitor binding and selectivity, supported by relevant case studies. We hope that this chapter can help foster the development of new experimental strategies for metalloenzymes and advance the research on their catalytic and inhibitory mechanisms.

* S.Q.W. and Z.Y.C. are co-first authors.

Drug Discovery Targeting Metalloenzymes: Strategies and Applications, First Edition. Edited by Guo-Bo Li.

4.2 Metalloenzyme Catalysis Mechanism

4.2.1 Detecting Reaction Intermediate by UV–Vis Spectroscopy

Ultraviolet–visible (UV–Vis) spectroscopy is a widely used technique for both qualitative and quantitative analysis, characterized by high sensitivity, excellent accuracy, ease of selective operation, and rapid analytical speed. UV–Vis spectroscopy can detect changes in metalloenzyme intermediates.

Tryptophan (Trp) is a vital amino acid for the human body, which is acquired mainly through dietary sources. The kynurenine (KYN) pathway is the primary metabolic route for Trp, with its metabolites closely associated with various diseases [5, 6]. The rate of Trp metabolism is regulated by tryptophan dioxygenase (hTDO) and indoleamine 2,3-dioxygenase (hIDO), both of which are thus considered as potential drug targets. IDO1 is a monomeric oxidase containing a heme iron, and can dioxygenate a broader range of substrates with indole moieties. TDO is a tetrameric hemoprotein specific to Trp metabolism, consisting of four non-covalently bonded subunits with molecular mass ranging from 35 to 45 kDa, each containing a heme group. These enzymes cleave the indole ring of Trp at the 2,3-position to produce *N*-formylkynurenine (NFK) [7] (Figure 4.1).

Figure 4.2 shows two proposed catalytic mechanisms of TDO and IDO. The initial indole activation step involves either an electrophilic or a radical addition, followed by formation of the common intermediate, indole epoxide [7]. The Fe = O resonance Raman peak at 799 cm^{-1} has been used to characterize the formation and decay of the ferryl intermediate during human IDO turnover [8]. Taking human IDO as an example, during the active catalytic cycle, the ferrous enzyme sequentially binds L-Trp and O_2 to form a ternary complex, which subsequently rearranges to produce NFK, returning the enzyme to its catalytically competent ferrous state. If the enzyme becomes inactive in the ferric state due to autoxidation, it needs to be reduced to Fe(II) to reenter the active catalytic cycle (Figure 4.3) [9]. The changes in intermediates can be monitored using UV–Vis spectroscopy, which can be reflected in the peaks of the Soret band and Q band in the UV–Vis spectrum. Each peak corresponds to a distinct intermediate state (Table 4.1) [9].

Cytochrome P450 (CYP) enzymes, which like IDO/TDO, utilize heme cofactors to catalyze oxidation reactions, are a family of self-oxidizing ferrous hemoproteins classified as heme monooxygenase [10]. They play a crucial role in the metabolism of exogenous and endogenous substances, including drugs, making CYP enzymes

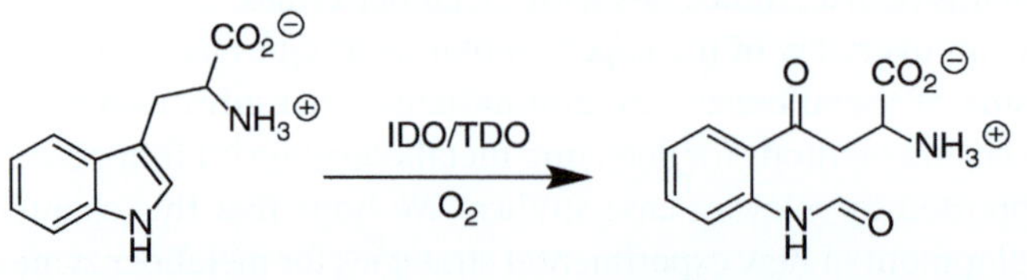

Figure 4.1 IDO/TDO-catalyzed transformation of Trp to NFK.

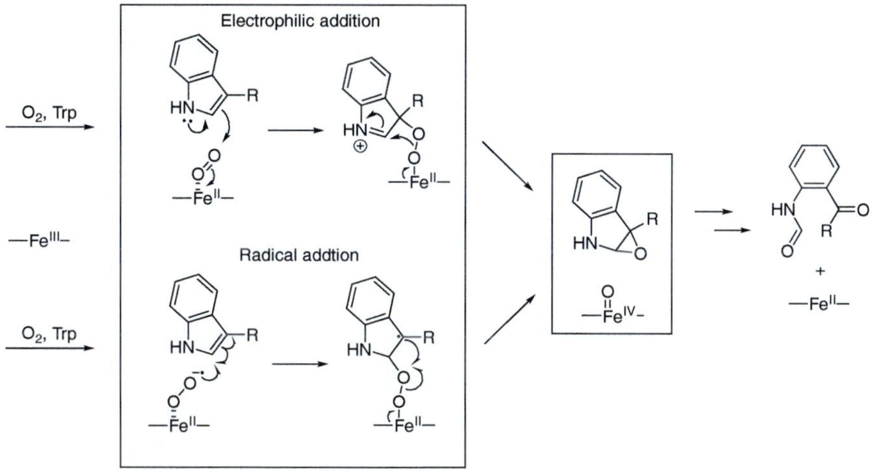

Figure 4.2 Two proposed mechanisms of IDO/TDO deoxygenating tryptophan: an electrophilic or a radical addition.

Figure 4.3 Catalytic cycle of human indoleamine 2,3-dioxygenase.

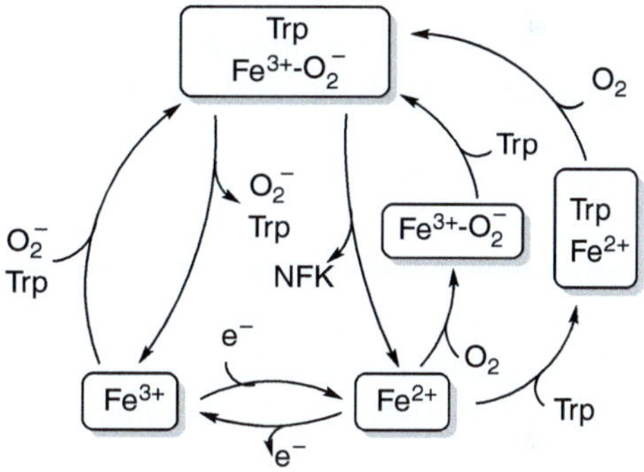

Table 4.1 Soret bands and Q-bands of the various derivatives of hIDO.

Condition	λ_{Soret}(nm)	λ_{vis}(nm)
Fe^{3+}	404	499,533,633
Fe^{3+}-L-Trp	410	540,576
Fe^{2+}	429	588
Fe^{2+}-L-Trp	425	555

important drug targets [11]. Lockart's team [12] elucidated cytochrome P450 ligand-binding modes using continuous wave (CW) EPR spectroscopy. Since CYP3A4 and CYP2C9 metabolize more than 50% of all pharmaceutical drugs, their ligand-binding modes were studied using EPR. The g values, which depend on the orientation of the magnetic field relative to the heme, include g_x, g_y, and g_z. Analyses of g_z shifts, ligand field parameters, and principal components revealed that the main variations in the EPR spectra are driven by differences in heme ligation. These findings demonstrated that the ligand field of the heme is closely associated with CYP ligand-binding modes.

4.2.2 Capturing the Intermediate Binding Mode by Crystallography

Investigating the three-dimensional structures of biomacromolecules is crucial for understanding their functional mechanisms. X-ray crystallography plays a pivotal role in this endeavor by providing diffraction patterns that can be translated into electron-density maps, unveiling the true structure of biomacromolecules. For instance, in 1958, Kendrew and coworkers [13] determined the first three-dimensional model of the myoglobin molecule by X-ray analysis, and in 1960, Perutz and coworkers [14] obtained the three-dimensional structure of Hemoglobin after six years to produce its electron-density map at a resolution of 5.5 Å. Furthermore, a milestone achievement in the early applications of X-ray crystallography was the elucidation of the DNA structure, confirming its double-helix conformation in 1953 by Watson and Crick [15].

In some cases, crystallography can directly capture the catalytic intermediate of a metalloenzyme, providing valuable insights for forming rational hypotheses about the catalytic process and exploring potential mechanisms. Urease was the first enzyme to be crystallized and confirmed as proteinaceous, as well as the first enzyme established to depend on the presence of Ni^{2+} as an essential element. Urease facilitates the hydrolysis of urea into ammonia and carbamate. As revealed by crystallographic analyses, the carbonyl and/or amide groups coordinate with Ni^{2+} to form a plane perpendicular to the bridging hydroxide (Figure 4.4a). Supported by these structural bases, the proposed catalytic mechanisms of urease are shown in Figure 4.4b. However, the extremely short lifetime of the urease-urea intermediate adduct hindered the confirmation of its structure, which in turn impeded the understanding of the catalytic mechanism and the development of urease inhibitors. To address this mechanistic controversy, Ciurli and colleagues [16] published the high-resolution structure of the urease-urea complex (Figure 4.4c), which replaced the co-substrate hydroxide with unreactive fluoride, thereby blocking subsequent catalytic steps. The crystal structure shows that the oxygen atom of carbonyl and one amide nitrogen atom of urea bind to Ni(1) and Ni(2), respectively, while another amide group points away from the Ni^{2+} and forms hydrogen bonds with Gly280 and Ala366. These findings support the first hypothesis and provide more detailed insights into the mechanism of urease-mediated hydrolysis.

4.2.3 Investigating Intermediate Transformation by Serial Crystallography

X-ray crystallography has long been a powerful tool for analyzing structures of biomacromolecules. However, this method typically requires the growth of sufficiently large crystals and involves prolonged exposure of these crystals to X-rays, leading to radiation-induced damage that significantly compromises

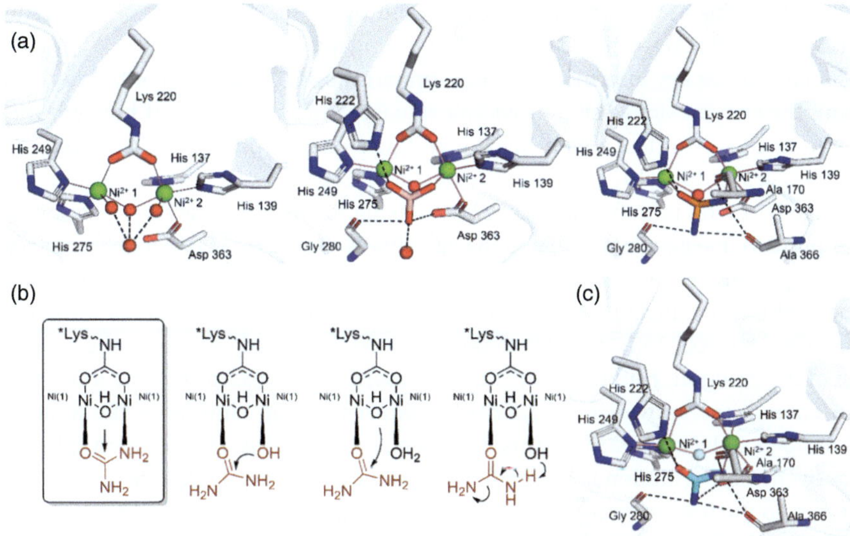

Figure 4.4 (a) Crystal structure of the active core of urease, urease-boric acid complex, and urease-diamidophosphate complex; (b) Hypothesis about the hydrolysis reaction mechanism of urease; (c) Crystal structure of urease-urea complex published by Ciurli's group.

the quality of diffraction data and can even cause irreversible alterations to the biomacromolecular structure [17]. Cryocooling of crystals can mitigate radiation damage during data collection, but this approach may limit the structural insights into molecular dynamics [18]. With the advent of X-ray free electron lasers (XFELs), synchrotron sources, and new sample delivery systems, serial crystallography (SX) has developed to overcome the limitations of traditional X-ray crystallography (Figure 4.5). By exposing crystals to X-rays for extremely brief durations, SX effectively minimizes radiation damage, and realizes "diffraction-before-destruction". Furthermore, SX allows data collection at room temperature or near-physiological conditions, facilitating investigations into the functional mechanisms of biomacromolecules in their native environments [18]. Consequently, SX has become a

Figure 4.5 Schematic representation showing the experimental setup for TR-SX measurement.

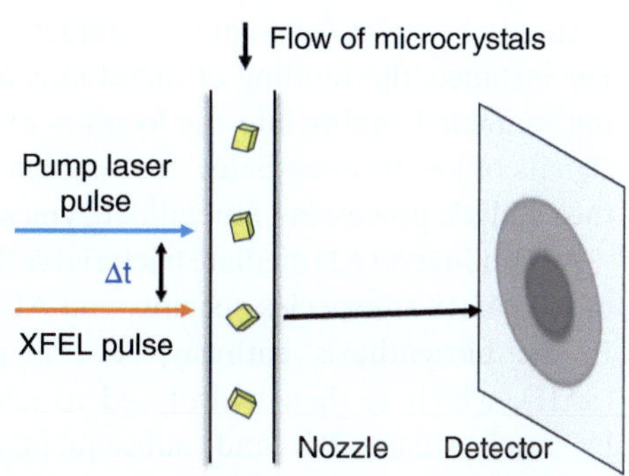

preferred method for elucidating the structures of metalloenzymes, unraveling metalloprotein catalysis processes, and informing drug design efforts.

SX can capture key intermediates and support the actual position of the substrate within the enzyme active site, providing valuable information about how enzymes interact with substrates, which helps investigate enzymatic reaction mechanisms. Joachimiak's group [19] published a detailed study on the process of β-lactam cleavage by L1 metallo-β-lactamase (MBL) using SX techniques. They employed a laser pulse to release a zinc ion, which was initially locked by a UV-labile photocage, allowing them to initiate the reaction at a controlled time and capture real-time structural images during β-lactam hydrolysis. The time-resolved crystal structures (20, 40, 60, 80, 100, 150, 300, 500, 2000, and 4000 ms) clearly illustrate the progression of the reaction. Initially, a 347 nm UV-laser pulse released the zinc ion, which then entered the active site of L1 MBL, followed by the binding of the β-lactam substrate moxalactam within 20 ms. Between 20 and 100 ms, the β-lactam substrate underwent conformational adjustments, primarily covering the carboxyl group adjacent to the four-membered ring. The open-ring reaction occurred between 100 and 150 ms, and the open-ring product then continued to adjust its conformation to achieve stability (Figure 4.6b). Unexpectedly, it was discovered that during hydrolysis, the oxazine ring rotates counterclockwise by about 30° and then recovers by rotating clockwise during the 500–4000 ms timeframe (Figure 4.6c). While previous crystallographic studies at low temperatures have suggested possible mechanisms for MBL-mediated β-lactam hydrolysis, this time-resolved approach provides more detailed insights into the reaction process and supports the hypothesis raised by Vila [20] that the two main steps – C—N bond cleavage and protonation of the nitrogen atom – occur synchronously.

4.2.4 Studying Intermediate Transformation by NMR

X-ray crystallography is widely used to determine static protein structures, elucidate mechanisms, and aid in drug design. However, it faces limitations when dealing with flexible regions of proteins, as these areas fail to produce clear electron density maps. In contrast, NMR spectroscopy can be employed to explore ensembles of structures representing different conformations in solution, providing a complementary perspective on protein structure and ligand-receptor interactions [21]. Due to the sensitivity of chemical shifts to changes in the chemical environment, NMR is particularly useful for studying interactions between proteins and other molecules. For instance, the binding of metal ions to proteins induces chemical shifts, offering valuable insights into the location of metal-binding sites. By identifying NMR signals of key intermediates, researchers can formulate rational hypotheses about the catalytic processes of metalloenzymes.

Autoinducers (AI) mediate bacterial cell–cell communication. There are two types of AIs, AI-1s are species-specific, and AI-2 is a universal signal used by all species. In the biosynthesis pathway, AI-2 is produced from *S*-adenosylhomocysteine (SAH), which is then hydrolyzed to adenine and *S*-ribosylhomocysteine (SRH) by nucleosidase Pfs and subsequently transformed into homocysteine and

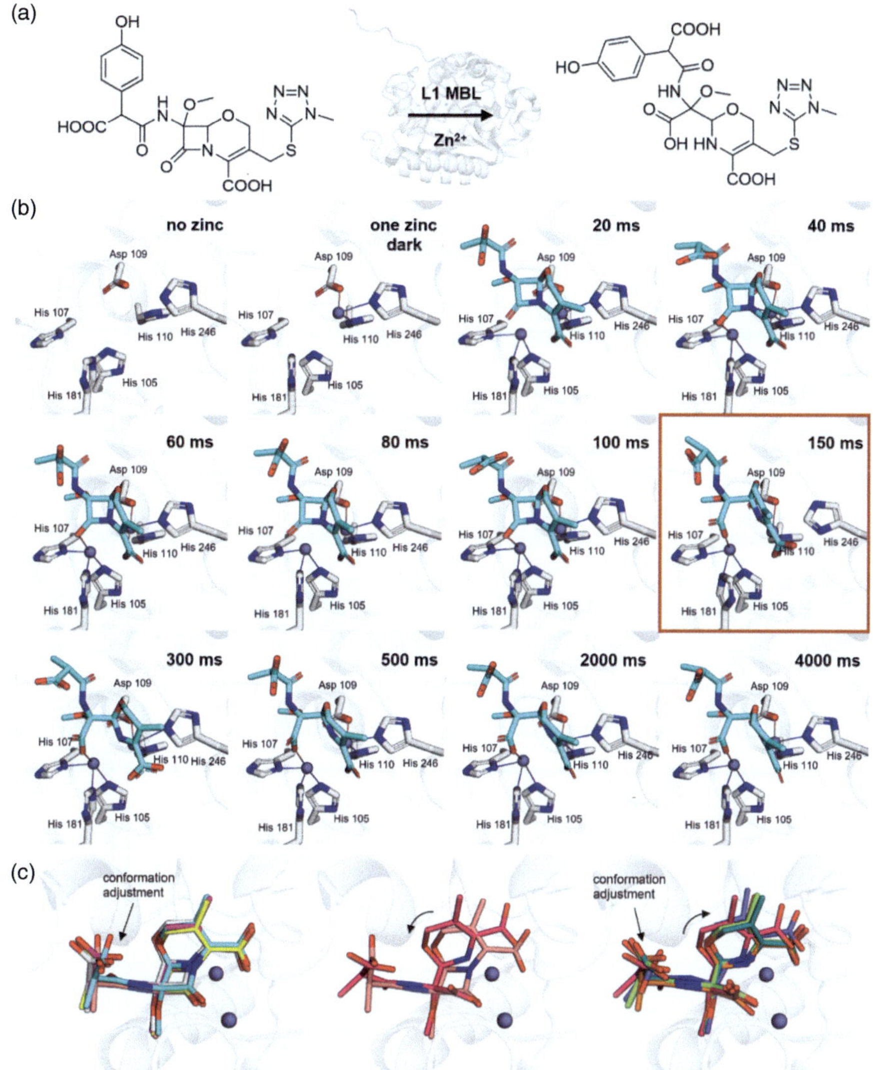

Figure 4.6 (a): Schematics of moxalactam hydrolysis; (b): Room temperature SSX and TR-SSX structures of L1 active site representing different states; (c): Conformation adjustments of β-lactam substrate moxalactam before hydrolysis, in hydrolysis and after hydrolysis.

4,5-dihydroxy-2,3-pentanedione (DHPD) by *S*-ribosylhomocysteinase (LuxS). DHPD will finally form a furanosyl borate diester as the AI-2. Based on the position of deuterium in the product DHPD from reactions processed in D_2O (Figure 4.7a), Pei's group [22] proposed a possible mechanism of how LuxS catalyzes SRH to form DHPD and conducted a ^{13}C NMR experiment to prove their hypothesis. They brought ^{13}C at the 2-/3-positions of SRH and then explored the time-dependent ^{13}C NMR of the substrate mixed with the enzyme. The results reveal the existence of

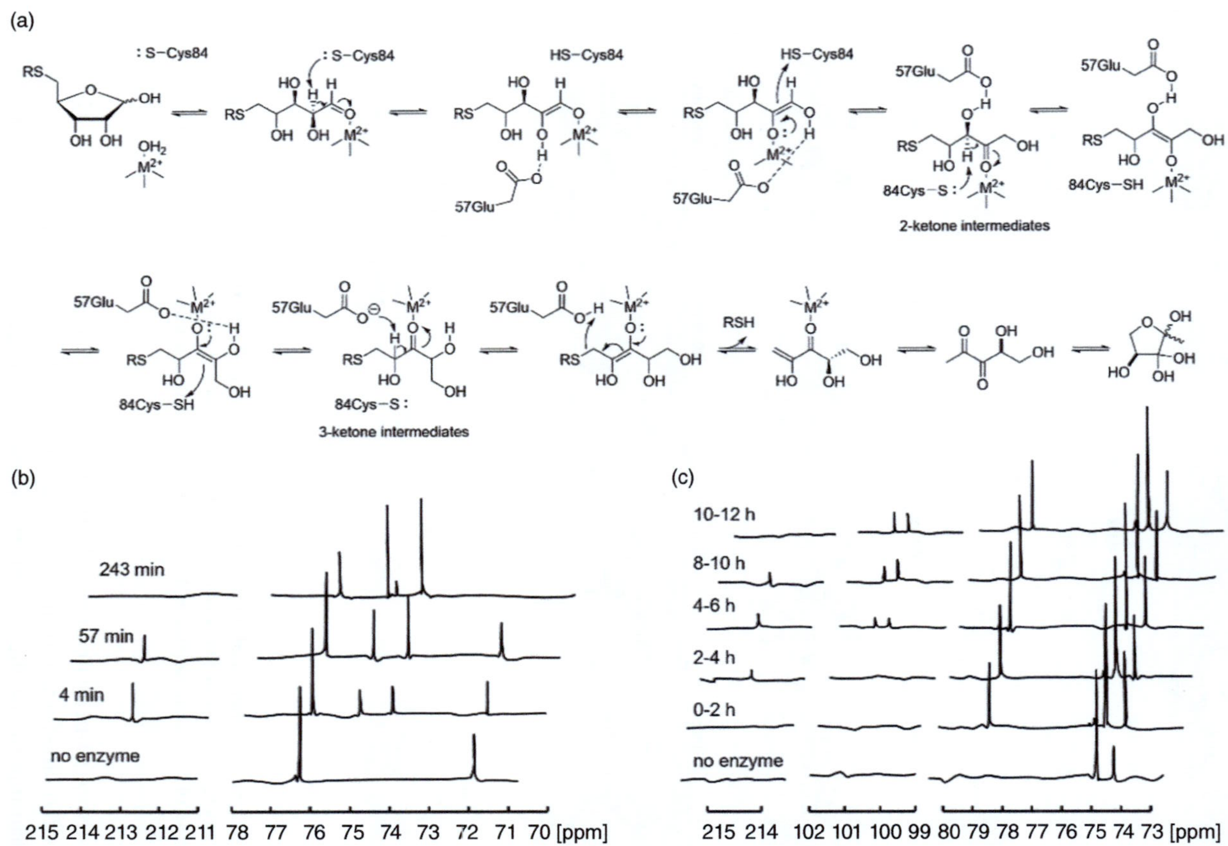

Figure 4.7 (a) Proposed mechanism for LuxS-catalyzed reaction; (b) [2-^{13}C]SRH (2.0 mM) and wild-type *B. subtilis* LuxS (2.0 mM) were mixed at 4 °C, and spectra were recorded every 4.1 min; (c) [3-^{13}C]SRH (1.8 mM) and E57A LuxS (1.4 mM) were mixed at 4 °C, and spectra were recorded every 2 h.

a 2-keto intermediate (213.3 ppm) (Figure 4.7b). The signal at 214.5 ppm can also be monitored when ^{13}C is brought at the 3-position, suggesting the existence of a 3-keto intermediate (Figure 4.7c). They then synthesized a 2-keto intermediate and mixed it with LuxS, which successfully afforded the downstream product DHPD, and conducted kinetic experiments to prove the kinetic character of the 2-keto intermediate. Finally, they successfully obtained direct evidence for the involvement of 2- and 3-ketone intermediates in the LuxS-catalyzed reaction, thereby validating the catalytic mechanism previously proposed.

4.3 Metalloenzyme Inhibition Mechanism

4.3.1 Investigating Inhibitor Binding by NMR

NMR has become a widely used technology for studying metalloenzyme inhibitor binding [23], owing to the presence of metal ion(s) in the active sites of metalloenzymes. A representative example is the combination of virtual screening and NMR in the discovery of new MBL inhibitors [24]. Since MBLs contain one or two zinc ions for catalysis, the authors used ethylenediaminetetraacetic acid (EDTA) to remove the zinc ions from the MBL active sites to obtain apo-enzymes for a control study. They tested the hits from virtual screening with di-Zn(II)-VIM-2 and apo-VIM-2 by using the ^{1}H Carr-Purcell-Meiboom-Gill (CPMG) NMR spectroscopy. The results can indicate whether the zinc ions are essential for inhibitor binding, which partly reflects the inhibitor's binding with VIM-2. The most effective inhibitors **1** and **2** can both bind with di-Zn(II)-VIM-2 and apo-VIM-2. A stronger binding with di-Zn(II)-VIM-2 suggests that the zinc ions may play a role in indirectly interacting with both the inhibitor and VIM-2 (Figure 4.8a), as supported by the subsequent crystallographic analyses (Figure 4.8b).

NMR can also be used to investigate the position at which the compounds interact with metalloenzymes. Schofield's group [25] applied the PrOF NMR technique to study MBL by using the 3-bromo-1,1,1-trifluoroacetone (BTFA) reagent to label Tyr58C and Phe151C in variants of São Paulo Metallo-β-lactamase (SPM-1). This approach allowed them to observe changes in the L3 loop (Tyr58C*) and the α3 region (Phe151*) of SPM-1 induced by ligand binding (Figure 4.9). When SPM-1 was mixed with the zinc chelator 1,10-*o*-phenanthroline, the chemical shifts of Tyr58C* and Phe151C* were altered, aligning with the positions observed in apo-SPM-1. This suggests that 1,10-*o*-phenanthroline removes the zinc ion from the active site of SPM-1 without binding to the enzyme.

The isoquinoline derivative **3**, a broad-spectrum MBL inhibitor, was also studied using ^{19}F NMR. The spectrum indicated that both the L3 loop and α3 region interact with compound **3**. The ^{19}F NMR spectrum of **3** suggested that it can coordinate with SPM-1 without the need for a metal ion.

For the SPM-1 substrates meropenem and piperacillin, the ^{19}F NMR spectrum indicated that these compounds interact with the L3 loop but do not affect the α3 region, as no significant chemical shifts of Phe151C* were observed. Additionally, ^{1}H NMR and ^{19}F NMR were used to investigate the binding modes of

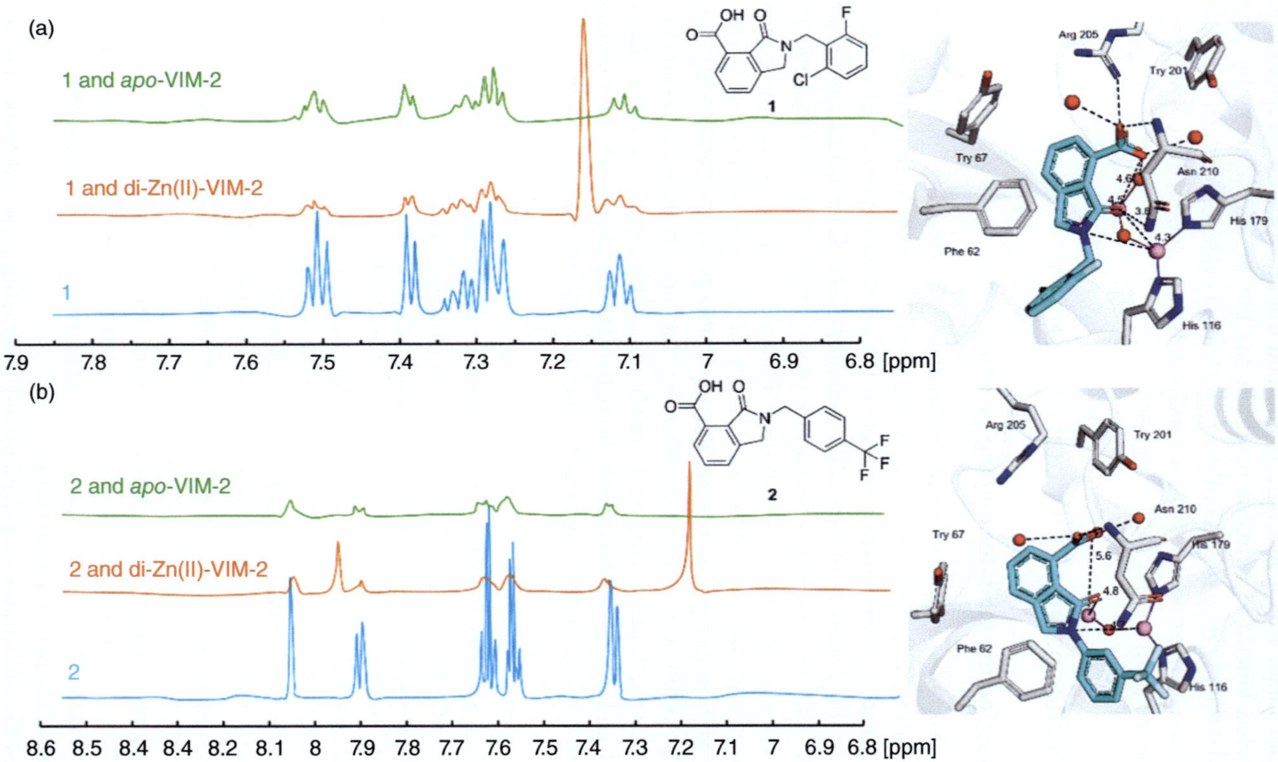

Figure 4.8 (a): ^{1}H CPMG NMR spectroscopy and crystallographic structure of **1** and apo/di-Zn(II)-VIM-2; (b): ^{1}H CPMG NMR spectroscopy and crystallographic structure of **2** and apo/di-Zn(II)-VIM-2.

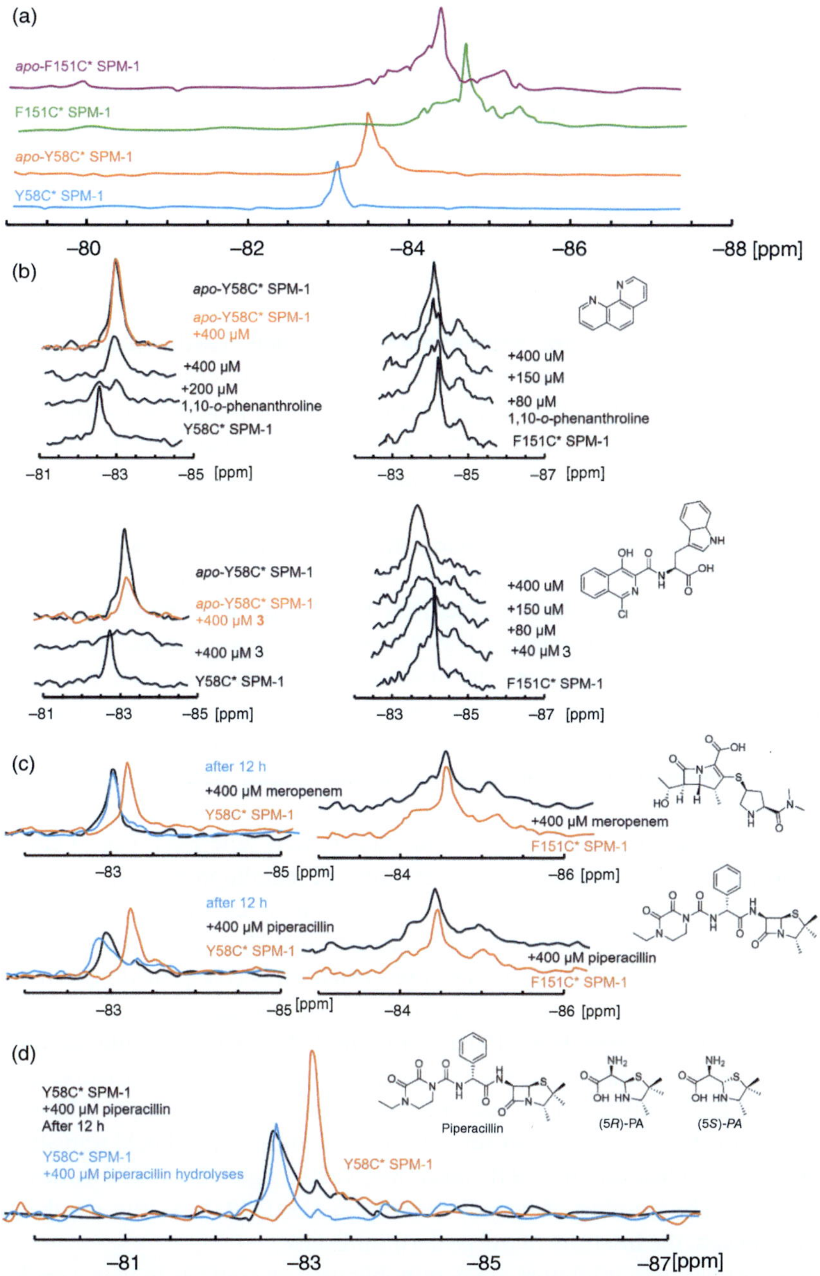

Figure 4.9 (a): PrOF NMR spectra of apo- and di-Zn(II)-SPM-1* variants; (b): ^{19}F-NMR spectra of the interactions of 1,10-*o*-phenanthroline with Y58C* SPM-1, F151C* SPM-1, and interactions of **3** with Y58C* SPM-1, F151C* SPM-1; (c): Time-course analyses (after 12 hours) of meropenem and piperacillin with Y58C* SPM-1 are consistent with a stable protein-product peak with an additional shift in the case of piperacillin, which indicates the formation of a new species. Titration of meropenem and piperacillin into a solution of F151C* SPM-1 shows no substantial changes; (d): ^{19}F-NMR spectra of Y58C* SPM-1 interacting with hydrolyzed piperacillin. Structures of piperacillin and its hydrolyzed products [(5*R*)-PA and (5*S*)-PA] are also shown.

piperacillin hydrolysis products, (5*S*)/(5*R*)-penicilloic acid, with SPM-1. The results revealed that (5*R*)-penicilloic acid is released more quickly from the enzyme, while (5*S*)-penicilloic acid binds more readily to SPM-1, with the L3 loop playing a key role in product binding and release.

4.3.2 Exploring Inhibitor Binding by UV–Vis Spectroscopy

UV–Vis spectroscopy provides extensive information about the binding of inhibitors to metalloproteins [26]. Since UV–Vis spectroscopy is capable of detecting changes in metalloenzyme intermediates, it is useful for examining the inhibitor binding. β-Lactam antibiotics are among the most widely used small molecule antibacterial agents in clinical practice [4]. However, the efficacy of β-lactams has been increasingly diminished due to the spread of β-lactamases, including serine-β-lactamases (SBLs) and metallo-β-lactamases (MBLs) [4, 27]. The SBLs cleave the β-lactam ring through a nucleophilic serine residue at the active site, while zinc ions in MBLs activate water molecules for substrate hydrolysis [28]. Although SBL inhibitors, such as avibactam, have been clinically successful, no MBL inhibitors are available for clinical use to combat the rapidly increasing MBL-mediated resistance [4, 27]. Scientists have made numerous attempts to address this issue, with IMiPenemase (IMP), Verona Integron-encoded MBL (VIM), and New Delhi MBL (NDM) being the most clinically relevant enzyme types [29]. Although spectroscopic techniques can be used to probe inhibitor mechanisms, MBLs predominantly bind zinc ions in the active site, which are diamagnetic and can only be accessed through X-ray crystallography and X-ray absorption spectroscopy (XAS) [26].

To overcome the challenge of spectroscopically inert zinc ions, Co(II) can be used as a spectroscopic probe for the active sites of metalloproteins. Co(II) binds to MBLs in the same manner as zinc ions and remains catalytically active [30]. UV–Vis spectroscopy can probe Co(II) binding to metalloenzymes based on the absorption of UV–Vis radiation by the d electrons in Co(II), providing valuable information [26]. Most MBLs with Co(II) in the active sites appear pink, and when their concentration ranges from 100 mM to 1 mM, two peaks should be noted [26, 31]. An intense peak at 320–350 nm appears when a cysteine sulfhydryl binds to Co(II) and disappears when the cysteine dissociates from Co(II) due to inhibitors. Another group of peaks at 500–650 nm, referred to as d-d or ligand field transitions, arise from the d electrons in Co(II) absorbing visible light. Their intensities are determined by the number of ligands binding to Co(II) [31]. As the number of ligands increases, the intensity of the peaks diminishes.

In these studies, two inhibitors are commonly used as controls to better explore the inhibition modes of unknown compounds: EDTA and captopril [32]. The former is a metal chelator, inhibiting MBLs by removing or sequestering metal ions in the active site [33]. The latter is a sulfhydryl-containing compound that forms ternary complexes with MBLs and competitively inhibits MBLs by chelating zinc ions in the active site via the thiolate anion [34]. The formation of a complex between the inhibitor (e.g. captopril) and MBLs results in additional ligand binding to Co(II),

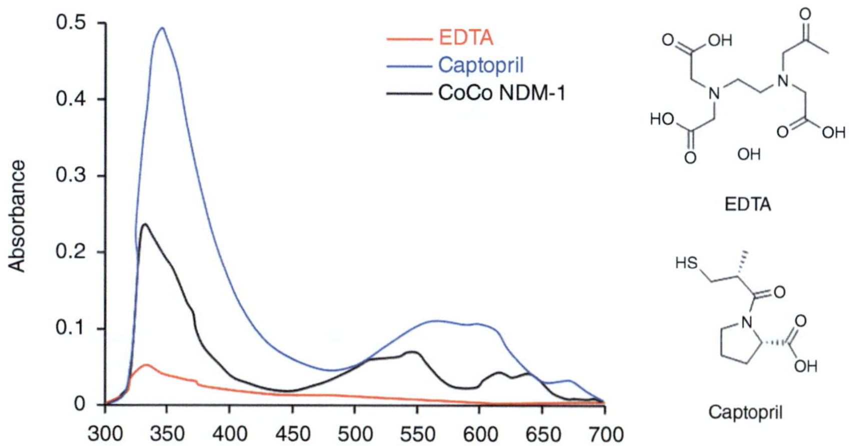

Figure 4.10 UV–visible (UV–Vis) spectroscopy of CoCo NDM-1 with two equivalent EDTA (red line), CoCo NDM-1 with two equivalent captopril (blue line), and CoCo NDM-1 (black line).

leading to a decrease in the intensity of the d-d peak or a significant change [31]. Furthermore, additional thiolate coordination to Co(II) by the inhibitor increases the intensity of the peak at 320–350 nm [26]. Conversely, if Co(II) is stripped by the inhibitor (e.g. EDTA), resulting in a multi-coordinated complex, the intensity of the d-d peak is significantly reduced, and the 320–350 nm peak disappears [31] (Figure 4.10).

Based on the structure of 2,6-dipicolinic acid (DPA) (Figure 4.11a), Chen's team [35] employed fragment-based drug discovery (FBDD) to identify inhibitor **4** (Figure 4.11b), which is highly selective for MBLs compared to other zinc-containing metalloenzymes. The combination of **4** with imipenem effectively inhibited *E.coli* and *Klebsiella pneumoniae* harboring MBLs. To explore the inhibition mode, they incubated di-Co(II)-substituted NDM-1 with DPA and **4**, and the samples were analyzed by UV–Vis spectroscopy. When DPA at 1 or 2 equivalents was combined with NDM-1, the ligand field intensity decreased, showing a trend similar to that observed with EDTA, though less pronounced. This suggested that DPA inhibited NDM by chelating metal ions from NDM-1, but did not bind as tightly as EDTA to Co(II). Meanwhile, the increasing intensity of the peak at approximately 300 nm and the retention of the d-d band intensity strongly suggested that **4** formed a ternary complex with NDM-1, similar to the competitive inhibitor captopril (Figure 4.12).

As mentioned earlier, the Soret peak is the characteristic optical absorption peak at 405 nm and can reflect the heme-iron electronic state [9]. A series of 6-bromo-1*H*-indazol-4-amine derivatives were identified as hIDO1 inhibitors (Figure 4.13) [36]. To explore the inhibition mode of the 6-bromo-1*H*-indazol-4-amine scaffold, the authors used UV–Vis to investigate how derivatives **5** and **6** interact with IDO/TDO. When hIDO1 was incubated in the reductive assay buffer, the Soret peak decreased with a redshift, while OD421.5 increased, indicating that the combination with **5** influenced the electronic state of heme iron (Figure 4.14).

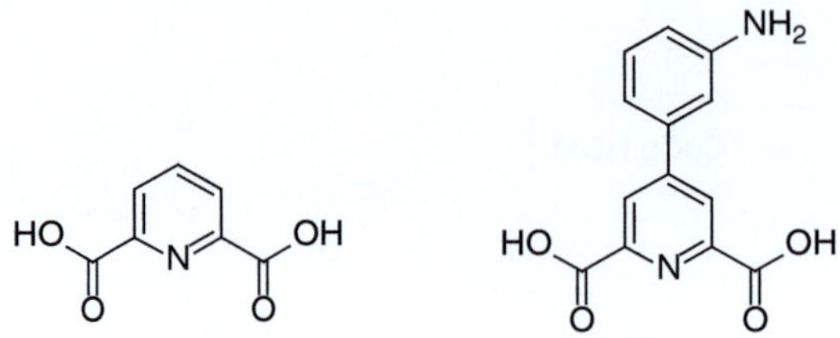

DPA inhibitior **4**

Figure 4.11 Structure of DPA and inhibitor **4**.

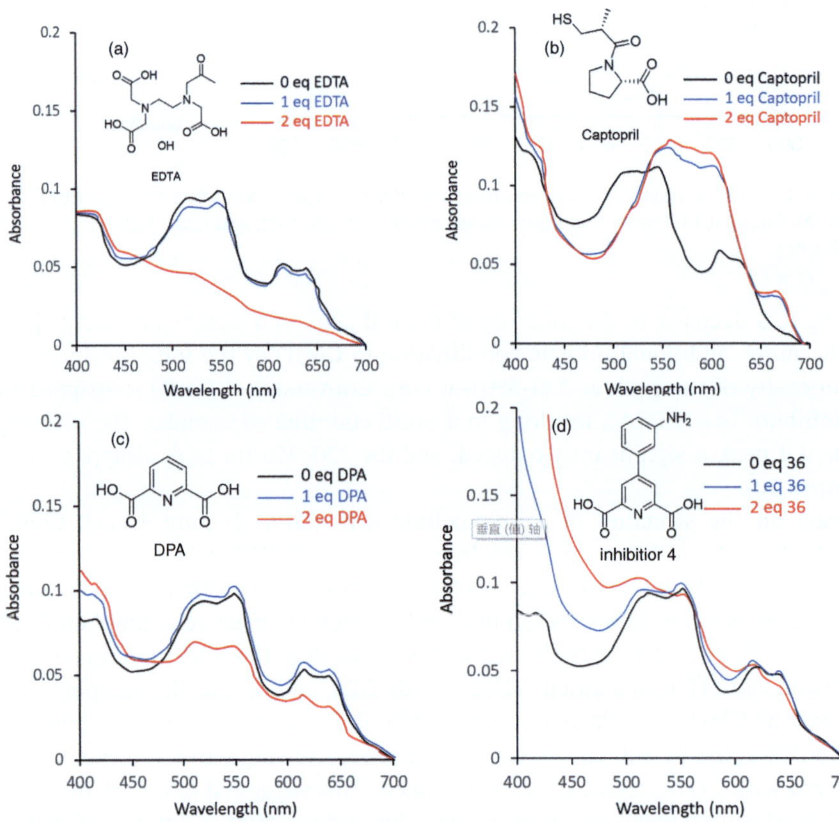

Figure 4.12 UV–Vis spectroscopy of CoCo-NDM-1 (black lines) and CoCo-NDM-1 (300 μM) with EDTA (a) and L-captopril (b) as control, and 1–2 equivalents of added DPA (c), and **4** (d).

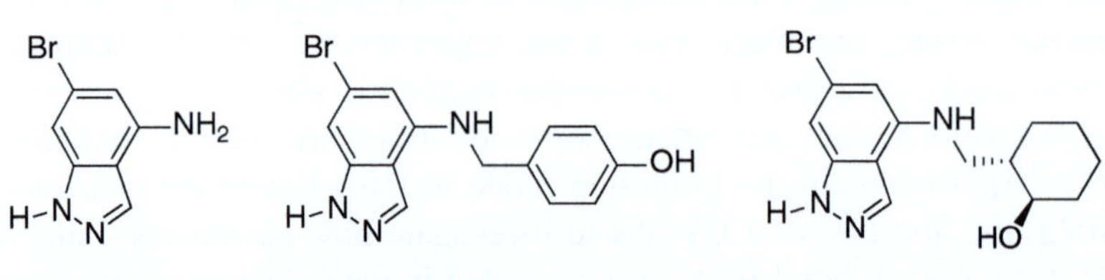

5 **6** **7**

Figure 4.13 Chemical structure of 6-bromo-1*H*-indazol-4-amine derivatives **5–7**.

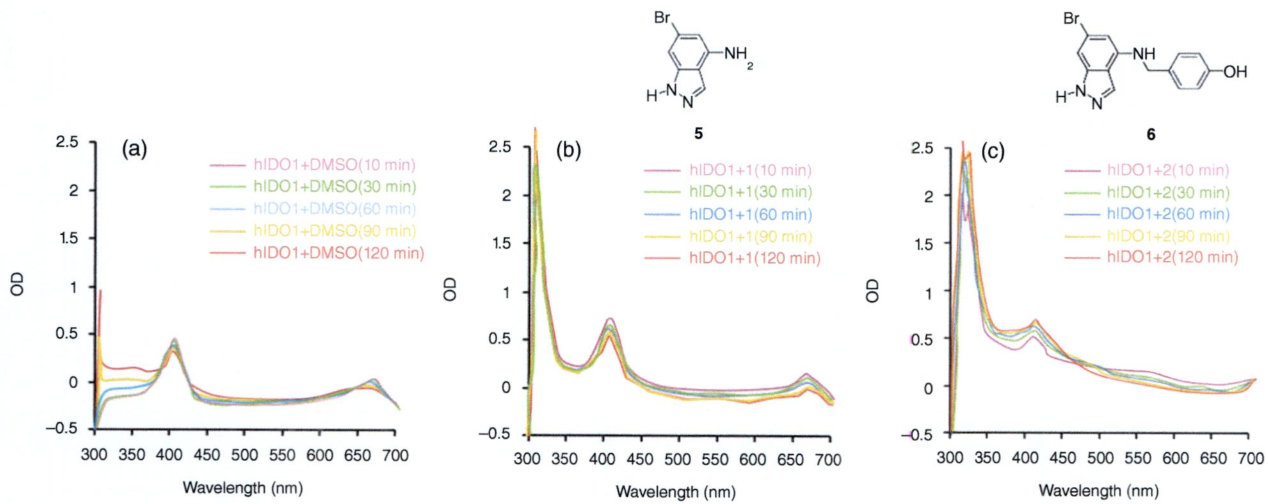

Figure 4.14 UV–Vis absorption spectra of hIDO1 in complex with dimethylsulfoxide (DMSO), **5**, or **6** under the assay buffer over 2 h.

In the spectra of hTDO, the trends in the changes of OD405.5 and OD421.5 are similar to those observed for hIDO. Similar experiments were conducted with the derivative **7**, and it showed a similar effect in combination with hTDO, indicating that it inhibits hIDO1 and hTDO *via* coordination bonding with both heme ferric and ferrous states.

To elucidate inhibitor selectivity in hIDO1 and hTDO, Khoa's team [5] used PF-06840003 (IPD) as a structural probe, demonstrating that IPD is a hIDO1-selective inhibitor, exhibiting 400-fold higher inhibitory activity toward hIDO1 than hTDO. They employed UV–Vis spectroscopy to explore the binding modes of IPD in hIDO1 versus hTDO by monitoring the heme coordination state in both enzymes. The Soret peak at 404 nm and visible/charge transfer bands at 504/632 nm of ferric hIDO1 indicated a water-coordinated six-coordinate (6C) ferric heme. The Soret peak decreased with a blueshift, and the bandwidth broadened upon IPD binding to hIDO1 (Figure 4.15a). These differences occurred as a result of the molecules in the 6C water-coordinated state transitioning to the five-coordinate (5C) state, devoid of water. In both the ferric and ferrous states, the spectra of hTDO were similar to those of hIDO1; however, the addition of IPD did not affect the hTDO spectra. It can be concluded that IPD did not directly coordinate with the heme iron but bound to ferric hIDO1, leading to the dissociation of the water ligand

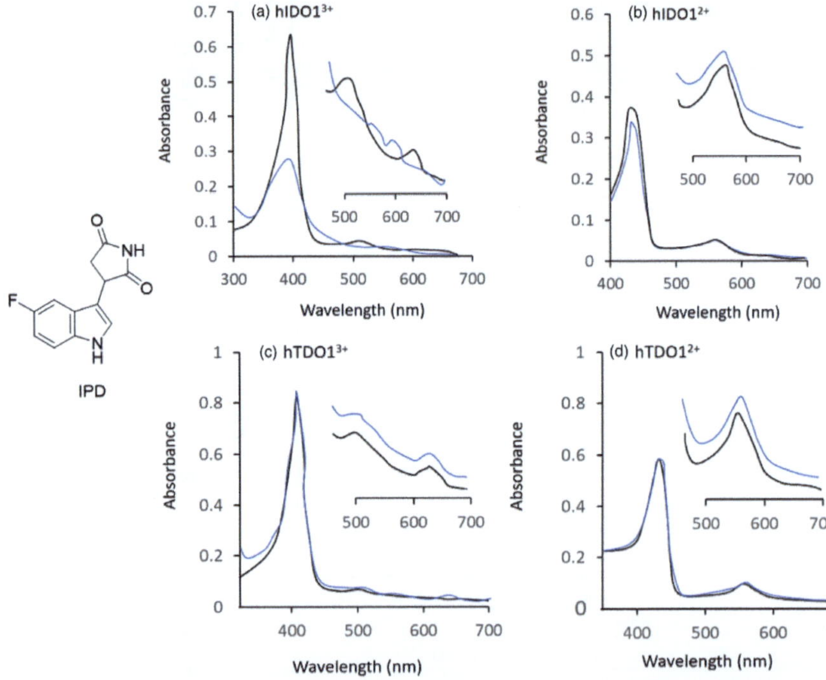

Figure 4.15 Spectral changes introduced by IPD binding to ferric and ferrous hIDO1 (a, b) and hTDO (c, d). The black and blue spectra shown in each panel were obtained in the absence or presence of IPD, respectively.

from the heme iron. Combined with crystallographic structures, these data provide new insights into the design of subsequent mono- and dual inhibitors.

4.3.3 Inhibition Mechanism by Equilibrium Dialysis

Equilibrium dialysis is a straightforward method used to study inhibition patterns, allowing for the determination of the binding of small molecules (or metal ions) to proteins in solution. The principle of equilibrium dialysis is based on the use of a dialysis membrane with a specific molecular weight cutoff, which separates small molecules (or metal ions) from the mixed solution, while large molecules are retained in the membrane. When equilibrium is reached during dialysis, the concentration of small molecules (or metal ions) in the solution on both sides of the membrane becomes equal. By measuring the concentration of small molecules (or metal ions), the binding of small molecules (or metal ions) with proteins can be analyzed. In metalloenzymes, unbound and loosely bound metal ions can be removed using equilibrium dialysis [37].

Equilibrium dialysis offers several advantages, including simple operation, easy control and adaptation of conditions, and low equipment costs. However, equilibrium dialysis alone cannot provide information about the specific binding sites between small molecules and proteins, nor the structural changes of proteins following their interaction. Therefore, it must be combined with other techniques, such as UV–Vis spectroscopy, fluorescence spectroscopy, high-performance liquid chromatography, mass spectrometry, and thermal proteome profiling, to obtain more precise information about the interaction.

To explore the inhibitory mechanisms of the MBL inhibitors, MBLs are incubated with the inhibitors, and the buffer is changed several times for dialysis. The metal content of the MBL is then determined using other techniques, such as atomic absorption (AA) spectroscopy [26]. In the presence of the inhibitor, a reduction in metal content indicates that the inhibitors exhibit a metal-stripping mechanism of inhibition, while no change in metal content suggests that the inhibitors exhibit a metal-coordination mechanism of inhibition [26].

Through a cell-based screen for inhibitors of the NDM-1 MBL, King's team [27] identified aspergillomarasmine A (compound **8**) (Figure 4.16), a fungus-derived molecule from a strain of *Aspergillus versicolor*, as a new MBL inhibitor. **8** was previously known as an inhibitor of the angiotensin-converting enzyme (ACE). ACE is also a zinc-dependent metalloproteinase and shares some mechanistic similarities with MBL [38], suggesting that **8** may inhibit NDM-1 through interaction

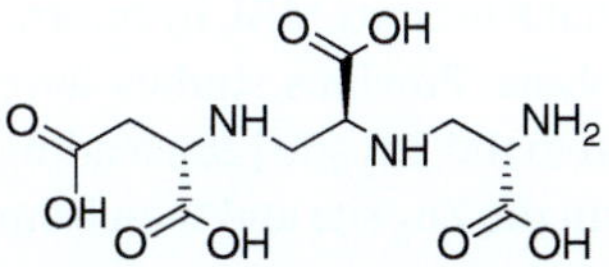

8

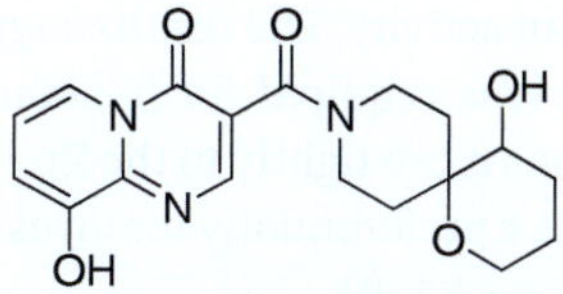

9

Figure 4.16 Chemical structures of Aspergillomarasmine A (**8**) compound **9**.

with zinc ions in the active site. In subsequent minimum inhibitory concentration (MIC) experiments, combining **8** with the antibiotic meropenem killed most NDM-1 and VIM-2 strains and was even effective against *Pseudomonas spp.* (mainly *Pseudomonas aeruginosa*). Furthermore, antibiotic-inhibitor combination therapy (**8** and meropenem) resulted in a survival rate of more than 95% in mice infected for five days with the lethal NDM-1-positive *Klebsiella pneumoniae*, while either meropenem or **8** monotherapy was unable to prevent the infection. Dialysis and inductively coupled plasma mass spectrometry (ICP-MS) were used to explore the selectivity of **8** for the MBLs [38]. To avoid interference from contaminating metals, they used cutoff dialysis tubing to remove the metals and simultaneously concentrate the protein. The proteins were then incubated with **8** at different concentrations to form protein-**8** samples, which were subsequently dialyzed in the same buffer using cutoff D-tube dialyzer mini micro-dialysis cassettes with smaller molecular weight cut-offs. The samples were analyzed using a NexION 3000 ICP mass spectrometer (Perkin Elmer) after post-processing to determine the percent residual activity following metalloenzyme incubation with **8**. The results showed a significant decline in the residual activity of the MBLs, with NDM-1 and VIM-2 being completely inactivated. IMP-7 and ACE activities were inhibited by approximately 70% and 50%, respectively, demonstrating selectivity toward NDM and VIM MBLs, suggesting that **8** can overcome resistance mediated by these enzymes. In the future, **8** or its semi-synthetic derivatives could be potential synergistic antimicrobial agents that may become clinically available for the treatment of MBL infections [38].

However, the inhibition mode of **8** was unclear, specifically whether **8** acts by chelating metal ions after the release of the active site's metal ions, or by participating in the removal of metals from the MBLs. Bergstrom's team [33] further investigated the inhibition of **8** with the MBLs using equilibrium dialysis. They diluted the native Zn(II)-metalloform of MBL to a micromolar level and removed unbound and loosely bound metal ions via dialysis.NDM-1, VIM-2, and IMP-7 were incubated with **8** at varying concentrations for several cycles, bringing **8** and zinc ions into equilibrium. The metal content was determined by ICP-AES, and it decreased with increasing **8** concentration. However, it is important to note that this change was not linear, as the effect on zinc content became less significant with increasing **8** concentration. When 2 mol equivalents of **8** were added, the zinc content was reduced by approximately 1 mol equivalent, leaving ~1.0–1.1 mol equivalents, while the final content was 0.8–0.9 equivalents with 10 equivalents of **8**. EDTA, used as the control, exhibited more effective metal removal than **8**. They also performed kinetic measurements on the post-equilibrium dialysis fractions, and the results showed a significant reduction in activity. The results suggested that **8** inhibits MBL by removing active site metal ions required for β-lactam hydrolysis. Previous studies have revealed that zinc binds more tightly to the Zn_1 site than to the Zn_2 site [26], leading to the assumption that **8** preferentially removes zinc from the Zn_2 site and then from the Zn_1 site under excess **8** [39].

Cheng's team [40] developed a computer algorithm that combined machine learning with quantitative high-throughput screening (qHTS) to identify inhibitors of MBLs. Through this approach, they discovered compound **9** (9-hydroxy-3-[(5-hydroxy-1-oxa-9-azaspiro[5.5]undec-9-yl)carbonyl]-4*H*-pyrido[1,2-a]pyrimidin-4-one) (Figure 4.16) as a novel inhibitor of NDM-1. The MIC results demonstrated that **9** could partially restore the susceptibility of a panel of *Escherichia coli* and *Klebsiella pneumoniae* clinical isolates expressing NDM-1 to meropenem. Additionally, equilibrium dialysis, along with other techniques, was employed to investigate the inhibition mechanism of this compound. NDM-1 was dialyzed with varying concentrations of captopril, EDTA, and compound **9**, and the metal ion content was measured. The zinc ion content did not decrease with increasing concentrations of compound **9**, indicating that the compound did not inhibit NDM-1 by stripping zinc ions. In conjunction with equilibrium dialysis and spectroscopic analysis, it was concluded that compound **9** inhibited NDM-1 through the formation of ternary complexes.

4.3.4 Inhibition Mechanism Study by X-band EPR Spectroscopy

Electron paramagnetic resonance (EPR) spectroscopy provides valuable information that other spectroscopic techniques cannot, by monitoring the electron relaxation properties of unpaired electrons in paramagnetic compounds. This allows for the elucidation of the inhibition mechanism of metal-binding inhibitors [30]. The interaction of these electrons with the molecule results in modifications to the magnetic field of the electrons under an external magnetic field [41]. Three microwave frequencies are commonly employed in EPR spectroscopy: X-band, K-band, and Q-band. The X-band is the most commonly used for studying metalloenzymes. Molecules with fully filled electronic shells cannot be detected by EPR, as this technique is sensitive only to spin-active electrons [42]. The solvent and protein backbone are EPR-silent, while the metal ions at the active sites of metalloenzymes are easily detected, providing abundant information. Therefore, EPR spectroscopy is well-suited for studying metalloproteins in solution [42].

However, only paramagnetic and EPR-active ions(such as Co^{2+}, Fe^{3+}, and Mn^{2+}) are detectable by EPR, while diamagnetic and EPR-silent ions(such as Zn^{2+} and Cu^{2+}) are not [42]. Two important parameters, obtained through computer simulations, are used to analyze EPR spectra. The first is the g-value, which indicates the position of a line in the spectrum and can be used to characterize the active center of a metalloprotein [42]. The second is hyperfine coupling, which characterizes the interaction between electron and nuclear spins in the studied molecules, providing information about the atoms surrounding the metal ions [42].

Since multiple techniques are often combined to probe the inhibition modes of inhibitors, the cases discussed in the following sections have already been mentioned in previous chapters and will focus on the application of EPR in these studies. Since MBLs are Zn(II)-containing metalloenzymes and Zn(II) is diamagnetic, MBLs can only be accessed by EPR when Zn(II) is replaced by other metal ions [26]. When Co(II), a preferred active probe, substitutes for Zn(II) in the metal-binding site, it generates a paramagnetic, high-spin Co(II) ion, providing EPR spectral data [30]. However, it should be noted that at temperatures higher than optimal, relaxation causes significant broadening of the Co(II) EPR spectra [30]. As mentioned in chapter 4.3.2, Chen's team [35] identified inhibitor **4** and employed

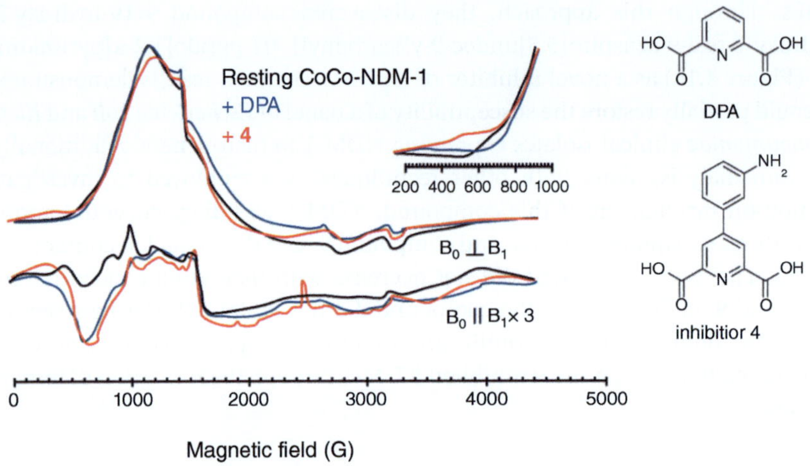

Figure 4.17 X-band EPR spectroscopy of CoCo-NDM-1 (black) and CoCo-NDM-1 with 1 equivalent of added DPA (blue) and **4** (red). Standard perpendicular mode spectra are on top, parallel mode spectra (scaled threefold) are shown below. Inset: Expansion of the low-field region.

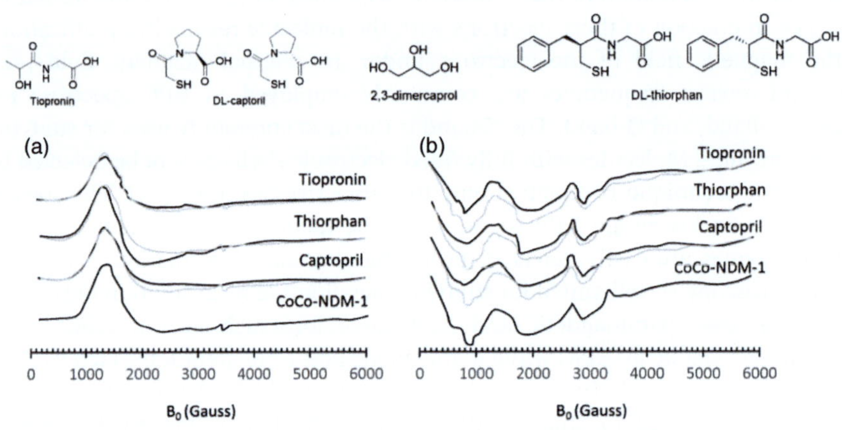

Figure 4.18 Perpendicular- (a) and parallel-mode (b) EPR of CoCo-NDM-1 thiol-inhibitor complexes. The features at~1600 and ~ 3400 G in part A are attributed to minor contamination from iron and copper, respectively. Gray lines symbolize the uncomplexed enzyme.

various experimental techniques, including EPR, to gain a better understanding of its inhibition mechanism. In the EPR spectra (Figure 4.17), 1 equivalent of DPA and inhibitor **4** induced only minor perturbations, with extremely small changes in the signal, suggesting that they did not modify the electronic structure of the metal ions. However, in the parallel mode spectra, inhibitor **4** significantly enhanced the NMD-1 spectra at 600 G, generated by the weak ferromagnetic coupling of the Co(II) ions. This suggests that the inhibitor bridged the Co(II) ions in MBLs to form a ternary complex.

Fullington's team [43] investigated the inhibition mechanisms of several FDA-approved sulfhydryl-containing MBL inhibitors, including L-captopril, DL-thiorphan, tiopronin, and 2,3-dimercaprol (Figure 4.18). All four drugs were first shown to form a ternary complex with NDM-1 through equilibrium dialysis, and were subsequently analyzed using UV–Vis and EPR spectroscopy. In the perpendicular mode spectra, the addition of the inhibitors influenced the width of the low-field perpendicular features, suggesting that all of these drugs bound to the metal ions in the active site. Tiopronin elicited the least perturbation, indicating that it bound to only one metal ion. In parallel mode EPR, the signal intensities decreased in each group due to reduced spin coupling, with the attenuation at 800 G being more pronounced. This suggests that the thiol-sulfur substitution of the inhibitor bridges the hydroxyl group.

4.3.5 Determining Inhibitor Binding Mode by Crystallography

Crystallography provides real images of metalloenzyme-inhibitor complexes, which help confirm binding modes, understanding inhibition mechanisms, and guiding drug design and optimization. As mentioned previously, discovery of new, safe, and effective MBL inhibitors is crucial. Crystallography plays a vital role in the development of new MBL inhibitors. For instance, Li's group [44] developed a series of 2-aminothiazole-4-carboxylic acids as MBL inhibitors by mimicking carbapenem hydrolysate binding (Figure 4.19a), demonstrating a broad-spectrum inhibitory profile across B1, B2, and B3 MBLs. They used crystallography to reveal the binding modes of the 2-aminothiazole-4-carboxylic acid core with the enzymatic active site, showing interactions similar to those involved in enzyme hydrolysis of penems.

In the VIM-2 complex (a B1 MBL subtype) with compound **10**, crystallographic analysis revealed that the zinc ion is chelated by Asp120 and coordinates with **10** through the carboxylic oxygen atom and the nitrogen atom of the thiazole ring. In addition to interacting with the zinc ion, the 2-amino group of **10** forms hydrogen bonds with Asp120, while the 4-carboxyl group forms a hydrogen bond with Arg228 (Figure 4.19b).

In the L1:**11** complex (L1 being a B3 MBL subtype), the crystal structure shows that Asp120 chelates the zinc ion and forms a hydrogen bond with the 2-amino group. The zinc ion also coordinates with compound **11** via the carboxylic oxygen atom and the nitrogen atom of the thiazole ring, similar to the VIM-2 : **10** binding mode. However, the 4-carboxyl group of **11** forms hydrogen bonds with Ser221 and Ser223, rather than Arg228 (Figure 4.19c).

For B2 MBLs, despite differences in the active site zinc geometry compared to B1 and B3 MBLs, the 2-aminothiazole-4-carboxylic acids (AtCs) can still form stable coordination with the zinc ion via the carboxylic oxygen atom and thiazole nitrogen atom, as revealed by the crystal structure of Sfh-I : **12**. Compound **12** also forms hydrogen bonds with Asn223 and Lys224 through its 4-carboxyl group, while the 2-amino group forms a hydrogen bond with Asp120 (Figure 4.19d).

Notably, when investigating the influence of the 5-substituent group on inhibitory activity, researchers found that as the carbon chain length increased, Asn233 gradually adopted an outward-flipping conformation, resulting in a wider

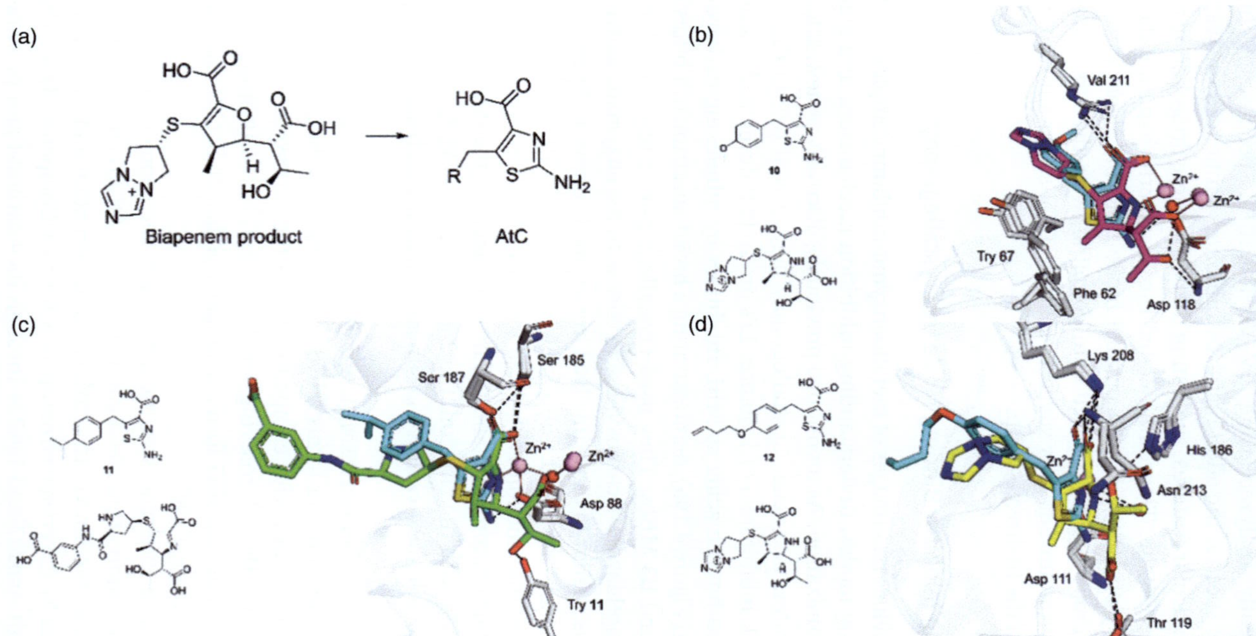

Figure 4.19 (a) Design AtCs by mimicking carbapenem hydrolysate; (b) Superimposition of the VIM-2 : **10** complex and the VIM-2:biapenem enamine hydrolysis product complex revealed that **10** mimicked the binding of the biapenem product with VIM-2; (c) Superimposition of L1 : **11** and L1 : hydrolyzed ertapenem reveals that **11** binds with L1 via the product imitation binding mode; (d) Superimposition of Sfh-I : **12** and CphA:hydrolyzed biapenem reveals that **12** has a similar mode as that of hydrolyzed biapenem with B2 CphA.

active site pocket. This provided valuable insights into how the flexibility of active site loops facilitates the accommodation of structurally diverse ligands. They subsequently investigated the activities of AtC derivatives, which showed that the derivatives are MBL-selective, nonhemolytic, and capable of restoring the antibacterial activity of penems.

Crystallography can also be used to optimize the structure of leading compounds. An example of this is from Christianson's group [45], who designed, synthesized, and evaluated a series of 2-aminoimidazole amino acids as arginase I inhibitors. Arginase I is a binuclear Mn^{2+} metalloenzyme found in extrahepatic tissues, which regulates L-arginine homeostasis by catalyzing the hydrolysis of L-arginine to form L-ornithine and urea. The expression of arginase I is thought to contribute to atopic asthma, and inhibitors of arginase I can significantly reduce airway hyperresponsiveness induced by IL-13 or aeroallergens.

The researchers previously synthesized compounds **13** and **14** and evaluated their inhibitory effects. The X-ray crystal structure of the enzyme-inhibitor complex revealed that 2-aminoimidazole binds to the active site and indirectly interacts with Mn^{2+} (Figure 4.20b), explaining its low effectiveness (K_i = 3600 μM). In contrast, **13** demonstrated much stronger inhibition (K_i = 300 μM) due to a more potent interaction. Crystallographic analysis showed that **13** recruits a tetrahedral anion, interpreted as sulfate, which coordinates with Mn^{2+}. The α-amino group of **13** forms hydrogen bonds with Asp183 and two water molecules, while the α-carboxylate

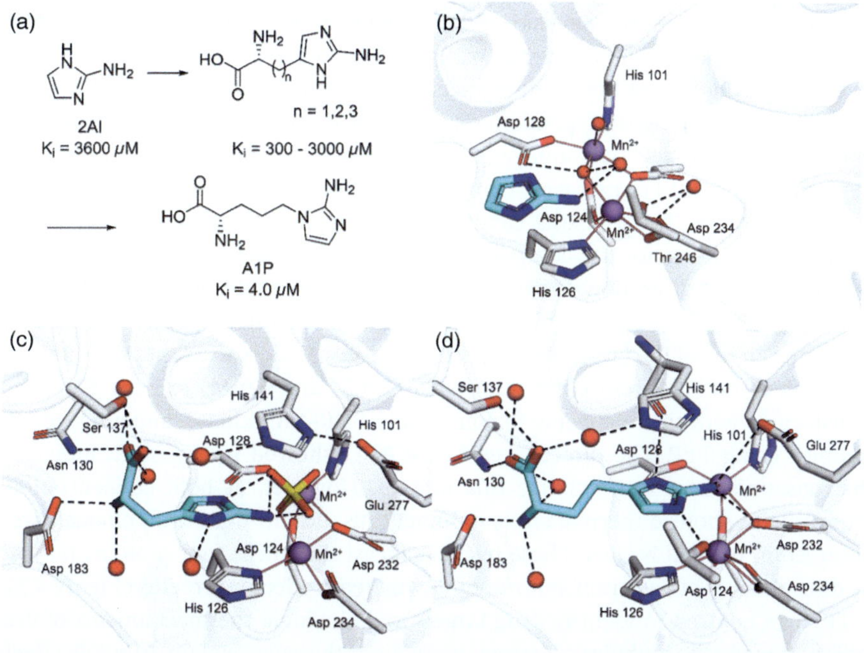

Figure 4.20 (a) Process of optimization of Arginase I inhibitor; (b) Crystal structure of human arginase I and 2-aminoimidazole complex; (c) Crystal structure of human arginase I and **13** complex; (d) Crystal structure of human arginase I and **14** complexes.

group accepts hydrogen bonds from Asn130, Ser137, and two water molecules (Figure 4.20c). For **14**, the α-amino and α-carboxylate groups are expected to interact via hydrogen bonds in the active site, similar to other inhibitors. However, the distance between the 2-aminoimidazole group and the Mn^{2+} cluster is too long (Figure 4.20d), likely explaining its lower effectiveness (K_i = 3000 μM). Encouraged by these structural insights, the researchers hypothesized that the optimal distance between the 2-amino group and the Mn^{2+} cluster should be around 2.0 Å. They then synthesized the derivative **15**, which extended the chain by one carbon atom, leading to a sharp increase in inhibition (K_i = 4.0 μM). Further, in a murine model of allergic airway inflammation, **15** significantly reduced airway hyperresponsiveness to methacholine in OVA-sensitized and -challenged Balb/C mice.

4.4 Metalloenzyme Inhibitor Selectivity by Thermal Proteome Profiling

Proteins will unfold and aggregate, becoming insoluble when heated to denature. Thermal stability of a protein can be assessed by the amount of residual soluble proteins. The protein stability can be changed when proteins interact with small molecules, manifested as a thermal shift. Thermal proteome profiling (TPP), first developed by Savitski and colleagues in 2014, is based on the combination of the cellular thermal shift assay (CETSA) with mass spectrometry (MS)-based proteomics. TPP enables a proteome-wide assessment of how small molecules affect protein thermal stability. Savitski and colleagues selected two kinase inhibitors, staurosporine, and compound **16**, which differ in structure and known target profiles. They analyzed K562 cell extracts treated with staurosporine and a vehicle control, generating two independent replicates. A sharp thermal shift was observed in 92% of the proteins, indicating significant thermal shifts induced by ligand binding. Among these, 13 targets were common to both staurosporine and **16**, exhibiting similar T_m shifts. These results validate the principles of the TPP method. Additionally, TPP allows for the comparison of Tm shifts in cell extracts where ligand binding occurs but no downstream effects are observed, versus intact cells where active signaling is present. This comparison can potentially reveal downstream effector proteins of the target. In their study, the researchers used the ABL inhibitor dasatinib at two different concentrations (0.5 mM and 5 mM) to treat K562 cells transformed with the oncogenic fusion protein BCR-ABL kinase, and analyzed the samples using TPP. The direct target, BCR-ABL, showed no T_m shift, indicating that dasatinib does not stabilize this protein. However, at both concentrations, four proteins showed thermal shifts in intact cells, but no significant changes were observed in the cell lysates. These results suggest that these four proteins may not be direct targets of dasatinib, but rather downstream effector proteins (Figure 4.21).

TPP can be used to identify drug targets and elucidate the mechanisms of drug action, as well as to pinpoint off-target interactions that may explain drug side effects. Savitski's group employed TPP to identify the protein targets of the histone deacetylase (HDAC) inhibitor panobinostat, which is associated with side effects such as

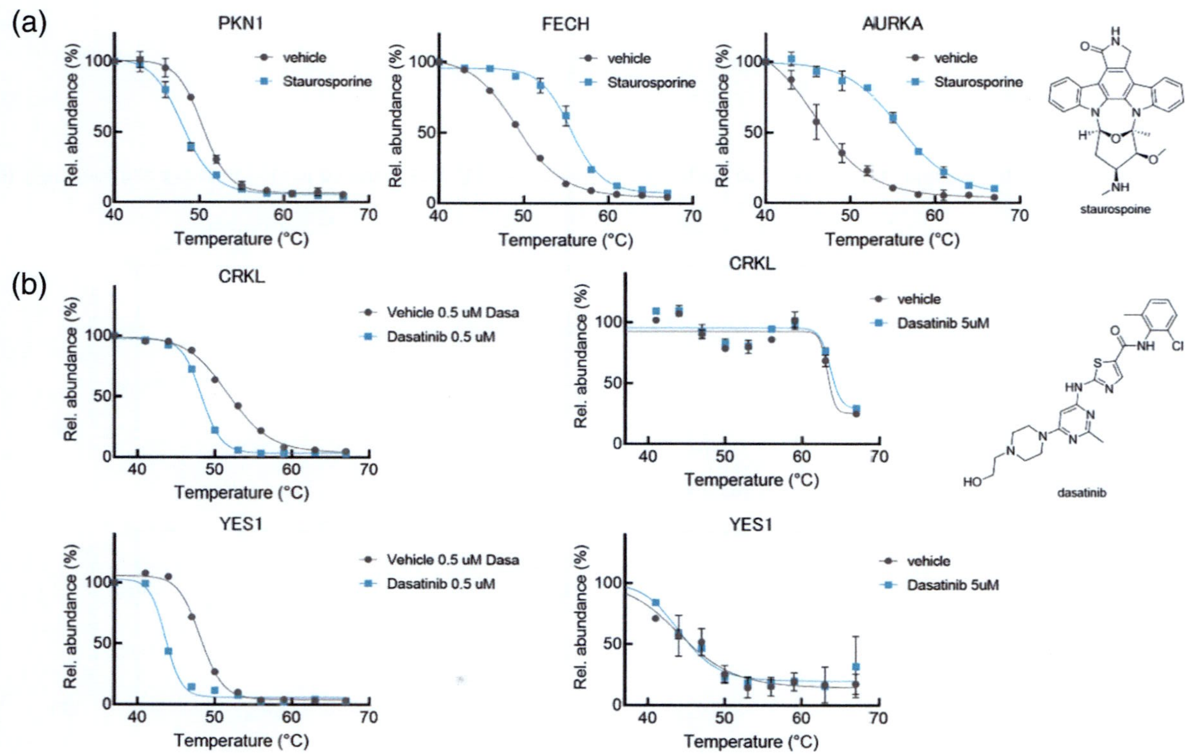

Figure 4.21 (a): TPP identifies targets of staurosporine; (b): TPP identifies downstream effector proteins by comparing T_m shifts of cell extracts (direct binding, no signaling)with T_m shifts of intact cells where active signaling and direct binding occurs.

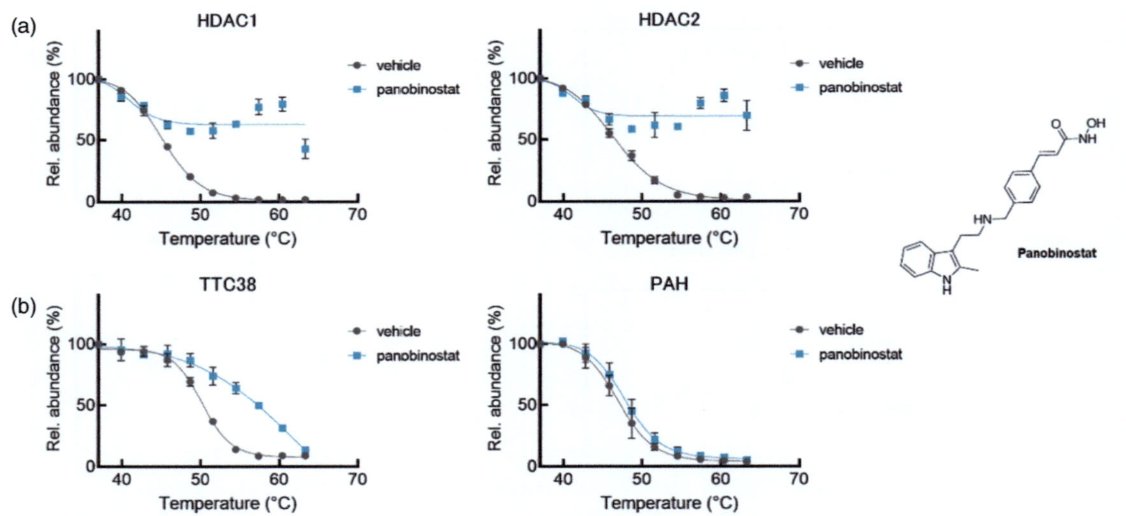

Figure 4.22 (a) TPP identifies direct targets of panobinostat; (b) TPP identifies off-targets of panobinostat, which might induce side effects.

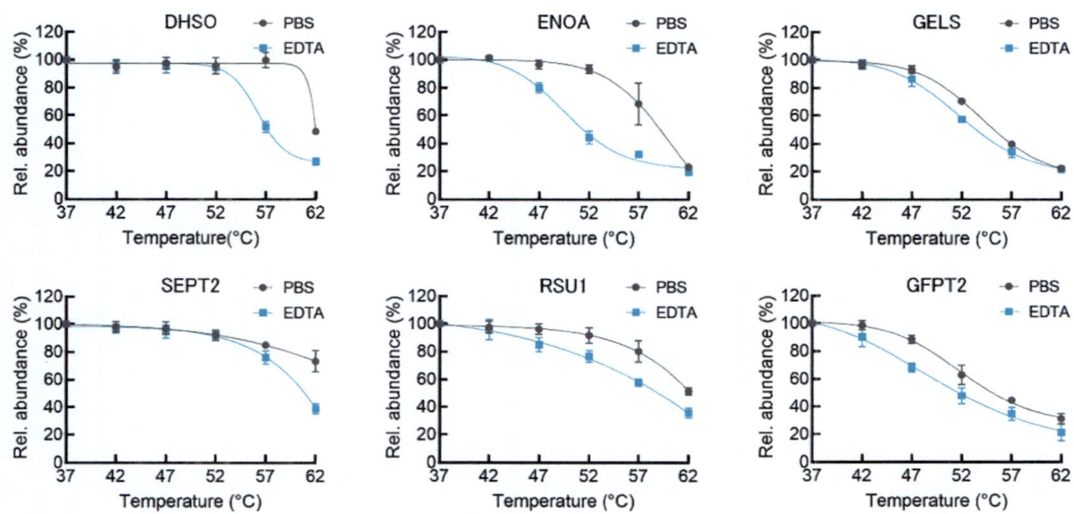

Figure 4.23 TPP identifies metal-binding protein by comparing the T_m shift of MBP and apo-MBP produced by chelator.

hypothyroidism, seizures, and tremors – adverse effects not observed with other hydroxamate-based HDAC inhibitors [46]. They found that HDAC1 and HDAC2 showed significant T_m shifts upon binding with panobinostat, indicating that these proteins are targets of panobinostat. Additionally, they identified two other proteins, tetratricopeptide repeat domain 38 (TTC38) and phenylalanine hydroxylase (PAH), which both displayed increased thermal stability at low concentrations of panobinostat (Figure 4.22), suggesting that these proteins are also targets of panobinostat. Subsequent cellular experiments confirmed that panobinostat reduces cellular tyrosine levels and increases phenylalanine levels by inhibiting PAH, thereby explaining the mechanism behind some of panobinostat's adverse drug effects.

Ligand binding can influence the thermal stability of proteins, and similarly, metal binding can also alter protein thermal stability. Based on this principle, Wang's group developed a novel TPP method named METAL-TPP, which uses the broad-spectrum chelator EDTA to extract metal ions from metalloproteins and monitors the resulting thermal shifts using TPP. Most metalloproteins show reduced thermal stability when metal ions are removed. METAL-TPP can be used to identify metalloproteins [1].

In their METAL-TPP analysis, the researchers quantified a total of 5821 proteins. Of these, 3596 proteins were quantified in both EDTA and Phosphate Buffer Saline (PBS) treatments across three biological replicates. After filtering with strict criteria, thermal shift curves for 2478 proteins were obtained with high confidence under both conditions. From these results, they discovered 23 proteins with decreased thermal stability that had not previously been identified as metalloproteins. Six of these proteins were confirmed to form complexes with known metalloproteins, which may explain their altered stability due to indirect perturbation, while the remaining 17 proteins were identified as potential metal-binding proteins (Figure 4.23). This work highlights the potential of METAL-TPP in metalloproteome study.

4.5 Concluding Remarks

The experimental strategies summarized above play crucial roles in metalloenzyme mechanism research and drug discovery. Each method offers distinct advantages but also has its limitations. A promising approach is the integration of multiple experimental techniques along with computational strategies, which can provide complementary benefits. Continuous refinement and innovation of these methods are essential to minimize their limitations and broaden their applicability. For instance, thermal proteome profiling could be further optimized to identify novel metalloenzymes or investigate the selectivity of metalloenzyme inhibitors, potentially requiring the use of specialized chemical probes. More importantly, it is vital to develop metalloenzyme-specific experimental strategies tailored to the unique metal ions in these enzymes. Such strategies would be instrumental in addressing critical challenges in metalloenzyme-targeted drug discovery, including inhibitor selectivity and the elucidation of metalloenzyme catalytic mechanisms.

References

1 Zeng, X., Wei, T., Wang, X. et al. (2024). Discovery of metal-binding proteins by thermal proteome profiling. *Nature Chemical Biology* 20: 770–778.

2 Li, H. and Sun, H. (2012). NMR studies of metalloproteins. *Topics in Current Chemistry* 326: 69–98.

3 Li, G., Su, Y., Yan, Y.H. et al. (2020). MeLAD: an integrated resource for metalloenzyme-ligand associations. *Bioinformatics* 36: 904–909.

4 Yan, Y.H., Li, G., and Li, G.B. (2020). Principles and current strategies targeting metallo-β-lactamase mediated antibacterial resistance. *Medicinal Research Reviews* 40: 1558–1592.

5 Pham, K.N., Lewis-Ballester, A., and Yeh, S.R. (2019). Structural basis of inhibitor selectivity in human indoleamine 2,3-dioxygenase 1 and tryptophan dioxygenase. *Journal of the American Chemical Society* 141: 18771–18779.

6 Ye, Z., Yue, L., Shi, J. et al. (2019). Role of IDO and TDO in cancers and related diseases and the therapeutic implications. *Journal of Cancer* 10: 2771–2782.

7 Mondal, P. and Wijeratne, G.B. (2020). Modeling tryptophan/indoleamine 2,3-dioxygenase with heme superoxide mimics: is ferryl the key intermediate? *Journal of the American Chemical Society* 142: 1846–1856.

8 Booth, E.S., Basran, J., Lee, M. et al. (2015). Substrate oxidation by indoleamine 2,3-dioxygenase: evidence for a common reaction mechanism. *The Journal of Biological Chemistry* 290: 30924–30930.

9 Lu, C., Lin, Y., and Yeh, S.R. (2010). Spectroscopic studies of ligand and substrate binding to human indoleamine 2,3-dioxygenase. *Biochemistry* 49: 5028–5034.

10 Finnigan, J.D., Young, C., Cook, D.J. et al. (2020). Cytochromes P450 (P450s): a review of the class system with a focus on prokaryotic P450s. *Advances in Protein Chemistry and Structural Biology* 122: 289–320.

11 Guengerich, F.P., Waterman, M.R., and Egli, M. (2016). Recent structural insights into cytochrome P450 function. *Trends in Pharmacological Sciences* 37: 625–640.

12 Lockart, M.M., Rodriguez, C.A., Atkins, W.M., and Bowman, M.K. (2018). CW EPR parameters reveal cytochrome P450 ligand binding modes. *Journal of Inorganic Biochemistry* 183: 157–164.

13 Kendrew, J.C., Bodo, G., Dintzis, H.M. et al. (1958). A three-dimensional model of the myoglobin molecule obtained by X-ray analysis. *Nature* 181: 662–666.

14 Perutz, M.F., Rossmann, M.G., Cullis, A.F. et al. (1960). Structure of hæmoglobin: a three-dimensional fourier synthesis at 5.5-Å. resolution, obtained by X-ray analysis. *Nature* 185: 416–422.

15 Watson, J.D. and Crick, F.H.C. (1953). Molecular structure of nucleic acids: a structure for deoxyribose nucleic acid. *Nature* 171: 737–738.

16 Mazzei, L., Cianci, M., Benini, S., and Ciurli, S. (2019). The structure of the elusive urease-urea complex unveils the mechanism of a paradigmatic nickel-dependent enzyme. *Angewandte Chemie (International ed. in English)* 58: 7415–7419.

17 Chapman, H.N., Fromme, P., Barty, A. et al. (2011). Femtosecond X-ray protein nanocrystallography. *Nature* 470: 73–77.

18 Barends, T.R.M., Stauch, B., Cherezov, V., and Schlichting, I. (2022). Serial femtosecond crystallography. *Nature Reviews Methods Primers* 2: 59.

19 Wilamowski, M., Sherrell, D.A., Kim, Y. et al. (2022). Time-resolved β-lactam cleavage by L1 metallo-β-lactamase. *Nature Communications* 13.

20 Tioni, M.F., Llarrull, L.I., Poeylaut-Palena, A.A. et al. (2008). Trapping and characterization of a reaction intermediate in carbapenem hydrolysis by B. cereus metallo-β-lactamase. *Journal of the American Chemical Society* 130: 15852–15863.

21 Cuniasse, P., Tavares, P., Orlova, E.V., and Zinn-Justin, S. (2017). Structures of biomolecular complexes by combination of NMR and cryoEM methods. *Current Opinion in Structural Biology* 43: 104–113.

22 Zhu, J., Hu, X., Dizin, E., and Pei, D. (2003). Catalytic mechanism of S-ribosylhomocysteinase (LuxS): direct observation of ketone intermediates by 13C NMR spectroscopy. *Journal of the American Chemical Society* 125: 13379–13381.

23 Ju, L.-C., Cheng, Z., Fast, W. et al. (2018). The continuing challenge of metallo-β-lactamase inhibition: mechanism matters. *Trends in Pharmacological Sciences* 39: 635–647.

24 Li, G.B., Abboud, M.I., Brem, J. et al. (2017). NMR-filtered virtual screening leads to non-metal chelating metallo-β-lactamase inhibitors. *Chemical Science* 8: 928–937.

25 Abboud, M.I., Hinchliffe, P., Brem, J. et al. (2017). 19F-NMR reveals the role of mobile loops in product and inhibitor binding by the São Paulo metallo-β-lactamase. *Angewandte Chemie International Edition* 56: 3862–3866.

26 Ju, L.C., Cheng, Z., Fast, W. et al. (2018). The continuing challenge of metallo-β-lactamase inhibition: mechanism matters. *Trends in Pharmacological Sciences* 39: 635–647.

27 Yang, Y., Yan, Y.H., Schofield, C.J. et al. (2023). Metallo-β-lactamase-mediated antimicrobial resistance and progress in inhibitor discovery. *Trends in Microbiology* 31: 735–748.

28 Bush, K. and Jacoby, G.A. (2010). Updated functional classification of beta-lactamases. *Antimicrobial Agents and Chemotherapy* 54: 969–976.

29 Mojica, M.F., Bonomo, R.A., and Fast, W. (2016). B1-metallo-β-lactamases: where do we stand? *Current Drug Targets* 17: 1029–1050.

30 Bennett, B. (2010). EPR of Cobalt-Substituted Zinc Enzymes. In: *Metals in Biology. Biological Magnetic Resonance*, vol. 29 (eds. G. Hanson, and L. Berliner). New York, NY: Springer.

31 Yang, H., Aitha, M., Marts, A.R. et al. (2014). Spectroscopic and mechanistic studies of heterodimetallic forms of metallo-β-lactamase NDM-1. *Journal of the American Chemical Society* 136: 7273–7285.

32 Zhang, H., Yang, K., Cheng, Z. et al. (2021). Spectroscopic and biochemical characterization of metallo-β-lactamase IMP-1 with dicarboxylic, sulfonyl, and thiol inhibitors. *Bioorganic & Medicinal Chemistry* 40: 116183.

33 Thomas, C.A., Cheng, Z., Yang, K. et al. (2020). Probing the mechanisms of inhibition for various inhibitors of metallo-β-lactamases VIM-2 and NDM-1. *Journal of Inorganic Biochemistry* 210: 111123.

34 Brem, J., van Berkel, S.S., Zollman, D. et al. (2016). Structural basis of metallo-β-lactamase inhibition by captopril stereoisomers. *Antimicrobial Agents and Chemotherapy* 60: 142–150.

35 Chen, A.Y., Thomas, P.W., Stewart, A.C. et al. (2017). Dipicolinic acid derivatives as inhibitors of New Delhi metallo-β-lactamase-1. *Journal of Medicinal Chemistry* 60: 7267–7283.

36 Ning, X.L., Li, Y.Z., Huo, C. et al. (2021). X-ray structure-guided discovery of a potent, orally bioavailable, dual human indoleamine/tryptophan 2,3-dioxygenase (hIDO/hTDO) inhibitor that shows activity in a mouse model of Parkinson's disease. *Journal of Medicinal Chemistry* 64: 8303–8332.

37 Bergstrom, A., Katko, A., Adkins, Z. et al. (2017). Probing the interaction of Aspergillomarasmine a with metallo-β-lactamases NDM-1, VIM-2, and IMP-7. *ACS Infectious Diseases* 4: 135–145.

38 King, A.M., Reid-Yu, S.A., Wang, W. et al. (2014). Aspergillomarasmine a overcomes metallo-β-lactamase antibiotic resistance. *Nature* 510: 503–506.

39 Orellano, E.G., Girardini, J.E., Cricco, J.A. et al. (1998). Spectroscopic characterization of a binuclear metal site in Bacillus cereus beta-lactamase II. *Biochemistry* 37: 10173–10180.

40 Cheng, Z., Aitha, M., Thomas, C.A. et al. (2024). Machine learning models identify inhibitors of New Delhi metallo-β-lactamase. *Journal of Chemical Information and Modeling* 64: 3977–3991.

41 Ubbink, M., Worrall, J.A., Canters, G.W. et al. (2002). Paramagnetic resonance of biological metal centers. *Annual Review of Biophysics and Biomolecular Structure* 31: 393–422.

42 Gambarelli, S. and Maurel, V. (2014). Study of metalloproteins using continuous wave electron paramagnetic resonance (EPR). In: *Methods in Molecular Biology*, vol. 1122, 139–151. Clifton, N.J.

43 Fullington, S., Cheng, Z., Thomas, C. et al. (2020). An integrated biophysical approach to discovering mechanisms of NDM-1 inhibition for several thiol-containing drugs. *Journal of Biological Inorganic Chemistry: JBIC: a Publication of the Society of Biological Inorganic Chemistry* 25: 717–727.

44 Yan, Y.-H., Zhang, T.-T., Li, R. et al. (2023). Discovery of 2-aminothiazole-4-carboxylic acids as broad-spectrum metallo-β-lactamase inhibitors by mimicking carbapenem hydrolysate binding. *Journal of Medicinal Chemistry* 66: 13746–13767.

45 Ilies, M., Di Costanzo, L., North, M.L. et al. (2010). 2-Aminoimidazole amino acids as inhibitors of the binuclear manganese metalloenzyme human arginase I. *Journal of Medicinal Chemistry* 53: 4266–4276.

46 Becher, I., Werner, T., Doce, C. et al. (2016). Thermal profiling reveals phenylalanine hydroxylase as an off-target of panobinostat. *Nature Chemical Biology* 12: 908–910.

5

Targeting Metalloenzymes by Metallo-Drugs

Cheng Chen[1,2], Kewu Yang[3], Hongyan Li[1], and Hongzhe Sun[1]

[1] *The University of Hong Kong, Department of Chemistry, CAS-HKU Joint Laboratory of Metallomics for Health and Environment, Pokfulam Road, Hong Kong SAR, P. R. China*
[2] *Northwest A&F University, Department of Forest Product Chemical Engineering, 3 Taicheng Road, Yangling, Shaanxi, 712100, P. R. China*
[3] *Northwest University, College of Chemistry and Materials Science, Key Laboratory Synthetic and Natural Functional Molecular Chemistry of Ministry of Education, 1 Xuefu Road, Xi'an, 710127, P. R. China*

5.1 Introduction

The effective management of bacterial infections is a foundation of modern health care, enabling medical technologies such as transplantation, cancer chemotherapy, and surgery [1]. The rise of antibiotic-resistant bacteria represents a silent pandemic, eroding the safety of these basic medical interventions. This resistance is responsible for severe and deadly infections, leading to increased morbidity and mortality that have disseminated worldwide, posing a great threat to public health [1, 2]. **A**nti**m**icrobial **r**esistance (AMR) has become the largest threat to human health in the twenty-first century. Gram-negative bacteria (GNB) show higher intrinsic resistance to many antibiotics that are effective against Gram-positive bacteria, due to their complex outer membrane, which prevents the penetration of these drugs [3, 4]. Therefore, infections caused by GNB present a greater challenge in clinical settings. Carbapenems, including meropenem and imipenem, are among the commonly used antibiotics in clinics for severe infections, offering a broad spectrum of activity and high potency. They are often used as the last-line agents for the treatment of serious GNB infections [5–7]. However, the misuse and over-prescribing of antibiotics, coupled with evolutionary events, have led to the emergence and spread of carbapenem-resistant pathogens, which has become a global health challenge for both animals and humans. Carbapenem-resistant *Acinetobacter baumannii* and carbapenem-resistant *Enterobacteriaceae* have been listed by the World Health Organization (WHO) as "critical priority pathogens" in 2024 [8, 9].

The production of metallo-β-lactamases (MBLs) including New Delhi metallo-β-lactamase-1 (NDM-1) first identified in 2009, represents the most clinically important bacterial strategy for resistance to carbapenems, owing to the ability of these enzymes to catalyze the hydrolysis of carbapenems and virtually all other

Drug Discovery Targeting Metalloenzymes: Strategies and Applications, First Edition. Edited by Guo-Bo Li.

β-lactams [10, 11]. GNB producing NDM-1 has spread globally in over 70 countries, seriously weakening the efficacy of carbapenems [12, 13]. To combat multidrug-resistant GNB, colistin, a cationic cyclic peptide antibiotic, has been increasingly applied as a last-line defense in clinical treatment. Colistin acts by associating with the anionic lipopolysaccharide (LPS) component of the GNB outer membrane, leading to membrane disruption, leakage of intracellular contents, and ultimately cell death. Unfortunately, the efficacy of colistin has been seriously compromised in the regular treatment of lethal bacterial infections owing to the emergence of plasmid-mediated mobile colistin resistance (MCR-1) discovered in 2015 [14, 15]. In contrast to chromosomally mediated resistance, *mcr-1* gene can be transferred between different bacterial species, such as *Escherichia coli*, *Klebsiella pneumoniae*, and other pathogens, resulting in the wide spread of colistin resistance across over 40 countries/regions covering five continents [16]. To date, there are no effective drugs available to deal with these complex drug-resistant bacterial infections. Therefore, new strategies are urgently required to counteract the AMR mediated by metalloenzymes (MBLs and MCRs).

In recent decades, the discovery of new classes of antibiotics has been relatively stagnant due to the reduced investment in drug discovery by major pharmaceutical companies, the depletion of low-hanging fruits from the previous decades, and the exhaustion of new drug candidates [4, 17, 18]. Combination therapies for bacterial infections are an emerging field of research that may offer a complementary strategy to combat AMR in pathogenic bacteria [19, 20]. β-Lactam antibiotics in combination with serine-β-lactamase (SBL) inhibitors have proven to be an effective clinical approach to overcome resistance mediated by SBLs [21, 22]. However, these inhibitors are ineffective against MBLs and MCRs [23]. Compared with the clinical success of SBL inhibitors, currently, there are no equivalent inhibitors available for MBLs and MCR-1. The insufficiency of available therapeutics to surmount the resistance mediated by metalloenzymes underscores the urgent need for the development of inhibitors targeting MBLs and MCRs.

Metallo-drugs and metallo-agents have emerged as pivotal entities within the realm of medicinal chemistry, serving as chemotherapeutic agents for a spectrum of human diseases, such as cancer, neurological and cardiovascular disorders, diabetes, arthritis, infectious diseases, and as diagnostic agents for nuclear medicine [24, 25]. Notably, their application as antimicrobial agents spans centuries. Auranofin (AUR), a drug for rheumatoid arthritis, exerts broad-spectrum bactericidal effects by inhibiting bacterial thioredoxin reductase [26]. Silver nitrate and gallium nitrate have been shown to augment the activity of antibiotics against multidrug-resistant bacteria [27]. Bismuth-based compounds (e.g. colloidal bismuth subcitrate and ranitidine bismuth citrate) are clinically used drugs in combination with antibiotics to treat peptic ulcer and *Helicobacter pylori* infections, including those resistant to clarithromycin and metronidazole [24]. Recently, metal compounds have garnered attention as a viable alternative in addressing the AMR crisis [28]. The development of a clinically available inhibitor necessitates a comprehensive understanding of the interplay between the chemistry properties of metallo-drugs/metallo-agents and the biological mechanisms of resistance. In this chapter, we summarize the AMR mechanism caused by metalloenzymes, specifically MBLs and MCR-1, and review the progress made in developing metallo-drugs/metallo-agents aimed at reversing antibiotic resistance in these superbugs.

5.2 Mechanisms of Bacterial Resistance Mediated by Metalloenzymes

5.2.1 MBLs-Mediated Carbapenem Resistance

β-Lactam antibiotics exert their bactericidal effect by binding to penicillin-binding proteins (PBPs), thereby inhibiting bacterial cell wall synthesis and preventing peptidoglycan cross-linking, which ultimately induces bacterial death. However, the efficacy of these antibiotics is increasingly threatened by the emergence of resistance mechanisms involving β-lactamases, enzymes capable of hydrolyzing the β-lactam ring and thus causing β-lactam inactivation [29]. β-Lactamases are categorized into SBLs and MBLs. SBL inhibitors, e.g. clavulanic acid (1981), sulbactam (1987), tazobactam (1992), avibactam (2015), vaborbactam (2017), and relebactam (2019), have been developed and are currently in clinical use to enhance the activity of β-lactams. In contrast, MBL inhibitors are not yet available in clinics, which presents a considerable challenge in the clinical management of infections caused by bacteria produced by these metalloenzymes [12, 30].

MBLs are classified into three molecular subclasses B_1, B_2, and B_3 based on differences in their active site residues, metal content requirement, and substrate profile (Figure 5.1). B_1 subclass enzymes, require two Zn(II) ions for full activity, possess a wide substrate range [30–32]. B_1 MBLs, such as IMPs (imipenemases), VIMs (Verona integron-encoded metallo-β-lactamases), and NDMs (New Delhi metallo-β-lactamases), are spreading globally via mobile genetic elements, thereby aggravating the geographical proliferation of antibiotic resistance [22]. B_2 subclass MBLs are chromosomally encoded, require only one Zn(II) ion for activity, and exhibit specificity for carbapenems while showing poor hydrolytic capacities against penicillins and cephalosporins, including CphA from *Aeromonas hydrophila*, SfhI from *Serratia fonticola,* and ImiS from *Aeromonas sobria* [33]. B_3 subclass enzymes, with two Zn(II) ions at active site, have a broad substrate spectrum and displace less conservation among their residues, including GOB from *Elizabethkingia meningoseptica*, L1 from *Stenotrophomonas maltophilia,* and FEZ from *Legionella gormanii* [21, 34]. Furthermore, the identification of new MBLs is continually being reported, as evidenced by recent reports on CrxA, GMB-1, and PJM-1 MBLs.

Two Zn(II) ions of B1 enzymes are bound to the active site, with a bridging water/hydroxide (Wat1) [29]. The first Zn(II), referred to as Zn_1, is coordinated by His^{116}, His^{118}, His^{196}, and Wat^1 (standard MBL numbering scheme). The second Zn(II) ions, are coordinated by Asp^{120}, Cys^{221}, His^{263}, Wat^1, and a second water molecule (Wat^2). B_3 MBLs share the same ligands as B_1 enzymes, except Cys^{221} is displaced by the His^{121}, a modification that mirrors the Zn_2 site found in B_1 MBLs (Figure 5.1). During the catalytic cycle, a water molecule (W_1) or hydroxide

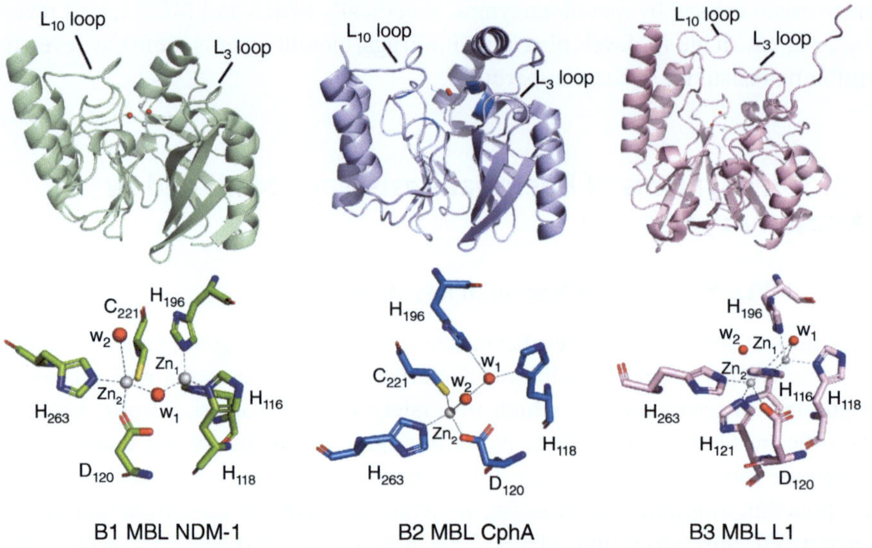

Figure 5.1 Metallo-β-Lactamases (MBLs) have a conserved αβ/βα fold structure. B_1 MBLs, such as NDM-1 (PDBID: 3SPU), feature two conserved Zn(II) binding sites and flexible loops for binding with various substrates including all bicyclic β-lactam antibiotics. B_2 MBLs, like CphA (PDBID: 1X8G), are mono-zinc enzymes that display a preference for the hydrolysis of carbapenems. B_3 MBLs, shown by L1 (PDBID: 2FM6), are characterized by a di-zinc-binding active site and flexible loops that contribute to a wide substrate profile.

in B_1 enzymes bridges the two zinc ions in the resting state and is activated by both Zn_1 and Zn_2 to act as a nucleophile in the reaction with the substrate β-lactam. This nucleophilic attack leads to the formation of a high-energy tetrahedral intermediate, which then transitions to a more stable anionic intermediate, culminating in the production of an inactive β-amino acid (Figure 5.2) [30].

5.2.2 MCR-1-Mediated Colistin Resistance

Polymyxins are a class of cyclic cationic lipopeptides that exhibit bactericidal activity primarily through electrostatic attraction associating with the anionic phosphate group of lipid A, which is a component of the outer membrane in GNB. This interaction leads to the destabilization of the membrane structure, an increase in membrane permeability, and the leakage of intracellular contents, ultimately leading to cell death [35]. Colistin (polymyxin E) and polymyxin B are two clinically used antibiotics that are employed as the last-resort treatment for infections caused by multidrug-resistant Gram-negative bacteria (MDR GNB). The extensive use of colistin, particularly in agriculture settings, has increased the prevalence of acquired colistin resistance. In 2015, a plasmid-mediated resistance gene, *mcr-1*, which confers MCR, was first identified in *Enterobacterales* isolates from a pig farm in China [36, 37].

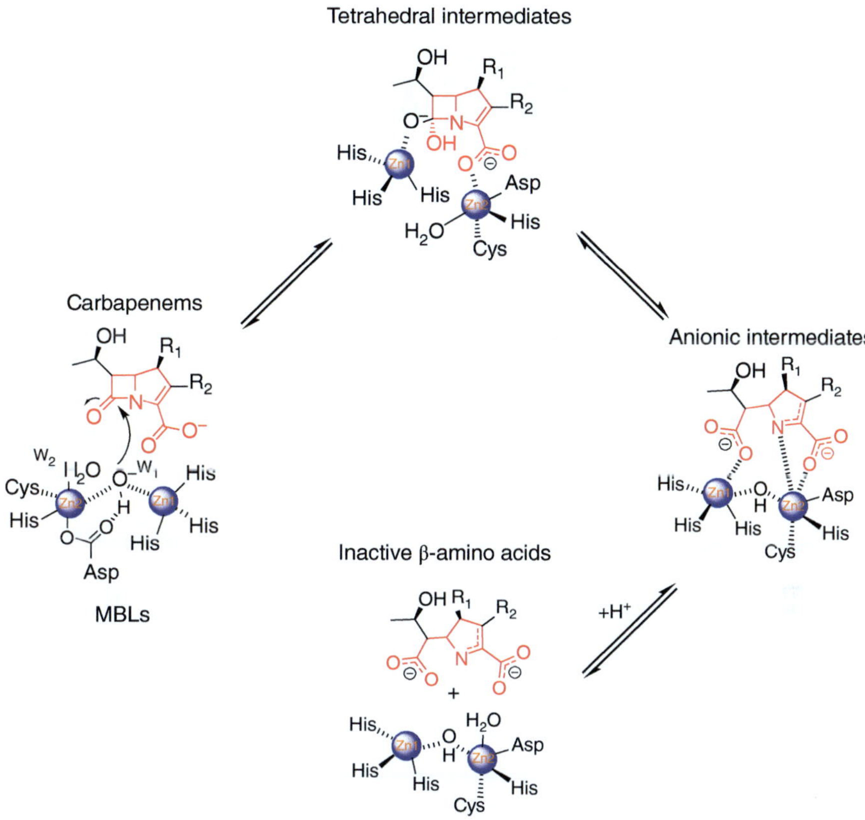

Figure 5.2 Mechanism of carbapenems resistance mediated by B1 MBL.

The MCR-1 enzyme features a Zn(II) cofactor within its active site, which is coordinated by Glu^{246}, Asp^{465}, His^{466}, and the phosphorylated Thr^{285}, a conserved nucleophilic attack group. A catalyzed mechanism for MCR-1 has been proposed based on the multiple sequence and crystal structure alignments (Figure 5.3). Initially, the highly conserved nucleophilic Thr^{285} in the active center of cMCR is activated by transferring a proton from its side chain to Glu^{246}. This activation allows Thr^{285} to execute a nucleophilic attack on the phosphate group of the phosphoethanolamine (PEA) moiety of phosphatidylethanolamine (PE), resulting in the formation of diacylglycerol and a Thr^{285}-pEtN intermediate, which is referred to as the MCR/pEtN complex [38]. In the subsequent step, the 1′- or 4′-phosphate of lipid A performs a nucleophilic attack on the Thr^{285}-pEtN intermediate. Subsequently, Glu^{246} transfers a proton to Thr^{285} of the Thr^{285}-pEtN intermediate, resulting in the formation of PEA-lipid A and the release of the MCR-1 enzyme (Figure 5.4). The ultimate result of these modifications is the neutralization of the surrounding negative charges, consequently eliminating the electrostatic attraction that dictates the initial binding of colistin to lipid A [39].

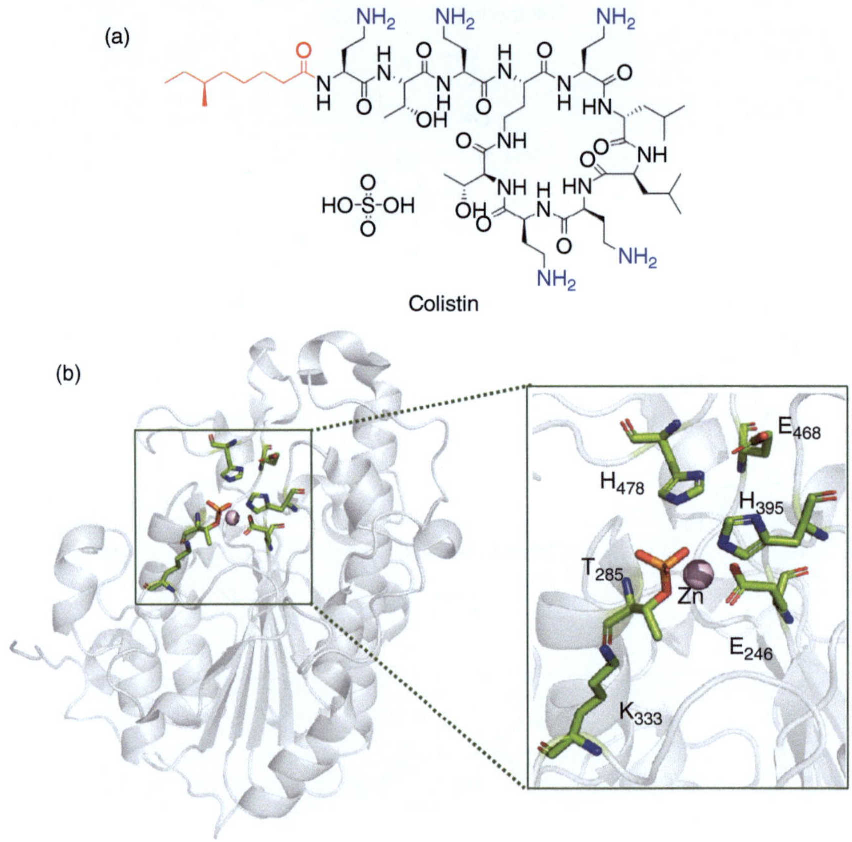

Figure 5.3 The structure of the last-line antibiotic colistin (a). Overall fold of MCR-1 catalytic domain, and the active site with zinc ion coordination with key residues including the phosphorylation of Thr^{285} (b).

5.3 Metallo-drugs/Metallo-agents: Targeting Metalloenzymes Against Superbugs

The emergence of Gram-negative superbugs that produce metalloenzymes has significantly complicated the management of infectious diseases [26]. Metallo-drugs and metallo-agents are increasingly seen as potential arsenals against antibiotic resistance in these superbugs. The development of a clinically available inhibitor necessitates a thorough understanding of the relationship between the chemical properties of metallo-drugs/metallo-agents and the biological underpinnings of the resistance mechanisms. In the following section, we summarize the advancements in developing metallo-drugs/metallo-agents aimed at reversing antibiotic resistance mediated by metalloenzymes (MBLs and MCRs). These examples can be segmented into five different categories: (i) Bismuth (Bi(III)); (ii) Gold (Au(I)); (iii) Silver (Ag(I) or AgNP); (iv) Copper (Cu(I)/Cu(II)); (v) other metal complexes, each of which will be discussed in detail below.

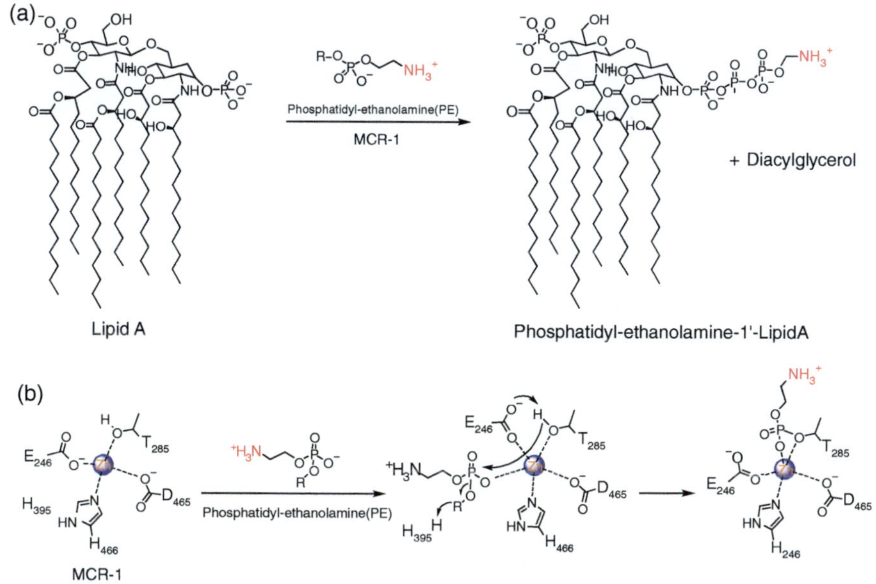

Figure 5.4 The proposed phosphoethanolamine transfer reaction catalyzed by MCR-1. (a). Possible mechanism for PE addition to Thr285 of mono-zinc MCR-1 to form Thr285 adduct (b).

5.3.1 Bismuth

Bi(III) complexes have a long-standing history in medical application, having been employed for over 200 years to treat various diseases, including stomach disorders and *Helicobacter pylori* infection. The non-toxic feature of Bi(III) is attributed to its low absorption and the self-clearance mechanism in mammalian cells, which involve glutathione (GSH) and multi-drug resistance transporters. Colloidal bismuth citrate (CBS), an anti-*H. pylori* drug, along with related Bi(III) compounds, has been shown to irreversibly inhibit MBLs by cell-based and enzyme-based assays, exhibiting IC_{50} values of 2.81, 3.54, and 0.70 μM for NDM-1, VIM-2, and IMP-4, respectively (Figure 5.5a) [40]. The inhibitory mechanism involves the displacement of two Zn(II) ions in the active site by a single Bi(III) ion, as revealed from X-ray crystallography and biophysical studies (Figure 5.5b,c). This displacement leads to the release of Zn(II) cofactors and restoration of meropenem's efficacy, as evidenced by the fractional inhibitory concentration index (FICI) values ranging from 0.047 to 0.375, and the minimum inhibitory concentration (MIC) of meropenem decreased by 8–64-folds against MBL-producing bacteria *in vitro*. In murine peritonitis models, the co-administration of CBS boosts the effectiveness of meropenem, leading to increased mouse survival time and reduced mortality rates in mice infected with NDM-HK strain [40]. Notably, CBS also retards the development of higher-level resistance in NDM-1-positive bacteria.

Depletion of Zn(II) to inactivate MBLs presents an effective approach to reversing carbapenem resistance in NDM-producing bacteria. However, achieving specific Zn(II) deprivation and enhancing bacterial outer membrane penetrability

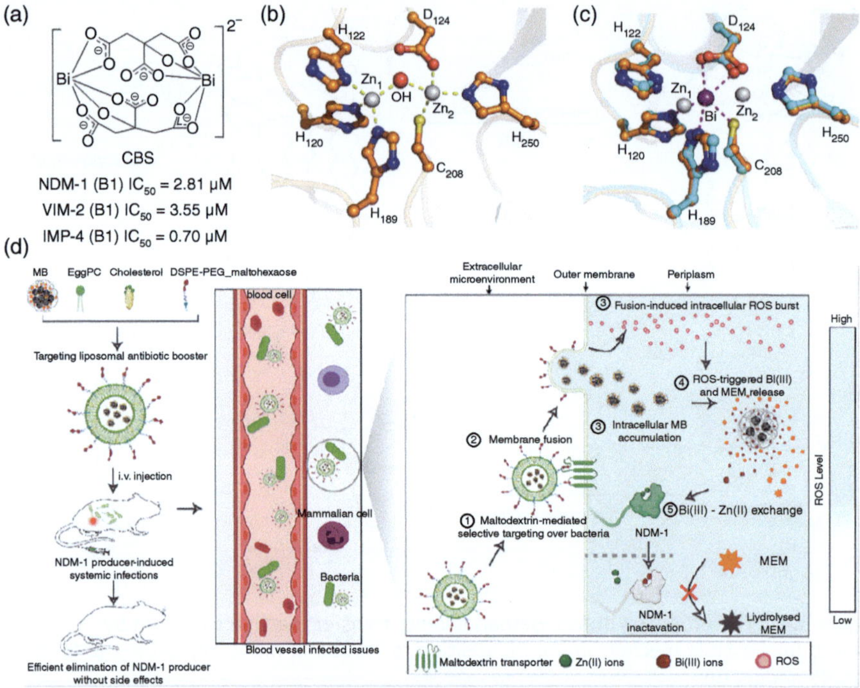

Figure 5.5 Chemical structure of colloidal bismuth citrate (CBS), (a). The active site of native Zn-bound NDM-1 with two Zn(II) ions shown as gray spheres and the bridging hydroxyl nucleophile as a red sphere (b). An overlay image comparing the relative position of Bi(III) with the two Zn(II) ions. Bi(III) is located in between the two Zn(II) ions slightly closer to Zn_1 site (c). Schemes for construction of liposomal antibiotic booster (M-MFL@MB) that targets and inactivates NDMs via Bi(III)-mediated Zn(II) removal (d). *Source:* [40] / Springer Nature / CC BY 4.0.

in vivo poses significant challenges. A pathogen-primed liposomal antibiotic booster (M-MFL@MB) that facilitates drugs delivery into bacteria and sequesters Zn(II) from NDMs was developed by Wu et al. [41]. As shown in Figure 5.5d, M-MFL@MB incorporates bismuth nanoclusters (BiNCs) as a reservoir of Bi(III) to initiate Zn(II) removal upon reactive oxygen species (ROS) activation. Inspired by the bacteria-specific maltodextrin transport pathway, meropenem-loaded BiNCs are encapsulated within a maltodextrin-cloaked membrane fusion liposome, enabling selective bacterial targeting and direct outer membrane fusion, bypassing the bacterial envelope barrier. This fusion disturbs bacterial membrane homeostasis, then triggers intracellular ROS amplification, which activates Bi(III)-mediated Zn(II) replacement and meropenem release, realizing more precise and efficient NDMs producer treatment. Benefiting from specific bacteria-targeting, adequate intracellular drugs accumulation, and self-activating Zn(II) replacement, M-MFL@MB rescues all mice infected by NDM producers without systemic side effects [41]. Additionally, M-MFL@MB decreases bacterial outer membrane vesicle secretion, slowing down transmission from NDM producers by over 35 times. Taken together, liposomal antibiotic booster as an efficient and safe tool provides a new strategy for tackling NDM producer-induced infections.

5.3.2 Gold (Au)

Gold has been utilized in medicine since antiquity. As a noble metal, the therapeutic potential of Au, particularly in the form of Au(I) complexes for rheumatoid arthritis, was first recognized in the 1930s. The first oral Au(I) drug, tetraacetyl-β-D-thioglucose Au(I) triethylphosphine (auranofin, Ridaura®) approved by Federal Drug Administration (FDA), has been used for anti-arthritis therapy since 1985. Since then, an array of gold complexes has been developed, exhibiting great promise for diverse therapies, especially in anti-arthritis and anticancer. In light of the global emergence of GNB carrying the plasmid-borne resistance genes, bla_{MBL} and *mcr*, the treatment of life-threatening infections with the antibiotics, carbapenems and colistin faces a significant challenge. Auranofin (AUR), an anti-rheumatic drug, has recently been reported as an effective dual inhibitor of MBLs and MCRs with IC_{50} of 437.9 ± 29.1 nM for NDM-1 and K_d of 3.36 ± 0.38 μM for MCR-1, respectively (Figure 5.6a) [26]. Importantly, AUR synergized with meropenem and colistin in killing a spectrum of bacterial pathogens carrying bla_{MBL} and/or *mcr* genes with FIC index values of 0.125–0.375. Significantly, the combination suppressed the resistance development of either MBL or MCR. Notably, AUR potently restored the susceptibility of MCR-1- and NDM-5-co-producing pathogens to colistin in murine peritonitis models (Figure 5.6b) [26].

Mechanistic studies show that AUR irreversibly inhibits NDM-1 activity and disrupts the function of MCR-1 via displacing Zn(II) ions in their active sites.

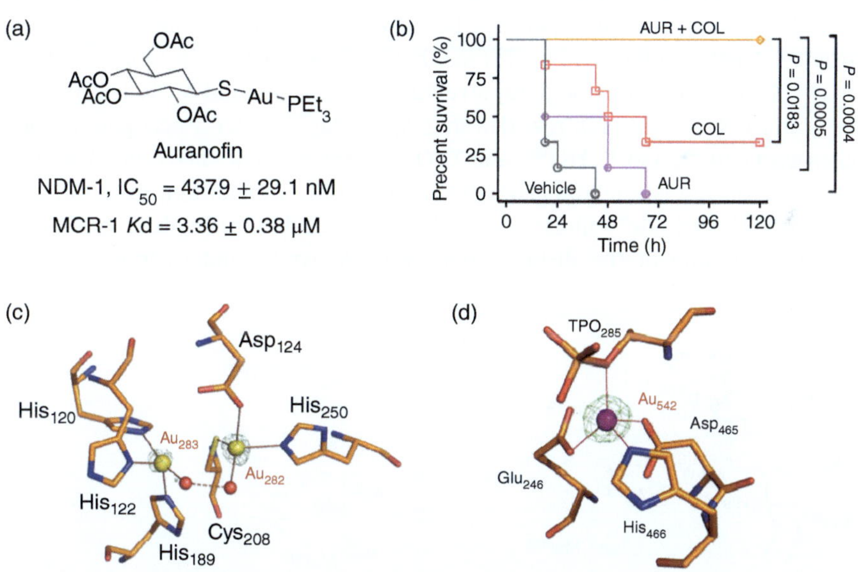

Figure 5.6 Chemical structure of auranofin (a). Survival curves showing combination efficacies in the peritonitis infection model. Balb/c mice were infected by a lethal dose of *E. coli* CKE (MCR-1⁺, NDM-5⁺), (b). Structure of the active site of Au-NDM-1 (PDBID: 6LHE), (c). Structure of the active site of Au-MCR-1-S (PDBID: 6LI6), (d). *Source:* [26] / Springer Nature / CC BY 4.0.

The crystal structure of Au-NDM-1 was obtained at 1.20 Å resolution (PDB ID: 6LHE), as shown in Figure 5.6c, two Au(I) ions (Au^{282} and Au^{283}) were clearly observed in the active site, tetrahedrally coordinated to Cys^{208}, His^{250}, Asp^{124}, a water molecule (W^{291}), and His^{122}, His^{120}, His^{189}, and a water molecule (W^{410}), respectively. The distance between two Au ions (~3.8 Å) is much shorter than that between two Zn ions (~4.6 Å) in the intact NDM-1 crystal. In addition, a Zn(II)-bound crystal of MCR-1-S (PDBID: 6LI4) and Au(I)-bound MCR-1-S crystal (PDBID: 6LI6) was obtained by a soaking method (Figure 5.6d) [26]. From the density map, three Au(I) ions were clearly visible in one chain in an asymmetric unit, and a single Au(I) ion (Au^{542}) was found in the Zn(II)-dependent catalytic core, coordinating with four residues, i.e. Glu^{246}, Asp^{465}, His^{466}, and TPO^{285} to form a distorted tetrahedral geometry. This crystallographic analysis demonstrates that AUR binds to NDM-1 and MCR-1, displacing Zn(II) in the active site through Au(I) [26].

5.3.3 Silver (Ag)

Silver has long been used as an antimicrobial agent for the management of infected wounds and burns. Silver sulfadiazine (silvadene), is an FDA-approved antimicrobial drug that forms a polymeric complex between Ag(I) and sulfadiazine. For many years, the development of Ag(I) complexes as antimicrobial agents was overshadowed by the widespread application of antibiotics. However, with the escalating concern over antibiotic resistance, silver compounds have reemerged as a viable option against superbugs because of their low tendency to induce resistance. Recent studies have confirmed that Ag(I) is capable of inhibiting MCR-1 activity [27]. Furthermore, the X-ray structure of the Ag-bound MCR-1-S (PDBID: 7WAA) at a 1.58 Å resolution revealed that Ag(I) (Ag^{617} with 0.7 occupancy) coordinates with Glu^{246}, Asp^{465}, His^{466}, and TPO^{285} in the original Zn(II) site of MCR-1, forming a distorted tetrahedral geometry (Figure 5.7a). In addition, the binding of Ag^{620} to Met^{392} and His^{395} induced ca. 66° rotation of the imidazole ring of His^{395} and the shortening of the distance between $N\delta_1/His^{395}$ and $C\alpha$/ethanolamine

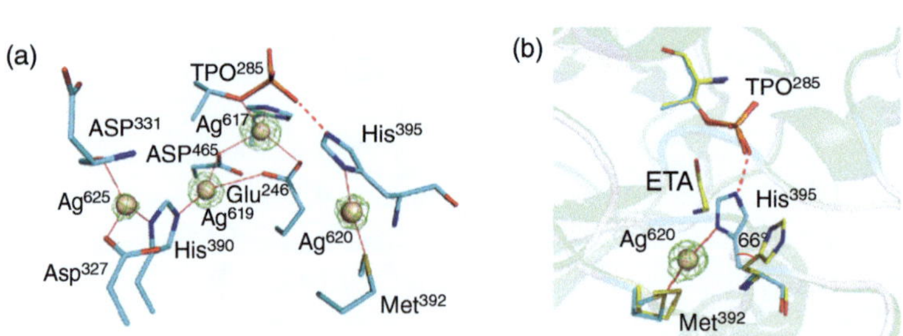

Figure 5.7 The cartoon of the tetranuclear silver center within the active-site pocket of the MCR-1-S enzyme. Ag(I) ions are bridged in a narrow pocket by either coordination bonds or hydrogen bonds (a). Superimposition of Ag(I)-bound MCR-1-S (PDB ID: 7WAA) onto substrate analog (ETA)-bound MCR-1-S (PDB ID: 5YLE), (b). *Source:* [27] / National Academy of Sciences.

(ETA) from 3.94 to 1.32 Å in the substrate-binding site of MCR-1 (Figure 5.7b), in comparison to the MCR-1 complex with substrate analog ETA (PDBID: 5YLE). These data indicated that Ag(I) played dual roles in abolishing MCR-1 activity by replacing Zn(II) with Ag(I) in the catalytic site and exhibiting steric effects in the substrate-binding site, thus reversing *mcr-1*-mediated resistance [27]. Moreover, Ag(I) could restore colistin efficacy against bacteria carrying *mcr-1* gene, with FICI values ranging from 0.25 to 0.37. Significantly, Ag(I) effectively slows down the development of higher-level resistance and reduces mutation frequency. Combination of Ag(I) with colistin could relieve dermonecrotic lesions and reduce the bacterial load of mice infected with *mcr-1*-carrying pathogens [27].

Considering the urgency of treatment of infections caused by carbapenem-resistant bacteria that produce MBLs, bio-surfactin-stabilized silver nanoparticles (AgNPs) have been reported to inhibit NDMs, possibly binding to the sulfhydryl group of cysteine in the active site of NDMs, inactivating these enzymes [42]. AgNPs combined with various β-lactams exhibited synergistic increase in sensitivity. Moreover, Li et al. introduced a bioresponsive silver peroxide-based nanovesicle, i.e. Ag_2O_2@BP-MT@MM, that serves as a broad-spectrum MBL inhibitor for combating MBL-producing bacterial pneumonia (Figure 5.8a). The Ag_2O_2@BP-MT@MM effectively abrogates MBL activity by displacing the Zn(II) cofactor in MBLs with Ag(I) and displays potent bactericidal and anti-inflammatory properties, specific targeting abilities, and great bioresponsive characteristics (Figure 5.8b) [42]. Moreover, Ag(I) released from Ag_2O_2 decomposition at the infection sites effectively inhibits MBL activity and overcomes the resistance of MBL-producing bacteria to meropenem, resulting in synergistic elimination of bacteria in conjunction with meropenem (Figure 5.8c). Importantly, in two murine infection models of NDM-1-positive *Klebsiella pneumoniae*-induced severe pneumonia and NDM-1-positive *Escherichia coli*-induced sepsis-related bacterial pneumonia, the Ag_2O_2@BP-MT@MM nanoparticles significantly reduce bacterial loading, pro-inflammatory cytokine levels locally and systemically, and the recruitment and activation of neutrophils and macrophages [42].

5.3.4 Copper (Cu)

Copper has a well-documented history as an antimicrobial agent, dating back to its use in ancient civilizations. Extensive research has elucidated both the efficacy and mechanism underlying copper's antimicrobial activity against various microorganisms. Interestingly, Djoko et al. have demonstrated that copper ions potently inhibit the activity of NDM-1 enzyme, exhibiting a noncompetitive mode of inhibition, with a lower K_i (3.7 μM), which was in agreement with a study that reported a noncompetitive mode of inhibition by Cu(II) with a similar magnitude for the MBL AIM-1 [43, 44]. Moreover, copper increases the susceptibility of NDM-positive isolates of *E. coli* to carbapenems, with FIC indices of 0.11 for both ertapenem and meropenem. Copper pyrithione ($Cu(PyS)_2$), an FDA-approved antifungal agent, exerts an antimicrobial effect and has been found to increase the susceptibility of MS6192 and MS8485 to ertapenem and meropenem [43]. The FIC indices were

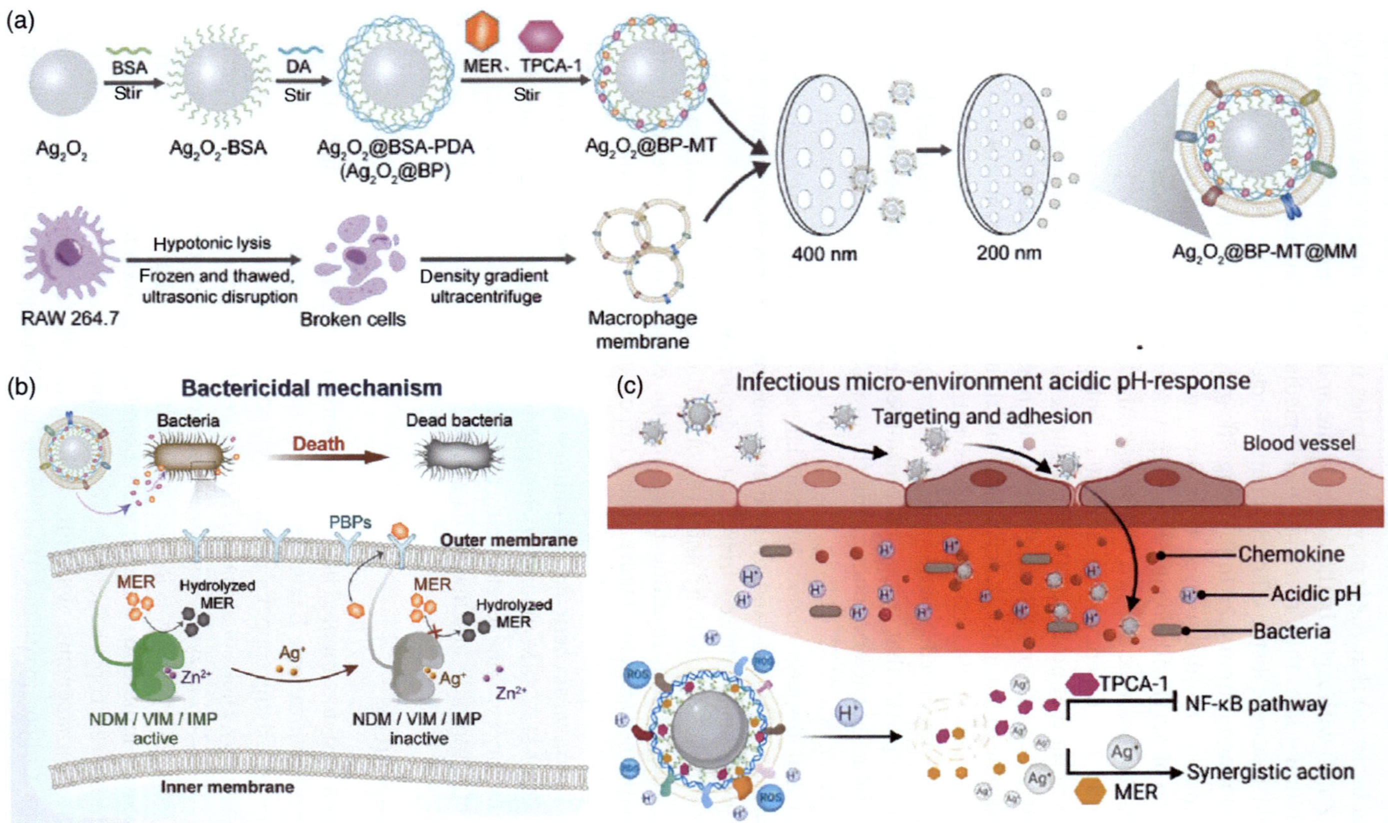

Figure 5.8 Schematic illustration of synthetic procedures for Ag_2O_2@BP-MT@MM (a). The released Ag(I) exerted its ability of enzyme binding and replaced Zn(II) in MBLs, thus leading to inactivation of enzyme and restoration of superbugs susceptibility to meropenem (b). Schematic illustration of inflammation targeting and acid-responsive macrophage membrane (MM) disruption as well as drugs release (c). *Source:* [42] / John Wiley & Sons.

0.18 ± 0.07 (ertapenem) and 0.13 ± 0.05 (meropenem) for MS6192, and 0.28 ± 0.11 (ertapenem) and 0.17 ± 0.08 (meropenem) for MS8485, respectively. The possible mechanism showed that copper disrupts binding of one or both of the zinc ions in the active site of NDM-1. Alternatively, copper ions may bind to an allosteric site outside the zinc-containing pocket. Additionally, the immunoblot results indicated that copper may also affect the synthesis, maturation (enzyme folding and zinc site assembly), or stability of NDM-1 [43].

$Cu(DTC)_2$, a copper-containing metabolite *in vivo* of disulfiram, was reported to inactivate B1 and B2 subclass MBLs (NDM-1, IMP-1, ImiS), with IC_{50} ranges of 3.9–39 nM [45]. The proposed inhibition mechanism is oxidizing the thiolate in the active site of NDM-1. Moreover, $Cu(DTC)_2$ effectively enhances the susceptibility of clinical isolates of *E. coli*, *K. pneumoniae*, and *P. aeruginosa* producing-NDM-1 to carbapenems (imipenem), with a MIC reduction of 2–16 folds. Furthermore, a library of dithiocarbamates combined with copper was comprehensively assessed for their synergistic antibacterial effects, further underscoring the efficacy of copper coordination complexes as potent adjuvants for carbapenems [46]. The use of copper complexes in conjunction with antibiotics may represent a synergistic strategy to address the rising threat of antibiotic-resistant bacteria.

5.3.5 Other Metallo-agents

Having conducted an exhaustive analysis of the initial four categories of metallo-drugs/metallo-agents, it is important to acknowledge an additional class of metallo-agents that cannot be fully incorporated into the aforementioned categories. Cisplatin, Pd(II), and Ru(II) complexes have been reported to be potent broad-spectrum inhibitors of MBLs from B_1 and B_2 subclasses, exhibiting an IC_{50} value of 0.14–0.76 μM (Figure 5.9) [47, 48]. These metal complexes irreversibly inhibited NDM-1 through a novel inhibition mode involving binding to the Cys^{208} residue and displacing one Zn(II) ion of the enzyme with one Pt(II) containing two NH_3's or one Pd(II) ion, which was testified by enzyme kinetics, thermodynamics, site-directed mutation assays, inductively coupled plasma-atomic emission spectrometry (ICP-AES), and matrix-assisted desorption/ionization time-of-flight mass spectrometry (MALDI-TOF-MS) [48]. Interestingly, the Cys^{208} residue at the Zn(II)-binding site and Met^{67} residue at the β-hairpin loop of the active pocket are critical for Ru(II) complexes to inhibit NDM-1 [47]. Importantly, these metallo-agents effectively revived meropenem efficacy against MBL-expressing bacteria and suppressed the development of higher-level resistance in bacteria-producing NDM-1. These results undoubtedly aid efforts to develop metal-based MBL inhibitors in combination with carbapenems to deal with the clinical crisis of carbapenem-resistant *E. coli* harboring MBLs.

By high-throughput screening of a pharmacologically characterized compound library, Thomas et al. identified two NDM-1 inhibitors: p-chloromecuribenzoate (p-CMB) and nitroprusside (Figure 5.9), with an IC_{50} value of 2.3 and 9.0 μM, respectively [49]. The unambiguous identification of the covalent adduction site of p-CMB to the NDM-1 using bottom-up LC-MS/MS revealed that p-CMB formed

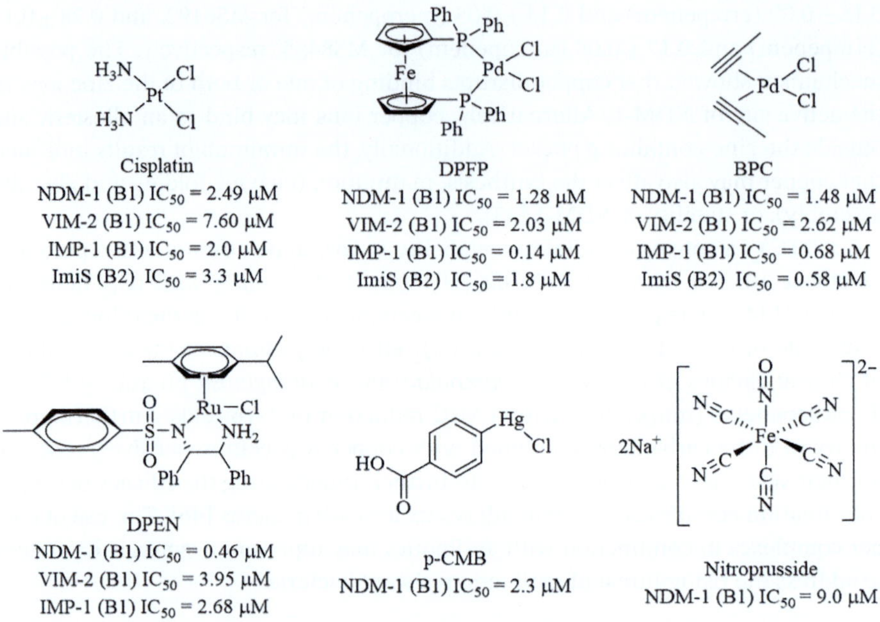

Figure 5.9 Chemical structures of cisplatin, Pd(II) complex (DPFP, BPC), Ru(II) complex (DPEN), p-chloromecuribenzoate (p-CMB), and nitroprusside, and their inhibition activity (IC_{50}, μM) against MBLs.

an Hg-S bond with the Cys^{208} residue of NDM-1 [49]. Similarly, nitroprusside, a nitric oxide (NO) donor, could inactivate NDM-1 with a possible conversion of the reactive thiol group of cysteine residue into N-hydroxysulfenamide ($RSONH_2$) [49]. This paves the way for the development of bacterial-specific NO donors, especially the macrophage-derived reactive nitrogen species to combat MBL-mediated bacterial infections. Additionally, Zn, Ni, Co, and Fe complexes of pyridine-2,6-dithiocarboxylic acid (DPTC) were also found to be novel NDM-1 inhibitors [50]. DPTC-Ni complex had the best inhibitory activity against NDM-1, exhibiting an IC_{50} of 3.5 μM. PDTC-metal complexes effectively increased the potency of meropenem, reducing the MIC by as much as 10-fold, against clinical isolates of *Enterobacteriaceae* [50].

5.4 Conclusion and Perspectives

The ongoing challenge of AMR, particularly through the mechanism of MBLs and MCR-1, necessitates innovative approaches in drug development. Current efforts have highlighted the potential of various metallo-drugs/metallo-agents to effectively combat MBLs/MCR-1-producing pathogens [26, 40]. Considering the global emergence of GNB carrying the plasmid-borne resistance genes, *bla*$_{MBL}$ and *mcr*, the treatment of life-threatening infections with the antibiotics, carbapenems and colistin faces a significant challenge [26]. The future trend lies in the development of metal-based dual inhibitors that simultaneously target MBLs and MCR-1. For instance, Au(I) and Ag(I) have been reported to be as an effective dual inhibitor of MBLs and MCR-1 [26, 27, 42].

Given that the mechanisms by which most metallo-drugs/metallo-agents inhibit metalloenzymes involve targeting the Cys^{208} residues in the active center of the metalloenzymes [47, 48], one significant challenge is the development of resistance to existing metallo-drugs, which can undermine their efficacy over time. For instance, it was reported that despite its sequence conservation, the Cys residue in the active site of B1 MBL IMP-1 can be substituted by Asp or Gly and still confer resistance to β-lactams [51]. In addition, Pei et al. demonstrated that C208D mutations in NDM-1 can confer resistance to covalent inactivators that target a conserved active-site Cys^{208}, thus highlighting the potential drawbacks of this drug design strategy [49].

Resistance and adverse side effects are always the main obstacles to the widespread use of different metallo-drugs [52]. Targeted therapy is a new trend for the design of metallo-drugs/metallo-agents which may maximize the antibacterial efficiency of metallo-drugs/metallo-agents and minimize the related unwanted side effects. Thereby, innovative formulation and delivery systems are critical for improving the efficacy of metallo-drugs/metallo-agents against Gram-negative superbugs. In this chapter, we summarize recent advancements including the development of bioresponsive nanocarriers that enhance targeted delivery to infection sites. For example, Li et al. reported a bioresponsive silver peroxide-based nanovesicle that serves as a broad-spectrum MBL inhibitor for treating severe pneumonia [42]. This system effectively releases Ag(I) ions at the infection site, displacing Zn(II) cofactors in MBLs and exhibiting potent bactericidal properties. The targeted delivery mechanism facilitated by macrophage membrane encapsulation significantly improves the therapeutic outcomes against MBL-producing bacteria. Similarly, Wu et al. presented a liposomal antibiotic booster designed to enhance the penetration of drugs into bacteria while simultaneously removing Zn(II) from NDMs [41]. This novel formulation employs bismuth nanoclusters to facilitate the removal of Zn(II), which is crucial for restoring the activity of carbapenems against resistant strains. The liposomal structure not only improves drug delivery but also enhances the selectivity and efficacy of the therapeutic agents. Additionally, the exploration of copper coordination complexes as delivery vehicles has shown promise in sensitizing resistant bacteria to carbapenems [43, 53]. By effectively delivering copper at low concentrations, these complexes can synergistically enhance the antibacterial activity of existing drugs.

Given that the spatial conformation of bacterial metalloenzymes (MBLs, MCR-1) and targeted delivery systems have been reported, with the cross-fusion of disciplines, the boom in structural biology, and the application of machine learning (ML) and artificial intelligence (AI) in drug development, a metallo-drug (or agent) with sensitivity, efficiency, selectivity, and stability to counter carbapenem and cloistin resistance will be developed and approved in the future.

Acknowledgments

Our work has been supported by the Research Grants Council of Hong Kong SAR (C7034-20E, R7070-18, 17308921, SRFS2122-7S04, 17306323, and 17304323), the University of Hong Kong (URC (202107185074) and Norman & Cecilia Yip Foundation), the National Natural Science Foundation of China (22307103), the China Postdoctoral Science Foundation (2023 M732885) and Natural Science Foundation of Shaanxi Province (2023-JC-QN-0133).

References

1 Luther, A., Urfer, M., Zahn, M. et al. (2019). Chimeric peptidomimetic antibiotics against Gram-negative bacteria. *Nature* 576: 452–458.
2 Shukla, R., Peoples, A.-J., Ludwig, K.-C. et al. (2023). An antibiotic from an uncultured bacterium binds to an immutable target. *Cell* 186: 4059–4073.
3 Singh, K.-S., Sharma, R., Reddy, P.-A.-N. et al. (2021). IspH inhibitors kill Gram-negative bacteria and mobilize immune clearance. *Nature* 589: 597–602.
4 Theuretzbacher, U., Blasco, B., Duffey, M., and Piddock, L.-J.-V. (2023). Unrealized targets in the discovery of antibiotics for Gram-negative bacterial infections. *Nature Review Drug Discovery* 22: 957–975.
5 Wu, K.-J.-Y., Tresco, B.-I.-C., Ramkissoon, A. et al. (2024). An antibiotic preorganized for ribosomal binding overcomes antimicrobial resistance. *Science* 383: 721–726.
6 Smith, P.-A., Koehler, M.-F.-T., Girgis, H.-S. et al. (2018). Optimized arylomycins are a new class of Gram-negative antibiotics. *Nature* 561: 189–194.
7 Okano, A., Isley, N.-A., and Boger, D.-L. (2017). Total syntheses of vancomycin-related glycopeptide antibiotics and key analogues. *Chemical Review* 117: 11952–11993.
8 Durand-Reville, T.-F., Guler, S., Comita-Prevoir, J. et al. (2017). ETX2514 is a broad-spectrum beta-lactamase inhibitor for the treatment of drug-resistant Gram-negative bacteria including *Acinetobacter baumannii*. *Nature Microbiology* 2: 17104.
9 Richter, M.-F., Drown, B.-S., Riley, A.-P. et al. (2017). Predictive compound accumulation rules yield a broad-spectrum antibiotic. *Nature* 545: 299–304.
10 Yang, Y., Yan, Y.-H., Schofield, C.-J. et al. (2023). Metallo-β-lactamase-mediated antimicrobial resistance and progress in inhibitor discovery. *Trends in Microbiology* 31: 735–748.
11 Gonzalez, L.-J., Bahr, G., Gonzalez, M.-M. et al. (2023). In-cell kinetic stability is an essential trait in metallo-β-lactamase evolution. *Nature Chemical Biology* 19: 1116–1126.
12 Davies, D.-T. and Everett, M. (2021). Designing inhibitors of β-lactamase enzymes to overcome carbapenem resistance in Gram-negative bacteria. *Accounts of Chemical Research* 54: 2055–2064.

13 Ding, Y., Li, Z., Xu, C. et al. (2021). Recent progress of fluorogenic probes/inhibitors of β-lactamase and their applications in drug-resistant bacteria. *Angewandat Chemie International Education* 60: 24–40.

14 Cai, J., Shi, J., Chen, C. et al. (2023). Structural-activity relationship-inspired the discovery of saturated fatty acids as novel colistin enhancers. *Advanced Science* 10: e23021182.

15 Carfrae, L.-A., Rachwalski, K., French, S. et al. (2023). Inhibiting fatty acid synthesis overcomes colistin resistance. *Nature Microbiology* 8: 1026–1038.

16 Wang, S. and Shen, J. (2020). Active surveillance of the spread of mcr-1-positive *E. coli*. *Lancet Microbe* 1: e4–e5.

17 Zampaloni, C., Mattei, P., Bleicher, K. et al. (2024). A novel antibiotic class targeting the lipopolysaccharide transporter. *Nature* 625: 566–571.

18 Theuretzbacher, U., Bush, K., Harbarth, S. et al. (2020). Critical analysis of antibacterial agents in clinical development. *Nature Review Microbiology* 18: 286–298.

19 Zhanel, G.-G., Mansour, C., Mikolayanko, S. et al. (2024). Cefepime-Taniborbactam: a novel cephalosporin/β-lactamase inhibitor combination. *Drugs* 84: 1219–1250.

20 Si, Z., Pethe, K., and Chan-Park, M.-B. (2023). Chemical basis of combination therapy to combat antibiotic resistance. *JACS Au* 3: 276–292.

21 Yahav, D., Giske, C.-G., Gramatniece, A. et al. (2020). New β-lactam-β-lactamase inhibitor combinations. *Clinical Microbiology Reviews* 34: e00115-20.

22 Gonzalez-Bello, C., Rodriguez, D., Pernas, M. et al. (2020). β-Lactamase inhibitors to restore the efficacy of antibiotics against Superbugs. *Journal of Medicinal Chemistry* 63: 1859–1881.

23 Yan, Y.-H., Li, G., and Li, G.-B. (2020). Principles and current strategies targeting metallo-β-lactamase mediated antibacterial resistance. *Medicinal Research Reviews* 40: 1558–1592.

24 Griffith, D.-M., Li, H., Werrett, M.-V. et al. (2021). Medicinal chemistry and biomedical applications of bismuth-based compounds and nanoparticles. *Chemical Society Reviews* 50: 12037–12039.

25 Anthony, E.-J., Bolitho, E.-M., Bridgewater, H.-E. et al. (2020). Metallodrugs are unique: opportunities and challenges of discovery and development. *Chemical Science* 11: 12888–12917.

26 Sun, H., Zhang, Q., Wang, R. et al. (2020). Resensitizing carbapenem- and colistin-resistant bacteria to antibiotics using auranofin. *Nature Communications* 11: 5263.

27 Zhang, Q., Wang, R., Wang, M. et al. (2022). Re-sensitization of mcr carrying multidrug resistant bacteria to colistin by silver. *Proceedings of the National Academy of Sciences of the United States of America* 119: e2119417119.

28 Weng, C., Tan, Y.-L.-K., Koh, W.-G., and Ang, W.-H. (2023). Harnessing transition metal scaffolds for targeted antibacterial therapy. *Angewdate Chemie International Edition* 62: e202310040.

29 Mojica, M.-F., Rossi, M.-A., Vila, A.-J., and Bonomo, R.-A. (2021). The urgent need for metallo-β-lactamase inhibitors: an unattended global threat. *The Lancet Infectious Diseases* 22: e28–e34.

30 Bahr, G., Gonzalez, L.J., and Vila, A.-J. (2021). Metallo-β-lactamases in the age of multidrug resistance: from structure and mechanism to evolution, dissemination, and inhibitor design. *Chemical Reviews* 121: 7957–8094.

31 Li, H. and Sun, H. (2022). A hydroxide lock for metallo-β-lactamases. *Nature Chemistry* 14: 6–8.

32 King, A.-M., Reid-Yu, S.-A., Wang, W. et al. (2014). AMA overcomes metallo-β-lactamase antibiotic resistance. *Nature* 510: 503–506.

33 Chen, C., Oelschlaeger, P., Wang, D.-M. et al. (2022). Structure and mechanism-guided design of dual serine/metallo carbapenemase inhibitors. *Journal of Medicinal Chemistry* 65: 5954–5974.

34 Chen, C. and Yang, K.-W. (2020). Structure-based design of covalent inhibitors targeting metallo-β-lactamases. *European Journal of Medicinal Chemistry* 203: 112573.

35 Zhou, Y., Wang, J., Guo, Y. et al. (2019). Discovery of a potential MCR-1 inhibitor that reverses polymyxin activity against clinical mcr-1-positive *Enterobacteriaceae*. *Journal of Infection* 78: 364–372.

36 Liu, J.-H., Liu, Y.-Y., Shen, Y.-B. et al. (2023). Plasmid-mediated colistin-resistance genes: mcr. *Trends in Microbiology* 32: 365–378.

37 Huang, H., Dong, N., Shu, L. et al. (2020). Colistin-resistance gene mcr in clinical carbapenem-resistant *Enterobacteriaceae* strains in China, 2014–2019. *Emerging Microbes & Infections* 9: 237–245.

38 Son, S.-J., Huang, R., Squire, C.-J., and Leung, I.-K.-H. (2019). MCR-1: a promising target for structure-based design of inhibitors to tackle polymyxin resistance. *Drug Discovery Today* 24: 206–216.

39 Materon, I.-C. and Palzkill, T. (2023). Structural biology of MCR-1-mediated resistance to polymyxin antibiotics. *Current Opinion in Structural Biology* 82: 102647.

40 Wang, R., Lai, T.-P., Gao, P. et al. (2018). Bismuth antimicrobial drugs serve as broad-spectrum metallo-β-lactamase inhibitors. *Nature Communications* 9: 439.

41 Wu, S., Wei, Y., Wang, Y. et al. (2023). Liposomal antibiotic booster potentiates carbapenems for combating NDMs-producing *Escherichia coli*. *Advanced Science* 11: e2304397.

42 Li, H., Duan, S., Li, L. et al. (2023). Bio-responsive sliver peroxide-nanocarrier serves as broad-spectrum metallo-β-lactamase inhibitor for combating severe *Pneumonia*. *Advanced Materials* 36: e2310532.

43 Djoko, K.-Y., Achard, M.-E.-S., Phan, M.-D. et al. (2018). Copper ions and coordination complexes as novel carbapenem adjuvants. *Antimicrobial Agents and Chemotherapy* 62: e02280-17.

44 Selleck, C., Larrabee, J.-A., Harmer, J. et al. (2016). AIM-1: an antibiotic-degrading metallohydrolase that displays mechanistic flexibility. *Chemistry-A European Journal* 22: 17704–17714.

45 Chen, C., Yang, K.-W., Wu, L.-Y. et al. (2020). Disulfiram as a potent metallo-β-lactamase inhibitor with dual functional mechanisms. *Chemical Communications* 56: 2755–2758.

46 Chen, C., Yang, K.-W., Zhai, L. et al. (2022). Dithiocarbamates combined with copper for revitalizing meropenem efficacy against NDM-1-producing Carbapenem-resistant *Enterobacteriaceae. Bioorganic Chemistry* 118: 105474.

47 Chen, C. and Yang, K.-W. (2020). Ruthenium complex as prospective inhibitor of metallo-β-lactamases to reverse carbapenem resistance. *Dalton Transactions* 49: 14099–14105.

48 Chen, C., Sun, L.-Y., Gao, H. et al. (2020). Identification of Cisplatin and palladium(II) complexes as potent metallo-β-lactamases inhibitors for targeting carbapenem-resistant *Enterobacteriaceae* (CRE). *ACS Infectious Diseases* 6: 975–985.

49 Thomas, P.-W., Spicer, T., Cammarata, M. et al. (2013). An altered zinc-binding site confers resistance to a covalent inactivator of New Delhi metallo-β-lactamase-1 (NDM-1) discovered by high-throughput screening. *Bioorganic Medicinal Chemistry* 21: 3138–3146.

50 Thomas, C.-S., Braun, D.-R., Olmos, J.-L. et al. (2020). Pyridine-2,6-dithiocarboxylic acid and its metal complexes: new inhibitors of New Delhi metallo β-lactamase-1. *Marine Drugs* 18: 295.

51 Horton, L.-B., Shanker, S., Mikulski, R. et al. (2012). Mutagenesis of zinc ligand residue Cys^{221} reveals plasticity in the IMP-1 metallo-β-lactamase active site. *Antimicrobial Agents and Chemotherapy* 56: 5667–5677.

52 Zhou, Y., Ip, T.-K.-Y., Zhang, Q. et al. (2021). Metal complexes as drugs and therapeutic agents. In: *Comprehensive Coordination Chemistry III*, vol. 9 (ed. E.-C. Constable, G. Parkin, and L. Que Jr.,). Elsevier.

53 Zaengle-Barone, J.-M., Jackson, A.-C., Besse, D.-M. et al. (2018). Copper influences the antibacterial outcomes of a β-lactamase-activated prochelator against drug-resistant bacteria. *ACS Infectious Diseases* 4: 1019–1029.

6

Targeting Metallo-β-Lactamases to Combat Antibiotic Resistance

Mitchell A. Jeffs, Montserrat Mora-Ochomogo, Laila Masalha, Dylan W. Zhao, and Christopher T. Lohans

Queen's University, Department of Biomedical and Molecular Sciences, 18 Stuart Street, Kingston, Ontario, Canada

6.1 Introduction

β-Lactams, the most used class of antibiotics worldwide [1], are characterized by a core azetidinone (or β-lactam) ring. This reactive heterocyclic four-membered ring is essential for their bactericidal activity. Clinically used β-lactam antibiotics belong to four major subclasses, grouped according to the substituents attached to the β-lactam core. The structures of the penicillins and carbapenems feature the β-lactam ring fused to a five-membered thiazolidine or pyrroline ring, respectively, while the β-lactam ring in the cephalosporins is fused to a six-membered dihydrothiazine ring (Figure 6.1). The monobactams, however, lack a ring fused to the core β-lactam. The particular structures of these cyclic systems and their substituents define the spectra of activity and pharmacokinetic properties of the different β-lactam subclasses [2, 3].

β-Lactams act by inhibiting bacterial transpeptidase enzymes. The primary targets of the β-lactams are penicillin-binding proteins (PBPs), enzymes that catalyze the process of transpeptidation in the final steps of peptidoglycan synthesis. Peptidoglycan, a heteropolymer that plays major structural roles in the bacterial cell wall, consists of glycan strands cross-linked by peptide bridges [4]. The antibacterial activity of the β-lactams arises from their structural similarity to the terminal D-Ala-D-Ala moiety of the peptidoglycan stem pentapeptide [5]. This enables the β-lactam ring to react with an essential serine residue in the PBP transpeptidase domain active site, thereby preventing the formation of peptidoglycan cross-links and compromising the integrity of the cell wall [2, 5].

The first β-lactams to be discovered and used for medicinal purposes, the penicillins, laid the foundation for all subsequent β-lactam antibiotics. However, the spectrum of activity of the early penicillins was relatively limited, primarily targeting Gram-positive bacteria. Penicillin G, methicillin, oxacillin, cloxacillin, and

* Co-lead authorship for Mitchell Jeffs and Montserrat Mora-Ochomogo

Drug Discovery Targeting Metalloenzymes: Strategies and Applications, First Edition. Edited by Guo-Bo Li.

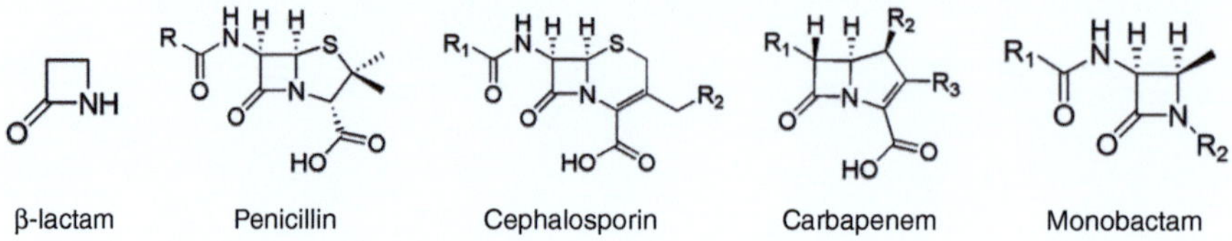

Figure 6.1 General structural features of the major subclasses of β-lactam antibiotics.

dicloxacillin were observed to be primarily active against Gram-positive cocci. However, some penicillins also exert antibacterial activity against Gram-negative pathogens [6]. Acting against both Gram-positive and Gram-negative bacteria, penicillins such as amoxicillin, piperacillin, carbenicillin, and ampicillin are categorized as broad-spectrum antibiotics [7, 8].

Many cephalosporins exhibit a broad spectrum of activity, when compared to the penicillins, and are generally classified into five generations based on their structures and antimicrobial properties. The first and second generations are predominantly active against Gram-positive pathogens, while third and fourth-generation cephalosporins extend coverage to a range of Gram-negative bacteria [3, 9]. These later generations are also less susceptible to degradation by β-lactamases, a major bacterial resistance mechanism against β-lactam antibiotics. Fifth-generation cephalosporins add an additional layer of protection by targeting some Gram-positive pathogens that are resistant to earlier generations of cephalosporins, including methicillin-resistant *Staphylococcus aureus* (MRSA) and *Listeria monocytogenes* [10].

Carbapenems are considered antibiotics of last resort and are often reserved for use against bacterial pathogens that are resistant to other β-lactams and other antibiotic classes. This is due in large part to their enhanced stability compared to penicillins and cephalosporins toward β-lactamase-catalyzed degradation [11]. Carbapenems have the broadest spectrum of activity among all β-lactams, potently targeting both Gram-negative and Gram-positive pathogens. Nonetheless, the carbapenems imipenem and doripenem have greater activity against Gram-positives, while meropenem and ertapenem are more effective against Gram-negative bacteria [11, 12].

Bacterial pathogens employ many different resistance mechanisms against β-lactams, threatening their clinical utility. These mechanisms include target modification (e.g. through mutations to genes that encode for PBPs), reduction of cell wall permeability (e.g. resulting from changes in porin structure or expression level), production of efflux pumps, and inactivation of β-lactams by β-lactamases. Although resistance can occur through a combination of these mechanisms, the production of β-lactamases represents the most prevalent resistance mechanism among Gram-negative bacteria [13, 14]. These enzymes hydrolyze the amide bond within the β-lactam ring, generating an inactive hydrolysis product that is incapable of inhibiting bacterial PBPs and cannot interfere with peptidoglycan synthesis.

One of the first classification systems used for β-lactamases was based on their substrate preferences, categorizing β-lactamases as penicillinases or cephalosporinases [15, 16]. In recent decades, β-lactamases that can hydrolyze carbapenem antibiotics (termed carbapenemases) have emerged globally. In 1980, the Ambler system was devised to classify β-lactamases according to their amino acid sequences and mechanism of activity [17]. The Ambler classification divides β-lactamases into classes A, B, C, and D; enzymes in classes A, C, and D are broadly referred to as serine β-lactamases (SBLs), while class B represents the metallo-β-lactamases (MBLs).

As the name suggests, SBLs possess an active site serine residue that is critical for their catalytic activity (Figure 6.2a). In a two-step hydrolytic mechanism, this serine residue first behaves as a nucleophile, attacking the carbonyl carbon of the β-lactam ring to form a covalent acyl-enzyme complex [2, 18, 19]. This complex is then hydrolyzed by a general base-activated water molecule, breaking the bond connecting the antibiotic to the serine [20, 21].

MBLs instead rely on one or more zinc ions to catalyze the hydrolysis of the β-lactam ring. These metal ions are strategically positioned in the active site to activate a water molecule that nucleophilically attacks the carbonyl of the β-lactam ring [22, 23]. MBLs exhibit a high level of diversity and are classified into subclasses B1, B2, and B3, with only low levels of sequence homology between these different subclasses (<30%) [24, 25]. Notably, B1 and B3 subclass enzymes use two active site zinc ions for catalysis, while enzymes belonging to subclass B2 generally require only one (Figure 6.2b,c) [26]. Many MBLs are of great clinical importance, particularly those belonging to the New Delhi MBL (NDM), Verona integron-encoded MBL (VIM), and imipenemase (IMP) families.

Because of their mechanistic differences, SBLs and MBLs differ greatly with respect to their susceptibility to β-lactamase inhibitors. There are several clinically approved SBL inhibitors that can restore β-lactam efficacy against resistant SBL-producing bacteria, including clavulanic acid, tazobactam, and avibactam (AVI) [27–30]. However, MBLs are impervious to currently used SBL inhibitors, resulting from their distinct mechanism of activity. The structural diversity of the MBLs further complicates the development of inhibitors that can broadly target all clinically relevant MBL variants. Consequently, there are currently no

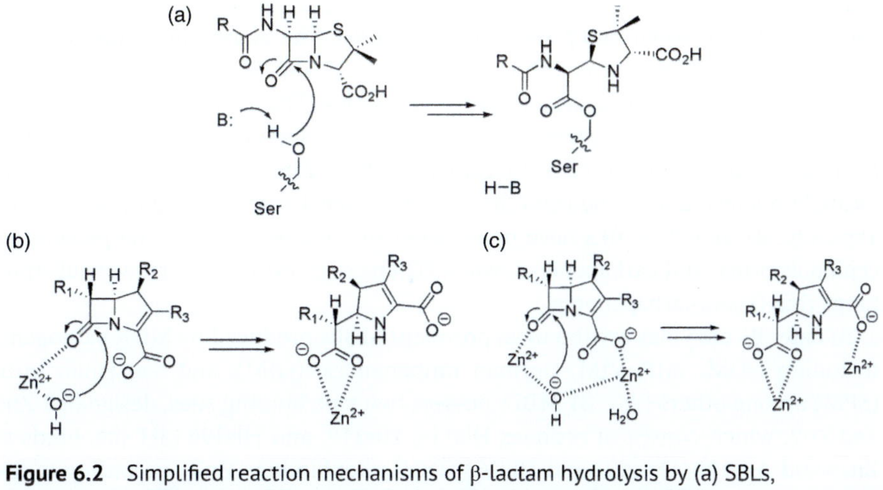

Figure 6.2 Simplified reaction mechanisms of β-lactam hydrolysis by (a) SBLs, (b) mono-zinc MBLs (class B2), and (c) di-zinc MBLs (classes B1 and B3).

MBL inhibitors approved for clinical use in the treatment of infections [31]. Coupled with their broad-spectrum activity against most of the different types of β-lactam antibiotics, MBLs are commonly found in important bacterial pathogens including *Escherichia coli*, *Klebsiella pneumoniae*, *Pseudomonas aeruginosa*, *Enterobacter cloacae*, and *Acinetobacter baumannii* [32–34]. Several of these species belong to the ESKAPE group of pathogens that have been identified as critical threats to global public health.

Antimicrobial resistance (AMR) represents one of the most pressing challenges to global health, driven by the widespread and often indiscriminate use of antibiotics in clinical and agricultural settings. The emergence and rapid dissemination of multidrug-resistant (MDR) organisms, including those producing MBLs, have severely limited the options available to treat infections, exerting a toll on human health and leading to higher healthcare costs [35]. As bacteria continue to evolve resistance mechanisms for the newest and most effective drugs, understanding the biochemical pathways, behavior, and transmission of these pathogens is critical.

MBLs play a critical role in bacterial resistance to β-lactam antibiotics, and an understanding of the properties of these enzymes is essential to appreciate the challenges posed by antibiotic resistance, particularly among Gram-negative pathogens. This chapter will provide an overview of the current state of knowledge regarding key topics related to MBL structure, function, evolution, and clinical significance. Additionally, it will explore recent advancements in the development of MBL inhibitors, as well as promising new antibiotics that are effective against MBL-producing bacteria.

6.2 Metallo-β-Lactamase Structure and Evolution

6.2.1 Structural Features of MBLs

Across the B1, B2, and B3 subclasses, MBLs share an αβ/βα fold in which the active site is located between two β-sheets (Figure 6.3a). The active site of the MBLs is centered on residues that coordinate zinc ions; B1 and B3 MBLs coordinate two zinc ions, while B2 MBLs are mono-zinc enzymes. The zinc ions coordinated at these sites interact with a catalytic water molecule, which upon deprotonation to a hydroxide, is directly involved in β-lactam hydrolysis. Zinc-coordinating residues are located on loops that extend from the flanking β-sheets surrounding the active site. Typically, B1 and B3 MBLs have broad-spectrum activity, hydrolyzing penicillins, cephalosporins, and carbapenems, while B2 enzymes exhibit a narrower substrate range that favors carbapenems.

To date, B1 enzymes are the most prevalent MBLs produced by MDR pathogens, including NDM, IMP, VIM, German imipenemase (GIM), and Sao Paulo MBL (SPM) among others [26]. B1 MBLs possess two zinc binding sites, designated Zn1 and Zn2, which consist of residues His116, His118, and His196 (3H site, binds to Zn1) and Asp120, Cys221, and His263 (DCH site; binds to Zn2), according to the metallo- or class B β-lactamase (BBL) numbering scheme [42] (Figure 6.3b–e).

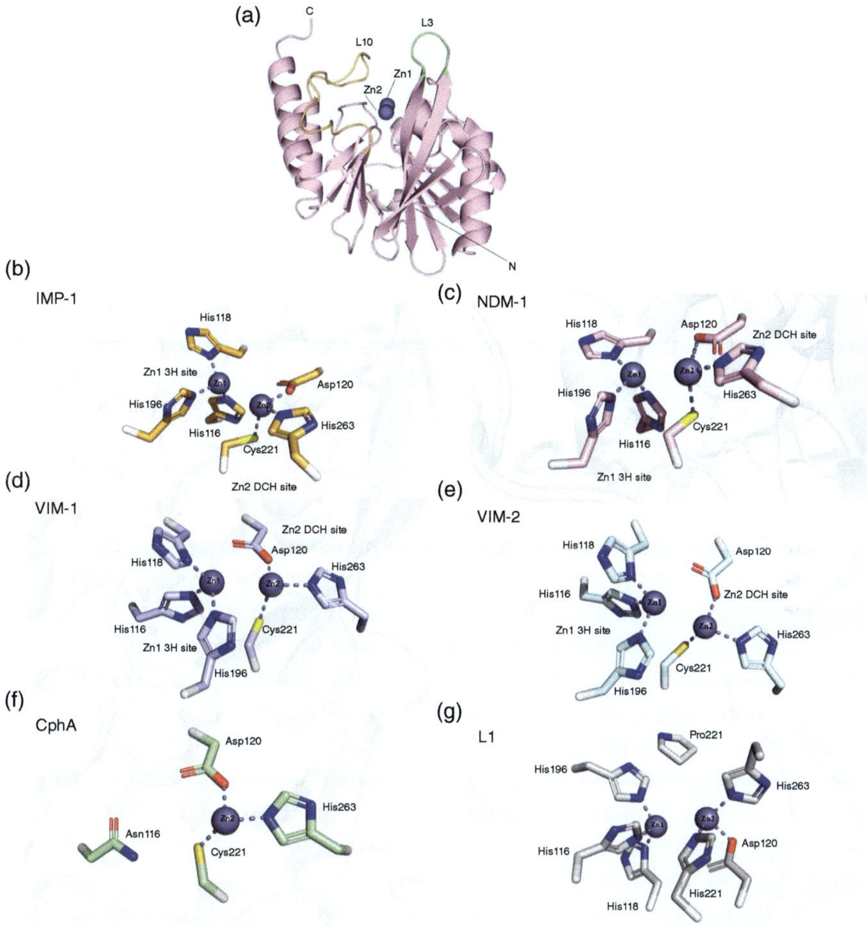

Figure 6.3 Global and active site structures of representative MBLs. (a) The global αβ/βα fold of NDM-1. Loops 3 and 10, which help form the active site are colored in light orange and green, respectively. The *N*- and *C*-termini are labeled. The coordination of zinc ions in the active sites of the class B1 MBLs (b) IMP-1, (c) NDM-1, (d) VIM-1, (e) VIM-2, (f) the class B2 MBL CphA, and (g) the class B3 MBL L1. The structural diagrams were generated in PyMOL using datasets available in the Research Collaboratory for Structural Bioinformatics (RCSB) Protein Data Bank (PDB): IMP-1 = 7XHW *Source:* Ref. [36]/Oxford University Press. NDM-1 = 3SPU *Source:* Ref. [37]/John Wiley & Sons. VIM-1 = 5N5I *Source:* Ref. [38]/John Wiley & Sons/CC BY 4.0. VIM-2 = 4NQ2 *Source:* Ref. [39]/American Chemical Society. CphA = 1X8G *Source:* Ref. [40]/with permission of Elsevier. *Source:* Ref. L1 = 1SML [41]/with permission of Elsevier.

MBLs belonging to the B2 subclass (e.g. CphA, Sfh, ImiS) are distinct in that they coordinate a single zinc ion at the DCH site (Figure 6.3f). Reduced zinc affinity at the Zn1 site is thought to result from the substitution of His116 with an asparagine residue [43]. B3 MBLs (e.g. L1, Adelaide imipenemase [AIM-1]) coordinate two zinc ions, with the Zn1 site possessing three histidine residues similar to what occurs in the B1 MBLs. However, the Zn2 site in B3 enzymes differs in that Cys221 is replaced with other amino acids that do not take part in zinc binding (Figure 6.3g). Instead,

His121 coordinates the second zinc ion, resulting in different active site geometry compared to B1 enzymes. Several review papers have described MBL structure and function in extensive detail [24, 26, 43, 44].

6.2.2 MBL Evolutionary Trajectories

The evolution of MBLs remains a daunting challenge for the prospect of overcoming AMR. The emergence of new MBL variants is thought to be driven by antibiotic stress as well as physiological stressors encountered within the host [45]. A particularly worrying development is the rise of clinical NDM and VIM variants that can better withstand zinc limitation. This could prove problematic for inhibitor development, especially concerning compounds that act by chelating to zinc. Additionally, these MBL variants may be better able to overcome nutritional immunity in the host, impeding immune-mediated clearing of an offending MBL-producing pathogen.

β-lactamases are principally found in the periplasmic space of Gram-negative organisms, located between the inner and outer membranes. Translocation of MBLs from the cytoplasm to the periplasm is typically mediated by the Sec pathway [46], which recognizes *N*-terminal signal sequences on protein cargo. Once transported to the periplasm, MBLs then undergo folding and are metalated with zinc [47]. NDM enzymes are unusual among MBLs in that they undergo lipidation at Cys26 in the *N*-terminal signal sequence, anchoring the enzyme to the outer membrane of Gram-negative bacteria [48]. Substitution of Cys26 with alanine leads to increased levels of soluble NDM-1 in the periplasm, with this enzyme exhibiting lower stability under zinc limitation compared to wild-type NDM-1 [49]. It has also been observed that the globular domain of NDM-1 can interact with bacterial membranes independently of lipidation [48].

Zinc acquisition by MBLs is thought to occur from free pools of zinc present in the periplasm, as no chaperones have been observed to mediate this process to date. Thus, the activity of MBLs is largely dependent on the availability of zinc in the cellular environment. For this reason, it has been argued that the clinical significance of MBLs has been overstated due to the reduced levels of resistance afforded by some MBLs under zinc-limiting conditions [50]. Zinc is often not readily available at the site of infection due to the production of zinc-chelating proteins such as calprotectin by the host during nutritional immune responses [51]. Calprotectin binds to zinc with a high affinity, inducing zinc deprivation, and treatment of MBL-producing *E. coli* with calprotectin has been shown to decrease NDM-1 activity [49]. Thus, the development of metal chelators has been an attractive strategy to inhibit MBLs, sequestering free zinc or directly stripping it from the enzyme active site.

Concerningly, clinical NDM variants have emerged that exhibit increased tolerance to zinc deprivation [52–55]. The M154L substitution is present in most NDM variants that exhibit increased zinc affinity, while other less common substitutions (e.g. D130N, D130G, and M154V) have similar effects [52]. *E. coli* expressing NDM-5, -7, -8, -12, -13, and -15 demonstrated a particularly high ability to resist zinc depletion with the metal chelator dipicolinic acid (DPA) [52], which has been proposed as a potential scaffold for MBL inhibitor development [56]. *E. coli* expressing NDM-4 and NDM-12 were also more resistant to ethylenediaminetetraacetic acid (EDTA) treatment compared to NDM-1 [53]. *E. coli* producing these NDM variants exhibit significantly increased minimum inhibitory concentrations (MICs) for penicillin, cephalosporin, and carbapenem antibiotics when tested under zinc stress, compared to NDM-1 [55]. Beyond NDM, VIM-2 variants (e.g. VIM-20 and VIM-28) have also demonstrated reduced susceptibility to zinc deprivation [57].

In contrast to NDM-1, the evolutionary trajectory of IMP enzymes has tended toward increased catalytic efficiency rather than a greater affinity for zinc. An extensive study revealed that bacteria producing IMP variants harboring S262G or V67F substitutions exhibited increased resistance to carbapenem antibiotics while sacrificing resistance to ampicillin [58]. However, none of the substitutions in these IMP variants conferred an advantage under zinc limitation. This may be because IMP-1 is less susceptible to zinc deprivation when compared to NDM-1 [58].

VIM enzymes have also acquired amino acid substitutions that alter their enzymatic properties. In contrast to many IMP- and NDM-type enzymes, some VIM variants exhibit increased hydrolytic activity against cephalosporins or cephems rather than carbapenems. For example, *E. coli* expressing VIM-1, -11, -23, -24, and -54 exhibited significantly elevated MICs for ceftazidime and cefepime compared to *E. coli* producing VIM-2 and VIM-4, often at the cost of reduced resistance to carbapenems [59]. Another study reported that VIM-24 exhibited 6- and 10-fold higher rates of ceftazidime and cefepime turnover, respectively, compared to VIM-2 [60].

The distinct evolutionary trajectories of the different MBL subtypes (e.g. NDM, VIM, and IMP) demonstrate the complexity of these enzymes. This poses a significant challenge in terms of addressing the heterogeneous nature of AMR resulting from the production of these enzymes. In the constant arms race against antibiotic-resistant bacteria, further research investigating the evolution of MBLs will help characterize selective pressures driving β-lactam resistance. For example, knowing how these enzymes can evolve to function more effectively under zinc limitation will help to inform on therapeutic development, particularly concerning de-prioritizing certain MBL inhibitor mechanisms (e.g. metal chelator-based inhibitors).

6.3 Clinical Impact of MBLs

6.3.1 Mechanisms of Dissemination

Globalization of travel has contributed to the widespread dissemination of AMR, posing a significant threat to public health. The emergence of MDR and pan-drug resistant (PDR) pathogens across different geographical hotspots demonstrates the dangerous transmissibility of antibiotic resistance. Among the most concerning threats, the spread of MBL-producing pathogens has been recognized by several public health agencies as a priority concern [61, 62]. MBL-encoding genes are harbored by several ESKAPE pathogens (e.g. *K. pneumoniae, A. baumannii,*

P. aeruginosa, and *Enterobacter* spp.), a group of organisms for which novel therapeutic strategies are urgently needed [63]. MBL production is also widespread in other pathogens of global significance, including *E. coli* and *Stenotrophomonas maltophilia* [64, 65].

The rapid spread of MBLs among bacterial pathogens can be attributed to the horizontal transfer of MBL-encoding genes via mobile genetic elements such as plasmids and transposons, and these genes are often incorporated into bacterial DNA in gene cassettes present in integrons. Plasmids harboring MBL genes frequently carry other resistance genes encoding resistance to multiple classes of antibiotics, contributing to the MDR phenotypes commonly associated with MBL-producing bacteria [66, 67]. Additionally, transposons and integrons facilitate the mobilization of MBL genes, enhancing their spread both within and between bacterial species, thereby increasing the dissemination of these genes [68–72]. Outer membrane vesicles (OMVs) may also play a role in the horizontal transfer of β-lactamase-encoding genes among Gram-negative bacteria [73–75].

6.3.2 Global Prevalence and Geographic Distribution

Among MBLs, the NDM, IMP, and VIM families are the most prevalent. The first report of NDM-1 was from a *K. pneumoniae* isolate described in 2008 [76]. In the years following the initial characterization of NDM-1, this enzyme and its variants have been widely reported in a variety of bacterial species, including *P. aeruginosa* and *E. coli*, throughout Asia, the Americas, Europe, and Africa [77]. A 2020 review indicated that the Asian continent has the highest prevalence of NDM-1-producing isolates, accounting for over half of the NDM-1 global reported cases from 2010 to 2019 [78]. The number of cases is particularly high in India and China, with India being the country where NDM-1 was first identified [76]. In the Americas, NDM-1-producing isolates account for approximately 11%, with the primary reservoir being Brazil [79].

In India, NDM-1-producing Enterobacterales have been widely detected in water sources, including tap water and seepage water in urban areas. Notably, several species not typically associated with NDM-1 production, such as *Shigella boydii* and *Vibrio cholerae,* have been found to harbor this enzyme, suggesting the potential for broad environmental dissemination [80]. Outside of India, NDM variants have also been reported in other Asian countries such as Pakistan [81, 82] and Hong Kong, with their occurrence often linked to travel [83].

Europe has also seen an increase in the prevalence of NDM enzymes. In Germany, *A. baumannii* isolates harboring NDM family enzymes have been increasingly reported, particularly from clinical settings involving blood cultures, skin infections, and urinary tract infections [84]. In 2022, researchers in Portugal reported an outbreak of NDM-1-producing *K. pneumoniae*, highlighting a novel plasmid backbone carrying the gene for this enzyme, further complicating control measures [85]. In the United Kingdom, NDM-producing bacteria have been predominantly isolated from urine samples and blood cultures that test positive for *Klebsiella* spp. and *E. coli* [86, 87].

A notable challenge in controlling the spread of NDM genes lies in their association with highly mobile plasmids that commonly carry additional resistance genes. Plasmids such as IncF, IncX3, and IncA/C are known for their broad host range and stability, facilitating the horizontal transfer of resistance genes across species and geographical regions. NDM-encoding plasmids have been observed to carry genes conferring resistance to polymyxins (such as *mcr-1*) [88, 89], aminoglycosides (including *rmtB* and *aacA4*) [90, 91], and macrolides (such as *msr(E)* and *mph(E)*) [92, 93]. Additionally, the presence of NDM-1 and NDM-5 genes is frequently associated with *sul1* genes that confer resistance to sulfonamides, further limiting therapeutic options [92].

IMP-1, the first enzyme of the IMP family, was initially discovered in 1988 from a *Serratia marcescens* isolate in Japan [94, 95]. Almost 10 years later, IMP-2 was identified in an *A. baumannii* isolate collected in Italy in 1997 [96]. Since then, the dissemination of IMP genes has been documented in over 24 countries, including significant reports from Asian countries such as China [97–99] and Singapore [100], as well as European nations like Italy [101, 102], Austria [103], and France [104]. In the Americas, the presence of IMP-producing strains has been reported in the United States [105], Canada [106], Brazil [107, 108], and Mexico [109]. In Canada, the first MBL to be identified was IMP-7, which was found in a *P. aeruginosa* isolate [110].

IMP enzymes have been detected in more than 26 different species of Gram-negative bacilli, with notable prevalence in *P. aeruginosa, E. coli, K. pneumoniae*, and *Enterobacter cloacae*. Reports have also noted the presence of IMP-19 in less typical species, such as *Aeromonas caviae* [104] and *Citrobacter youngae* [98]. These enzymes are predominantly carried by class 1 integrons, which are commonly found in both pathogenic and commensal Enterobacterales species [111–113]. The presence of IMP genes is frequently associated with co-resistance to other antibiotics, particularly aminoglycosides [114, 115].

The VIM family of enzymes was first identified in Italy in 1999 with the discovery of VIM-1 [116]. VIM enzymes have since become widespread throughout Europe, with Greece experiencing a great increase in *K. pneumoniae* hospital isolates that produce VIM enzymes, increasing from 1% to 20% within a five-year span [117]. VIM enzymes have been reported in numerous other European countries, including Spain [118, 119], Italy [120, 121], Hungary [122, 123], and France [124]. Initially, these enzymes were most frequently associated with *Pseudomonas* species [125], but recent reports document their spread to Enterobacterales, including *Klebsiella* spp. and *E. coli*. Like IMP, VIM genes are often located on class 1 integrons, frequently embedded within transposons, which facilitate their mobility and spread [116, 126–128]. The structural diversity of these integrons contributes to the broad dissemination of VIM enzymes and their frequent co-localization with other resistance genes, such as those conferring resistance to aminoglycosides (e.g. *aacA7*) and fosfomycin in *K. pneumoniae* [129].

SPM-1, another class B1 MBL, was first reported in Brazil in 2001 in a *P. aeruginosa* strain, and has since been detected in Europe in travel-related cases [130, 131]. In 2004, reports from Germany described the discovery of a new MBL, GIM-1, also in *P. aeruginosa* [132]. Similar to other MBLs, the GIM-1 gene was observed on a class 1 integron with aminoglycoside resistance genes, highlighting the complex genetic environments that facilitate the spread of these resistance mechanisms [125].

6.3.3 Current Treatment Options and Clinical Impact of MBL-Producing Pathogens

The treatment options for infections caused by MBL-producing pathogens are severely limited, largely due to the frequent co-occurrence of MBL genes with other antibiotic resistance genes. Currently, and in spite of their known nephrotoxicity and neurotoxicity, polymyxins such as colistin remain one of the only monotherapies available for the treatment of these infections, including those caused by *P. aeruginosa* [133, 134]. However, the efficacy of the polymyxins has been increasingly diminished by the emergence of colistin-resistant strains of *K. pneumoniae* and naturally resistant bacteria such as *Proteus* spp. and *Providencia* spp. [135].

Aztreonam (AZT), a monobactam β-lactam antibiotic resistant to hydrolysis by MBLs, is another treatment option, although its effectiveness is limited by the presence of other resistance mechanisms including SBL production [136]. Recently, the combination therapy of AZT with AVI has been proposed for the treatment of infections caused by MBL-producing pathogens; this novel combination will be covered in more detail in Section 7.4, which reviews recent advances in the development of therapeutics for infections caused by MBL-producing bacteria. Other therapeutic options include fosfomycin, which has shown efficacy against *E. coli* but is less effective against *Pseudomonas* spp. and often must be combined with other agents to mitigate resistance concerns [137, 138]. Tigecycline, although not effective against *P. aeruginosa*, has been used to treat infections caused by VIM-1-producing *K. pneumoniae* and other Enterobacterales [139–141].

Combination therapy has proven to be an effective approach for managing infections caused by MBL-producing bacteria. Carbapenems, while generally ineffective as monotherapy due to MBL-mediated resistance, have demonstrated some efficacy when used in combination with other antibiotics. For instance, the combination of imipenem and colistin has been associated with reduced mortality rates in patients with MBL-positive infections treated in clinical settings [142]. Combinations containing other β-lactams such as aztreonam-colistin-piperacillin–tazobactam and colistin-piperacillin–tazobactam have given positive outcomes in hospitalized patients infected with MBL-producing organisms [143].

The clinical impact of infections caused by MBL-producing pathogens is acute and complex, leading to markedly high morbidity and mortality. Infections caused by MBL-producing *P. aeruginosa* are particularly concerning, as they are associated with significantly higher mortality rates compared to infections caused by *P. aeruginosa* that do not produce MBLs [144, 145]. Patients infected with MBL-producing *P. aeruginosa* may experience a faster onset of infection and a more rapid progression of disease [146].

A comprehensive study conducted in Italy involving 343 patients infected with MBL-producing Enterobacterales revealed that patients who received a combination therapy of ceftazidime-avibactam (CAZ-AVI) and AZT had a reduced 30-day mortality rate compared to those treated with colistin [147]. A separate study conducted in Poland on 23 patients with nosocomial infections caused by NDM-1-producing *K. pneumoniae* reported 19 patients achieved clinical eradication of the pathogen following treatment with CAZ-AVI in combination with AZT [148]. More recently, a study focused on bloodstream infections with NDM-1-producing Enterobacterales found an alarmingly high 30-day mortality rate of 42.5% [149]. The reduced mortality in surviving patients was likely attributable to the combination therapy of CAZ-AVI and AZT.

Beyond the observed mortality rates, studies have identified key risk factors associated with infections caused by MBL-producing pathogens. These risk factors include prior exposure to β-lactams or fluoroquinolones, as well as prolonged stays in intensive care units and travel to endemic regions [144, 150–152]. This highlights the importance of antibiotic stewardship and strict infection control measures in healthcare settings.

Overall, the management of infections caused by MBL-producing pathogens is challenging due to their frequent resistance against multiple different classes of antibiotics. The development of new treatment regimens, particularly combination therapies, offers hope for better clinical outcomes. However, the high mortality rates associated with these infections highlight the urgent and unmet need for continued research and development of effective therapeutic strategies to combat MBL-producing pathogens.

6.3.4 Clinical Detection of MBL-Producing Bacteria

Phenotypic and genotypic tests are commonly employed to detect MBL-producing bacteria. Phenotypic methods directly or indirectly measure the production of MBL enzymes or their activity, while molecular techniques are based on the direct identification of resistance genes. Nonetheless, the detection of MBLs in healthcare settings presents substantial challenges. The sequence diversity of the MBLs complicates the development of universal molecular diagnostic tests using methods such as polymerase chain reaction (PCR). Additionally, MBLs often coexist with other β-lactamases, including extended-spectrum β-lactamases (ESBLs), complicating phenotypic detection methods. Overlapping substrate profiles between these different β-lactamases can lead to ambiguous test results that mask the presence of MBLs, making accurate identification more difficult.

Phenotypic methods are generally more accessible and cost-effective than molecular approaches. One such method involves a disk diffusion technique where two ceftazidime disks are placed on an agar plate along with a disk containing 2-mercaptopropionic acid (2-MPA), an MBL inhibitor. The impact of 2-MPA on the inhibition zones around the ceftazidime disks is indicative of MBL production. The modified Hodge test (MHT), which can detect both SBL and MBL carbapenemases, depends on the inactivation of the carbapenem imipenem by a carbapenemase-producing strain. This antibiotic inactivation allows a susceptible indicator strain to grow in proximity to a carbapenem-containing disk where the agar plate has been streaked with the organism being tested for carbapenemase production. However, some studies have obtained sensitivity values below 50% for the MHT when applied to the detection of NDM-producing isolates [153, 154].

In 2015, the carbapenem inactivation method (CIM) was introduced for the clinical detection of carbapenemase-producing organisms [155]. Later, the modified carbapenem inactivation method (mCIM) was developed, improving the sensitivity of detection of oxacillinase-48 (OXA-48)-type carbapenemases [156]. The mCIM involves incubating a disk containing the carbapenem meropenem in a suspension of test bacteria for a period of four hours. The disk is then transferred to an agar plate inoculated with a meropenem-susceptible *E. coli* strain. After overnight incubation, the test bacteria are revealed to be carbapenemase-producers if no zone of inhibition is observed around the meropenem disk. Subsequently, the eCIM (EDTA-modified mCIM) was introduced, which uses the metal-chelator EDTA to specifically inhibit MBL activity and allows SBLs and MBLs to be distinguished [157, 158]. The Clinical and Laboratory Standards Institute (CLSI) has endorsed the use of the mCIM in combination with eCIM for identifying MBL-producing Enterobacterales [159].

The biochemical CARBA-NP assay is also commonly employed for the detection of carbapenemase-producing organisms [160]. This test monitors the hydrolysis of the carbapenem imipenem by a bacterial lysate, as visualized using the pH indicator phenol red. A commercialized rapid test kit, RAPIDEC-CARBA-NP, is also available for increased ease of use [161, 162]. While the commercially available RAPIDEC-CARBA-NP test does not distinguish between SBLs and MBLs, modifications of the CARBA-NP assay employing EDTA have been reported which allow MBLs to be identified [163].

PCR is the gold standard genotypic method for the detection of MBLs. It offers a sensitivity and specificity of up to 100% by directly detecting genes encoding MBLs such as VIM, IMP, and NDM [164–166]. However, these methods are limited to identifying known genetic targets and may fail to detect novel or less common MBL variants. The high cost and the need for specialized equipment and training further restrict the widespread adoption of these techniques in lower-resource settings.

6.4 Recent Advances in the Development of Therapeutics to Target MBL-Producing Pathogens

6.4.1 β-Lactamase Inhibitors

Although β-lactam-β-lactamase inhibitor combinations exhibit potent activity against SBLs, the β-lactamase inhibitors that are currently available for clinical use do not target MBLs. Thus, there is a dire unmet need for new inhibitors that are effective against MBLs. In recent years, there have been extensive efforts made to discover and develop inhibitors targeting these enzymes. Several extensive reviews have been published describing ongoing efforts to develop MBL inhibitors [167–171]. In this part of the chapter, we will focus on some of the most promising clinical and pre-clinical candidates, and highlight novel mechanisms and chemical scaffolds for MBL inhibition. We will also further expand on potential therapeutic options for treating infections caused by MBL-producing pathogens that do not directly depend on MBL inhibitors.

6.4.2 MBL Inhibitors in Clinical Development

6.4.2.1 Taniborbactam

Taniborbactam (TAN) (Figure 6.4) is a cyclic boronate in development by Venatorx Pharmaceuticals. TAN was the first inhibitor to be reported that exhibits potent inhibitory activity against all four classes of β-lactamases, including MBLs such as VIM-2 and NDM-1 [172]. Crystallographic studies with TAN and VIM-2 have revealed that the boron atom in the drug can react with the hydroxide ion bridging the two active site zinc ions [173]. The resulting complex interacts with Zn1 and

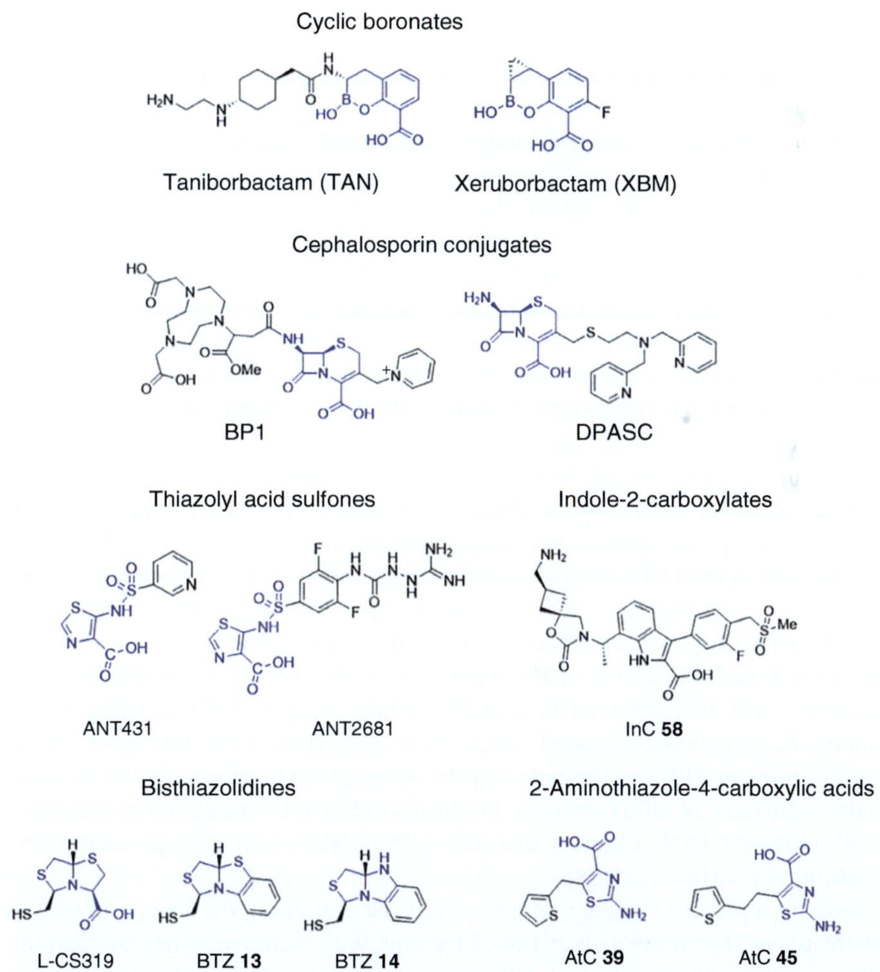

Figure 6.4 Chemical structures of the clinical and pre-clinical inhibitors discussed in this chapter, grouped according to their chemical scaffold.

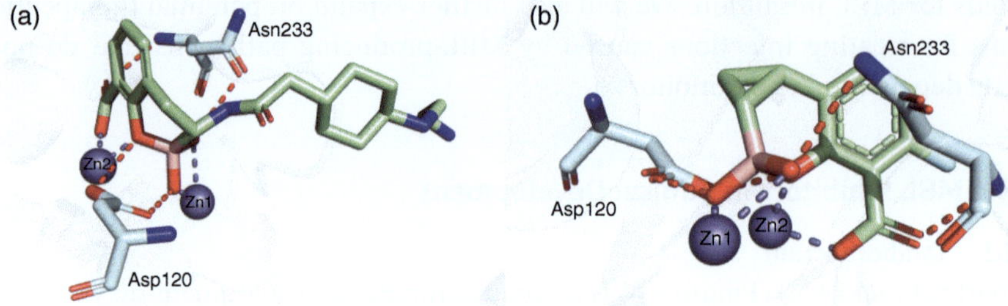

Figure 6.5 Binding mechanism of cyclic boronate inhibitors to VIM-2. VIM-2 in complex with (a) taniborbactam (TAN) and (b) xeruborbactam (XBM). Contacts between the inhibitors and surrounding amino acid residues are represented by red dashes, whereas contacts between the inhibitors and the zinc ions are represented by purple dashes. The structural diagrams were generated in PyMOL using datasets available in the RCSB Protein Data Bank (PDB IDs = 6SP7, 6VP1) *Source:* Ref. [172, 174].

the VIM-2 active site residues Asn233 and Asp120 (Figure 6.5a). Additionally, the carboxylate and oxygen atom of the cyclic oxaborinate group of TAN interacts with Zn2, mimicking the tetrahedral intermediate formed during β-lactam hydrolysis by class B1 MBLs.

Several studies have investigated the *in vitro* efficacy of cefepime-taniborbactam (FTB) against MBL-producing bacteria. Gerges et al. recently tested this drug combination against a collection of Enterobacterales isolates from blood cultures; out of 270 isolates, 98.9% demonstrated susceptibility to FTB [175]. Another study indicated that 97.6% of Enterobacterales isolates were susceptible to FTB, although the efficacy was lower against *Pseudomonas* spp. (with a susceptibility of just 67.1%) [176]. The large-scale Global Evaluation of Antimicrobial Resistance via Surveillance (GEARS) program investigated the efficacy of FTB against 13,731 Enterobacterales and 4619 *P. aeruginosa* isolates across 56 countries [177]. Among the tested library, 86.4% (203/235) of MBL-positive Enterobacterales and 66.5% of *P. aeruginosa* isolates were susceptible to FTB.

Resistance against FTB was associated with mutations to *ftsI* (the gene encoding for PBP3), production of NDM-5 in combination with OXA-181 or CTX-M-15, disruptions in the genes encoding for the porins OmpK35 (or OmpF) and OmpK35 (or OmpC), and alterations in the regulation of the AcrAB efflux system [177]. Resistance was also observed in Enterobacterales carrying IMP-encoding genes. Among *P. aeruginosa*, elevated MICs were associated with IMP production, modifications to PBP3 or the porin OprD, overexpression of *ampC,* and changes to the regulation of efflux systems. Production of NDM-9 also confers resistance to inhibition by TAN, a variant that differs from NDM-1 by a single amino acid substitution (Glu149Lys) [178].

Recently, a phase 3 clinical trial was completed examining the efficacy of FTB in the treatment of complex urinary tract infections, with meropenem as a comparator. FTB was superior to meropenem with regard to clinical and microbiological success (composite success = 70.6% vs 58%, respectively) [179]. Following these positive results, FTB was submitted for Federal Drug Administration (FDA) approval in August 2023. A press release from Venatorx issued in February 2024 indicated the new drug application was rejected by the FDA, citing the need for further data related to chemistry manufacturing and controls [180]. However, the FDA did not request further clinical testing demonstrating safety or efficacy.

6.4.2.2 Xeruborbactam (QPX7728)

Xeruborbactam (XBM) (Figure 6.4), a cyclic boronate in clinical development by Qpex pharmaceuticals, displays inhibitory activity against all four Ambler classes of β-lactamases. This compound potently inhibits class A and C ESBLs and class A and D carbapenemases [181]. XBM also exhibits strong inhibitory potency against several MBLs, with IC_{50} values in the nanomolar range [181]. X-ray crystallographic studies with VIM-2 indicate that XBM has a similar binding mode to TAN (Figure 6.5b) [174].

The combination of meropenem-XBM exhibited potent activity against Enterobacterales, *P. aeruginosa* and *A. baumanii* isolates, with meropenem MICs reduced to below the CLSI susceptibility breakpoint [174]. More recently, XBM was evaluated in comparison with meropenem, AZT, piperacillin, ceftolozane, or cefepime against a panel of MBL-producing *P. aeruginosa* isolates [182]. The most effective combination was piperacillin-XBM, with 72.1% of 61 isolates testing as susceptible. Ceftolozane-XBM and meropenem-XBM possessed lower levels of efficacy, and 27.9% and 31.1% of strains were susceptible to these combinations, respectively.

The potential impact of resistance mechanisms in Enterobacterales, *P. aeruginosa,* and *A. baumannii* on the potency of XBM has also been investigated [183]. Disruption of *ompK36* in an isogenic *Klebsiella pneumoniae* carbapenemase (KPC)-3-producing *K. pneumoniae* strain reduced the potency of XBM in combination with meropenem by 8–16-fold, while disruption of *ompK35* did not have any impact. Additionally, an isolate producing OmpK36 with modifications to the L3 loop (which acts to constrict the channel) exhibited reduced susceptibility to meropenem-XBM. Inactivation of the *oprD* porin-encoding gene in *P. aeruginosa* did not impact inhibitor potency, and the presence of efflux systems in *P. aeruginosa* and *A. baumannii* had minimal impact, causing just a twofold increase in MIC.

XBM completed a phase 1 clinical trial in 2022, which evaluated the safety profile of orally administered prodrug in 48 healthy subjects [184]. The drug exhibited high oral bioavailability (90–100%) and was well tolerated in all administered doses (100–1000 mg). Another phase 1 trial set to conclude at the end of 2024 is evaluating the safety and pharmacokinetics of ceftibuten in combination with an oral prodrug of XBM.

6.4.3 Recent Advances in Pre-Clinical MBL Inhibitor Development

A widely investigated strategy for MBL inhibition involves the development of compounds that either bind to zinc in the MBL active site, or act as chelators that strip the zinc away from the enzyme [56, 185–195]. However, there are several key limitations associated with this general approach. MBLs such as NDM are evolving to better withstand zinc deprivation at the site of infection, with several clinical variants exhibiting either increased affinity for zinc or increased stability under zinc limitation [52, 53, 55]. These NDM variants were observed to have reduced susceptibility to inhibition by the zinc chelator DPA [52]. Thus, inhibitors that act via zinc binding or stripping mechanisms should be evaluated against such variants during drug development campaigns.

A second limitation with these types of inhibitors is the risk of off-target effects due to interactions with human metalloenzymes [196]. Specifically, the αβ/βα fold characteristic of bacterial MBLs is also present in human MBL-fold proteins involved in numerous cellular processes such as nucleic acid metabolism and detoxification of aldehydes [197]. Efforts have been made to address this limitation by developing conjugates in which metal chelators are covalently attached to other scaffolds. Peters et al. reported BP1 (Figure 6.4), a cephalosporin-zinc chelator conjugate that restored the activity of meropenem against bacterial isolates producing an array of MBLs including NDM-1, NDM-4, IMP-1, IMP-8, and VIM-1 [198]. Additionally, BP1 did not inhibit the activity of the human metalloprotein glyoxalase II at the concentrations tested, while metal chelators EDTA and tetrakis-(2-pyridylmethyl) ethylenediamine (TPEN) significantly reduced glyoxalase II activity. The combination of meropenem and BP1 was shown to be effective in a murine thigh infection model, reducing the number of viable NDM-producing *K. pneumoniae* by $3\log_{10}$ colony forming units (CFUs). Another study by Tian et al. reported the development of cephalosporin-tripodalamine conjugate (DPASC) (Figure 6.4), a cephalosporin conjugate of *N*-(mercaptoethyl)-di-(2-pyridylmethyl)amine (DPASH) in which the cephalosporin moiety reduces the metal-binding capacity of the compound, reducing its toxicity [199]. DPASC exhibited potent inhibition of NDM-1 and VIM-2, with IC_{50} values of 91 and 67 nM, respectively. Microbiological testing with a panel of MBL-producing clinical isolates indicated that DPASC was able to reduce the MIC of meropenem by up to 512-fold, with all isolates tested susceptible to the combination. DPASC did not show significant activity against the human metalloenzyme alcohol dehydrogenase at the concentrations tested, while the unconjugated DPASH had an IC_{50} of 20 μM. Additionally, DPASC was not toxic to human hepatoma HepG2 cells, even though DPASH exhibited significant toxicity (50% of lethal dose [LD_{50}] = 2 μg/mL).

Leiris et al. reported a promising group of thiazolyl acid sulfone MBL inhibitors derived from a pyridine-2-carboxylic acid scaffold [200–202]. ANT431 (Figure 6.4) was identified as a promising hit, exhibiting potent inhibition of NDM-1 and VIM-2 with IC_{50} values of 2.6 and 6.7 μM, respectively. However, this compound exhibited less potency against IMP-1 (IC_{50} = 54 μM) and VIM-1 (IC_{50} > 200 μM). X-ray crystallographic studies with VIM-2 indicate that this compound fits between Phe61 and Tyr66 of the enzyme active site, with its carboxylate group forming a salt bridge with the positively charged side chain of Arg228 (Figure 6.6). The lack of inhibition observed for VIM-1 compared to VIM-2 was proposed to result from the substitution of Arg228 in VIM-2 with serine in VIM-1. Follow-up microbiological testing on ANT431 in combination with meropenem indicated that this

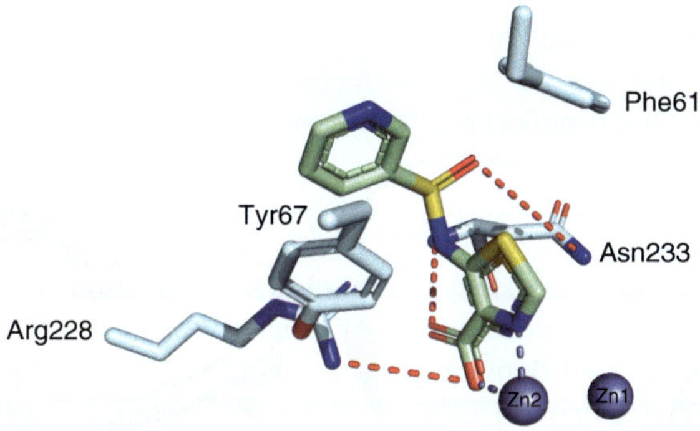

Figure 6.6 Binding mechanism of ANT431 to VIM-2. Contacts between the inhibitors and surrounding amino acid residues are represented by red dashes, whereas contacts between the inhibitor and the zinc ions are represented by purple dashes. The interaction diagram was generated in PyMOL with a dataset from the RCSB Protein Data Bank (PDB ID = 6HF5) *Source:* Adapted from [200].

inhibitor was able to reduce the MIC of meropenem below the susceptibility limit (European Committee on Antimicrobial Susceptibility Testing [EUCAST] breakpoint of 2 μg/mL) in 72% of the 94 VIM- and NDM-producing clinical Enterobacterales isolates tested [201]. The combination of meropenem-ANT431 also showed promise in an animal study employing a murine infection model with NDM-1-producing *E. coli* [201].

Using the structure of ANT431 as a starting point, further structure–activity relationship (SAR) studies led to the development of the pre-clinical lead candidate, ANT2681 [202]. ANT2681 (Figure 6.4) exhibits an expanded spectrum of inhibition against MBLs compared to ANT431, with activity against IMP, VIM, and NDM enzymes. Zalacain et al. evaluated the efficacy of meropenem-ANT2681 against a panel of 1687 MBL-producing Enterobacterales isolates, demonstrating its efficacy against 92.5% of NDM producers, 74.7% of VIM producers, and 85.7% of IMP producers [203]. Not surprisingly, this combination was significantly less effective against strains co-producing MBLs and KPC or OXA-type SBL carbapenemases, inhibiting growth of just 21.2% of these isolates. Interestingly, meropenem-ANT2861 exhibited weaker activity against isolates producing NDM-9, a variant that has also been associated with resistance to cefepime-taniborbactam as described above.

Other carboxylate-containing scaffolds have also shown promise for MBL inhibition. Brem et al. reported the development of indole-2-carboxylates (InCs) with potent activity against NDM-1, IMP-1, and VIM-2 [204]. Structural analyses revealed that the InCs can mimic β-lactam substrate binding and do not rely on displacement of zinc from the MBL active site. Lead optimization resulted in the development of compound InC **58** (Figure 6.4), which was demonstrated to successfully restore susceptibility to meropenem among a panel of clinical Enterobacterales isolates.

The combination of meropenem-InC **58** was also evaluated *in vivo* in murine peritoneum/septicemia and thigh infection models with four different bacterial strains; of these strains, one was an MBL-producer (positive for NDM-7). Meropenem-InC **58** treatment (30/30 mg/kg) resulted in >3$\log_{10}$ reduction in the number of viable bacterial cells in the peritoneal model, but was less effective in the thigh infection model (30/30 mg/kg treatment yielded less than 1$\log_{10}$ reduction in viable bacteria).

Bisthiazolidine (BTZ) scaffolds have also shown promise as substrate-mimicking MBL inhibitors. The bicyclic ring structure in the BTZs allows them to act as β-lactam mimics, with carboxylate and thiol groups contributing to zinc binding [205]. The first report of BTZs (compound LCS319, Figure 6.4) acting as MBL inhibitors indicates these compounds can inhibit NDM-1 and restore the activity of imipenem against NDM-1-producing *K. pneumoniae, A. baumannii,* and *Providencia rettgeri* [205]. This class of compounds has been expanded in further work that suggests that BTZs can function as pan-MBL inhibitors [206, 207]. Crystallographic studies with IMP-1 and L1 confirm that BTZ binding results in displacement of the zinc-bridging water molecule in the MBL active site, involving interactions between the BTZ carboxylate group and active site residues Lys224 in IMP-1 and Ser223 in L1 [206]. Additionally, BTZs can make further contact with the L1 and L3 loops of these MBLs. Work by Villamil et al. revealed that replacement of the BTZ carboxylate group with aromatic groups increased the potency of inhibition [207]. This yielded compounds BTZ **13** and BTZ **14** (Figure 6.4) that exert low or sub-micromolar IC_{50} values against B1 (NDM-1, IMP-1, VIM-2), B2 (Sfh-1), and B3 (L1) enzymes. In microbiological testing, BTZ **13** and BTZ **14** restored susceptibility to meropenem and imipenem when tested against VIM and IMP-producing *K. pneumoniae.* Although the compounds were able to significantly reduce the MICs of imipenem and meropenem against NDM-producing isolates, none of the isolates tested exhibited MICs at or below the susceptibility breakpoint for these antibiotics. Nonetheless, BTZs hold promise as a scaffold for future MBL inhibitor development, providing that cellular efficacy can be further improved.

Recently, aminothiazole carboxylic acid scaffolds have also seen success as substrate-mimicking inhibitors. Yan et al. reported the development of 2-aminothiazole-4-carboxylic acids (AtCs) that inhibit MBLs by mimicking the binding of a carbapenem hydrolysis product [208]. After extensive SAR analyses with purified enzymes and follow-up microbiological testing with a subset of compounds, AtC **39** and AtC **45** (Figure 6.4) were identified as potential lead candidates. These compounds reduced the MICs of meropenem to or slightly above the susceptible breakpoint against NDM-, IMP-, and VIM-producing isolates. However, they were not effective against L1- or CphA-producing isolates. *In vivo* experiments employing a murine sepsis model infected with NDM-1-expressing *K. pneumoniae* indicated that the combination of meropenem + AtC **39** (and to a lesser extent, meropenem + AtC **45**) reduced bacterial loads in the kidney, spleen, and liver of infected mice compared to meropenem treatment alone. Both compounds were confirmed to be non-hemolytic and no toxicity was observed in mouse models.

6.4.4 New Clinical and Pre-Clinical Compounds to Overcome MBL-Mediated Resistance That Do Not Rely on Direct Inhibition

6.4.4.1 Aztreonam + Avibactam

The combination of aztreonam + avibactam (AZT-AVI) (Figure 6.7) is currently under clinical development by Pfizer for the treatment of infections caused by MBL-producing pathogens; the monobactam AZT is not efficiently degraded by MBLs, and AVI protects AZT against SBL-catalyzed hydrolysis. Some groups have also investigated the triple combination of AZT-AVI with the cephalosporin ceftazidime (CAZ). Marshall et al. initially tested this triple combination against 21 Enterobacterales isolates co-producing MBLs and SBLs; all isolates were resistant to CAZ-AVI, but the addition of AZT resulted in 17/21 isolates testing susceptible to the combination [209]. *In vivo* efficacy was also demonstrated in a neutropenic murine thigh infection model, where administration of 32/8 mg/kg CAZ-AVI + 32 mg/kg AZT resulted in a significant CFU reduction of an MBL-producing *K. pneumoniae* isolate, reducing viability by $3.79\log_{10}$ CFU compared 32/8 mg/kg CAZ-AVI treatment alone. A large-scale *in vitro* efficacy study employing 1192 carbapenem-resistant Enterobacterales indicated an overall susceptibility of 95.5% to CAZ-AVI + AZT [139]. The ATLAS Global Surveillance program tested the *in vitro* activity of the combination of AZT-AVI against 24,937 clinical isolates collected across 27 countries [210]. In broth microdilution assays, the growth of 99.8% of isolates was inhibited by AZT-AVI and just 61 of 24,937 strains exhibited MICs greater than 8 µg/mL when treated with this combination. Within the isolate library that was tested, 1610 were found to carry MBL-encoding genes; AZT-AVI successfully inhibited the growth of 100% of VIM- and IMP-producers, and 98.7% of NDM-producers.

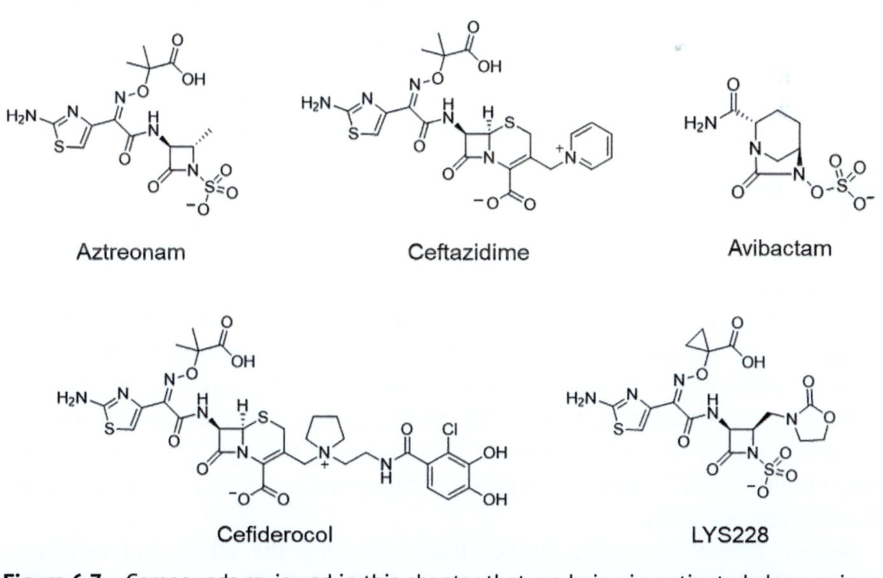

Figure 6.7 Compounds reviewed in this chapter that are being investigated alone or in combination for efficacy against MBL-producing pathogens, but that do not directly inhibit MBL activity.

The efficacy of the combination of CAZ-AVI + AZT has also been evaluated in several clinical studies. Falcone et al. compared the outcomes of 102 patients with bloodstream infections caused by MBL-producing Enterobacterales who were treated either with CAZ-AVI + ATM or other active antibiotic combinations [211]. The 30-day mortality rate among patients treated with CAZ-AVI + AZT (19.2%) was significantly lower than the mortality rates for comparator antibiotics (colistin, fosfomycin, tigecycline, meropenem, or gentamicin) alone and in different combinations (44%).

Recently, a phase 3 clinical trial examined the efficacy and safety of AZT-AVI for the treatment of complicated intra-abdominal infections (cIAI) and hospital-acquired infections (HAI) caused by Gram-negative bacteria (including MBL-producing organisms) [212]. A population of 422 patients were enrolled and randomized in the study, where they received treatment with either AZT-AVI or meropenem + colistin. Overall, 28-day all-cause mortality was reduced in the group that received AZT-AVI (1.9% and 10.8% for cIAI and HAI, respectively) compared to the group that received meropenem + colistin (2.9% and 19.4% for cIAI and HAI, respectively).

Although AZT-AVI provides a very promising alternative to the development of novel MBL inhibitors, resistance to this combination has already been reported. Sadek et al. evaluated 118 clinical *E. coli* isolates for susceptibility to AZT-AVI, finding that 19 isolates were characterized as resistant according to the EUCAST clinical breakpoint of 4 μg/mL [213]. Resistance was associated with the production of PBP3 variants bearing four-amino acid insertions (YRIN or YRIK) and the presence of plasmid-encoded cephalosporinase CMY-42. Several other studies have reported elevated MICs for AZT-AVI for isolates producing ESBLs and/or MBLs in combination with PBP3 insertions [214–217]. Additionally, there is evidence that some MBLs can slowly hydrolyze both AZT and AVI [218]. With extended clinical use of this combination, new MBLs could evolve that are better able to hydrolyze AZT and/or AVI. Thus, the future clinical utility of AZT-AVI could be impacted when treating infections caused by organisms possessing these resistance mechanisms.

6.4.4.2 Cefiderocol

Cefiderocol (Figure 6.7) is a cephalosporin-siderophore conjugate of particular interest, as it is poorly degraded by many KPC, NDM, IMP, VIM, and OXA-type carbapenemases [219, 220]. For instance, the catalytic efficiencies of VIM-2 and NDM-1 are 260- and threefold lower, respectively, for cefiderocol when compared to meropenem. A unique feature of this compound is the catechol moiety, which chelates iron and allows cefiderocol to be taken up into bacterial cells via iron transport systems [221]. Unlike typical β-lactam-based antibiotics, cefiderocol does not primarily enter bacterial cells through non-specific porins (e.g. OmpC, OmpF, OmpK35, OmpK36), limiting the impact of porin modifications on drug efficacy [222].

Several recent large-scale studies have evaluated the efficacy of cefiderocol against MBL-producing clinical isolates [223–226]. Five consecutive multinational studies (designated SIDERO-WT) tested cefiderocol against a total of 452 MBL-producing strains, observing that 91.5% of Enterobacterales had

MICs ≤4 μg/mL (CLSI susceptibility breakpoint for cefiderocol) and 67.5% of isolates had MICs ≤2 μg/mL (EUCAST susceptibility breakpoint) [223]. Cefiderocol was also highly effective against *P. aeruginosa* strains, with all isolates having MICs ≤4 μg/mL and 97.4% of strains having an MIC ≤2 μg/mL. However, the effectiveness of cefiderocol was significantly lower against MBL-producing *A. baumannii* strains, with only 60% or 44% of isolates having MICs ≤4 or 2 μg/mL, respectively. Another study examined the efficacy of cefiderocol compared to other antimicrobials against a collection of 806 carbapenem-resistant *P. aeruginosa* strains from the ERACE-PA surveillance program [224]. Cefiderocol was the most active agent, with 98% and 95% of isolates testing susceptible based on CLSI and EUCAST criteria; the next most active agents were amikacin and imipenem-relebactam, with 70% and 48% of isolates being susceptible to these treatments. A multicenter study in Spain tested cefiderocol against a collection of 232 MBL-producing strains in which 85.3% and 96.6% of isolates tested susceptible based on EUCAST and CLSI breakpoints [225]. Among resistant isolates, it was noted that 70.6% of isolates co-produced MBLs and ESBLs. Lower efficacy against VIM-1 and NDM-1-producing isolates was also noted, with 72.8% and 73.7% of these isolates being susceptible. Another study comparing cefiderocol to other antimicrobial agents against isolates collected from France and Belgium also noted lower efficacy of cefiderocol against NDM-producing Enterobacterales (48% susceptible, EUCAST criteria) and *Acinetobacter* spp. (30% susceptible, EUCAST criteria) [226]. Notably, several resistance mechanisms to cefiderocol have been reported, including mutations to the siderophore receptor gene *cirA* [227–230], production of KPC variants [231, 232], PBP3 modifications [229, 230], increased expression of NDM-5 [233] and production of AmpC variants [234, 235].

To evaluate the clinical efficacy of cefiderocol, the APEKS-NP and CREDIBLE-CR Phase 3 randomized controlled trials tested this drug for the treatment of infections caused by carbapenem-resistant pathogens [236, 237]. Results from the APEKS-NP trial indicate cefiderocol was non-inferior to a high-dose extended infusion of meropenem. All-cause mortality at day 14 was 12.4% for cefiderocol and 11.6% for meropenem. Findings from the CREDIBLE-CR trial concluded that cefiderocol had similar clinical and microbiological efficacy compared to best-available treatment options. In patients with pneumonia, clinical cure was achieved in 50% of patients with cefiderocol and 53% of patients in the best-available therapy group. For patients with sepsis or bloodstream infections, clinical cure rates were 43% for both treatment populations. Lastly, in the urinary tract infection group, the clinical cure rate was markedly higher for cefiderocol at 53% compared to 20% for the best-available therapy group. An observational retrospective study involving 124 patients compared the efficacy of cefiderocol vs. colistin for the treatment of carbapenem-resistant *Acinetobacter baumannii* infections, reporting that 30-day mortality was higher in patients who received colistin compared to cefiderocol (55.8% vs 34%) [238]. Several other smaller-scale reports on the real-world usage of cefiderocol have been published [239–242], and the drug is currently approved for clinical use in the United States and Europe for the treatment of infections caused by carbapenem-resistant Gram-negative pathogens.

6.4.4.3 LYS228

Currently, AZT is the only clinically used monobactam antibiotic. Reck et al. reported the development of the novel monobactam, LYS228 (Figure 6.7), which, unlike AZT, is resistant to hydrolysis by SBLs [243, 244]. *In vitro* microbiological testing of this compound against a panel of MDR Enterobacterales strains yielded MICs of ≤2 μg/mL for 95.9% of the 271 isolates tested [244]. Among the 33 MBL producers in the library, 84.8% of isolates had an MIC ≤2 μg/mL, and all isolates had MICs ≤16 μg/mL. Mechanism of action studies indicate that LYS228 primarily binds to PBP3 in *E. coli* and to a lesser extent PBP1a and 1b [245]. Notably, the susceptibility of *E. coli* American Type Culture Collection (ATCC) 25922 was reduced 256-fold after serial passaging in the presence of LYS228, with mutations occurring in *fstI* (the gene encoding PBP3), as well as several other genes (e.g. *baeR, acrD, envZ, sucB,* and *rfaI*). LYS228 was demonstrated to be effective *in vivo* in neutropenic thigh infection and pyelonephritis models with *K. pneumoniae* producing NDM-1 or KPC-2 [246]. LYS228 was acquired by Boston Pharmaceuticals (re-branding it to BOS-228) and it is currently in clinical testing.

6.5 Concluding Remarks

MBL-producing organisms pose a dire threat to public health on a global scale due to the widespread dissemination of MBL genes among bacterial pathogens. The diversity of MBL structures and evolutionary trajectories will continue to pose a major challenge as these enzymes evolve to function more efficiently under nutrient-limiting conditions at the site of infection, to degrade a broader spectrum of β-lactam antibiotics, and to become less susceptible to inhibitors currently in the clinical and pre-clinical pipelines. Although novel options such as FTB, cefiderocol, and CAZ-AVI + AZT show promise for the treatment of infections caused by MBL-producing bacteria, resistance is already emerging to these drug combinations. Thus, research efforts should continue to advance our understanding of the complex and expanding evolutionary landscape of this class of enzymes and prioritize the identification of novel inhibition mechanisms to drive therapeutic development. As MBL-producing pathogens increase in prevalence, the development of new diagnostics should also continue, specifically with regard to easily implementable phenotypic assays which can distinguish between SBLs and MBLs. With promising treatments entering clinical use, the rapid identification of MBL-producing pathogens is critical to ensure that critically ill patients receive appropriate treatment. Moving forward, addressing β-lactam resistance caused by MBLs will require international multidisciplinary efforts led by pharmaceutical, clinical, and academic research laboratories.

References

1 Bush, K. and Bradford, P.A. (2016). β-Lactams and β-lactamase inhibitors: an overview. *Cold Spring Harbor Perspectives in Medicine* 6 (8): a025247.

2 Mora-Ochomogo, M. and Lohans, C.T. (2021). β-Lactam antibiotic targets and resistance mechanisms: from covalent inhibitors to substrates. *RSC Medicinal Chemistry* 12 (10): 1623–1639.

3 Balsalobre, L., Blanco, A., and Alarcón, T. (2019). Beta-lactams. In: *Antibiotic Drug Resistance* (ed. J.-L. Capelo-Martínez and G. Igrejas), 57–72. Hoboken, NJ, USA: Wiley.

4 Lima, L.M., Silva, B.N.M.D., Barbosa, G., and Barreiro, E.J. (2020). β-Lactam antibiotics: an overview from a medicinal chemistry perspective. *European Journal of Medicinal Chemistry* 208: 112829.

5 Tooke, C.L., Hinchliffe, P., Bragginton, E.C. et al. (2019). β-Lactamases and β-lactamase inhibitors in the 21st century. *Journal of Molecular Biology* 431 (18): 3472–3500.

6 Perry, C.M. and Markham, A. (1999). Piperacillin/Tazobactam: an updated review of its use in the treatment of bacterial infections. *Drugs* 57 (5): 805–843.

7 Morán-Díaz, J.R., Jiménez-Vázquez, H.A., Gómez-Pliego, R. et al. (2019). Correlation study of antibacterial activity and spectrum of Penicillins through a structure-activity relationship analysis. *Medicinal Chemistry Research* 28 (9): 1529–1546.

8 Miller, E.L. (2002). The penicillins: a review and update. *Journal of Midwifery and Women's Health* 47 (6): 426–434.

9 Klein, N.C. and Cunha, B.A. (1995). Third-generation cephalosporins. *The Medical Clinics of North America* 79 (4): 705–719.

10 Zhanel, G.G., Sniezek, G., Schweizer, F. et al. (2009). Ceftaroline: a novel broad-spectrum cephalosporin with activity against methicillin-resistant *Staphylococcus aureus*. *Drugs* 69 (7): 809–831.

11 Papp-Wallace, K.M., Endimiani, A., Taracila, M.A., and Bonomo, R.A. (2011). Carbapenems: past, present, and future. *Antimicrobial Agents and Chemotherapy* 55 (11): 4943–4960.

12 El-Gamal, M.I., Brahim, I., Hisham, N. et al. (2017). Recent updates of carbapenem antibiotics. *European Journal of Medicinal Chemistry* 131: 185–195.

13 Bush, K. and Jacoby, G.A. (2010). Updated functional classification of β-lactamases. *Antimicrobial Agents and Chemotherapy* 54 (3): 969–976.

14 Bush, K. (2018). Past and present perspectives on β-lactamases. *Antimicrobial Agents and Chemotherapy* 62 (10): e01076–e01018.

15 Sawai, T., Mitsuhashi, S., and Yamagishi, S. (1968). Drug resistance of enteric bacteria: XIV. Comparison of β-lactamases in gram-negative rod bacteria resistant to α-aminobenzylpenicillin. *Japanese Journal of Microbiology* 12 (4): 423–434.

16 Jack, G.W. and Richmond, M.H. (1970). Comparative amino acid contents of purified β-lactamases from enteric bacteria. *FEBS Letters* 12 (1): 30–32.

17 Ambler, R.P., Baddiley, J., and Abraham, E.P. (1980). The structure of β-lactamases. *Philosophical Transactions of the Royal Society of London*. Series B, Biological Sciences 289 (1036): 321–331.

18 Massova, I. and Mobashery, S. (1998). Kinship and diversification of bacterial penicillin-binding proteins and β-lactamases. *Antimicrobial Agents and Chemotherapy* 42: 17.

19 Hermann, J.C., Hensen, C., Ridder, L. et al. (2005). Mechanisms of antibiotic resistance: QM/MM modeling of the acylation reaction of a class A β-lactamase with benzylpenicillin. *Journal of the American Chemical Society* 127 (12): 4454–4465.

20 Saves, I., Burlet-Schiltz, O., Maveyraud, L. et al. (1995). Mass spectral kinetic study of acylation and deacylation during the hydrolysis of penicillins and cefotaxime by β-lactamase TEM-1 and the G238S mutant. *Biochemistry* 34 (37): 11660–11667.

21 Tripathi, R. and Nair, N.N. (2013). Mechanism of the acyl-enzyme complex formation from the Henry- Michaelis complex of class C β-lactamases with β-lactam antibiotics. *Journal of the American Chemical Society* 135 (39): 14679–14690.

22 Wang, J.F. and Chou, K.C. (2013). Metallo-β-lactamases: structural features, antibiotic recognition, inhibition, and inhibitor design. *Current Topics in Medicinal Chemistry* 13 (10): 1242–1253.

23 Wang, Z., Fast, W., Valentine, A.M., and Benkovic, S.J. (1999). Metallo-β-lactamase: structure and mechanism. *Current Opinion in Chemical Biology* 3 (5): 614–622.

24 Bahr, G., González, L.J., and Vila, A.J. (2021). Metallo-β-lactamases in the age of multidrug resistance: from structure and mechanism to evolution, dissemination, and inhibitor design. *Chemical Reviews* 121 (13): 7957–8094.

25 González, J.M. (2021). Visualizing the superfamily of metallo-β-lactamases through sequence similarity network neighborhood connectivity analysis. *Heliyon* 7 (1): e05867.

26 Palzkill, T. (2013). Metallo-β-lactamase structure and function. *Annals of the New York Academy of Sciences* 1277: 91–104.

27 Bush, K. (2018). Game changers: new β-lactamase inhibitor combinations targeting antibiotic resistance in gram-negative bacteria. *ACS Infectious Diseases* 4 (2): 84–87.

28 Ehmann, D.E., Jahić, H., Ross, P.L. et al. (2013). Kinetics of avibactam inhibition against class A, C, and D β-lactamases. *The Journal of Biological Chemistry* 288 (39): 27960–27971.

29 Shirley, M. (2018). Ceftazidime-avibactam: a review in the treatment of serious gram-negative bacterial infections. *Drugs* 78 (6): 675–692.

30 Liscio, J.L., Mahoney, M.V., and Hirsch, E.B. (2015). Ceftolozane/tazobactam and ceftazidime/avibactam: two novel β-lactam/β-lactamase inhibitor combination agents for the treatment of resistant Gram-negative bacterial infections. *International Journal of Antimicrobial Agents* 46 (3): 266–271.

31 Jeffs, M.A. and Lohans, C.T. (2022). Inhibiting the metallo-β-lactamases: challenges and strategies to overcome bacterial β-lactam resistance. *Future Medicinal Chemistry* 14 (14): 1021–1025.

32 Sader, H.S., Rhomberg, P.R., and Jones, R.N. (2005). *in vitro* activity of β-lactam antimicrobial agents in combination with aztreonam tested against metallo-β-lactamase-producing *Pseudomonas aeruginosa* and *Acinetobacter baumannii. Journal of Chemotherapy* 17 (6): 622–627.

33 Shakil, S., Azhar, E.I., Tabrez, S. et al. (2011). New Delhi metallo-β-lactamase (NDM-1): an update. *Journal of Chemotherapy* 23 (5): 263–265.

34 Somboro, A.M., Sekyere, J.O., Amoako, D.G. et al. (2018). Diversity and proliferation of metallo-β-lactamases: a clarion call for clinically effective metallo-β-lactamase inhibitors. *Applied and Environmental Microbiology* 84: e00698-18–18.

35 Murray, C.J., Ikuta, K.S., Sharara, F. et al. (2022). Global burden of bacterial antimicrobial resistance in 2019: a systematic analysis. *The Lancet* 399 (10325): 629–655.

36 Yamamoto, K., Tanaka, H., Kurisu, G. et al. (2022). Structural insights into the substrate specificity of IMP-6 and IMP-1 metallo-β-lactamases. *The Journal of Biochemistry* (Tokyo) 173 (1): 21–30.

37 King, D. and Strynadka, N. (2011). Crystal structure of New Delhi metallo-β-lactamase reveals molecular basis for antibiotic resistance. *Protein Science* 20 (9): 1484–1491.

38 Salimraj, R., Hinchliffe, P., Kosmopoulou, M. et al. (2019). Crystal structures of VIM-1 complexes explain active site heterogeneity in VIM-class metallo-β-lactamases. *The FEBS Journal* 286 (1): 169–183.

39 Aitha, M., Marts, A.R., Bergstrom, A. et al. (2014). Biochemical, mechanistic, and spectroscopic characterization of metallo-β-lactamase VIM-2. *Biochemistry* 53 (46): 7321–7331.

40 Garau, G., Bebrone, C., Anne, C. et al. (2005). A metallo-beta-lactamase enzyme in action: crystal structures of the monozinc carbapenemase CphA and its complex with biapenem. *Journal of Molecular Biology* 345 (4): 785–795.

41 Ullah, J.H., Walsh, T.R., Taylor, I.A. et al. (1998). The crystal structure of the L1 metallo-beta-lactamase from *Stenotrophomonas maltophilia* at 1.7 A resolution. *Journal of Molecular Biology* 284 (1): 125–136.

42 Galleni, M., Lamotte-Brasseur, J., Rossolini, G.M. et al. (2001). Standard numbering scheme for class B beta-lactamases. *Antimicrobial Agents and Chemotherapy* 45 (3): 660–663.

43 Krco, S., Davis, S.J., Joshi, P. et al. (2023). Structure, function, and evolution of metallo-β-lactamases from the B3 subgroup—emerging targets to combat antibiotic resistance. *Frontiers in Chemistry* 11: 1196073.

44 Yun, Y., Han, S., Park, Y.S. et al. (2022). Structural insights for core scaffold and substrate specificity of B1, B2, and B3 metallo-β-lactamases. *Frontiers in Microbiology* 12: https://doi.org/10.3389/fmicb.2021.752535.

45 López, C., Delmonti, J., Bonomo, R.A., and Vila, A.J. (2022). Deciphering the evolution of metallo-β-lactamases: a journey from the test tube to the bacterial periplasm. *The Journal of Biological Chemistry* 298 (3): 101665.

46 Morán-Barrio, J., Limansky, A.S., and Viale, A.M. (2009). Secretion of GOB metallo-beta-lactamase in *Escherichia coli* depends strictly on the cooperation between the cytoplasmic DnaK chaperone system and the sec machinery: completion of folding and Zn(II) ion acquisition occur in the bacterial periplasm. *Antimicrobial Agents and Chemotherapy* 53 (7): 2908–2917.

47 Bahr, G., González, L.J., and Vila, A.J. (2022). Metallo-β-lactamases and a tug-of-war for the available zinc at the host–pathogen interface. *Current Opinion in Chemical Biology* 66: 102103.

48 Prunotto, A., Bahr, G., González, L.J. et al. (2020). Molecular bases of the membrane association mechanism potentiating antibiotic resistance by New Delhi metallo-β-lactamase 1. *ACS Infectious Diseases* 6 (10): 2719–2731.

49 González, L.J., Bahr, G., Nakashige, T.G. et al. (2016). Membrane anchoring stabilizes and favors secretion of New Delhi metallo-β-lactamase. *Nature Chemical Biology* 12 (7): 516–522.

50 Asempa, T.E., Abdelraouf, K., and Nicolau, D.P. (2020). Metallo-β-lactamase resistance in Enterobacteriaceae is an artefact of currently utilized antimicrobial susceptibility testing methods. *The Journal of Antimicrobial Chemotherapy* 75 (4): 997–1005.

51 Murdoch, C.C. and Skaar, E.P. (2022). Nutritional immunity: the battle for nutrient metals at the host–pathogen interface. *Nature Reviews Microbiology* 20 (11): 657–670.

52 Bahr, G., Vitor-Horen, L., Bethel, C.R. et al. (2018). Clinical evolution of New Delhi metallo-β-lactamase (NDM) optimizes resistance under Zn(II) deprivation. *Antimicrobial Agents and Chemotherapy* 62 (1): e01849-17.

53 Stewart, A.C., Bethel, C.R., VanPelt, J. et al. (2017). Clinical variants of New Delhi metallo-β-lactamase are evolving to overcome zinc scarcity. *ACS Infectious Diseases* 3 (12): 927–940.

54 Farhat, N. and Khan, A.U. (2020). Evolving trends of New Delhi metallo-beta-lactamase (NDM) variants: a threat to antimicrobial resistance. *Infection, Genetics and Evolution* 86: 104588.

55 Cheng, Z., Thomas, P.W., Ju, L. et al. (2018). Evolution of New Delhi metallo-β-lactamase (NDM) in the clinic: Effects of NDM mutations on stability, zinc affinity, and mono-zinc activity. *The Journal of Biological Chemistry* 293 (32): 12606–12618.

56 Chen, A.Y., Thomas, P.W., Stewart, A.C. et al. (2017). Dipicolinic acid derivatives as inhibitors of New Delhi metallo-β-lactamase-1. *Journal of Medicinal Chemistry* 60 (17): 7267–7283.

57 Cheng, Z., Shurina, B.A., Bethel, C.R. et al. (2019). A single salt bridge in VIM-20 increases protein stability and antibiotic resistance under low-zinc conditions. *MBio* 10 (6): e02412-19.

58 Cheng, Z., Bethel, C.R., Thomas, P.W. et al. (2021). Carbapenem use is driving the evolution of imipenemase 1 variants. *Antimicrobial Agents and Chemotherapy* 65 (4): e01714–e01720.

59 Martínez-García, L., González-Alba, J.M., Baquero, F. et al. (2018). Ceftazidime is the key diversification and selection driver of VIM-type carbapenemases. *MBio* 9 (3): e02109-17.

60 Mojica, M.F., Mahler, S.G., Bethel, C.R. et al. (2015). Exploring the role of residue 228 in substrate and inhibitor recognition by VIM metallo-β-lactamases. *Biochemistry* 54 (20): 3183–3196.

61 Centers for Disease Control and Prevention (U.S.) (2019). Antibiotic Resistance Threats in the United States, 2019.

62 World Health Organization (2014). *Antimicrobial Resistance: Global Report on Surveillance*. Geneva: World Health Organization.

63 Miller, W.R. and Arias, C.A. (2024). ESKAPE pathogens: antimicrobial resistance, epidemiology, clinical impact and therapeutics. *Nature Reviews Microbiology* https://doi.org/10.1038/s41579-024-01054-w. Epub ahead of print.

64 Bajaj, P., Singh, N.S., and Virdi, J.S. (2016). *Escherichia coli* β-lactamases: what really matters. *Frontiers in Microbiology* 7: 417.

65 Mojica, M.F., Humphries, R., Lipuma, J.J. et al. (2022). Clinical challenges treating *Stenotrophomonas maltophilia infections*: an update. *JAC-Antimicrobial Resistance* 4 (3): dlac040.

66 Bennett, P.M. (2008). Plasmid encoded antibiotic resistance: acquisition and transfer of antibiotic resistance genes in bacteria. *British Journal of Pharmacology* 153 (S1): S347–S357.

67 Ito, H., Arakawa, Y., Ohsuka, S. et al. (1995). Plasmid-mediated dissemination of the metallo-beta-lactamase gene blaIMP among clinically isolated strains of *Serratia marcescens*. *Antimicrobial Agents and Chemotherapy* 39 (4): 824–829.

68 Pecora, N., Zhao, X., Nudel, K. et al. (2019). Diverse vectors and mechanisms spread New Delhi metallo-β-lactamases among Carbapenem-resistant enterobacteriaceae in the Greater Boston Area. *Antimicrobial Agents and Chemotherapy* 63 (2): e02040-18.

69 Laraki, N., Galleni, M., Thamm, I. et al. (1999). Structure of In31, a *bla* IMP-containing *Pseudomonas aeruginosa* integron phyletically related to In5, which carries an unusual array of gene cassettes. *Antimicrobial Agents and Chemotherapy* 43 (4): 890–901.

70 Yamamoto, M., Nagao, M., Matsumura, Y. et al. (2013). Regional dissemination of Acinetobacter species harbouring metallo-β-lactamase genes in Japan. *Clinical Microbiology and Infection* 19 (8): 729–736.

71 Peleg, A.Y., Franklin, C., Bell, J.M., and Spelman, D.W. (2005). Dissemination of the metallo-β-lactamase gene blaIMP-4 among Gram-negative pathogens in a clinical setting in Australia. *Clinical Infectious Diseases* 41 (11): 1549–1556.

72 Macesic, N., Hawkey, J., Vezina, B. et al. (2023). Genomic dissection of endemic carbapenem resistance reveals metallo-beta-lactamase dissemination through clonal, plasmid and integron transfer. *Nature Communications* 14 (1): 4764.

73 López, C., Ayala, J.A., Bonomo, R.A. et al. (2019). Protein determinants of dissemination and host specificity of metallo-β-lactamases. *Nature Communications* 10 (1): 3617.

74 Bin, T., Awen, Y., Peilin, L. et al. (2023). Outer membrane vesicles transmitting blaNDM-1 mediate the emergence of carbapenem-resistant hypervirulent *Klebsiella pneumoniae*. *Antimicrobial Agents and Chemotherapy* 67 (5): e01444-22.

75 Rumbo, C., Fernández-Moreira, E., Merino, M. et al. (2011). Horizontal transfer of the OXA-24 carbapenemase gene via outer membrane vesicles: a new mechanism of dissemination of carbapenem resistance genes in *Acinetobacter baumannii*. *Antimicrobial Agents and Chemotherapy* 55 (7): 3084–3090.

76 Yong, D., Toleman, M.A., Giske, C.G. et al. (2009). Characterization of a new metallo-β-lactamase gene, blaNDM-1, and a novel erythromycin esterase gene carried on a unique genetic structure in *Klebsiella pneumoniae* sequence type 14 from India. *Antimicrobial Agents and Chemotherapy* 53 (12): 5046–5054.

77 Rolain, J.M., Parola, P., and Cornaglia, G. (2010). New Delhi metallo-beta-lactamase (NDM-1): towards a new pandemia? *Clinical Microbiology and Infection* 16 (12): 1699–1701.

78 Safavi, M., Bostanshirin, N., Hajikhani, B. et al. (2020). Global genotype distribution of human clinical isolates of New Delhi metallo-β-lactamase-producing *Klebsiella pneumoniae*; a systematic review. *Journal of Global Antimicrobial Resistance* 23: 420–429.

79 Khan, A.U., Maryam, L., and Zarrilli, R. (2017). Structure, genetics and worldwide spread of New Delhi metallo-β-lactamase (NDM): a threat to public health. *BMC Microbiology* 17 (1): 101.

80 Walsh, T.R., Weeks, J., Livermore, D.M., and Toleman, M.A. (2011). Dissemination of NDM-1 positive bacteria in the New Delhi environment and its implications for human health: an environmental point prevalence study. *The Lancet Infectious Diseases* 11 (5): 355–362.

81 Perry, J.D., Naqvi, S.H., Mirza, I.A. et al. (2011). Prevalence of faecal carriage of Enterobacteriaceae with NDM-1 carbapenemase at military hospitals in Pakistan, and evaluation of two chromogenic media. *The Journal of Antimicrobial Chemotherapy* 66 (10): 2288–2294.

82 Sidjabat, H.E. and Paterson, D.L. (2015). Multidrug-resistant *Escherichia coli* in Asia: epidemiology and management. *Expert Review of Anti-Infective Therapy* 13 (5): 575–591.

83 Tsang, K., Luk, S., Lo, J.Y. et al. (2012). Hong Kong experiences the 'ultimate superbug': NDM-1 Enterobacteriaceae. *Hong Kong Medical Journal* 18 (5): 439–441.

84 Wareth, G., Brandt, C., Sprague, L.D. et al. (2020). Spatio-temporal distribution of *Acinetobacter baumannii* in Germany–a comprehensive systematic review of studies on resistance development in humans (2000–2018). *Microorganisms* 8 (3): 375.

85 Novais, Â., Ferraz, R.V., Viana, M. et al. (2022). NDM-1 Introduction in Portugal through a ST11 KL105 *Klebsiella pneumoniae* Widespread in Europe. *Antibiotics* 11 (1): 92.

86 Jain, A., Hopkins, K.L., Turton, J. et al. (2014). NDM carbapenemases in the United Kingdom: an analysis of the first 250 cases. *The Journal of Antimicrobial Chemotherapy* 69 (7): 1777–1784.

87 Kumarasamy, K.K., Toleman, M.A., Walsh, T.R. et al. (2010). Emergence of a new antibiotic resistance mechanism in India, Pakistan, and the UK: a molecular, biological, and epidemiological study. *The Lancet Infectious Diseases* 10 (9): 597–602.

88 Yao, X., Doi, Y., Zeng, L. et al. (2016). Carbapenem-resistant and colistin-resistant *Escherichia coli* co-producing NDM-9 and MCR-1. *The Lancet Infectious Diseases* 16 (3): 288–289.

89 Xu, L., Wang, P., Cheng, J. et al. (2019). Characterization of a novel blaNDM-5-harboring IncFII plasmid and an mcr-1-bearing IncI2 plasmid in a single *Escherichia coli* ST167 clinical isolate. *Infection and Drug Resistance* 12: 511–519.

90 Costa, A., Figueroa-Espinosa, R., Gaudenzi, F. et al. (2021). Co-Occurrence of NDM-5 and RmtB in a clinical isolate of *Escherichia coli* belonging to CC354 in Latin America. *Frontiers in Cellular and Infection Microbiology* 11: 654852.

91 Bonnin, R.A., Poirel, L., Carattoli, A., and Nordmann, P. (2012). Characterization of an IncFII plasmid encoding NDM-1 from *Escherichia coli* ST131. *PLoS One* 7 (4): e34752.

92 Li, Y., Yang, Y., Wang, Y. et al. (2023). Molecular characterization of blaNDM-harboring plasmids reveal its rapid adaptation and evolution in the Enterobacteriaceae. *One Health Advances* 1 (1): 30.

93 Sugawara, Y., Akeda, Y., Sakamoto, N. et al. (2017). Genetic characterization of blaNDM-harboring plasmids in carbapenem-resistant *Escherichia coli* from Myanmar. *PLoS One* 12 (9): e0184720.

94 Osano, E., Arakawa, Y., Wacharotayankun, R. et al. (1994). Molecular characterization of an enterobacterial metallo beta-lactamase found in a clinical isolate of *Serratia marcescens* that shows imipenem resistance. *Antimicrobial Agents and Chemotherapy* 38 (1): 71–78.

95 Watanabe, M., Iyobe, S., Inoue, M., and Mitsuhashi, S. (1991). Transferable imipenem resistance in *Pseudomonas aeruginosa*. *Antimicrobial Agents and Chemotherapy* 35 (1): 147–151.

96 Riccio, M.L., Franceschini, N., Boschi, L. et al. (2000). Characterization of the metallo-β-lactamase determinant of *Acinetobacter baumannii* AC-54/97 reveals the existence of blaIMP allelic variants carried by gene cassettes of different phylogeny. *Antimicrobial Agents and Chemotherapy* 44 (5): 1229–1235.

97 Yang, Q., Wang, H., Sun, H. et al. (2010). Phenotypic and genotypic characterization of Enterobacteriaceae with decreased susceptibility to carbapenems: results from large hospital-bsased surveillance studies in China. *Antimicrobial Agents and Chemotherapy* 54 (1): 573–577.

98 Hawkey, P.M., Xiong, J., Ye, H. et al. (2001). Occurrence of a new metallo-beta-lactamase IMP-4 carried on a conjugative plasmid in *Citrobacter youngae* from the People's Republic of China. *FEMS Microbiology Letters* 194 (1): 53–57.

99 Xiong, J., Hynes, M.F., Ye, H. et al. (2006). bla(IMP-9) and its association with large plasmids carried by *Pseudomonas aeruginosa* isolates from the People's Republic of China. *Antimicrobial Agents and Chemotherapy* 50 (1): 355–358.

100 Koh, T.H., Khoo, C.T., Tan, T.T. et al. (2010). Multilocus sequence types of carbapenem-resistant *Pseudomonas aeruginosa* in Singapore carrying metallo-beta-lactamase genes, including the novel bla(IMP-26) gene. *Journal of Clinical Microbiology* 48 (7): 2563–2564.

101 Pagani, L., Colinon, C., Migliavacca, R. et al. (2005). Nosocomial outbreak caused by multidrug-resistant *Pseudomonas aeruginosa* producing IMP-13 metallo-beta-lactamase. *Journal of Clinical Microbiology* 43 (8): 3824–3828.

102 Docquier, J.D., Riccio, M.L., Mugnaioli, C. et al. (2003). IMP-12, a new plasmid-encoded metallo-beta-lactamase from a *Pseudomonas putida* clinical isolate. *Antimicrobial Agents and Chemotherapy* 47 (5): 1522–1528.

103 Duljasz, W., Gniadkowski, M., Sitter, S. et al. (2009). First organisms with acquired metallo-beta-lactamases (IMP-13, IMP-22, and VIM-2) reported in Austria. *Antimicrobial Agents and Chemotherapy* 53 (5): 2221–2222.

104 Neuwirth, C., Siebor, E., Robin, F., and Bonnet, R. (2007). First occurrence of an IMP metallo-beta-lactamase in *Aeromonas caviae*: IMP-19 in an isolate from France. *Antimicrobial Agents and Chemotherapy* 51 (12): 4486–4488.

105 Hanson, N.D., Hossain, A., Buck, L. et al. (2006). First occurrence of a *Pseudomonas aeruginosa* isolate in the United States producing an IMP metallo-beta-lactamase, IMP-18. *Antimicrobial Agents and Chemotherapy* 50 (6): 2272–2273.

106 Gibb, A.P., Tribuddharat, C., Moore, R.A. et al. (2002). Nosocomial outbreak of carbapenem-resistant *Pseudomonas aeruginosa* with a new bla(IMP) allele, bla(IMP-7). *Antimicrobial Agents and Chemotherapy* 46 (1): 255–258.

107 Lincopan, N., Leis, R., Vianello, M.A. et al. (2006). Enterobacteria producing extended-spectrum beta-lactamases and IMP-1 metallo-beta-lactamases isolated from Brazilian hospitals. *Journal of Medical Microbiology* 55: 1611–1613.

108 Gales, A.C., Tognim, M.C.B., Reis, A.O. et al. (2003). Emergence of an IMP-like metallo-enzyme in an *Acinetobacter baumannii* clinical strain from a Brazilian teaching hospital. *Diagnostic Microbiology and Infectious Disease* 45 (1): 77–79.

109 Garza-Ramos, U., Morfin-Otero, R., Sader, H.S. et al. (2008). Metallo-beta-lactamase gene bla(IMP-15) in a class 1 integron, In95, from *Pseudomonas aeruginosa* clinical isolates from a hospital in Mexico. *Antimicrobial Agents and Chemotherapy* 52 (8): 2943–2946.

110 Cornaglia, G., Giamarellou, H., and Rossolini, G.M. (2011). Metallo-β-lactamases: a last frontier for β-lactams? *The Lancet Infectious Diseases* 11 (5): 381–393.

111 Zhao, W.-H. and Hu, Z.-Q. (2011). IMP-type metallo-β-lactamases in Gram-negative bacilli: distribution, phylogeny, and association with integrons. *Critical Reviews in Microbiology* 37 (3): 214–226.

112 Weldhagen, G.F. (2004). Integrons and β-lactamases–a novel perspective on resistance. *International Journal of Antimicrobial Agents* 23 (6): 556–562.

113 Houang, E.T.S., Yiu-Wai, C., Wai-Sing, L. et al. (2003). Epidemiology of rifampin ADP-ribosyltransferase (arr-2) and metallo-β-lactamase (blaIMP-4) gene cassettes in class 1 integrons in *Acinetobacter* strains isolated from blood cultures in 1997 to 2000. *Antimicrobial Agents and Chemotherapy* 47 (4): 1382–1390.

114 Stoesser, N., Sheppard, A.E., Peirano, G. et al. (2016). First report of *bla* IMP-14 on a plasmid harboring multiple drug resistance genes in *Escherichia coli* sequence type 131. *Antimicrobial Agents and Chemotherapy* 60 (8): 5068–5071.

115 Mendes, R.E., Toleman, M.A., Julival, R. et al. (2004). Integron carrying a novel metallo-β-lactamase gene, blaIMP-16, and a fused form of aminoglycoside-resistant gene aac(6′)-30/aac(6′)-Ib': report from the SENTRY Antimicrobial Surveillance Program. *Antimicrobial Agents and Chemotherapy* 48 (12): 4693–4702.

116 Laura, L., Letizia, R.M., Annarita, M. et al. (1999). Cloning and characterization of blaVIM, a new integron-borne metallo-β-lactamase gene from a *Pseudomonas aeruginosa* clinical isolate. *Antimicrobial Agents and Chemotherapy* 43 (7): 1584–1590.

117 Vatopoulos, A. (2008). High rates of metallo-beta-lactamase-producing *Klebsiella pneumoniae* in Greece-a review of the current evidence. *Euro Surveillance* 13 (4): 8023.

118 Peña, C., Suarez, C., Tubau, F. et al. (2007). Nosocomial spread of *Pseudomonas aeruginosa* producing the metallo-beta-lactamase VIM-2 in a Spanish hospital: clinical and epidemiological implications. *Clinical Microbiology and Infection* 13 (10): 1026–1029.

119 Juan, C., Beceiro, A., Gutiérrez, O. et al. (2008). Characterization of the new metallo-beta-lactamase VIM-13 and its integron-borne gene from a *Pseudomonas aeruginosa* clinical isolate in Spain. *Antimicrobial Agents and Chemotherapy* 52 (10): 3589–3596.

120 Mazzariol, A., Mammina, C., Koncan, R. et al. (2011). A novel VIM-type metallo-beta-lactamase (VIM-14) in a *Pseudomonas aeruginosa* clinical isolate from a neonatal intensive care unit. *Clinical Microbiology and Infection* 17 (5): 722–724.

121 Luzzaro, F., Docquier, J.-D., Colinon, C. et al. (2004). Emergence *in Klebsiella pneumoniae* and *Enterobacter cloacae* clinical isolates of the VIM-4 metallo-beta-lactamase encoded by a conjugative plasmid. *Antimicrobial Agents and Chemotherapy* 48 (2): 648–650.

122 Libisch, B., Giske, C.G., Kovács, B. et al. (2008). Identification of the first VIM metallo-beta-lactamase-producing multiresistant *Aeromonas hydrophila* strain. *Journal of Clinical Microbiology* 46 (5): 1878–1880.

123 Libisch, B., Gacs, M., Csiszár, K. et al. (2004). Isolation of an integron-borne blaVIM-4 type metallo-beta-lactamase gene from a carbapenem-resistant *Pseudomonas aeruginosa* clinical isolate in Hungary. *Antimicrobial Agents and Chemotherapy* 48 (9): 3576–3578.

124 Poirel, L., Naas, T., Nicolas, D. et al. (2000). Characterization of VIM-2, a carbapenem-hydrolyzing metallo-beta-lactamase and its plasmid- and integron-borne gene from a *Pseudomonas aeruginosa* clinical isolate in France. *Antimicrobial Agents and Chemotherapy* 44 (4): 891–897.

125 Walsh, T.R., Toleman, M.A., Poirel, L., and Nordmann, P. (2005). Metallo-β-lactamases: the quiet before the storm? *Clinical Microbiology Reviews* 18 (2): 306–325.

126 Matsumura, Y., Peirano, G., Devinney, R. et al. (2017). Genomic epidemiology of global VIM-producing Enterobacteriaceae. *The Journal of Antimicrobial Chemotherapy* 72 (8): 2249–2258.

127 Tato, M., Coque, T.M., Baquero, F., and Cantón, R. (2010). Dispersal of carbapenemase *bla* VIM-1 gene associated with different Tn *402* variants, mercury transposons, and conjugative plasmids in Enterobacteriaceae and *Pseudomonas aeruginosa*. *Antimicrobial Agents and Chemotherapy* 54 (1): 320–327.

128 Zhao, W.H. and Hu, Z.-Q. (2011). Epidemiology and genetics of VIM-type metallo-β-lactamases in gram-negative bacilli. *Future Microbiology* 6 (3): 317–333.

129 Tang, Y., Zhou, Y., Meng, C. et al. (2020). Co-occurrence of a novel VIM-1 and FosA3-encoding multidrug-resistant plasmid and a KPC-2-encoding pKP048-like plasmid in a clinical isolate of *Klebsiella pneumoniae* sequence type 11. *Infection, Genetics and Evolution* 85: 104479.

130 Toleman, M.A. (2003). Genetic characterization of a novel metallo-β-lactamase gene, blaIMP-13, harboured by a novel Tn5051-type transposon disseminating carbapenemase genes in Europe: report from the SENTRY worldwide antimicrobial surveillance programme. *The Journal of Antimicrobial Chemotherapy* 52 (4): 583–590.

131 El, S.A., Toleman, M.A., Janis, W. et al. (2010). First report of the metallo-β-lactamase SPM-1 in Europe. *Antimicrobial Agents and Chemotherapy* 54 (1): 582–582.

132 Castanheira, M., Toleman, M.A., Jones, R.N. et al. (2004). Molecular characterization of a beta-lactamase gene, blaGIM-1, encoding a new subclass of metallo-beta-lactamase. *Antimicrobial Agents and Chemotherapy* 48 (12): 4654–4661.

133 Sabuda, D.M., Laupland, K., Pitout, J. et al. (2008). Utilization of colistin for treatment of multidrug-resistant *Pseudomonas aeruginosa*. *Canadian Journal of Infectious Diseases and Medical Microbiology* 19 (6): 413–418.

134 Carmeli, Y., Akova, M., Cornaglia, G. et al. (2010). Controlling the spread of carbapenemase-producing Gram-negatives: therapeutic approach and infection control. *Clinical Microbiology and Infection* 16 (2): 102–111.

135 Antoniadou, A., Kontopidou, F., Poulakou, G. et al. (2007). Colistin-resistant isolates *of Klebsiella pneumoniae* emerging in intensive care unit patients: first report of a multiclonal cluster. *The Journal of Antimicrobial Chemotherapy* 59 (4): 786–790.

136 Crandon, J.L. and Nicolau, D.P. (2013). Human simulated studies of aztreonam and aztreonam-avibactam to evaluate activity against challenging gram-negative organisms, including metallo-β-lactamase producers. *Antimicrobial Agents and Chemotherapy* 57 (7): 3299–3306.

137 Kaye, K.S., Rice, L.B., Dane, A.L. et al. (2019). Fosfomycin for injection (ZTI-01) versus piperacillin-tazobactam for the treatment of complicated urinary tract infection including acute pyelonephritis: ZEUS, a phase 2/3 randomized trial. *Clinical Infectious Diseases* 69 (12): 2045–2056.

138 Falagas, M.E., Kastoris, A.C., Karageorgopoulos, D.E., and Rafailidis, P.I. (2009). Fosfomycin for the treatment of infections caused by multidrug-resistant non-fermenting Gram-negative bacilli: a systematic review of microbiological, animal and clinical studies. *International Journal of Antimicrobial Agents* 34 (2): 111–120.

139 Sonnevend, Á., Ghazawi, A., Darwish, D. et al. (2020). in vitro efficacy of ceftazidime-avibactam, aztreonam-avibactam and other rescue antibiotics against carbapenem-resistant Enterobacterales from the Arabian Peninsula. *International Journal of Infectious Diseases* 99: 253–259.

140 Johnston, B.D., Thuras, P., Porter, S.B. et al. (2020). Activity of cefiderocol, ceftazidime-avibactam, and eravacycline against carbapenem-resistant *Escherichia coli* isolates from the United States and international sites in relation to clonal background, resistance genes, coresistance, and region. *Antimicrobial Agents and Chemotherapy* 64 (10): e00797-20.

141 Boyd, S.E., Livermore, D.M., Hooper, D.C., and Hope, W.W. (2020). Metallo-β-lactamases: structure, function, epidemiology, treatment options, and the development pipeline. *Antimicrobial Agents and Chemotherapy* 64 (10): e00397-20.

142 Souli, M., Rekatsina, P.D., Chryssouli, Z. et al. (2009). Does the activity of the combination of imipenem and colistin in vitro exceed the problem of resistance in metallo-beta-lactamase-producing *Klebsiella pneumoniae* isolates? *Antimicrobial Agents and Chemotherapy* 53 (5): 2133–2135.

143 Parkins, M.D., Pitout, J.D.D., Church, D.L. et al. (2007). Treatment of infections caused by metallo-β-lactamase-producing *Pseudomonas aeruginosa* in the Calgary Health Region. *Clinical Microbiology and Infection* 13 (2): 199–202.

144 Zavascki, A.P., Barth, A.L., Gaspareto, P.B. et al. (2006). Risk factors for nosocomial infections due to *Pseudomonas aeruginosa* producing metallo-β-lactamase in two tertiary-care teaching hospitals. *The Journal of Antimicrobial Chemotherapy* 58 (4): 882–885.

145 Laupland, K.B., Parkins, M.D., Church, D.L. et al. (2005). Population-based epidemiological study of infections caused by carbapenem-resistant *Pseudomonas aeruginosa* in the Calgary Health Region: importance of metallo-β-lactamase (MBL)–producing strains. *The Journal of Infectious Diseases* 192 (9): 1606–1612.

146 Lucena, A., Dalla Costa, L.M., Nogueira, K.S. et al. (2014). Nosocomial infections with metallo-beta-lactamase-producing *Pseudomonas aeruginosa*: molecular epidemiology, risk factors, clinical features and outcomes. *The Journal of Hospital Infection* 87 (4): 234–240.

147 Falcone, M., Giordano, C., Leonildi, A. et al. (2024). Clinical features and outcomes of infections caused by metallo-β-lactamase–producing Enterobacterales: A 3-year prospective study from an endemic area. *Clinical Infectious Diseases* 78 (5): 1111–1119.

148 Guzek, A., Rybicki, Z., Tomaszewski, D. et al. (2024). Outcomes of 23 patients diagnosed with New Delhi metallo-beta-lactamase (NDM)-producing *Klebsiella pneumoniae* infection treated with ceftazidime/avibactam and aztreonam at a single center in Poland. *European Journal of Clinical Microbiology & Infectious Diseases* 43 (8): 1579–1587.

149 Falcone, M., Tiseo, G., Antonelli, A. et al. (2020). Clinical features and outcomes of bloodstream infections caused by New Delhi metallo-β-lactamase–producing Enterobacterales during a regional outbreak. *Open Forum Infectious Diseases* 7 (2): ofaa011.

150 Snyder, B.M., Montague, B.T., Anandan, S. et al. (2019). Risk factors and epidemiologic predictors of blood stream infections with New Delhi Metallo-b-lactamase (NDM-1) producing *Enterobacteriaceae*. *Epidemiology and Infection* 147: e137.

151 Nouér, S.A., Nucci, M., de Oliveira, M.P. et al. (2005). Risk factors for acquisition of multidrug-resistant *Pseudomonas aeruginosa* producing SPM metallo-β-lactamase. *Antimicrobial Agents and Chemotherapy* 49 (9): 3663–3667.

152 Daikos, G.L., Vryonis, E., Psichogiou, M. et al. (2010). Risk factors for bloodstream infection with *Klebsiella pneumoniae* producing VIM-1 metallo-β-lactamase. *The Journal of Antimicrobial Chemotherapy* 65 (4): 784–788.

153 Doyle, D., Peirano, G., Lascols, C. et al. (2012). Laboratory detection of enterobacteriaceae that produce carbapenemases. *Journal of Clinical Microbiology* 50 (12): 3877–3880.

154 Girlich, D., Poirel, L., and Nordmann, P. (2012). Value of the modified hodge test for detection of emerging carbapenemases in Enterobacteriaceae. *Journal of Clinical Microbiology* 50 (2): 477–479.

155 van der Zwaluw, K., de Haan, A., Pluister, G.N. et al. (2015). The carbapenem inactivation method (CIM), a simple and low-cost alternative for the carba NP test to assess phenotypic carbapenemase activity in gram-negative rods. *PLoS One* 10 (3): e0123690.

156 Pierce, V.M., Simner, P.J., Lonsway, D.R. et al. (2017). Modified carbapenem inactivation method for phenotypic detection of carbapenemase production among Enterobacteriaceae. *Journal of Clinical Microbiology* 55 (8): 2321–2333.

157 Sfeir, M.M., Hayden, J.A., Fauntleroy, K.A. et al. (2019). EDTA-modified carbapenem inactivation method: a phenotypic method for detecting metallo-β-lactamase-producing Enterobacteriaceae. *Journal of Clinical Microbiology* 57 (5): e01757-18.

158 Tsai, Y.M., Wang, S., Chiu, H.C. et al. (2020). Combination of modified carbapenem inactivation method (mCIM) and EDTA-CIM (eCIM) for phenotypic detection of carbapenemase-producing Enterobacteriaceae. *BMC Microbiology* 20 (1): 315.

159 Gill, C.M., Lasko, M.J., Asempa, T.E., and Nicolau, D.P. (2020). Evaluation of the EDTA-modified carbapenem inactivation method for detecting metallo-β-lactamase-producing *Pseudomonas aeruginosa*. *Journal of Clinical Microbiology* 58 (6): e02015-19.

160 Nordmann, P., Poirel, L., and Dortet, L. (2012). Rapid detection of carbapenemase-producing Enterobacteriaceae. *Emerging Infectious Diseases* 18 (9): 1503–1507.

161 Suryavanshi, K.T. and Lahiri, K.K. (2018). Assessment of Rapidec Carba NP Test, as screening test to detect carbapenemase, specially metallo β-lactamase producing gram negative bacteria at tertiary care centre. *International Journal of Health Sciences & Research* 8 (8): 56–61.

162 Garg, A., Garg, J., Upadhyay, G.C. et al. (2015). Evaluation of the Rapidec Carba NP Test kit for detection of carbapenemase-producing Gram-negative bacteria. *Antimicrobial Agents and Chemotherapy* 59 (12): 7870–7872.

163 Kumar, N., Singh, V.A., Beniwal, V., and Pottathil, S. (2018). Modified carba NP test: simple and rapid method to differentiate KPC- and MBL-producing *Klebsiella* species. *Journal of Clinical Laboratory Analysis* 32 (7): e22448.

164 Mendes, R.E., Kiyota, K.A., Jussimara, M. et al. (2007). Rapid detection and identification of metallo-β-lactamase-encoding genes by multiplex real-time PCR assay and melt curve analysis. *Journal of Clinical Microbiology* 45 (2): 544–547.

165 Shibata, N., Doi, Y., Yamane, K. et al. (2003). PCR typing of genetic determinants for metallo-β-lactamases and integrases carried by Gram-negative bacteria isolated in Japan, with focus on the class 3 isntegron. *Journal of Clinical Microbiology* 41 (12): 5407–5413.

166 Ellington, M.J., Kistler, J., Livermore, D.M., and Woodford, N. (2006). Multiplex PCR for rapid detection of genes encoding acquired metallo-β-lactamases. *The Journal of Antimicrobial Chemotherapy* 59 (2): 321–322.

167 Gu, X., Zheng, M., Chen, L., and Li, H. (2022). The development of New Delhi metallo-β-lactamase-1 inhibitors since 2018. *Microbiological Research* 261: 127079.

168 Palacios, A.R., Rossi, M.-A., Mahler, G.S., and Vila, A.J. (2020). Metallo-β-lactamase inhibitors inspired on snapshots from the catalytic mechanism. *Biomolecules* 10 (6): 854.

169 Yang, Y., Yan, Y.-H., Schofield, C.J. et al. (2023). Metallo-β-lactamase-mediated antimicrobial resistance and progress in inhibitor discovery. *Trends in Microbiology* 31 (7): 735–748.

170 Nagulapalli Venkata, K.C., Ellebrecht, M., and Tripathi, S.K. (2021). Efforts towards the inhibitor design for New Delhi metallo-beta-lactamase (NDM-1). *European Journal of Medicinal Chemistry* 225: 113747.

171 Denakpo, E., Naas, T., and Iorga, B.I. (2023). An updated patent review of metallo-β-lactamase inhibitors (2020-2023). *Expert Opinion on Therapeutic Patents* 33 (7–8): 523–538.

172 Liu, B., Trout, R.E.L., Chu, G.-H. et al. (2020). Discovery of taniborbactam (VNRX-5133): a broad-spectrum serine- and metallo-β-lactamase Inhibitor for carbapenem-resistant bacterial infections. *Journal of Medicinal Chemistry* 63 (6): 2789–2801.

173 Hamrick, J.C., Docquier, J.-D., Uehara, T. et al. (2020). VNRX-5133 (Taniborbactam), a broad-spectrum inhibitor of serine- and metallo-β-lactamases, restores activity of cefepime in Enterobacterales and *Pseudomonas aeruginosa*. *Antimicrobial Agents and Chemotherapy* 64 (3): e01963-19.

174 Hecker, S.J., Reddy, K.R., Lomovskaya, O. et al. (2020). Discovery of cyclic boronic acid QPX7728, an ultrabroad-spectrum inhibitor of serine and metallo-β-lactamases. *Journal of Medicinal Chemistry* 63 (14): 7491–7507.

175 Gerges, B., Rosenblatt, J., Truong, Y.-L. et al. (2024). *in vitro* activity of cefepime/taniborbactam and comparator agents against Gram-negative bacterial bloodstream pathogens recovered from patients with cancer. *JAC-Antimicrobial Resistance* 6 (2): dlae060.

176 Hernández-García, M., García-Castillo, M., Ruiz-Garbajosa, P. et al. (2022). *in vitro* activity of cefepime-taniborbactam against carbapenemase-producing Enterobacterales and *Pseudomonas aeruginosa* isolates recovered in Spain. *Antimicrobial Agents and Chemotherapy* 66 (3): e02161-21.

177 Karlowsky, J.A., Hackel, M.A., Wise, M.G. et al. (2023). *in vitro* activity of cefepime-taniborbactam and comparators against clinical isolates of gram-negative bacilli from 2018 to 2020: results from the gGlobal Evaluation of Antimicrobial Resistance via Surveillance (GEARS) Program. *Antimicrobial Agents and Chemotherapy* 67 (1): e01281-22.

178 Drusin, S.I., Le Terrier, C., Poirel, L. et al. (2023). Structural basis of metallo-β-lactamase resistance to taniborbactam. *Antimicrobial Agents and Chemotherapy* 68 (2): e01168-23.

179 Wagenlehner, F.M., Gasink, L.B., McGovern, P.C. et al. (2024). Cefepime-taniborbactam in complicated urinary tract infection. *The New England Journal of Medicine* 390 (7): 611–622.

180 Pharmaceuticals, V. (2024). Venatorx and Melinta Provide Update on Status of U.S. *New Drug Application for Cefepime-Taniborbactam.* .

181 Tsivkovski, R., Totrov, M., and Lomovskaya, O. (2020). Biochemical characterization of QPX7728, a new ultrabroad-spectrum beta-lactamase inhibitor of serine and metallo-beta-lactamases. *Antimicrobial Agents and Chemotherapy* 64 (6): e00130-20.

182 Lomovskaya, O., Rubio-Aparicio, D., Nelson, K. et al. (2021). *in vitro* activity of the ultrabroad-spectrum beta-lactamase inhibitor QPX7728 in combination with multiple beta-lactam antibiotics against *Pseudomonas aeruginosa*. *Antimicrobial Agents and Chemotherapy* 65 (6): e00210-21.

183 Lomovskaya, O., Nelson, K., Rubio-Aparicio, D. et al. (2020). Impact of intrinsic resistance mechanisms on potency of QPX7728, a new ultrabroad-spectrum beta-lactamase inhibitor of serine and metallo-beta-lactamases in Enterobacteriaceae, *Pseudomonas aeruginosa*, and *Acinetobacter baumannii*. *Antimicrobial Agents and Chemotherapy* 64 (6): e00552-20.

184 Griffith, D., Roberts, J., Wallis, S. et al. (2022). 218. A phase 1 study of the single-dose safety, tolerability, and pharmacokinetics of the beta-lactamase inhibitor xeruborbactam administered as the isobutyryloxymethyl oral prodrug to healthy adult subjects. *Open Forum Infectious Diseases* 9 (Supplement_2): ofac492.296.

185 Sychantha, D., Rotondo, C.M., Tehrani, K.H.M.E. et al. (2021). Aspergillomarasmine a inhibits metallo-β-lactamases by selectively sequestering Zn (2). *The Journal of Biological Chemistry* 297 (2): 100918.

186 Aoki, N., Ishii, Y., Tateda, K. et al. (2010). Efficacy of calcium-EDTA as an inhibitor for metallo-β-lactamase in a mouse model of *Pseudomonas aeruginosa* pneumonia. *Antimicrobial Agents and Chemotherapy* 54 (11): 4582–4588.

187 Tehrani, K.H.M.E., Brüchle, N.C., Wade, N. et al. (2020). Small molecule carboxylates inhibit metallo-β-lactamases and resensitize carbapenem-resistant bacteria to meropenem. *ACS Infectious Diseases* 6 (6): 1366–1371.

188 Somboro, A.M., Tiwari, D., Bester, L.A. et al. (2015). NOTA: a potent metallo-β-lactamase inhibitor. *The Journal of Antimicrobial Chemotherapy* 70 (5): 1594–1596.

189 Principe, L., Vecchio, G., Sheehan, G. et al. (2020). Zinc chelators as carbapenem adjuvants for metallo-β-lactamase-producing bacteria: *in vitro* and *in vivo* evaluation. *Microbial Drug Resistance* 26 (10): 1133–1143.

190 Schnaars, C., Kildahl-Andersen, G., Prandina, A. et al. (2018). Synthesis and preclinical evaluation of TPA-based zinc chelators as metallo-β-lactamase inhibitors. *ACS Infectious Diseases* 4 (9): 1407–1422.

191 La Piana, L., Viaggi, V., Principe, L. et al. (2021). Polypyridine ligands as potential metallo-β-lactamase inhibitors. *Journal of Inorganic Biochemistry* 215: 111315.

192 Liénard, B.M.R., Garau, G., Horsfall, L. et al. (2008). Structural basis for the broad-spectrum inhibition of metallo-β-lactamases by thiols. *Organic and Biomolecular Chemistry* 6 (13): 2282–2294.

193 Brem, J., van Berkel, S.S., Aik, W. et al. (2014). Rhodanine hydrolysis leads to potent thioenolate mediated metallo-β-lactamase inhibition. *Nature Chemistry* 6 (12): 1084–1090.

194 Brem, J., van Berkel, S.S., Zollman, D. et al. (2016). Structural basis of metallo-β-lactamase inhibition by captopril stereoisomers. *Antimicrobial Agents and Chemotherapy* 60 (1): 142–150.

195 Roll, D.M., Yang, Y., Wildey, M.J. et al. (2010). Inhibition of metallo-β-lactamases by pyridine monothiocarboxylic acid analogs. *Journal of Antibiotics* (Tokyo) 63 (5): 255–257.

196 Thomas, C.A., Cheng, Z., Yang, K. et al. (2020). Probing the mechanisms of inhibition for various inhibitors of metallo-β-lactamases VIM-2 and NDM-1. *Journal of Inorganic Biochemistry* 210: 111123.

197 Pettinati, I., Brem, J., Lee, S.Y. et al. (2016). The chemical biology of human metallo-β-lactamase fold proteins. *Trends in Biochemical Sciences* 41 (4): 338–355.

198 Peters, B.K., Reddy, N., Shungube, M. et al. (2023). *in vitro* and *in vivo* development of a β-lactam-metallo-β-lactamase inhibitor: targeting carbapenem-resistant Enterobacterales. *ACS Infectious Diseases* 9 (3): 486–496.

199 Hongyan, T., Yiwan, W., Yang, D. et al. (2022). A cephalosporin-tripodalamine conjugate inhibits metallo-β-lactamase with high efficacy and low toxicity. *Antimicrobial Agents and Chemotherapy* 66 (10): e00352-22.

200 Leiris, S., Coelho, A., Castandet, J. et al. (2019). SAR studies leading to the identification of a novel series of metallo-β-lactamase inhibitors for the treatment of carbapenem-resistant Enterobacteriaceae infections that display efficacy in an animal infection model. *ACS Infectious Diseases* 5 (1): 131–140.

201 Everett, M., Sprynski, N., Coelho, A. et al. (2018). Discovery of a novel metallo-β-lactamase inhibitor that potentiates meropenem activity against carbapenem-resistant Enterobacteriaceae. *Antimicrobial Agents and Chemotherapy* 62 (5): e00074-18.

202 Davies, D.T., Leiris, S., Sprynski, N. et al. (2020). ANT2681: SAR studies leading to the identification of a metallo-β-lactamase inhibitor with potential for clinical use in combination with meropenem for the treatment of infections caused by NDM-producing Enterobacteriaceae. *ACS Infectious Diseases* 6 (9): 2419–2430.

203 Zalacain, M., Lozano, C., Llanos, A. et al. (2021). Novel specific metallo-β-lactamase inhibitor ANT2681 restores meropenem activity to clinically effective levels against NDM-positive Enterobacterales. *Antimicrobial Agents and Chemotherapy* 65 (6): e00203-21.

204 Brem, J., Panduwawala, T., Hansen, J.U. et al. (2022). Imitation of β-lactam binding enables broad-spectrum metallo-β-lactamase inhibitors. *Nature Chemistry* 14 (1): 15–24.

205 González, M.M., Kosmopoulou, M., Mojica, M.F. et al. (2015). Bisthiazolidines: a substrate-mimicking scaffold as an inhibitor of the NDM-1 carbapenemase. *ACS Infectious Diseases* 1 (11): 544–554.

206 Hinchliffe, P., González, M.M., Mojica, M.F. et al. (2016). Cross-class metallo-β-lactamase inhibition by bisthiazolidines reveals multiple binding modes. *Proceedings of the National Academy of Sciences* 113 (26): e3745–e3754.

207 Villamil, V., Rossi, M.-A., Mojica, M.F. et al. (2024). Rational design of benzobisheterocycle metallo-β-lactamase inhibitors: a tricyclic scaffold enhances potency against target enzymes. *Journal of Medicinal Chemistry* 67 (5): 3795–3812.

208 Yan, Y.-H., Zhang, T.-T., Li, R. et al. (2023). Discovery of 2-aminothiazole-4-carboxylic acids as broad-spectrum metallo-β-lactamase inhibitors by mimicking carbapenem hydrolysate binding. *Journal of Medicinal Chemistry* 66 (19): 13746–13767.

209 Marshall, S., Hujer, A.M., Rojas, L.J. et al. (2017). Can ceftazidime-avibactam and aztreonam overcome β-lactam resistance conferred by metallo-β-lactamases in Enterobacteriaceae? *Antimicrobial Agents and Chemotherapy* 61 (4): e02243-16.

210 Wise, M.G., Karlowsky, J.A., Mohamed, N. et al. (2023). *in vitro* activity of aztreonam–avibactam against Enterobacterales isolates collected in Latin America, Africa/Middle East, Asia, and Eurasia for the ATLAS Global Surveillance Program in 2019–2021. *European Journal of Clinical Microbiology and Infectious Diseases* 42 (9): 1135–1143.

211 Falcone, M., Daikos, G.L., Tiseo, G. et al. (2021). Efficacy of Ceftazidime-avibactam plus aztreonam in patients with bloodstream infections caused by metallo-β-lactamase-producing Enterobacterales. *Clinical Infectious Diseases* 72 (11): 1871–1878.

212 Carmeli, Y., Cisneros, J.-M., Paul, M. et al. (2023). 2893 A. efficacy and safety of aztreonam-avibactam for the treatment of serious infections due to gram-negative bacteria, including metallo-β-lactamase-producing pathogens:

phase 3 REVISIT study. *Open Forum Infectious Diseases* 10 (Supplement_2): ofad500.2476.

213 Sadek, M., Juhas, M., Poirel, L., and Nordmann, P. (2020). Genetic features leading to reduced susceptibility to aztreonam-avibactam among metallo-β-lactamase-producing *Escherichia coli* isolates. *Antimicrobial Agents and Chemotherapy* 64 (12): e01659-20.

214 Periasamy, H., Joshi, P., Palwe, S. et al. (2020). High prevalence of *Escherichia coli* clinical isolates in India harbouring four amino acid inserts in PBP3 adversely impacting activity of aztreonam/avibactam. *The Journal of Antimicrobial Chemotherapy* 75 (6): 1650–1651.

215 Tellapragada, C., Razavi, M., Peris, P.S. et al. (2024). Resistance to aztreonam-avibactam among clinical isolates of *E. coli* is primarily mediated by altered penicillin binding protein 3 and impermeability. *International Journal of Antimicrobial Agents* 64 (3): 107256.

216 Ma, K. and Zong, Z. (2022). Resistance to aztreonam-avibactam due to CTX-M-15 in the presence of penicillin-binding protein 3 with extra amino acids in *Escherichia coli*. *Frontiers in Microbiology* 13: 1047109.

217 Ma, K., Feng, Y., and Zong, Z. (2022). Aztreonam-avibactam may not replace ceftazidime/avibactam: the case of KPC-21 carbapenemase and penicillin-binding protein 3 with four extra amino acids. *International Journal of Antimicrobial Agents* 60 (3): 106642.

218 Lohans, C.T., Brem, J., and Schofield, C.J. (2017). New Delhi metallo-β-lactamase 1 catalyzes avibactam and aztreonam hydrolysis. *Antimicrobial Agents and Chemotherapy* 61 (12): e01224-17.

219 Aoki, T., Yoshizawa, H., Yamawaki, K. et al. (2018). Cefiderocol (S-649266), a new siderophore cephalosporin exhibiting potent activities against *Pseudomonas aeruginosa* and other gram-negative pathogens including multi-drug resistant bacteria: structure activity relationship. *European Journal of Medicinal Chemistry* 155: 847–868.

220 Kaye, K.S., Naas, T., Pogue, J.M., and Rossolini, G.M. (2023). Cefiderocol, a siderophore cephalosporin, as a treatment option for infections caused by carbapenem-resistant Enterobacterales. *Infectious Disease and Therapy* 12 (3): 777–806.

221 Ito, A., Nishikawa, T., Matsumoto, S. et al. (2016). Siderophore cephalosporin cefiderocol utilizes ferric iron transporter systems for antibacterial activity *against Pseudomonas aeruginosa*. *Antimicrobial Agents and Chemotherapy* 60 (12): 7396–7401.

222 Ito, A., Sato, T., Ota, M. et al. (2018). *in vitro* antibacterial properties of cefiderocol, a novel siderophore cephalosporin, against Gram-negative bacteria. *Antimicrobial Agents and Chemotherapy* 62 (1): e01454-17.

223 Takemura, M., Wise, M.G., Hackel, M.A. et al. (2023). *in vitro* activity of cefiderocol against MBL-producing Gram-negative bacteria collected in North America and Europe in five consecutive annual multinational SIDERO-WT surveillance studies (2014-2019). *The Journal of Antimicrobial Chemotherapy* 78 (8): 2019–2027.

224 Gill, C.M., Santini, D., Nicolau, D.P., and the ERACE-PA Global Study Group (2024). in vitro activity of cefiderocol against a global collection of carbapenem-resistant *Pseudomonas aeruginosa* with a high level of carbapenemase diversity. *The Journal of Antimicrobial Chemotherapy* 79 (2): 412–416.

225 Delgado-Valverde, M., Portillo-Calderón, I., Recacha, E. et al. (2023). *in vitro* activity of cefiderocol compared to other antimicrobials against a collection of metallo-beta-lactamase-producing Gram-negative bacilli from Southern Spain. *Microbiology Spectrum* 11 (3): e04936-22.

226 Oueslati, S., Bogaerts, P., Dortet, L. et al. (2022). *in vitro* activity of cefiderocol and comparators against carbapenem-resistant Gram-negative pathogens from France and Belgium. *Antibiotics* 11 (10): 1352.

227 Klein, S., Boutin, S., Kocer, K. et al. (2022). Rapid development of cefiderocol resistance in carbapenem-resistant *Enterobacter cloacae* during therapy is associated with heterogeneous mutations in the catecholate siderophore receptor cirA. *Clinical Infectious Diseases* 74 (5): 905–908.

228 McElheny, C.L., Fowler, E.L., Iovleva, A. et al. (2021). *in vitro* evolution of cefiderocol resistance in an NDM-producing Klebsiella pneumoniae due to functional loss of *cirA*. *Microbiology Spectrum* 9 (3): e01779-21.

229 Wang, Q., Jin, L., Sun, S. et al. (2022). Occurrence of high levels of cefiderocol resistance in carbapenem-resistant *Escherichia coli* before its approval in China: a report from China CRE-network. *Microbiology Spectrum* 10 (3): e02670-21.

230 Barker, K.R., Rebick, G.W., Fakharuddin, K. et al. (2024). When the Trojan horse is unable to reach inside the city: investigation of the mechanism of resistance behind the first reported cefiderocol-resistant *E. coli* in Canada. *Microbiology Spectrum* 12 (5): e03223-23.

231 Hobson, C.A., Cointe, A., Jacquier, H. et al. (2021). Cross-resistance to cefiderocol and ceftazidime–avibactam in KPC β-lactamase mutants and the inoculum effect. *Clinical Microbiology and Infection* 27 (8): 1172.e7–1172.e10.

232 Castillo-Polo, J.A., Hernández-García, M., Maruri-Aransolo, A. et al. (2024). Evolution of ceftazidime-avibactam and cefiderocol resistance in ST131-H30R1-*Escherichia coli* isolates with KPC-3 mutants and application of FTIR biotyping. *Microbiology Spectrum* 12 (4): e02776-23.

233 Simner, P.J., Mostafa, H.H., Bergman, Y. et al. (2022). Progressive development of cefiderocol resistance in *Escherichia coli* during therapy is associated with an increase in $bla_{\text{NDM-5}}$ copy number and gene expression. *Clinical Infectious Diseases* 75 (1): 47–54.

234 Shields, R.K., Iovleva, A., Kline, E.G. et al. (2020). Clinical evolution of AmpC-mediated ceftazidime-avibactam and cefiderocol resistance in *Enterobacter cloacae* complex following exposure to cefepime. *Clinical Infectious Diseases* 71 (10): 2713–2716.

235 Kawai, A., McElheny, C.L., Iovleva, A. et al. (2020). Structural basis of reduced susceptibility to ceftazidime-avibactam and cefiderocol in *Enterobacter cloacae* due to AmpC R2 loop deletion. *Antimicrobial Agents and Chemotherapy* 64 (7): e00198-20.

236 Bassetti, M., Echols, R., Matsunaga, Y. et al. (2021). Efficacy and safety of cefiderocol or best available therapy for the treatment of serious infections caused by carbapenem-resistant Gram-negative bacteria (CREDIBLE-CR): a randomised, open-label, multicentre, pathogen-focused, descriptive, phase 3 trial. *The Lancet Infectious Diseases* 21 (2): 226–240.

237 Wunderink, R.G., Matsunaga, Y., Ariyasu, M. et al. (2021). Cefiderocol versus high-dose, extended-infusion meropenem for the treatment of Gram-negative nosocomial pneumonia (APEKS-NP): a randomised, double-blind, phase 3, non-inferiority trial. *The Lancet Infectious Diseases* 21 (2): 213–225.

238 Falcone, M., Tiseo, G., Leonildi, A. et al. (2022). Cefiderocol- compared to colistin-based regimens for the treatment of severe infections caused by carbapenem-resistant *Acinetobacter baumannii. Antimicrobial Agents and Chemotherapy* 66 (5): e02142-21.

239 de la Fuente, C., Rodríguez, M., Merino, N. et al. (2023). Real-life use of cefiderocol for salvage therapy of severe infections due to carbapenem-resistant Gram-negative bacteria. *International Journal of Antimicrobial Agents* 62 (1): 106818.

240 Hoellinger, B., Simand, C., Jeannot, K. et al. (2023). Real-world clinical outcome of cefiderocol for treatment of multidrug-resistant non-fermenting, gram negative bacilli infections: a case series. *Clinical Microbiology and Infection* 29 (3): 393–395.

241 Sajib, M.I., Monteforte, M., and Go, R. (2023). Clinical outcome of cefiderocol for infections with carbapenem-resistant organisms. *Antibiotics* 12 (5): 936.

242 Petrucci, F., Perciballi, B., Rivano Capparuccia, M. et al. (2024). Compassionate use of cefiderocol in a complex case of extensively drug-resistant *Acinetobacter baumannii* fracture-related infection: a comprehensive approach and multidisciplinary management. *Infection* https://doi.org/10.1007/s15010-024-02294-x.

243 Reck, F., Bermingham, A., Blais, J. et al. (2018). Optimization of novel monobactams with activity against carbapenem-resistant Enterobacteriaceae – identification of LYS228. *Bioorganic and Medicinal Chemistry Letters* 28 (4): 748–755.

244 Blais, J., Lopez, S., Li, C. et al. (2018). *in vitro* activity of LYS228, a novel monobactam antibiotic, against multidrug-resistant Enterobacteriaceae. *Antimicrobial Agents and Chemotherapy* 62 (10): e00552-18.

245 Dean, C.R., Barkan, D.T., Bermingham, A. et al. (2018). Mode of action of the monobactam LYS228 and mechanisms decreasing in vitro susceptibility *in Escherichia coli* and *Klebsiella pneumoniae. Antimicrobial Agents and Chemotherapy* 62 (10): e01200-18.

246 Weiss, W.J., Pulse, M.E., Nguyen, P., and Growcott, E.J. (2019). *in vivo* efficacy of novel monobactam LYS228 in murine models of carbapenemase-producing *Klebsiella pneumoniae* infection. *Antimicrobial Agents and Chemotherapy* 63 (4): e02214-18.

7

Targeting Disease-Linked Metalloenzymes Involved in RNA Metabolism

Simranjeet Kaur and Wei Shen Aik*

Department of Chemistry, Hong Kong Baptist University, Kowloon Tong, Hong Kong SAR, China

Section I

7.1 Background

RNA is an important class of macromolecules in the cell. It plays essential roles in gene expression and regulation, generally as an "intermediary" between the genome encoded by DNA and effector proteins, in accordance with the central dogma of molecular biology [1–4]. For a gene to be expressed as effector proteins, pre-messenger RNA, which is transcribed from the DNA code, will first have to be processed into mature messenger RNA (mRNA) before it can be translocated from the nucleus to the cytoplasm. In the cytoplasm, mRNA binds to the ribosomes, which are comprised of ribosomal RNA (rRNA) and ribosomal proteins, for decoding and protein synthesis. During protein synthesis, transfer RNAs (tRNA) are responsible for transporting amino acids for polymerization in the ribosome into polypeptides/proteins. The gene expression process is tightly regulated, which can be done through RNA metabolism involving complex biochemistry at different stages of the lifespan of RNA molecules. Many of the biochemical reactions affecting RNA metabolism are carried out by metalloenzymes. Some of these key regulatory steps of RNA metabolism are also associated with diseases, especially cancer, due to their links with dysregulation of gene expression leading to tumorigenesis [5–8]. Therefore, metalloenzymes that are involved in RNA modifications and processing have now been explored as potential drug targets.

* Current address: School of Biological Sciences, The University of Hong Kong, Hong Kong SAR, China

Drug Discovery Targeting Metalloenzymes: Strategies and Applications, First Edition. Edited by Guo-Bo Li.

Metalloenzymes are involved in different stages of the RNA life cycle, including RNA synthesis, processing, modifications, and degradation. In humans, RNA is synthesized by DNA-dependent-RNA-polymerases, which are Zn^{2+}-dependent metalloenzymes [9]. After RNA synthesis, most of the RNAs will have to undergo processing and cleavage [10, 11]. For example, a majority of the mRNAs will first need to undergo 5′-capping, pre-mRNA splicing, and 3′-end cleavage and polyadenylation. Metalloenzymes are also involved in 3′-end cleavage, e.g. CPSF73 endonuclease [12–14]. RNA can also undergo chemical modifications and editing, both of which will alter the levels of gene expression. Several enzymes that are involved in RNA modifications and editing are also metalloenzymes [15–18]. In this chapter, we will discuss several human homologues of the AlkB family of ferrous iron- and 2-oxoglutarate-dependent oxygenases (2OG oxygenases) and the Zn^{2+}-dependent adenine deaminases acting on RNA (ADARs).

Overall, this chapter will discuss selected human metalloenzymes acting on RNA that are associated with diseases and thus are potential drug targets. We will also discuss reported strategies for inhibitor discovery for these enzymes.

7.2 Fe(II) and 2-Oxoglutarate-Dependent Oxygenases Involved in Epitransciptomic Regulation of RNA Metabolism

Several members of the ferrous iron and 2-oxoglutarate-dependent oxygenase superfamily (2OG oxygenases) are involved in RNA modifications. 2OG oxygenases are Fe(II)-dependent enzymes that catalyze 2-electron oxidations using 2OG (a tricarboxylic acid [TCA] cycle metabolite) and molecular oxygen as cosubstrates (Figure 7.1a) [19–24]. Among 2OG oxygenases, members that are involved in nucleic acid modifications are mostly from the AlkB and Ten-eleven-translocation (TET) subfamilies [25], with one unique 2OG oxygenase TYW5 from the JmjC domain subfamily [26, 27]. AlkB was originally identified as a bacterial DNA repair protein that repairs N-alkylated base damage [19, 28, 29]. For example, AlkB can demethylate N^1-methyldeoxyadenosine (1meA) and N^3-methyldeoxycytosine (3meC) by first hydroxylating 1meA/3meC, which results in hemiaminals that fragment into adenine/cytosine and formaldehyde (Figure 7.1b) [19, 28]. AlkB has 9 human homologues: ALKBH1–8 and FTO [25, 30]. ALKBH1, 3, 5, 8, and FTO have been known to catalyze demethylation or hydroxylation of RNAs. In this section, we will discuss inhibition efforts of ALKBH3, ALKBH5, and FTO that have been reported.

7.3 Fat Mass and Obesity Associated Protein (FTO)

7.3.1 Biological Functions of FTO

The fat mass and obesity associated protein (FTO) is one of the best characterized human homologues of the AlkB subfamily. FTO was first identified as a product of

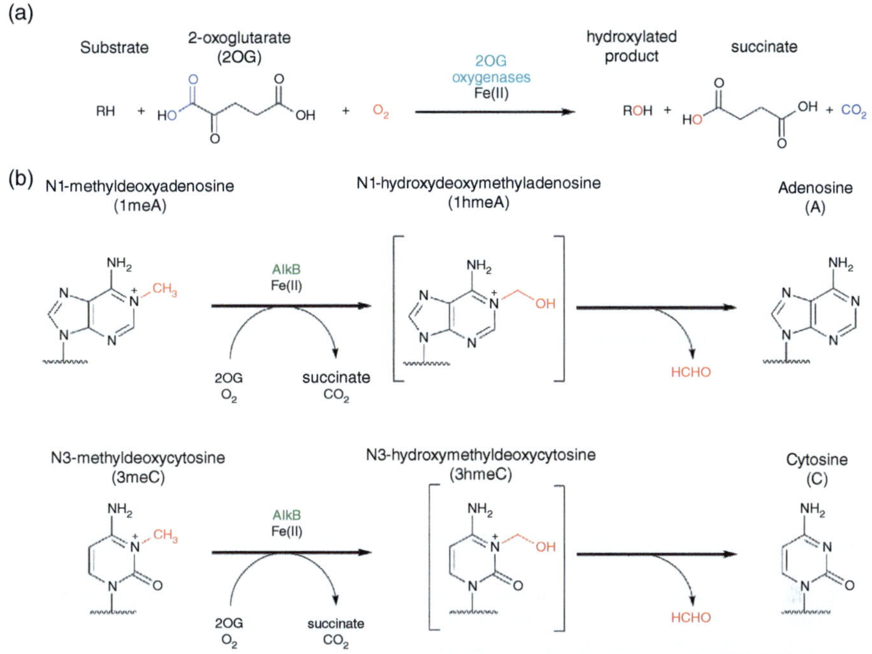

Figure 7.1 Nucleic acid oxidation reactions as catalyzed by 2OG oxygenases. (a) General reaction scheme for ferrous iron and 2OG-dependent oxygenases. During enzyme catalysis, the substrate is hydroxylated as a result of oxidation using 2OG and molecular oxygen as cosubstrates. (b) Schematic representation of alkylated base (1meA/3meC) repair as catalyzed by DNA repair enzyme AlkB. The methylated bases are first hydroxylated to generate hemiaminals (1hmeA/3hmeC) which then are rapidly fragmented to give the canonical nucleobases, adenosine, and cytosine, along with the release of formaldehyde. *Source:* [19] / Springer Nature.

the *FTO* gene, of which single nucleotide polymorphisms (SNPs) in the first intron were identified by genome-wide association studies (GWAS) to be linked to body mass index and type II diabetes in certain human populations. [31–34]. The function of FTO in inducing pre-adipocyte differentiation due to alternate splicing was validated by knockdown studies [35, 36].

FTO later generated further interest as an RNA-modifying metalloenzyme, implicating it in epitranscriptomic regulation. Research on the catalytic activity of FTO established that FTO is a nucleic acid demethylase through its Fe(II) and 2OG-dependent oxygenase activity by demethylating 3-methylthymidine (3mT) in single-stranded DNA (ssDNA) [32] and 3-methyluracil (m^3U) in ssRNA [37]. Subsequently, FTO was reported to efficiently catalyze the oxidative demethylation of m^6A in ssRNA, thereby affecting nuclear translocation [15, 38]. FTO-catalyzed oxidation of m^6A initiates with initial hydroxylation which produces the hemiaminal hm^6A. Unlike the hemiaminals of other nucleobases such as hm^1A and hm^3C, the hm^6A is relatively stable [39]. Subsequently, hm^6A can either be further oxidized to form N^6-formyladenosine (f^6A) or fragment into adenosine and formaldehyde [15, 38]. MALDI-based mass spectrometry assays have also detected N^6-methyleneadenosine

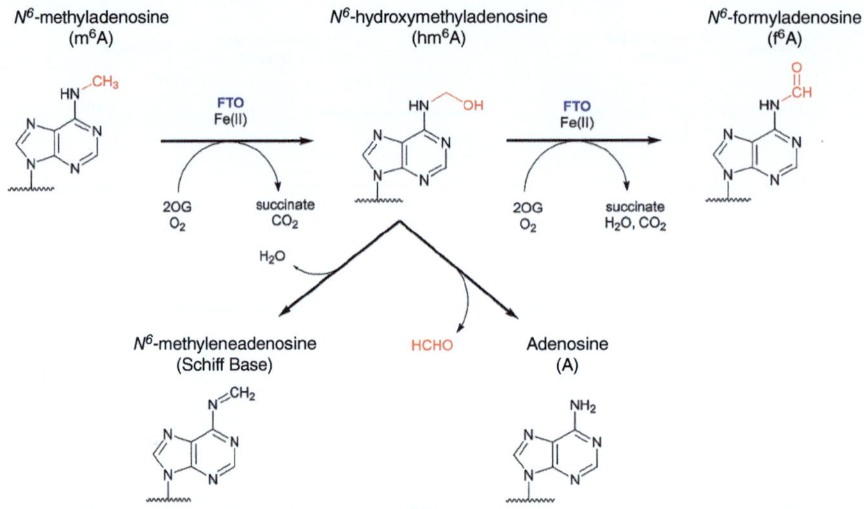

Figure 7.2 Scheme of m^{6}A oxidation by FTO. FTO catalyzed oxidation of m^{6}A produces a mixture of products including hm^{6}A, f^{6}A, and the demethylated adenosine [38] / Springer Nature. The N^6-hemiaminal hm^{6}A formed is fragmented to adenosine or forms a Schiff base [40] / National Academy of Sciences. hm^{6}A can potentially undergo another round of oxidation to produce f^{6}A [38] / Springer Nature.

(an imine species) which is generated upon the loss of a water molecule from hm^{6}A [38] (Figure 7.2). m^{6}A in mRNA has been actively studied in the past decade to play important roles in RNA metabolism and diseases. Recent evidence suggests that FTO can also demethylate N^6,2′O-dimethyladenosine (m^{6}A$_m$) adjacent to the 5′ N^7-methylguanosine (m^{7}G) triphosphate cap in mRNA and small nuclear RNA (snRNA) [41–43]. Notably, FTO's activity on m^{6}A$_m$ by the 5′-cap was reported to have a 100-fold higher K_{cat}/K_m when compared with internal m^{6}A in ssRNA [41–43], suggesting that m^{6}A$_m$ by the 5′-cap is the major physiological substrate of FTO. The FTO-catalyzed demethylation of m^{7}Gpppm^{6}A$_m$ can impact mRNA stability, mRNA splicing, and degradation [41–43]. For instance, FTO-catalyzed demethylation of m^{6}A$_m$ by the 5′-cap caused the RNA to be more easily degraded by the DCP2 decapping enzyme [41]. Similarly, the consequences of m^{6}A regulation by FTO have been implicated in various biological processes such as mediating heat shock response [44], altering protein translation [45], reversing the effects of m^{6}A methyltransferase complex METTL3:METTL14 in modulating DNA damage response, Hepatitis C viral infection [46, 47], and in several neurodegenerative disorders [48].

In addition to its role in human biology, FTO is also implicated in cancers such as endometrial cancer [49–51], breast cancer [52, 53], acute myeloid leukemia [54], pancreatic cancer [51], and glioblastoma [55]. Therefore, FTO as an RNA-modifying metalloenzyme is of interest as a target for potential anticancer therapies. Aberrant expression of FTO alters the cellular levels of m^{6}A and dictates its role either as a tumor suppressor or tumor promoter in the pathogenesis of various cancers (Table 7.1).

Table 7.1 The roles of FTO in cancers.

Cancer type	Role	Downstream target	Mechanism and physiological outcome	Reference
Acute myeloid leukemia (AML)	Promoter	ASB2 RARA mRNA	Overexpression of FTO in AML reduces m^6A levels and promotes cell proliferation and leukemogenesis while decreasing drug sensitivity.	[54]
Non-small cell lung cancer (NSCLC)	Promoter	E2F1 mRNA	Upregulation of FTO enhances the overexpression of E2F1. FTO/E2F1/NELL2 axis accelerates the migration and invasion of NSCLC tumor cells.	[56]
Cervical cancer	Promoter	ZEB1, Myc mRNA	High expression of FTO mediates the demethylation of ZEB1 and Myc impacting cell proliferation, invasion, and migration of tumor cells.	[57]
Esophageal squamous cell carcinoma	Promoter	LINC00022 lncRNA	FTO overexpression demethylates LINC00022 *in vivo* and results in cell proliferation and tumor progression.	[58]
Gastric cancer	Promoter	HDAC3, FOXA2, Myc	FTO-catalyzed demethylation upregulates the expression of HDAC3 while FOXA2 expression decreases. It also stabilizes Myc mRNA expression and promotes tumorigenesis and metastasis.	[59]
		CAV1 mRNA	FTO-induced degradation of CAV1 mRNA modulates mitochondrial metabolic processes.	[60]
Endometrial cancer	Promoter	HOXB13 mRNA	Elevated expression of FTO is linked with HOXB13 mRNA demethylation and promotes tumor invasion and metastasis via the WNT signaling pathway.	[61]
Colorectal cancer	Suppressor	MTA1	Hypoxia-mediated downregulation of FTO protein exhibits an anti-tumor effect by regulating the MTA1 protein expression in an FTO/IGF2PB2-mediated, m^6A-dependent pathway, both *in vivo* and *in vitro*.	[62]
Breast cancer	Suppressor	KRT7	Upregulation of METTL3 stabilizes the KRT7-AS KRT7 duplex via IGF2BP1/HuR complex, FTO affects the translation elongation of KRT7. FTO overexpression is correlated with metastasis suppression.	[63]
Ovarian cancer	Suppressor	PDEIC, PDE4B	*in vivo*, FTO stabilizes PDEIC and PDE4B genes, activates the cAMP signaling pathway by demethylating the m^6A at 3′ end to suppress tumorigenesis and self-renewal of ovarian cancer cells.	[64]

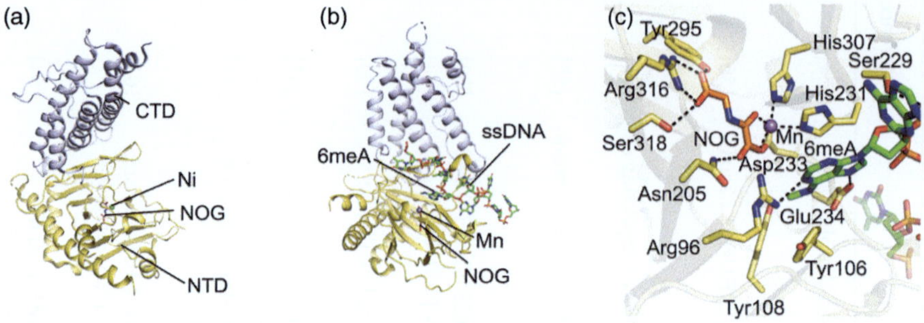

Figure 7.3 Crystal structure of human FTO. (a) Cartoon representation of the overall crystal structure of FTO(32–505) bound to an inert Ni(II) ion (green sphere) and NOG (orange sticks) (PDB ID: 4IDZ). *Source:* [66] / American Chemical Society. The two major domains NTD and CTD are colored yellow-orange and light blue, respectively. (b) Crystal structure of human FTO double mutant (Q86K/Q306K) in complex with Mn(II) (purple sphere) and 6meA modified ssDNA oligo (green sticks) (PDB ID: 5ZMD). *Source:* [67] / National Academy of Sciences. (c) A close-up view of the active site of FTO is shown. The metal ion is octahedrally coordinated by the conserved His231, Asp233, and His307 residues forming the facial triad. NOG (a 2OG mimetic) occupies the 2OG binding site and exhibits bidentate chelation to the metal ion. NOG is stabilized by its interactions with Arg316, Ser318, and Asn205 (black dashed lines). 6meA nucleobase is positioned into the substrate binding pocket facing the active site and forms critical interactions with Arg96 and Glu234.

7.3.2 Crystal Structures of FTO

The first X-ray structure of human FTO (residues 32–505) bound to 3meT nucleoside substrate (PDB ID: 3LFM) was solved in 2010 [65]. The overall structure revealed two well-defined domains: NTD (residues 32–326) and CTD (residues 327–498) with NTD forming the double-stranded β-helix (DSBH) catalytic core (Figure 7.3a). The DSBH fold is a conserved structural feature among 2OG oxygenases and is important for substrate binding as reviewed in [68]. The active site of the enzyme features an Fe(II) ion that is octahedrally coordinated by three conserved residues (His231, Asp233, and His307), which form a HxD/E…H catalytic triad. Consistent with other 2OG oxygenases, the cosubstrate 2OG chelates the active site Fe(II) in a bidentate fashion (Figure 7.3c). FTO exists as a trimer *in crystallo* due to crystal packing and this crystallographic trimer is predominantly mediated by Trp278 [65]. The CTD of FTO represented a novel domain mainly composed of an α-helix bundle and interacts extensively with the NTD. Biochemical studies support that this interaction between the two domains is crucial for enzymatic activity. Notably, FTO also harbors a unique loop L1 (residues 213–224), which is probably important for discriminating between single-stranded and double-stranded substrates [65]. More recently, a crystal structure of an FTO variant (Q86K/Q306K) in complex with a 6meA containing ssDNA oligo (PDB ID: 5ZMD) was determined (Figure 7.3b). The findings from this study rationalized how FTO recognizes its multiple substrates (*N6* methylated substrates) and demonstrates substrate selectivity [67]. Glu234 and Arg96 form major interactions with the 6meA nucleobase while a hydrophobic cavity stabilizes the m^6A nucleobase for demethylation [67].

7.3.3 FTO Inhibition

Among known members of the AlkB nucleic acid oxygenases, FTO is by far the most well-studied target for inhibition. Since FTO and other human AlkB proteins are Fe(II) and 2OG-dependent metalloenzymes, initial studies focused on metal ion chelators and 2OG analogues for FTO inhibition [66]. Complexes of FTO with various small molecule inhibitors have also been characterized by X-ray crystallography, providing insights into the binding modes of the inhibitors and mechanisms of FTO inhibition [66, 69, 70]. The biochemical and kinetic studies combined with crystallographic models serve as guides for rational design of more potent and selective small molecule inhibitors for FTO through structure-based virtual screening of multiple compound libraries [66, 69–72]. Some of the common strategies used for identification, development, and characterization of FTO inhibitors will be discussed below.

7.4 Generic 2OG Mimetic Inhibitors, Metal Ion Chelators

As FTO is a metalloenzyme, utilizing metal chelators for inhibition has been explored in the early stage of FTO inhibitor development. Most of the metal chelators are 2OG mimetics because 2OG chelates the Fe(II) in the active site for a majority of 2OG oxygenases, with only a few exceptions such as isopenicillin synthase (IPNS) [73], 1-aminocyclopropane-1-carboxylic acid (ACCO) [74], and (S)-2-hydroxypropylphosphonic acid epoxidase (HppE) [75]. Aik et. al first reported several classes of 2OG mimetics and their derivatives as inhibitors with the support of crystal structures of FTO-inhibitor complexes [66]. The inhibitor types include broad-spectrum 2OG analogues, such as N-oxalylglycine (NOG, **1**), pyridine-2,4-carboxylate (2,4-PDCA, **2**), 5-carboxy-8-hydroxyquinoline (IOX1, **3**), pyridine glycinamide and derivatives (**4–8**), and FG2216 (**9**). Crystallographic analyses of these inhibitors complexed to FTO (PDB ID: 4IDZ, 4IE0, 4IE4, 4IE5, 4IE6) revealed that they bind in the 2OG binding pocket, chelating to the active site metal (Zn^{2+} substituting Fe(II)) in a bidentate fashion (Figure 7.5a–c) [66]. A carboxylate group from each inhibitor interacted with Arg316, mimicking the 5-carboxylate of 2OG. Following attempts at derivatizing IOX1, pyridyl glycinamide, and FG2216, however, did not result in improved potencies. Steric hindrances of the derivatives can be rationalized from the crystal structures of the FTO-inhibitor scaffold complexes. Interestingly, the inhibition data from the stereoisomeric derivatives of FG2216, while all being less potent than FG2216, suggested stronger FTO inhibition by D-enantiomers (**10–12**) relative to the L-enantiomers (**13–15**) [66]. However, these observations contrasted with previous findings for bacterial AlkB and the HIF prolyl hydroxylase 2, PHD2, both of which are also members of the 2OG oxygenase superfamily, where L-enantiomers were reported as more potent inhibitors for these enzymes [76, 77]. This suggests that designing scaffolds with different stereoisomeric substitutions may be an effective strategy to achieve inhibitor selectivity among different AlkB enzymes.

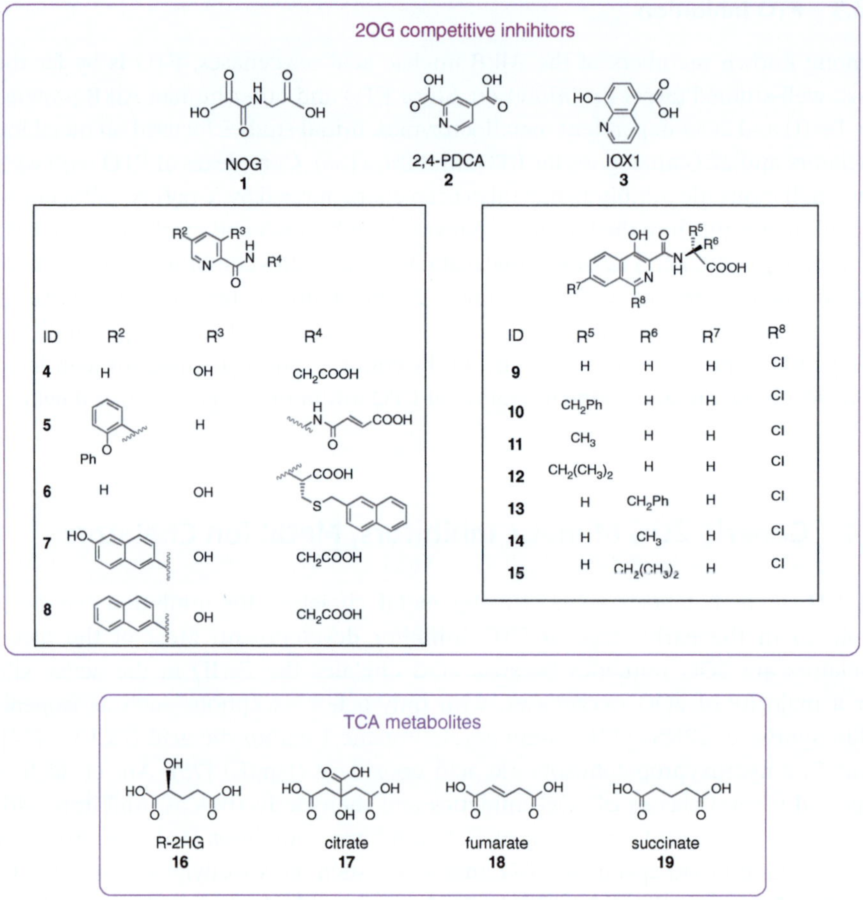

Figure 7.4 2OG competitive inhibitors of FTO. The structural analogues of 2OG and endogenous metabolites of the TCA cycle function as metal-chelating inhibitors of FTO. They have similar binding modes as observed for the natural cosubstrate and they bind within the 2OG binding pocket, thus, competing with 2OG. *Source:* [66] / American Chemical Society.

7.5 Endogenous TCA Metabolites as Inhibitors

7.5.1 R-2HG and Citrate

2-hydroxyglutarate (R-2HG, **16**), a prevalent oncometabolite in IDH1 and IDH2 mutated tumors has been shown to inhibit multiple 2OG oxygenases including TET enzymes and histone demethylases [78, 79]. Behaving as a weak competitor of 2OG, **16** was identified to inhibit FTO (IC_{50} 320 μM) [77] both *in vitro* and *in vivo* and exhibited broad tumor-suppressing effects in leukemia and glioma [78, 79]. In addition to its role as a cosubstrate of FTO and related AlkB enzymes, 2OG also participates in the tricarboxylic acid (TCA) cycle and is produced as an intermediate. Other such TCA metabolites such as citrate (**17**), fumarate (**18**), and succinate (**19**) demonstrated weak inhibition on FTO (**17**, IC_{50} 300 μM; **18**, IC_{50} 150 μM; **19**, IC_{50} 370 μM) [66]. Citrate, from the crystallization buffer, was found to be in the 2OG binding site of a crystal structure of FTO in complex with rhein (PDB ID: 4IE7, see below) (Figure 7.5d) [66]. Interestingly, these compounds displayed varying affinities against other AlkB oxygenases suggesting their role as competitive inhibitors against these enzymes. Furthermore, these observations also hinted toward the potential links between TCA cycle intermediates and 2OG oxygenases and their relevance to human physiology.

In general, the inhibitors discussed above are classified as 2OG competitors as they occupy the 2OG binding pocket. Largely identified and evaluated using virtual screening, X-ray crystallography, structure rationalized drug design, and dynamic combinatorial mass spectrometric techniques, their metal chelating scaffolds (such as oxalyl, pyridyl, carboxylate groups) facilitate their coordination to the active site metal ion in a similar bidentate manner to 2OG (Figure 7.4). The major limitation of these inhibitors is their broad selectivity toward other 2OG oxygenases such as AlkB enzymes acting on nucleic acid substrates, PHDs, KDMs, and JmjC demethylases [82, 83]. These enzymes share a conserved architecture of the active site which is amenable to inhibition by the 2OG competitive inhibitors. This precludes them from qualifying as drug candidates specifically targeting FTO. Nonetheless, these compounds serve as excellent templates that can be optimized to design inhibitors with improved selectivity and enhanced potency.

7.5.2 Substrate Competitive Inhibitors

An alternative strategy to inhibit FTO involves developing inhibitors that bind the primary nucleic acid substrate binding site. Most of the initial hits of the discovered inhibitors originated from high throughput and virtual screens, which were subsequently used for structure-based optimization to develop second-generation inhibitors. These FTO-substrate competitors have been classified based on the strategies used for their identification and are discussed in the following sections.

7.6 High Throughput Virtual Screening for Inhibitor Development

7.6.1 Rhein and Meclofenamic Acid

Chen *et. al* in 2012 reported the first reversible and competitive inhibition of FTO using a natural anthraquinone compound rhein (**20**) [84] through structure-based virtual screening. Rhein was determined as the lead compound for FTO with IC_{50} values ranging from 9 μM to 30 μM depending on the biochemical assays used to evaluate it [66, 84]. Subsequent crystallographic studies of the FTO-**20** complex (PDB ID: 4IE7) revealed the binding mode of rhein, which occupied the prime substrate binding site of FTO (Figure 7.5d). Rhein formed hydrogen bonds with the side chains of Ser229 and Arg96 and partial π-π stacking with the

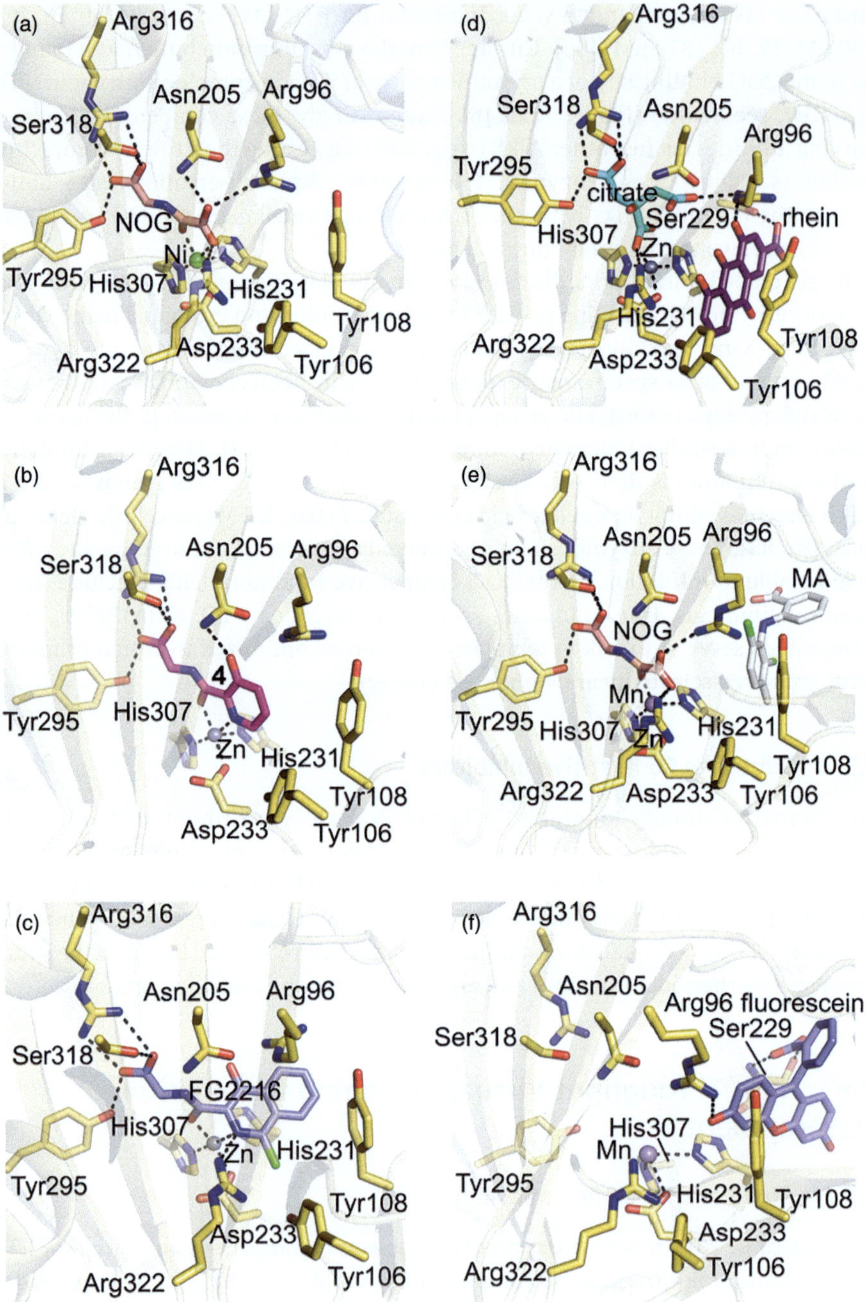
(a)
Arg316
Asn205
Arg96
Ser318
NOG
Ni
Tyr295
His307
His231
Tyr108
Arg322
Asp233
Tyr106
(b)
Arg316
Ser318
Asn205
Arg96
4
Tyr295
His307
Zn
His231
Tyr108
Asp233
Tyr106
(c)
Arg316
Asn205
Arg96
Ser318
FG2216
His307
Zn
His231
Tyr295
Tyr108
Asp233
Arg322
Tyr106
(d)
Arg316
Ser318
Asn205
Arg96
Tyr295
citrate
Ser229
rhein
His307
Zn
His231
Arg322
Tyr108
Asp233
Tyr106
(e)
Arg316
Asn205
Arg96
Ser318
MA
NOG
Mn
Tyr295
His307
His231
Zn
Tyr108
Arg322
Asp233
Tyr106
(f)
Arg316
Asn205
Arg96 fluorescein
Ser318
Ser229
His307
Mn
Tyr295
His231
Tyr108
Asp233
Arg322
Tyr106

Figure 7.5 FTO inhibition by 2OG competitive and substrate-competitive inhibitors. Active site views of FTO (32–505) complexed to (a) NOG (**1**) (PDB ID: 4IDZ, salmon sticks). *Source:* [66] / American Chemical Society, (b) Compound **4** (glycyl hydroxypyridine 2OG analogues) (PDB ID: 4 IE5, magenta sticks). *Source:* [66] / American Chemical Society, (c) FG2216 (9) (PDB ID: 4 IE6, purple sticks). *Source:* [66] / American Chemical Society, (d) Citrate (17) (cyan sticks) and rhein (**20**) (purple sticks) (PDB ID: 4 IE7). *Source:* [66] / American Chemical Society, (e) MA (**21**) (PDB ID: 4QKN, grey sticks). *Source:* [80] / Oxford University Press and (f) Fluorescein (**23**) (PDB ID: 4ZS2, purple sticks). *Source:* [81] / American Chemical Society. NOG, pyridine glycinamide, citrate, and FG2216 are 2OG competitors and predominantly bind in the 2OG binding pocket. Notably, FG2216 is seen partially extending into the substrate binding pocket. Rhein, MA, and fluorescein are substrate-competitive inhibitors and are seen residing in the substrate binding pocket. The interacting FTO residues are shown in sticks and the color scheme and labeling are the same as previously described in Figure 7.3.

imidazole ring of H231 (a catalytically important residue) [66]. Although rhein was shown as a cell-active inhibitor of FTO, the broad targeting exhibited by rhein toward other AlkB metalloenzymes limited its use as a therapeutic probe [85]. Meclofenamic acid (MA, **21**) was later discovered to be another cell-active substrate competitor of FTO by a fluorescence polarization-based high-throughput screening method [80]. Structural investigations on the FTO-**21** complex (PDB ID 4QKN) revealed that, similar to rhein (**20**), **21** occupied the substrate binding site and is stabilized by a network of hydrogen bonding and hydrophobic interactions (Figure 7.5e). Unlike rhein, MA demonstrated selectivity toward FTO over other AlkB enzymes. Structural findings reveal that MA interacts extensively with the residues on the β-hairpin loop of nucleotide recognition lid (NRL), and this interaction is a critical determinant for selectivity [80]. Both rhein and MA are among the earliest substrate-competitive inhibitors and have stimulated interest in the development of improved FTO inhibitors with enhanced potency using structure-based drug design (see below).

7.6.2 Rhein and MA Analogues via High-Throughput Screening

Besides rhein and MA, high-throughput virtual screening techniques have identified several other selective inhibitors with unique scaffolds for FTO such as the FDA-approved dihydroxybenzene compound entacapone (**22**) [86, 87]. Contrary to the methods described for MA and rhein, the screening techniques that led to the identification of amilorides and metizoline derivatives (rhein analogues) [88] and fluorescein (fluorescent MA analogue, **23**) [81], focused on monitoring the enzymatic activity of FTO upon inhibition. The screening assay for amilorides and metizoline pharmacophores used a fluorometric m^6A-Broccoli RNA as the substrate which exhibited fluorescence upon demethylation [88]. Similarly, fluorescein (**23**) and its structural derivatives FL2 (**24**) and FL2-DZ (**25**) demonstrated selective inhibition of FTO *in vitro* while enabling direct labeling of intracellular FTO [81]. Although the precise binding modes of amilorides and metizoline compounds remain elusive due to lack of availability of structural data, crystallographic complexes of fluorescein (PDB ID: 4ZS2) [81] (Figure 7.4) and 5-aminofluorescein

(**26**) (PDB ID: 4ZS3) [81] suggest a similar binding mode to MA [80]. The potential steric clashes between 5-amino group of **26** with neighboring hydrophobic residues explain the weakened inhibition effect (IC_{50} 6.55 μM) relative to (**23**, IC_{50} 3.23 μM) [81].

7.6.3 Other Scaffolds

In addition to the mentioned inhibitors, CS1 (**27**) and CS2 (**28**), were also discovered via structure-based virtual screening. Reports suggested that these compounds regulated the expression of MYC and RARA by inhibiting the binding of these mRNA to FTO [71]. Demonstrating enhanced inhibition potency in nanomolar range (**27**, IC_{50} 0.17 μM; **28**, IC_{50} 0.56 μM), both inhibitors were promising anticancer therapeutic candidates for AML [89].

In yet another example of exploiting the binding site of MA using molecular modeling and virtual-based screening, both FTO-02 (**29**) and FTO-04 (**30**) were found to be more potent inhibitors of FTO (**29**, IC_{50} 2.18 μM; **30**, IC_{50} 3.39 μM) over ALKBH5 (**29**, IC_{50} 85.5 μM; **30**, IC_{50} 39.4 μM) [90]. Interestingly, compound **30**-induced FTO inhibition increased the cellular levels of m^6A and m^6A_m in GSCs in a similar manner to FTO knockdown cells [90]. A similar study also reported that **30** impeded the neurosphere formation in glioblastoma without affecting the healthy human neural stem cells (hNSCs), thereby diminishing the self-renewal properties of GSCs [90].

Following this, the same group identified the oxetanyl derivatives of **30**, with FTO-43 (**31**) as the lead compound [91], which competitively inhibited FTO and demonstrated antiproliferation in multiple cancer stem cell models. Moreover, the improved potency of compound **31** (IC_{50} 1 μM) enabled the modulation of Wnt/PI3K-Akt signaling pathways and resulted in increased m^6A and m^6A_m in gastric cancer cells [91].

7.7 Structure-Based Rational Inhibitor Design

The wealth of structural knowledge of FTO inhibition with 2OG as well as substrate competitors has aided in the development of improved inhibitor design. The chemical structures of reported substrate-specific inhibitors are depicted in Figure 7.6 and Figure 7.7.

7.7.1 Two Component Acylhydrazine Derivatives

In the quest for developing cell-active inhibitors with enhanced selectivity for a specific AlkB enzyme, Toh *et al.* designed a series of "two component inhibitors" for FTO [92]. The structural differences within the substrate binding domains of different AlkB enzymes govern substrate specificity. Designing compounds that concurrently block the 2OG as well as the distinct substrate binding site of AlkB metalloenzymes is an effective strategy for developing selective inhibitors. Similar

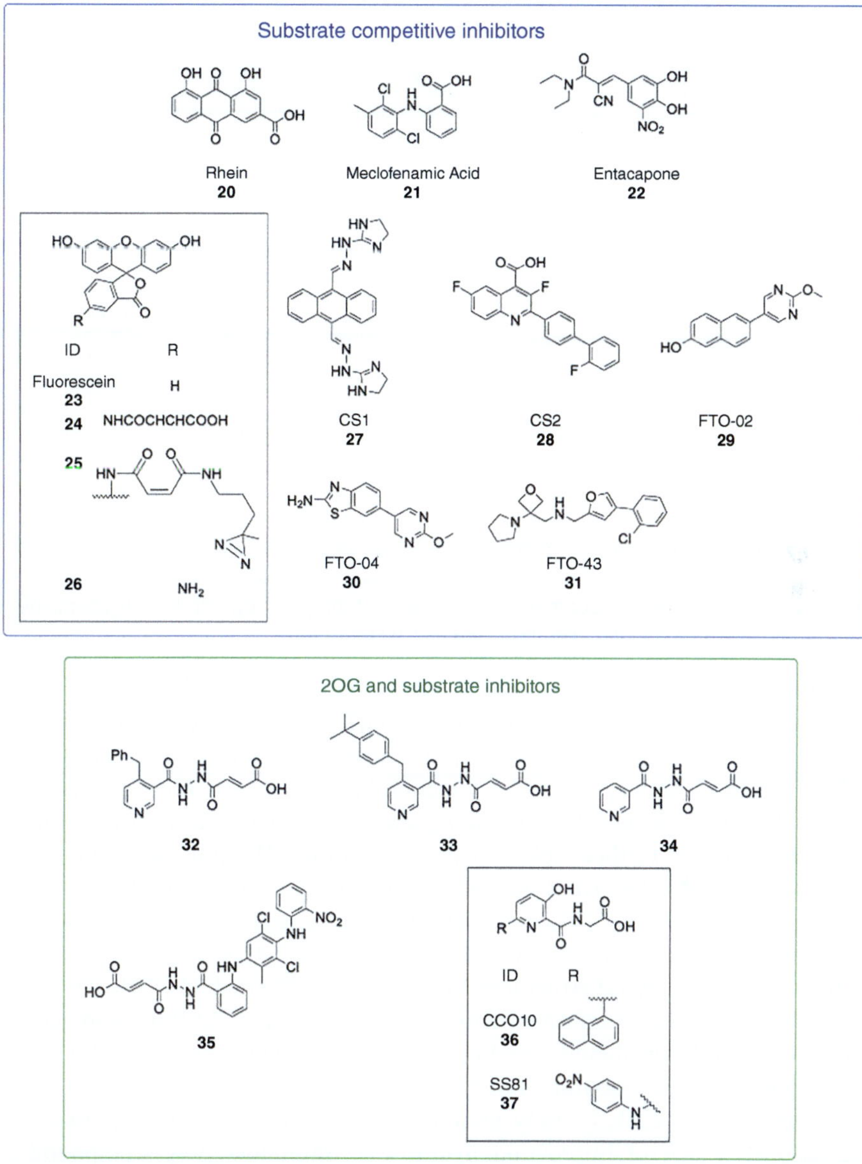

Figure 7.6 Substrate competitive inhibitors of FTO. This class of FTO inhibitors includes compounds that exclusively bind to the nucleic acid substrate binding pocket of FTO and bind both the 2OG and substrate binding sites developed by structure-based drug design approaches.

strategy has previously resulted in highly selective inhibitors for JmjC histone demethylases with enhanced potency [93].

For FTO, in particular, a compound possessing a fumarate hydrazide scaffold (2OG binding component) linked to 4-benzyl pyridine side chain (nucleotide-specific component) (**32**) effectively inhibited the demethylation (IC_{50} 0.81 μM) [92]. A

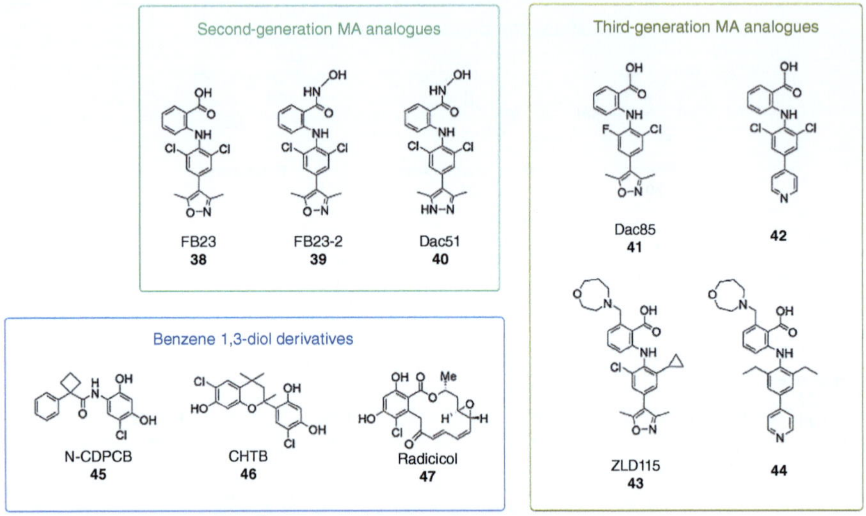

Figure 7.7 Chemical structures of FTO inhibitors developed by structure-based rationalization. Second and third-generation analogues of MA were developed by structure-based drug design approaches and showed high potency. Additionally, benzene 1,3-diol derivatives have also been reported as FTO inhibitors.

crystallographic structure of FTO.**32** (PDB ID: 4CXW) revealed that **32** occupied both the 2OG and the substrate binding site (3mT-FTO complex was chosen as the model substrate) [65], simultaneously preventing the binding of both substrate as well as the cosubstrate. A critical interaction between the pyridine nitrogen and Glu234 of FTO was responsible for binding selectivity [92]. HPLC and MALDI-based biochemical assays further validated that compound **32** significantly preferably inhibits FTO over other AlkB enzymes. Structural analogues of **32**, with either substituted 4-benzyl ring (**33**) or lacking the 4-benzyl ring altogether (**34**) were comparatively less potent (**33**, IC_{50} 2.11 μM, **34**, IC_{50} 11.8 μM) as rationalized by their respective crystal structures **33** (PDB ID 4CXX) and **34** (PDB ID: 4CXY) [92]. MTT assays were performed with an ester prodrug of **32** (for improved cell penetration and bioavailability) and reported over 80% cell viability in HeLa cells, suggesting that the compound is not cytotoxic.

Furthermore, in 2021, a study employed the fragment-merging approach for the rational design of improvised hybrid FTO inhibitors [94]. Compound **35** was synthesized by combining the acyl hydrazine moiety of **32** [92] with MA, **21** [80] and resulted in a highly potent and selective inhibitor of FTO (**35**, IC_{50} 0.087 μM) (Figure 7.8b). The ester prodrug of **35** was shown to effectively reduce the cell viability in AML by downregulating and upregulating MYC and RARA respectively [94].

7.7.2 Pyridyl Glycinamides Derivatives

Another study by Shishodia *et al.* reported a structure-informed approach to guide the design of inhibitors competing with both the 2OG cosubstrate and the substrate nucleobase for binding [69]. Based on the crystal structures of FTO-**04** (pyridinyl glycinamide) (PDB ID: 4IE5) and FTO-rhein (PDB ID: 4IE7), C-6 functionalization of pyridine glycinamides resulted in compound CCO10 (**36**) that contains a pyridinyl glycinamide that occupies the 2OG binding site and a naphthalene moiety mimicking rhein [69]. The binding mode of CCO10 was subsequently confirmed crystallographically (PDB ID: 4QHO) (Figure 7.8a). Subsequently, based on CCO10, a more potent inhibitor SS81 (**37**) was developed with its naphthalene portion being replaced by a nitropheyl aniline group to enhance flexibility. Both CCO10 and SS81 have enhanced inhibitory activity (**36**, IC_{50} 2.3 μM; **37**, IC_{50} 1.5 μM) relative to the parent compounds **4** and rhein, and selectivity over other related AlkB oxygenases [69]. The inhibition of FTO by these compounds was determined by nuclear magnetic resonance (NMR) studies (for competitive 2OG inhibition), liquid chromatography mass spectrometry (LCMS), and solid phase extraction-mass spectrometry (SPE-MS) based *in vitro* assays. In particular, the crystal structure of FTO.**37** (PDB ID: 7E8Z) manifested a conformational change in the side chain of Glu234 in the presence of **37** [69]. The nitrophenyl moiety of **37** pushes Glu234 away from the active site, plausibly explaining the enhanced inhibition exhibited by **37** (Figure 7.8a).

7.7.3 Second-Generation MA Analogues *(FB23, FB23-2, and Dac51)*

The crystal structure of FTO bound to MA revealed vacant space within the substrate binding pocket of FTO. Structure–activity relationship (SAR) analyses on MA facilitated the design of structural analogues with scaffolds that could extend further into the deep pocket and completely occupy the substrate binding site. To this end, tricyclic benzoic acid FB23 (**38**) was developed as a promising therapeutic probe for the treatment of AML and demonstrated remarkable inhibitory activity against FTO (**38**, IC_{50} 0.06 μM) [95]. The crystal structure of FTO.**38** was solved (PDB ID 6AKW) and the isoxazole ring of **38** was seen extending into the substrate binding region of FTO as compared to the binding pocket being partially occupied by MA (Figure 7.8c). The compound was stabilized via hydrogen bonding with Glu234 while the phenyl ring formed hydrophobic interactions with the NRL residues on FTO [95]. This largely rationalized the high potency of **38** for FTO *in vitro*.

To enhance cell permeability of FB23, the carboxylate group of FB23 was substituted for a hydroxamate moiety in benzohydroxamic acid (FB23-2) (**39**). Besides demonstrating selective inhibition against FTO both *in vitro* (IC_{50} 2.6 μM) as well as in NB4 and MONOMAC6 cell lines, FB23-2 greatly improved the cell-penetrating ability of **38** and significantly suppressed AML proliferation, as confirmed by cell-based assays [95]. Similarly, optimization of FB23 and FB23-2 led to the discovery of Dac51 (**40**) with a high potency (IC_{50} 0.4 μM) [98, 99]. *In vivo* studies concluded that Dac51 displays minimal cell toxicity and is majorly involved in regulating glycolytic metabolism in tumor cells. The inhibition of glycolytic activity is a consequence of FTO-mediated demethylation, which enhances T-cell production and inhibits solid tumor growth [98, 99].

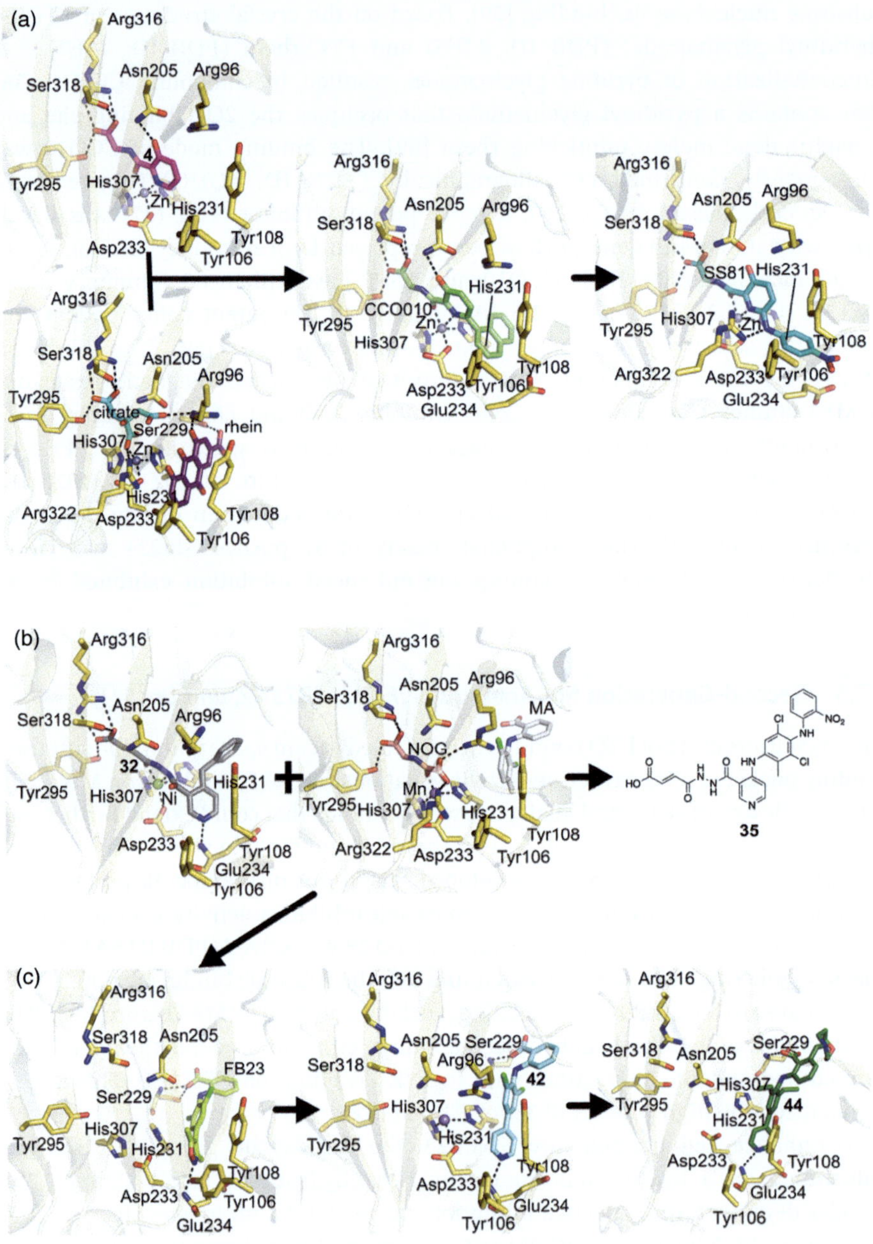
(a)
Arg316
Ser318
Asn205
Arg96
4
Tyr295
His307
Zn
His231
Tyr108
Asp233
Tyr106
CCO010
SS81
Arg322
Glu234
citrate
Ser229
rhein
(b)
32
Ni
NOG
MA
Mn
35
(c)
FB23
42
44

Figure 7.8 Structure-based FTO inhibitor development. (a) Active site views of FTO complexed to **4** (PDB ID: 4 IE5) and rhein (**20**) (PDB ID: 4 IE7), which were used to guide inhibitor design spanning across both 2OG and substrate binding sites. C6 functionalization of **4** enabled the design of CCO10 (**36**) (PDB ID: 4QHO, green sticks) [69] and SS81 (**27**) (PDB ID: 7E8Z, cyan sticks), *Source:* [69] / American Chemical Society / CC BY 4.0 both of which strongly inhibit FTO by binding to the substrate as well as the 2OG binding site. (b) Views from the active site of FTO complex with acylydrazine inhibitor (**32**) (PDB ID: 4CXW, dark gray sticks) [92] and MA (**21**) (PDB ID: 4QKN, gray sticks) [80]. In a fragment-merging approach, HZ and MA were combined to develop hybrid inhibitors that bind across both 2OG and the substrate binding region. (c) Views from the crystal structure of FTO bound to an MA analogue FB23 (**38**) (PDB ID: 6AKW, lime sticks) that extend into the vacant space within the substrate binding pocket [95]. Further substitution at either of the rings of FB23 prompted the design of **42** (PDB ID: 7WCV, cyan sticks) [96] and **44** (PDB ID: 8IT9, dark green sticks) [97].

7.7.4 Third-Generation MA Analogues *(SAR of tricyclic benzoic acids)*

As described, the investigation son tricyclic benzoic acid derivatives of MA (FB23 and FB23–2) showed great potential as therapeutic probes, opening avenues for further tuning the chemical space of MA via SAR analysis. Liu *et al.* (2022) designed a series of optimized inhibitors by individually substituting each ring in FB23 with aryl groups or heterocyclic scaffolds [96, 100, 101]. Notably, Dac85 (**41**) bearing halogen substituents (F and Cl) on the phenyl ring displayed remarkable inhibition against FTO *in vitro* (IC_{50} 0.7 μM) [96]. Compared to FB23, Dac85 demonstrated excellent antiproliferative effects on AML cells and significantly prolonged the survival in mice without displaying any visible side effects [96]. In the second series of optimization, the heterocyclic 3,5-dimethylisizole ring was replaced with a pyridine ring to synthesize compound **42** with a high potency (IC_{50} 1.5 μM) [96]. While fluorescence-based thermal shift assays indicated direct engagement between **42** and FTO, structural characterization of the FTO-bound **42** complex (PDB ID:7WCV) provided insights into the inhibitor binding mode (Figure 7.8c). The crystal structure showed that **42** extensively interacts with Glu234, Arg96, and Ser229 residues, and these interactions plausibly contribute to inhibition [96].

While Dac85 and FB23 exerted strong inhibition, the rigid chain structures of these compounds may limit their use as therapeutic probes in clinical trials. In 2023, the same research group attempted to ameliorate the tricyclic benzoic acid inhibitor design by incorporating a flexible basic side chain into the solvent-exposed regions of Dac85 [97]. To weaken this molecular rigidity and to improve the pharmacokinetic profile, they designed a series of FB23 derivatives with a 1,4-oxazepane pharmacore motif inserted at the 5- and 6- positions of the benzoic acid [97]. Among them, ZLD115 (**43**) was identified as the selective and potent FTO inhibitor with improved drug-like properties. The middle dichlorobenzene ring was substituted with the chlorine and cyclopropane functional group and displayed significant antiproliferative effects in AML cell lines as well as antileukemic activity in mice. Compared to FB23 and Dac85, the pharmacokinetics of ZLD115 were considerably enhanced. Further structural investigations on another related compound **44** from this series bound to FTO (PDB ID:8IT9) revealed that these tricyclic derivatives bind in a substrate-competitive manner (Figure 7.8c) [97].

7.8 Benzene-1,3-Diol Derivatives

From the class of benzene-1,3-diol derivatives, N-CDPCB (**45**) [102], CHTB (**46**) [103], and radicicol (**47**) [70] exhibited selective inhibition against FTO. Among these compounds, **45** showed the most effective inhibition (IC_{50} 4.95 μM) allowing for cell permeability [102]. This was followed by **47** (IC_{50} 16.04 μM) [70] and **46** (IC_{50} 39.24 μM) [103] and their respective crystal structures: FTO.**45** (PDB ID: 5DAB) and FTO.**46** (PDB ID: 5F8P) were determined by X-ray crystallography. The crystal structure of FTO.**45** presented an unprecedented binding mode with respect to other FTO-inhibitor complexes with MA [80] and rhein [66] and the 3mT substrate-bound structure [65]. In the active site of the enzyme, **45** was seen residing in the substrate binding site proximal to the solvent-exposed regions of FTO, partially masking the opening of the exterior groovc. The perpendicular binding orientation of **45** strikingly contrasted with previously established complex structures [65, 66, 80] enabling extensive interactions of N-CDPCB with antiparallel β-sheet of FTO and the extended NRL loop [102]. Compared to **45**, the binding mode of CHTB (PDB ID: 5F8P) resembled that of compound MA [80] and majority of the key interactions were conserved [103]. Radicicol, the 4-Cl-1,3-diol substituent of **45** and **46**, was identified through virtual-based screening and mirrored N-CDPCB [102] in occupying the binding site of FTO, predominantly in the L-shaped conformation [70]. However, the 1,3-diol group, conserved in both **45** and **47** adopted contrasting orientations in the enzyme's active site [70].

In summary, the evolution of FTO inhibitors highlights how structure-based drug discovery can prove to be an indispensable tool in enzyme inhibition. Over ~60 inhibitors for FTO have been identified to date (Figures 7.4, 7.6 and 7.7) and many of them are structurally characterized by X-ray crystallography (Figures 7.5 and 7.8). In general, the presently reported inhibitors can be roughly categorized into four groups based on their binding and inhibition mode: (i) 2OG competitors such as NOG, 2,4-PDCA, IOX1, R-2HG, (ii) Substrate competitors such as rhein, meclofenamic acid (MA), N-CDPCB that bind to the substrate outer pocket, (iii) Substrate competitors binding to the inner pocket such as FB23, FB23–2, Dac51, Dac85, and (iv) 2OG and substrate competitors such as acylhydrazines (HZ), pyridyl glycinamide derivatives, and HZ-MA hybrid. There are other inhibitors with undetermined binding modes as well. While most of these reported inhibitors demonstrated exceptional inhibitory strengths, a recurring limitation is their use *in vivo*. For the inhibitors with acidic groups, using ester prodrugs was previously reported to be an effective strategy that improves the drug-like properties of these compounds as demonstrated in the case of NOG [104], FB23 [95], and HZ-MA [94].

7.9 AlkB Human Homologue 5 (ALKBH5)

7.9.1 Biological Functions of ALKBH5 in RNA Metabolism

Following FTO, ALKBH5 was identified as another Fe(II) and 2OG-dependent m^6A demethylase [105]. ALKBH5 targets m^6A in both ssRNA and ssDNA substrates [105] with ssRNA being the physiological substrate. Besides m^6A, ALKBH5 has also been reported to exert demethylation activity on N^6, N^6-dimethyladenosine ($m^6{}_2A$), a modification commonly found on rRNA [106]. However, biochemical investigations reported that ALKBH5 demethylates m^6A more efficiently than $m^6{}_2A$, establishing itself as an m^6A demethylase [106]. Although both FTO and ALKBH5 catalyze the oxidative demethylation of the same m^6A substrate, their enzymatic activity varies in different cellular contexts (Figure 7.9). Factors such as subcellular localization of the enzymes, substrate sequence specificity, mRNA accessibility, and interactions with respective binding partner proteins potentially regulate the demethylation ability of the two enzymes, as reviewed in [108]. As a nuclear protein, ALKBH5 is predominantly found in the nucleus and associates with the mRNA processing machinery, indicating m^6A demethylation during mRNA biogenesis [105]. ALKBH5 is highly expressed in testis; knockout of ALKBH5 in male mice resulted in aberrant spermatogenesis [105]. Furthermore, knockdown of ALKBH5 in humans elevated the levels of m^6A in polyadenylated mRNA and expedited translocation of mRNA into the cytoplasm from the nucleus, suggesting potential involvement of this demethylase in mRNA synthesis and splicing [105].

7.9.2 ALKBH5 in Human Diseases and Cancer

Aberrant expression of ALKBH5 is associated with various pathological disorders. In recurrent miscarriages, ALKBH5 overexpression represses the trophoblastic cell invasion and destabilizes the CYR61 mRNA in an m^6A-dependent manner [109]. Similarly, studies suggesting ALKBH5's involvement in ischemic heart diseases [110], osteogenesis [111], and Hirschsprung's disease [112] have been reported.

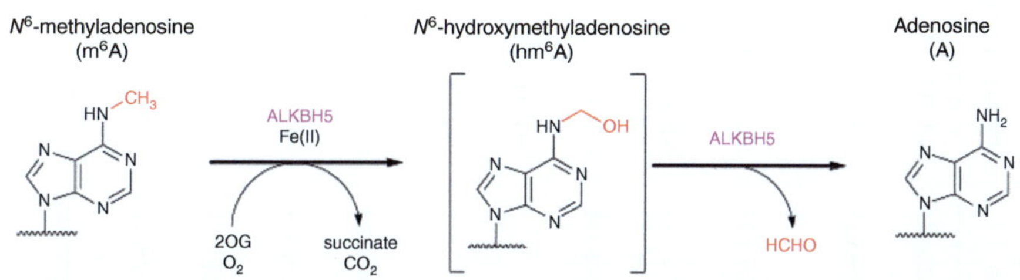

Figure 7.9 Reaction schematic for ALKBH5-catalyzed oxidation of m^6A. ALKBH5 catalyzes the oxidation of m^6A substrate producing a nascent hemiaminal species, hm^6A. Unlike FTO, the hm^6A formed is transient and rapidly fragments to produce demethylated adenosine and formaldehyde [40, 107]. The spontaneous fragmentation of the hydroxylated hm^6A is proposed to occur via an enzyme-mediated proton shuttle mechanism [107]. As a result, adenosine is generated as the sole reaction product during ALKBH5 catalysis of m^6A.

Table 7.2 The roles of ALKBH5 in cancers.

Cancer type	Role	Downstream target	Mechanism and physiological outcome	Reference
Breast cancer	Promoter	NANOG, KLF4	Overexpression of ALKBH5 under hypoxia reduces the m^6A levels in NANOG mRNA and stabilizes the transcripts leading to breast cancer initiation, metastasis, and maintenance.	[113, 117]
Glioblastoma	Promoter	FOXM1 mRNA	Knockdown of ALKBH5 suppresses GSC proliferation and tumor progression via FOXM1 overexpression. Silencing of ALKBH5 minimizes binding of the FOXM1 pre-mRNA to human antigen R (HuR), which is involved in mRNA stabilization.	[16]
Gastric cancer	Promoter	JAK1 mRNA	Expression of JAK1 is upregulated upon ALKBH5-induced m^6A demethylation, leading to cell proliferation and metastasis of gastric cancer cells.	[118]
		NEAT1 lncRNA	Overexpression of ALKBH5 promotes the upregulation of NEAT1 which subsequently affects the expression of downstream targets responsible for invasion and metastasis.	[119]
NSCLC	Promoter	SOCS2	The interleukin-6-regulated JAK–STAT pathway is activated upon ALKBH5-induced m^6A regulation of SOCS2.	[120]
		FOXM1	Elevated levels of ALKBH5 under intermittent hypoxia enhance FOXM1 mRNA translation, resulting in enhanced proliferation and cell invasion in lung adenocarcinoma.	[121]
		TIMP3	Ectopic upregulation of ALKBH5 is correlated with destabilization of TIMP3 mRNA and repressing translation, thereby leading to poor patient survival.	[122]
Ovarian cancer	Promoter	BCL2 mRNA	Overexpression of ALKBH5 in epithelial ovarian cancer is responsible for stabilizing BCL2 mRNA, which is associated with enhanced malignancy and poor survival rate.	[123]
AML	Promoter	TACC3 and AXL	Upregulation of ALKBH5 selectively enhances the self-renewal capacity of leukemia stem cells and promotes malignancy by regulating m^6A levels of TACC3 and AXL.	[120]
Pancreatic cancer	Suppressor	PER1	Overexpression of ALKBH5 is correlated with period circadian regulator 1 (PER1) demethylation in an m^6A-YTHDF2-dependent manner.	[125]
NSCLC	Suppressor	YAP1	ALKBH5 impacts the expression of YAP1 in a YTHDFs-dependent manner and decreases its activity to inhibit cell proliferation and metastasis.	[126]
Hepatocellular carcinoma	Suppressor	LYPD1	ALKBH5 acts as a tumor suppressor by demethylating the m^6A-containing LYPD1 transcripts and subsequently inhibiting its binding to IGF2BP1.	[127]
Bladder cancer	Suppressor	ITGA6	ALKBH5-induced m^6A demethylation of ITGA6 suppresses the YTHDF1/3-dependent translation, leading to altered cell adhesion patterns.	[128]

However, akin to FTO, ALKBH5 has also been investigated for its roles in tumor progression and suppression in several human cancers as listed in Table 7.2. Additionally, previous studies have also highlighted the potential links between hypoxia and dysregulation of ALKBH5 [113–115]. In 2011, an initial study by Thalhammer et al. reported that ALKBH5 is directly targeted by the hypoxia-inducible factor-1 (HIF-1) and influences the cellular responses under hypoxia [116]. For instance, in breast cancer, the microenvironment of tumor cells is hypoxic; ALKBH5 might aid cancer progression in these hypoxic environments [114, 115, 117]. The tumorigenic roles of ALKBH5 as an oncogene as well as a tumor suppressor have been summarized in Table 7.2. Since the majority of the downstream targets and associated tumorigenic pathways are impacted in an m^6A-dependent manner, the demethylation activity of ALKBH5 might be linked to oncogenesis. Therefore, it is imperative to elucidate the molecular mechanisms of ALKBH5 to understand the mechanisms of pathogenesis involving ALKBH5 because this would impact the design of anticancer therapies targeting ALKBH5.

7.9.3 Crystal Structures of ALKBH5 and Mechanisms of m^6A demethylation

Following the discovery of ALKBH5 as an m^6A RNA demethylase, four independent groups reported crystal structures of ALKBH5 from humans (PDB ID: 4NJ4, 4NRO, 4OCT) [129–131] and zebrafish (PDB ID: 4NPL) [132]. The catalytic DSBH core fold of ALKBH5 is divided into a major and minor beta sheet consisting of four antiparallel β-sheets each (Figure 7.10a). Three α helices flank the DSBH core that contains the active site. The active site Mn(II) ion (catalytically inactive ion substitute) exhibits octahedral coordination to His204, Asp206, His266, and 2OG (bidentate chelation) [129–131]. The 2OG binding site is in a cavity within two β-sheets and enables substrate access. The nucleotide recognition lid (NRL) of ALKBH5 is composed of two β-hairpin loops: NRL1 (β2-β3) and NRL2 (β4-β5).

More recently, three X-ray crystal structures of ALKBH5 complexed to m^6A-modified ssRNA oligo (PDB ID: 7WKV, 7WL0, and 7V4G) were reported providing significant insights into the substrate recognition and demethylation mechanisms of ALKBH5 (Figure 7.10b) [107]. Structural findings complemented with biochemical investigations allowed for a proposed proton shuttle mechanism on how ALKBH5 catalyzes the rapid fragmentation of the nascent hemiaminal N^6-hydroxymethyladenosine (hm^6A) intermediate to produce adenosine and formaldehyde, which contrasts with FTO that produces the hm^6A alongside the demethylated adenosine [107]. The results revealed that the 5′-3′ direction of the ssRNA substrate when bound to the active site of ALKBH5 is opposite to substrates bound to other AlkB subfamily members, including ssDNA bound to FTO, accounting for the differences in the demethylation mechanisms of ALKBH5 and FTO [107]. The complex structures of ALKBH5-RNA also revealed how ALKBH5 recognizes the consensus (A/G)m^6AC sequence motif.

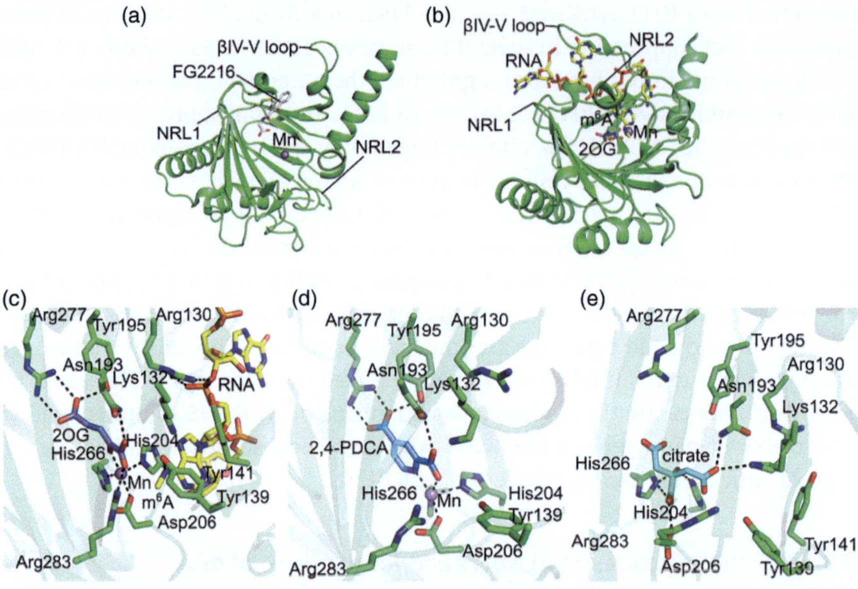

Figure 7.10 Representative crystal structures of human ALKBH5. Cartoon representation of (a) human ALKBH5(66–292) bound to Mn(II) (purple sphere) and FG2216 (**9**) (PDB ID: 4NJ4, light gray sticks). *Source:* [129] / Oxford University Press. (b) Human ALKBH5(74–292) complexed to Mn(II), 2OG (purple sticks) and m^{6}A modified ssRNA oligo (yellow sticks) (PDB ID: 7WKV). *Source:* [107] / Oxford University Press. The structural elements NRL1, NRL2, and βIV-V loop are critical for substrate recognition and binding and undergo conformational changes upon substrate binding. (c) Close-up view of active site of ALKBH5 highlighting the 2OG and the m^{6}A nucleobase binding sites. The metal chelating residues (His204, Asp206, and His266) and 2OG/m^{6}A interacting residues are shown as sticks and the black dashed lines represent the interactions. Notably, the m^{6}A substrate can be seen pointing toward the catalytic site in a position favorable for catalysis. Active site views of ALKBH5(66–292) inhibitor complexes are shown bound to (d) 2,4-PDCA (**2**) (PDB ID: 4NRQ, blue sticks) (e) Citrate (**17**) (PDB ID: 4NRM). Both the inhibitors bind in the 2OG binding site. *Source:* Adapted from [130].

7.10 ALKBH5 Inhibition

7.10.1 Citrate and 2OG Analogues

Initial studies reported several broad-spectrum 2OG competitors as inhibitors for ALKBH5 [87, 92, 129–132]. Like other 2OG oxygenases, these inhibitors were presumed to chelate to the metal ion center by displacing 2OG in the cosubstrate binding site. Among the endogenous TCA metabolites, citrate (**17**), for example, was identified as the moderate inhibitor (IC_{50} 488 μM) of ALKBH5 and the crystal structure of ALKBH5.**17** complex revealed that the binding of citrate into the 2OG binding site occurs without the presence of a metal in the active site (PDB ID: 4O61, 4NRM) (Figure 7.10e) [130, 131]. Crystallographic analyses of ALKBH5 complexes with 2OG structural analogues: NOG (**1**) (PDB ID: 4NRP, 4NRO) [130] and 2,4-PDCA (**2**) (PDB ID: 4NRQ) (Figure 7.10d) [130], and succinate (**19**) (PDB

ID: 4NPM) [132] demonstrated similar binding mode with all the compounds occupying the 2OG binding site. Besides, these structural analogues and metabolites of 2OG displayed weak coordination to the metal ion, potentially because they lacked an oxalyl group. While these compounds demonstrated varying potencies against the AlkB subfamily of proteins, the major drawback of 2OG competitive inhibitors is their lack of enzyme selectivity.

7.10.2 Structure–Activity Relationship

Several independent groups have started to develop small molecule inhibitors of ALKBH5 using a combination of virtual screening, derivative synthesis, and assessment of their SARs. Unlike FTO, many of the identified compounds lack support from crystal structures of ALKBH5-inhibitor complexes. So far, high-throughput virtual screening of inhibitors against ALKBH5 resulted in compounds with moderate potencies. For example, virtual screening of 180 000 compounds led to the identification of a pyrazolo[1,5-*a*]pyrimidine-based compound, DDO-2728 (**48**) as a novel selective inhibitor of ALKBH5 for AML [133]. The inhibition potency of **48** (IC_{50} 2.97 μM) was verified by a combination of biochemical assays and cell-based assays. *In vivo*, DDO-2728 markedly elevated the cellular levels of m^6A, directly targeted the ALKBH5-TACC3 signaling pathway, and demonstrated antiproliferative effects in AML cancer cells [133]. The binding mode of DDO-2728 is not structurally characterized. However, computational modeling analyses and site-directed mutagenesis assays suggested that DDO-2728 occupied the m^6A substrate binding site, rather than the 2OG binding pocket.

Interestingly, another group employed fluorescence-based polarization assays and structural-based screening techniques, resulting in a novel class of 1-aryl-1*H*-pyrazole scaffold-bearing compounds as potent and selective inhibitors of ALKBH5 [134]. Among these, 5-hydroxy-1-(3-(trifluoromethyl)phenyl)-1*H*-pyrazole-3-carboxylic acid (**49**) was discovered as the cell-active inhibitor with enhanced potency (IC_{50} 0.021 μM) [134]. *In vitro* biochemical techniques such as cellular thermal shift assays, fluorescence polarization assays, and dot-blot demethylation assays, confirmed that **49** preferentially inhibited ALKBH5 among other AlkB enzymes, implying it is a selective inhibitor for ALKBH5. Molecular docking studies predicted the inhibitory binding pose in which the *1H*-pyrazole moiety of **49** was located within the 2OG binding pocket of ALKBH5, chelating to the metal ion [134]. Notably, the trifluoromethyl group was observed extending into the substrate binding region, suggesting that designing inhibitors with 2OG and substrate binding motifs might be an effective strategy toward developing potent and selective inhibitors of ALKBH5, as previously demonstrated with FTO.

7.10.3 High-Throughput Screening

High throughput *in vitro* assays for screening of compound libraries also resulted in several types of ALKBH5 inhibitors. Employing an m^6A antibody-based enzyme-linked immunosorbent assay (ELISA), 2-[(1-hydroxy-2-oxo-2-phenylethyl) sulfanyl]acetic acid (**50**) and 4-[(furan-2-yl)methyl]amino-1,2-diazinane-3,6-dione (**51**) were discovered as potent inhibitors of ALKBH5 (**50**, IC_{50} 0.84 μM, **51**, IC_{50} 1.79 μM) against AML [135]. Both the compounds demonstrated significant antiproliferative effects when tested against several AML cell lines such as HL-60, CCRF-CEM, and K562 with inhibitory concentrations varying from 1.38 μM to 16.5 μM [135]. Another high-throughput method, ALPHA Screen, was successfully used to obtain inhibitors Ena15 (**52**) and Ena21 (**53**) with reported IC_{50} values of 18.3 μM and 15.7 μM, respectively [136]. Molecular modeling studies indicated that Ena15 does not compete with 2OG for inhibition due to steric clashes. On the contrary, Ena21 behaves as a 2OG competitive inhibitor [136]. Although the crystal structures of Ena15 and Ena21 highlighting their binding modes are yet to be determined, these compounds appeared to completely inhibit ssDNA binding, suggesting that they are prime substrate competitors. Ena15 and Ena21-induced ALKBH5 inhibition were also reported to inhibit GBM tumor growth in a similar manner as ALKBH5 knockdown. In all the tested GBM cell lines, the two compounds showed dose-dependent inhibition, stabilized the FOXM1 mRNA, and resulted in partial cell arrest in G0/G1 phase [136].

7.10.4 Covalent Inhibitor TD19

Covalent inhibition of ALKBH5 has also been recently reported. The authors of this study discussed the work of the first published ALKBH5 structure with an FG2216 adduct being covalently bonded to ALKBH5 in the crystal structure (PDB ID: 4NJ4) [129]. Using a targeted covalent inhibition approach, they identified a novel covalent inhibitor TD19 (**54**), which contains the thiadiazolidanone functional warhead. A structural analogue of tideglusib, TD19 inhibits the m^6A substrate binding to ALKBH5 by covalently linking to Cys100 and Cys267 residues [137]. The findings from this study indicate that **54** selectively inhibits the m^6A substrate binding to ALKBH5 over FTO by covalently modifying Cys100 and Cys267 of ALKBH5. Moreover, TD19 demonstrated high potency against ALKBH5 (IC_{50} 1.5–3 μM) as compared to FTO ($IC_{50} > 50$ μM). Molecular docking studies using the reported apo ALKBH5 (PDB ID:4NRO) [130] structure and 2OG and m^6A bound ALKBH5 (PDB ID: 7WKV) [107] structure predicted that the covalently modified Cys267 restricted the conformational changes occurring in the βIV-V loop, thereby preventing the binding of m^6A substrate to ALKBH5 [137]. While a crystallographic structure of **54** complexed to ALKBH5 remains unelucidated, supporting biochemical binding assays, inhibition assays, and cell-based analyses established the role of **54** as a promising selective and potent inhibitor for ALKBH5 over FTO [137].

7.10.5 Other Inhibitors

There were several other potential ALKBH5 inhibitors identified through *in silico* screenings and indirect cell-based assays. Direct and more thorough *in vitro* assays will be needed to verify their direct inhibitory activities against ALKBH5. One such example is the cell-active inhibitor of ALKBH5, Alk-04 (**55**) with an unreported chemical structure. It was shown to suppress tumor growth in mice and significantly increased the effectiveness of GVAX/anti-PD-1 immunotherapy against melanoma and other ALKBH5-sensitized cancer cells [138].

The search for ALKBH5 selective inhibitors led to the recent identification of MV1035 (**56**), an imidazobenzoxazin-5-thione compound via a high throughput *in silico* screening approach [139]. Initially discovered as a sodium channel blocker, **56** effectively impaired the enzymatic activity *in vitro* as well as diminished invasiveness and migration in U87 glioblastoma cells by regulating the translation of CD73 [139]. While IC_{50} data for **56** remains undetermined, molecular modeling studies suggested that the binding site of **56** is situated next to the 2OG binding site with potential overlap between the two regions. Following this, a recent study by Rivara et. al documented several structural analogues of **56** as potential inhibitors for ALKBH5 and ALKBH2 [140]. The study concluded that the length of the aliphatic substituents and presence of alkyl groups on the heterocyclic imidazole critically impact the enzymatic activity [140].

Recent years have witnessed significant progress in the development of enzyme-selective inhibitors of ALKBH5. While molecular docking studies have attempted to rationalize the binding mode for majority of the mentioned inhibitors, further structural investigations are imperative to validate these predictions. To our knowledge, the present small molecule inhibitors of ALKBH5 are proposed to occupy either the 2OG binding site or the m^{6}A substrate binding site. However, studies on FTO inhibition suggest that simultaneously exploiting the substrate as well as the cosubstrate binding sites may lead to the development of inhibitors with improved potency and specificity. The recently determined crystal structures of ALKBH5 complexed to its m^{6}A ssRNA substrate serve as a great starting point to explore the potential inhibitor design [107]. Detailed investigations are also required to validate the inhibition of the reported inhibitors *in vitro* and in cells. The structures of the reported ALKBH5 inhibitors are shown in (Figure 7.11).

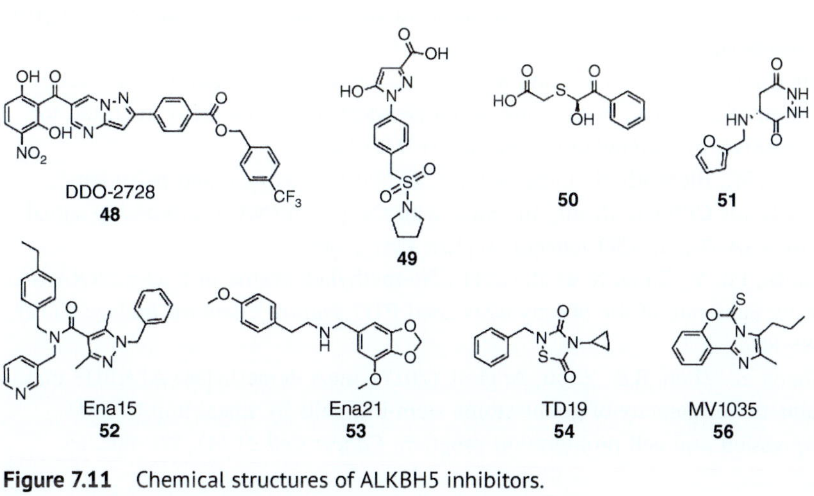

Figure 7.11 Chemical structures of ALKBH5 inhibitors.

References

1 Crick, F.H. (1958). On protein synthesis. *Symposia of the Society for Experimental Biology.*

2 Crick, F.H. (1968). The origin of the genetic code. *Journal of Molecular Biology* 38 (3): 367–379.

3 Crick, F. (1970). Central dogma of molecular biology. *Nature* 227 (5258): 561–563.

4 Crick, F.H.C., Barnett, L., Brenner, S., and Watts-Tobin, R.J. (1961). General nature of the genetic code for proteins. *Nature* 192 (4809): 1227–1232.

5 Cooper, T.A., Wan, L., and Dreyfuss, G. (2009). RNA and disease. *Cell* 136 (4): 777–793.

6 Lemmens, R., Moore, M.J., Al-Chalabi, A. et al. (2010). RNA metabolism and the pathogenesis of motor neuron diseases. *Trends in Neurosciences* 33 (5): 249–258.

7 Fu, Y., Dominissini, D., Rechavi, G. et al. (2014). Gene expression regulation mediated through reversible m6A RNA methylation. *Nature Reviews Genetics* 15 (5): 293–306.

8 Goodall, G.J. and Wickramasinghe, V.O. (2021). RNA in cancer. *Nature Reviews Cancer* 21 (1): 22–36.

9 Westover, K.D., Bushnell, D.A., and Kornberg, R.D. (2004). Structural basis of transcription: separation of RNA from DNA by RNA polymerase II. *Science* 303 (5660): 1014–1016.

10 Chan, S., Choi, E.-A., and Shi, Y. (2011). Pre-mRNA 3′-end processing complex assembly and function. *WIREs RNA* 2 (3): 321–335.

11 Shi, Y. and Manley, J.L. (2015). The end of the message: multiple protein-RNA interactions define the mRNA polyadenylation site. *Genes & Development* 29 (9): 889–897.

12 Sheets, M.D., Ogg, S.C., and Wickens, M.P. (1990). Point mutations in AAUAAA and the poly (A) addition site: effects on the accuracy and efficiency of cleavage and polyadenylation in vitro. *Nucleic Acids Research* 18 (19): 5799–5805.

13 Takagaki, Y., Ryner, L.C., and Manley, J.L. (1988). Separation and characterization of a poly(A) polymerase and a cleavage/specificity factor required for pre-mRNA polyadenylation. *Cell* 52 (5): 731–742.

14 Keller, W., Bienroth, S., Lang, K.M. et al. (1991). Cleavage and polyadenylation factor CPF specifically interacts with the pre-mRNA 3′ processing signal AAUAAA. *The EMBO Journal* 10 (13): 4241–4249.

15 Jia, G., Fu, Y., Zhao, X. et al. (2011). N6-methyladenosine in nuclear RNA is a major substrate of the obesity-associated FTO. *Nature Chemical Biology* 7 (12): 885–887.

16 Zhang, S., Zhao, B.S., Zhou, A. et al. (2017). m6A demethylase ALKBH5 maintains tumorigenicity of glioblastoma stem-like cells by sustaining FOXM1 expression and cell proliferation program. *Cancer Cell* 31 (4): 591–606. e6.

17 Tasaki, M., Shimada, K., Kimura, H. et al. (2011). ALKBH3, a human AlkB homologue, contributes to cell survival in human non-small-cell lung cancer. *British Journal of Cancer* 104 (4): 700–706.

18 Nishikura, K. (2010). Functions and regulation of RNA editing by ADAR deaminases. *Annual Review of Biochemistry* 79: 321–349.

19 Falnes, P.Ø., Johansen, R.F., and Seeberg, E. (2002). AlkB-mediated oxidative demethylation reverses DNA damage in Escherichia coli. *Nature* 419 (6903): 178–182.

20 Clifton, I.J., McDonough, M.A., Ehrismann, D. et al. (2006). Structural studies on 2-oxoglutarate oxygenases and related double-stranded β-helix fold proteins. *Journal of Inorganic Biochemistry* 100 (4): 644–669.

21 Hausinger, R.P. (2004). Fe (II)/α-ketoglutarate-dependent hydroxylases and related enzymes. *Critical Reviews in Biochemistry and Molecular Biology* 39 (1): 21–68.

22 Loenarz, C. and Schofield, C.J. (2011). Physiological and biochemical aspects of hydroxylations and demethylations catalyzed by human 2-oxoglutarate oxygenases. *Trends in Biochemical Sciences* 36 (1): 7–18.

23 McDonough, M.A., Loenarz, C., Chowdhury, R. et al. (2010). Structural studies on human 2-oxoglutarate dependent oxygenases. *Current Opinion in Structural Biology* 20 (6): 659–672.

24 Schofield, C.J. and Zhang, Z. (1999). Structural and mechanistic studies on 2-oxoglutarate-dependent oxygenases and related enzymes. *Current Opinion in Structural Biology* 9 (6): 722–731.

25 Kurowski, M.A., Bhagwat, A.S., Papaj, G., and Bujnicki, J.M. (2003). Phylogenomic identification of five new human homologs of the DNA repair enzyme AlkB. *BMC Genomics* 4: 1–6.

26 Noma, A., Ishitani, R., Kato, M. et al. (2010). Expanding role of the jumonji C domain as an RNA hydroxylase. *The Journal of Biological Chemistry* 285 (45): 34503–34507.

27 Kato, M., Araiso, Y., Noma, A. et al. (2011). Crystal structure of a novel JmjC-domain-containing protein, TYW5, involved in tRNA modification. *Nucleic Acids Research* 39 (4): 1576–1585.

28 Trewick, S.C., Henshaw, T.F., Hausinger, R.P. et al. (2002). Oxidative demethylation by Escherichia coli AlkB directly reverts DNA base damage. *Nature* 419 (6903): 174–178.

29 Aravind, L. and Koonin, E.V. (2001). The DNA-repair protein AlkB, EGL-9, and leprecan define new families of 2-oxoglutarate- and iron-dependent dioxygenases. *Genome Biology* 2 (3): Research0007.

30 Müller, T.A. and Hausinger, R.P. (2015). AlkB and its homologues–DNA repair and beyond. *2-oxoglutarate-Dependent Oxygenases* 246–262.

31 Dina, C., Henshaw, T.F., Hausinger, R.P. et al. (2007). Variation in FTO contributes to childhood obesity and severe adult obesity. *Nature Genetics* 39 (6): 724–726.

32 Gerken, T., Girard, C.A., Tung, Y.C. et al. (2007). The obesity-associated FTO gene encodes a 2-oxoglutarate-dependent nucleic acid demethylase. *Science* 318 (5855): 1469–1472.

33 Scott, L.J., Mohlke, K.L., Bonnycastle, L.L. et al. (2007). A genome-wide association study of type 2 diabetes in Finns detects multiple susceptibility variants. *Science* 316 (5829): 1341–1345.

34 Frayling, T.M., Timpson, N.J., and Weedon, M.N. (2007). A common variant in the FTO gene is associated with body mass index and predisposes to childhood and adult obesity. *Science* 316 (5826): 889–894.

35 Zhao, X., Yang, Y., Sun, B.F. et al. (2014). FTO-dependent demethylation of N6-methyladenosine regulates mRNA splicing and is required for adipogenesis. *Cell Research* 24 (12): 1403–1419.

36 Wang, X., Zhu, L., and Chen, J. (2015). mRNA m6A methylation downregulates adipogenesis in porcine adipocytes. *Biochemical and Biophysical Research Communications* 459 (2): 201–207.

37 Jia, G., Yang, C.G., and Yang, S. (2008). Oxidative demethylation of 3-methylthymine and 3-methyluracil in single-stranded DNA and RNA by mouse and human FTO. *FEBS Letters* 582 (23–24): 3313–3319.

38 Fu, Y., Jia, G., Pang, X. et al. (2013). *FTO-mediated formation of N 6-hydroxymethyladenosine and N 6-formyladenosine in mammalian RNA. Nature Communications* 4 (1): 1798.

39 Shishodia, S., Zang, D., El-Sagheer, A.H. et al. (2018). *NMR analyses on N-hydroxymethylated nucleobases–implications for formaldehyde toxicity and nucleic acid demethylases. Organic & Biomolecular Chemistry* 16 (21): 4021–4032.

40 Toh, J.D., Crossley, S.W.M., Bruemmer, K.J. et al. (2020). *Distinct RNA N-demethylation pathways catalyzed by nonheme iron ALKBH5 and FTO enzymes enable regulation of formaldehyde release rates. Proceedings of the National Academy of Sciences* 117 (41): 25284–25292.

41 Mauer, J., Luo, X., Blanjoie, A. et al. (2017). *Reversible methylation of m6Am in the 5′ cap controls mRNA stability. Nature* 541 (7637): 371–375.

42 Mauer, J., Sindelar, M., Guez, T. et al. (2018). *The RNA demethylase FTO targets m6Am in snRNA to establish distinct methyl isoforms that influence splicing. BioRXiv* 327924.

43 Mauer, J., Sindelar, M., Despic, V. et al. (2019). *FTO controls reversible m6Am RNA methylation during snRNA biogenesis. Nature Chemical Biology* 15 (4): 340–347.

44 Zhou, J., Wan, J., Gao, X. et al. (2015). *Dynamic m6A mRNA methylation directs translational control of heat shock response. Nature* 526 (7574): 591–594.

45 Zhou, J., Wan, J., and Shu, X.E. (2018). *N6-methyladenosine guides mRNA alternative translation during integrated stress response. Molecular Cell* 69 (4): 636–647. e7.

46 Xiang, Y., Laurent, B., Hsu, C.H. et al. (2017). *RNA m6A methylation regulates the ultraviolet-induced DNA damage response. Nature* 543 (7646): 573–576.

47 Gokhale, N.S., McIntyre, A.B.R., McFadden, M.J. et al. (2016). *N6-methyladenosine in flaviviridae viral RNA genomes regulates infection. Cell Host & Microbe* 20 (5): 654–665.

48 Yu, J., Chen, M., Huang, H. et al. (2018). *Dynamic m6A modification regulates local translation of mRNA in axons. Nucleic Acids Research* 46 (3): 1412–1423.

49 Delahanty, R.J., Beeghly-Fadiel, A., Xiang, Y.B. et al. (2011). *Association of obesity-related genetic variants With endometrial cancer risk: a report from the Shanghai endometrial cancer genetics study. American Journal of Epidemiology* 174 (10): 1115–1126.

50 Lurie, G., Gaudet, M.M., Spurdle, A.B. et al. (2011). *The obesity-associated polymorphisms FTO rs9939609 and MC4R rs17782313 and endometrial cancer risk in non-hispanic white women. PLOS ONE* 6 (2): e16756.

51 Huang, X., Zhao, J., Yang, M. et al. (2017). *Association between FTO gene polymorphism (rs9939609 T/A) and cancer risk: a meta-analysis. European Journal of Cancer Care* 26 (5): e12464.

52 Kaklamani, V., Yi, N., Sadim, M. et al. (2011). *The role of the fat mass and obesity associated gene (FTO) in breast cancer risk. BMC Medical Genetics* 12 (1): 52.

53 Garcia-Closas, M., Couch, F.J., Lindstrom, S. et al. (2013). *Genome-wide association studies identify four ER negative–specific breast cancer risk loci. Nature Genetics* 45 (4): 392–398.

54 Li, Z., Weng, H., Su, R. et al. (2017). *FTO plays an oncogenic role in acute myeloid leukemia as a N6-methyladenosine RNA demethylase. Cancer Cell* 31 (1): 127–141.

55 Cui, Q., Shi, H., Ye, P. et al. (2017). *m(6)A RNA methylation regulates the self-renewal and tumorigenesis of glioblastoma stem cells. Cell Reports* 18 (11): 2622–2634.

56 Wang, Y., Li, M., Zhang, L. et al. (2021). *m6A demethylase FTO induces NELL2 expression by inhibiting E2F1 m6A modification leading to metastasis of non-small cell lung cancer. Molecular Therapy-Oncolytics* 21: 367–376.

57 Wang, A., Jin, C., Wang, Y. et al. (2023). *FTO promotes the progression of cervical cancer by regulating the N6-methyladenosine modification of ZEB1 and Myc. Molecular Carcinogenesis* 62 (8): 1228–1237.

58 Cui, Y., Zhang, C., Ma, S. et al. (2021). *RNA m6A demethylase FTO-mediated epigenetic up-regulation of LINC00022 promotes tumorigenesis in esophageal squamous cell carcinoma. Journal of Experimental & Clinical Cancer Research* 40: 1–20.

59 Yang, Z., Jiang, X., Zhang, Z. et al. (2021). *HDAC3-dependent transcriptional repression of FOXA2 regulates FTO/m6A/MYC signaling to contribute to the development of gastric cancer. Cancer Gene Therapy* 28 (1): 141–155.

60 Zhou, Y., Wang, Q., Zheng, X. et al. (2022). *N6-methyladenosine demethylase FTO promotes growth and metastasis of gastric cancer via m6A modification of caveolin-1 and metabolic regulation of mitochondrial dynamics. Cell Death & Disease* 13 (1): 72.

61 Zhang, L., Wan, Y., Zhang, Z. et al. (2021). *FTO demethylates m6A modifications in HOXB13 mRNA and promotes endometrial cancer metastasis by activating the WNT signalling pathway. RNA Biology* 18 (9): 1265–1278.

62 Ruan, D.-Y., Li, T., Wang, Y.N. et al. (2021). *FTO downregulation mediated by hypoxia facilitates colorectal cancer metastasis. Oncogene* 40 (33): 5168–5181.

63 Chen, F., Chen, Z., Guan, T. et al. (2021). *N6-methyladenosine regulates mRNA stability and translation efficiency of KRT7 to promote breast cancer lung metastasis. Cancer Research* 81 (11): 2847–2860.

64 Huang, H., Wang, Y., Kandpal, M. et al. (2020). *FTO-dependent N 6-methyladenosine modifications inhibit ovarian cancer stem cell self-renewal by blocking cAMP signaling. Cancer Research* 80 (16): 3200–3214.

65 Han, Z., Niu, T., Chang, J. et al. (2010). *Crystal structure of the FTO protein reveals basis for its substrate specificity. Nature* 464 (7292): 1205–1209.

66 Aik, W., Demetriades, M., Hamdan, M.K. et al. (2013). *Structural basis for inhibition of the fat mass and obesity associated protein (FTO). Journal of Medicinal Chemistry* 56 (9): 3680–3688.

67 Zhang, X., Wei, L.H., Wang, Y. et al. (2019). *Structural insights into FTO's catalytic mechanism for the demethylation of multiple RNA substrates. Proceedings of the National Academy of Sciences* 116 (8): 2919–2924.

68 Aik, W., McDonough, M.A., Thalhammer, A. et al. (2012). *Role of the jelly-roll fold in substrate binding by 2-oxoglutarate oxygenases. Current Opinion in Structural Biology* 22 (6): 691–700.

69 Shishodia, S., Demetriades, M., Zhang, D. et al. (2021). *Structure-based design of selective fat mass and obesity associated protein (FTO) inhibitors. Journal of Medicinal Chemistry* 64 (22): 16609–16625.

70 Wang, R., Han, Z., Liu, B. et al. (2018). *Identification of natural compound radicicol as a potent FTO inhibitor. Molecular Pharmaceutics* 15 (9): 4092–4098.

71 Su, R., Dong, L., Li, Y. et al. (2020). *Targeting FTO suppresses cancer stem cell maintenance and immune evasion. Cancer Cell* 38 (1): 79–96.e11.

72 Selberg, S., Yu, L.Y., Bondarenko, O. et al. (2021). *Small-molecule inhibitors of the RNA M6A demethylases FTO potently support the survival of dopamine neurons. International Journal of Molecular Sciences* 22 (9): 4537.

73 Roach, P.L., Clifton, I.J., Fülöp, V. et al. (1995). *Crystal structure of isopenicillin N synthase is the first from a new structural family of enzymes. Nature* 375 (6533): 700–704.

74 Zhang, Z., Ren, J.S., Clifton, I.J. et al. (2004). *Crystal structure and mechanistic implications of 1-aminocyclopropane-1-carboxylic acid oxidase–the ethylene-forming enzyme. Chemistry & Biology* 11 (10): 1383–1394.

75 Higgins, L.J., Yan, F., Liu, P. et al. (2005). *Structural insight into antibiotic fosfomycin biosynthesis by a mononuclear iron enzyme. Nature* 437 (7060): 838–844.

76 Bailey, P.S.J. and Nathan, J.A. (2018). *Metabolic regulation of hypoxia-inducible transcription factors: the role of small molecule metabolites and iron. Biomedicines* 6 (2).

77 Perry, G.S., Das, M., and Woon, E.C.Y. (2021). *Inhibition of AlkB nucleic acid demethylases: promising new epigenetic targets. Journal of Medicinal Chemistry* 64 (23): 16974–17003.

78 Xu, W., Yang, H., Liu, Y. et al. (2011). *Oncometabolite 2-hydroxyglutarate Is a competitive inhibitor of α-ketoglutarate-dependent dioxygenases. Cancer Cell* 19 (1): 17–30.

79 Su, R., Dong, L., Li, C. et al. (2018). *R-2HG exhibits anti-tumor activity by targeting FTO/m(6)A/MYC/CEBPA signaling. Cell* 172 (1–2): 90–105.e23.

80 Huang, Y., Yan, J., Li, Q. et al. (2015). *Meclofenamic acid selectively inhibits FTO demethylation of m6A over ALKBH5. Nucleic Acids Research* 43 (1): 373–384.

81 Wang, T., Hong, T., Huang, Y. et al. (2015). *Fluorescein derivatives as bifunctional molecules for the simultaneous inhibiting and labeling of FTO protein. Journal of the American Chemical Society* 137 (43): 13736–13739.

82 Chowdhury, R., Yeoh, K.K., Tian, Y.M. et al. (2011). *The oncometabolite 2-hydroxyglutarate inhibits histone lysine demethylases. EMBO Reports* 12 (5): 463–469.

83 Rose, N.R., Ng, S.S., Mecinović, J. et al. (2008). *Inhibitor scaffolds for 2-oxoglutarate-dependent histone lysine demethylases. Journal of Medicinal Chemistry* 51 (22): 7053–7056.

84 Chen, B., Ye, F., Yu, L. et al. (2012). *Development of cell-active N6-methyladenosine RNA demethylase FTO inhibitor. Journal of the American Chemical Society* 134 (43): 17963–17971.

85 Li, Q., Huang, Y., Liu, X. et al. (2016). *Rhein inhibits AlkB repair enzymes and sensitizes cells to methylated DNA damage. The Journal of Biological Chemistry* 291 (21): 11083–11093.

86 Peng, S., Xiao, W., Ju, D. et al. (2019). *Identification of entacapone as a chemical inhibitor of FTO mediating metabolic regulation through FOXO1. Science Translational Medicine* 11 (488): eaau7116.

87 Cao, R., Liu, M., Yin, M. et al. (2012). *Discovery of novel tubulin inhibitors via structure-based hierarchical virtual screening. Journal of Chemical Information and Modeling* 52 (10): 2730–2740.

88 Svensen, N. and Samie, R. (2016). Jaffrey, *fluorescent RNA aptamers as a tool to study RNA-modifying enzymes. Cell Chemical Biology* 23 (3): 415–425.

89 Su, R., Dong, L., Li, Y. et al. (2019). *Effective novel fto inhibitors show potent anti-cancer efficacy and suppress drug resistance. Blood* 134: 233.

90 Huff, S., Tiwari, S.K., Gonzalez, G.M. et al. (2021). *m6A-RNA demethylase FTO inhibitors impair self-renewal in glioblastoma stem cells. ACS Chemical Biology* 16 (2): 324–333.

91 Huff, S., Kummetha, I.R., Zhang, L. et al. (2022). *Rational design and optimization of m6A-RNA demethylase FTO inhibitors as anticancer agents. Journal of Medicinal Chemistry* 65 (16): 10920–10937.

92 Toh, J.D.W., Sun, L., Lau, L.Z.M. et al. (2015). *A strategy based on nucleotide specificity leads to a subfamily-selective and cell-active inhibitor of N6-methyladenosine demethylase FTO. Chemical Science* 6 (1): 112–122.

93 Woon, E.C., Tumber, A., Kawamura, A. et al. (2012). *Linking of 2-oxoglutarate and substrate binding sites enables potent and highly selective inhibition of JmjC histone demethylases. Angewandte Chemie* 124 (7): 1663–1666.

94 Prakash, M., Itoh, Y., Fujiwara, Y. et al. (2021). *Identification of potent and selective inhibitors of fat mass obesity-associated protein using a fragment-merging approach. Journal of Medicinal Chemistry* 64 (21): 15810–15824.

95 Huang, Y., Su, R., Shang, Y. et al. (2019). *Small-molecule targeting of oncogenic FTO demethylase in acute myeloid leukemia. Cancer cell* 35 (4): 677–691e10.

96 Liu, Z., Duan, Z., Zhang, D. et al. (2022). *Structure-activity relationships and antileukemia effects of the tricyclic benzoic acid FTO inhibitors. Journal of Medicinal Chemistry* 65 (15): 10638–10654.

97 Xiao, P., Duan, Z., Liu, Z. et al. (2023). *Rational design of RNA demethylase FTO inhibitors with enhanced antileukemia drug-like properties. Journal of Medicinal Chemistry* 66 (14): 9731–9752.

98 Huang, Y., Su, R., Sheng, Y. et al. (2023). *Chemical inhibitors targeting the oncogenic m(6)a modifying proteins. Accounts of Chemical Research* 56 (21): 3010–3022.

99 Liu, Y., Liang, G., Xu, H. et al. (2021). *Tumors exploit FTO-mediated regulation of glycolytic metabolism to evade immune surveillance. Cell Metabolism* 33 (6): 1221–1233.e11.

100 Subbaiah, M.A.M. and Meanwell, N.A. (2021). *Bioisosteres of the phenyl ring: recent strategic applications in lead optimization and drug design. Journal of Medicinal Chemistry* 64 (19): 14046–14128.

101 St Jean, D.J. Jr., and Fotsch, C. (2012). *Correction to mitigating heterocycle metabolism in drug discovery. Journal of Medicinal Chemistry* 55 (22): 10315–10315.

102 He, W., Zhou, B., Liu, W. et al. (2015). *Identification of a novel small-molecule binding site of the fat mass and obesity associated protein (FTO). Journal of Medicinal Chemistry* 58 (18): 7341–7348.

103 Qiao, Y., Zhou, B., Zhang, M. et al. (2016). *A novel inhibitor of the obesity-related protein FTO. Biochemistry* 55 (10): 1516–1522.

104 Jaakkola, P., Mole, D.R., Tian, Y.M. et al. (2001). *Targeting of HIF-α to the von Hippel-Lindau ubiquitylation complex by O2-regulated prolyl hydroxylation. Science* 292 (5516): 468–472.

105 Zheng, G., Dahl, J.A., Niu, Y. et al. (2013). *ALKBH5 is a mammalian RNA demethylase that impacts RNA metabolism and mouse fertility. Molecular Cell* 49 (1): 18–29.

106 Ensfelder, T.T., Kurz, M.Q., Iwan, K. et al. (2018). *ALKBH5-induced demethylation of mono-and dimethylated adenosine. Chemical Communications* 54 (62): 8591–8593.

107 Kaur, S., Tam, N.Y., McDonough, M.A. et al. (2022). *Mechanisms of substrate recognition and N 6-methyladenosine demethylation revealed by crystal structures of ALKBH5–RNA complexes. Nucleic Acids Research* 50 (7): 4148–4160.

108 Jaafar, C. and Aguiar, R.C. (2024). *Dynamic multilayered control of m6A RNA demethylase activity. Proceedings of the National Academy of Sciences* 121 (46): e2317847121.

109 Li, X.-C., Jin, F., Wang, B.Y. et al. (2019). *The m6A demethylase ALKBH5 controls trophoblast invasion at the maternal-fetal interface by regulating the stability of CYR61 mRNA. Theranostics* 9 (13): 3853–3865.

110 Song, H., Feng, X., Zhang, H. et al. (2019). *METTL3 and ALKBH5 oppositely regulate m6A modification of TFEB mRNA, which dictates the fate of hypoxia/reoxygenation-treated cardiomyocytes. Autophagy* 15 (8): 1419–1437.

111 Wang, H.-F., Kuang, M.J., Han, S.J. et al. (2020). *BMP2 modified by the m6A demethylation enzyme ALKBH5 in the ossification of the ligamentum flavum through the AKT signaling pathway. Calcified Tissue International* 106 (5): 486–493.

112 Wang, B., Fang, X., Sun, X. et al. (2021). *m(6)A demethylase ALKBH5 suppresses proliferation and migration of enteric neural crest cells by regulating TAGLN in Hirschsprung's disease. Life Sciences* 278: 119577.

113 Zhang, C., Zhi, W.I., Lu, H. et al. (2016). *Hypoxia-inducible factors regulate pluripotency factor expression by ZNF217-and ALKBH5-mediated modulation of RNA methylation in breast cancer cells. Oncotarget* 7 (40): 64527.

114 Vaupel, P., Mayer, A., and Höckel, M. (2004). *Tumor hypoxia and malignant progression.* In: *Methods in Enzymology*, 335–354. Academic Press.

115 Harris, A.L. (2002). *Hypoxia – a key regulatory factor in tumour growth. Nature Reviews Cancer* 2 (1): 38–47.

116 Thalhammer, A., Bencokova, Z., Poole, R. et al. (2011). *Human AlkB homologue 5 is a nuclear 2-oxoglutarate dependent oxygenase and a direct target of hypoxia-inducible factor 1α (HIF-1α). Plos one* 6 (1): e16210.

117 Zhang, C., Samanta, D., Lu, H. et al. (2016). *Hypoxia induces the breast cancer stem cell phenotype by HIF-dependent and ALKBH5-mediated m6A-demethylation of NANOG mRNA. Proceedings of the National Academy of Sciences* 113 (14): E2047–E2056.

118 Fang, Y., Wu, X., Gu, Y. et al. (2023). *LINC00659 cooperated with ALKBH5 to accelerate gastric cancer progression by stabilising JAK1 mRNA in an m(6) A-YTHDF2-dependent manner. Clinical and Translational Medicine* 13 (3): e1205.

119 Zhang, J., Guo, S., Piao, H.Y. et al. (2019). *ALKBH5 promotes invasion and metastasis of gastric cancer by decreasing methylation of the lncRNA NEAT1. Journal of Physiology and Biochemistry* 75 (3): 379–389.

120 Cheng, C., Wang, P., Yang, Y. et al. (2023). *Smoking-induced M2-TAMs, via circEML4 in EVs, promote the progression of NSCLC through ALKBH5-regulated m6A modification of SOCS2 in NSCLC cells. Advanced Science* 10 (22): 2300953.

121 Chao, Y., Shang, J., and Ji, W. (2020). *ALKBH5-m6A-FOXM1 signaling axis promotes proliferation and invasion of lung adenocarcinoma cells under intermittent hypoxia. Biochemical and Biophysical Research Communications* 521 (2): 499–506.

122 Zhu, Z., Qian, Q., Zhao, X. et al. (2020). *N6-methyladenosine ALKBH5 promotes non-small cell lung cancer progress by regulating TIMP3 stability*. *Gene* 731: 144348.

123 Zhu, H., Gan, X., Jiang, X. et al. (2019). *ALKBH5 inhibited autophagy of epithelial ovarian cancer through miR-7 and BCL-2*. *Journal of Experimental & Clinical Cancer Research* 38 (1): 163.

124 Piekorz, R.P., Hoffmeyer, A., Duntsch, C.D. et al. (2002). *The centrosomal protein TACC3 is essential for hematopoietic stem cell function and genetically interfaces with p53-regulated apoptosis*. *The EMBO Journal* 21 (4): 653–664.

125 Guo, X., Li, K., Jiang, W. et al. (2020). *RNA demethylase ALKBH5 prevents pancreatic cancer progression by posttranscriptional activation of PER1 in an m6A-YTHDF2-dependent manner*. *Molecular Cancer* 19: 1–19.

126 Jin, D., Guo, J., Wu, Y. et al. (2020). *m(6)A demethylase ALKBH5 inhibits tumor growth and metastasis by reducing YTHDFs-mediated YAP expression and inhibiting miR-107/LATS2-mediated YAP activity in NSCLC*. *Molecular Cancer* 19 (1): 40.

127 Chen, Y., Zhao, Y., Chen, J. et al. (2020). *ALKBH5 suppresses malignancy of hepatocellular carcinoma via m(6)A-guided epigenetic inhibition of LYPD1*. *Molecular Cancer* 19 (1): 123.

128 Jin, H., Ying, X., Que, B. et al. (2019). *N(6)-methyladenosine modification of ITGA6 mRNA promotes the development and progression of bladder cancer*. *eBioMedicine* 47: 195–207.

129 Aik, W., Scotti, J.S., Choi, H. et al. (2014). *Structure of human RNA N 6-methyladenine demethylase ALKBH5 provides insights into its mechanisms of nucleic acid recognition and demethylation*. *Nucleic Acids Research* 42 (7): 4741–4754.

130 Feng, C., Liu, Y., Wang, G. et al., *Crystal structures of the human RNA demethylase Alkbh5 reveal basis for substrate recognition*.

131 Xu, C., Liu, K., Tempel, W. et al. (2014). *Structures of human ALKBH5 demethylase reveal a unique binding mode for specific single-stranded N6-methyladenosine RNA demethylation*. *Journal of Biological Chemistry* 289 (25): 17299–17311.

132 Chen, W., Zhang, L., Zheng, G. et al. (2014). *Crystal structure of the RNA demethylase ALKBH5 from zebrafish*. *FEBS Letters* 588 (6): 892–898.

133 Wang, Y.Z., Li, H.Y., Zhang, Y. et al. (2023). *Discovery of pyrazolo[1,5-a] pyrimidine derivative as a novel and selective ALKBH5 inhibitor for the treatment of AML*. *Journal of Medicinal Chemistry* 66 (23): 15944–15959.

134 Fang, Z., Mu, B., Liu, Y. et al. (2022). *Discovery of a potent, selective and cell active inhibitor of m(6)A demethylase ALKBH5*. *European Journal of Medicinal Chemistry* 238: 114446.

135 Selberg, S., Seli, N., Kankuri, E. et al. (2021). *Rational design of novel anticancer small-molecule RNA m6A demethylase ALKBH5 inhibitors*. *ACS Omega* 6 (20): 13310–13320.

136 Takahashi, H., Hase, H., Yoshida, T. et al. (2022). *Discovery of two novel ALKBH5 selective inhibitors that exhibit uncompetitive or competitive type and* *suppress the growth activity of glioblastoma multiforme. Chemical Biology & Drug Design* 100 (1): 1–12.

137 Lai, G.-Q., Li, Y., Zhu, H. et al. (2024). *A covalent compound selectively inhibits RNA demethylase ALKBH5 rather than FTO*. RSC. *Chemical Biology*.

138 Li, N., Kang, Y., Wang, L. et al. (2020). *ALKBH5 regulates anti-PD-1 therapy response by modulating lactate and suppressive immune cell accumulation in tumor microenvironment. Proceedings of the National Academy of Sciences of the United States of America* 117 (33): 20159–20170.

139 Malacrida, A., Rivara, M., Di Domizio, A. et al. (2020). *3D proteome-wide scale screening and activity evaluation of a new ALKBH5 inhibitor in U87 glioblastoma cell line. Bioorganic & Medicinal Chemistry* 28 (4): 115300.

140 Rivara, M., Nicolini, G., Malacrida, A. et al. (2024). *New ALKBH2 and ALKBH5 inhibitors for treating glioblastoma. Results in Chemistry* 9: 101645.

Section II

7.11 AlkB Human Homologue 3 (ALKBH3)

7.11.1 Biological Functions of ALKBH3

ALKBH3, another member of the AlkB subfamily 2OG oxygenase, acts on a wide range of alkylated substrates and reportedly performs similar repair activities as AlkB [1, 2]. Initially classified as a DNA demethylase, ALKBH3 is known to oxidatively demethylate a wide range of nucleic acid substrates including N^1-methyladenosine (1 mA/m^{1}A) in ssDNA and ssRNA (Figure 7.12) [2], ethenoadenosine (εA) in DNA, and N^3-methylcytosine (3mC/m^{3}C) in both DNA and ssRNA and tRNA. While most of these substrates are also targeted by ALKBH2, both these enzymes differ in their substrate selectivity [3]. Unlike ALKBH2 which strongly prefers dsDNA, ALKBH3 distinctively acts on single-stranded substrates with a slight bias toward m^{1}A over m^{3}C *in vitro* [3]. Interestingly, ALKBH3 has also been identified as the sole m^{1}A demethylase in mRNA [2]. ALKBH3 knockout studies in mammalian mRNA have been correlated with elevated levels of m^{1}A in

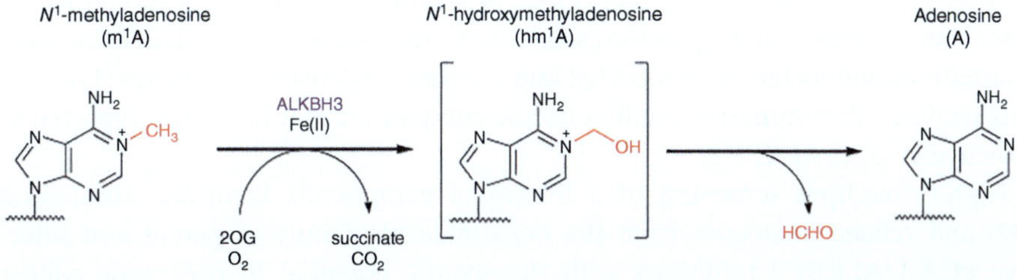

Figure 7.12 Reaction scheme of ALKBH3-catalyzed reaction of m^{1}A. ALKBH3 catalyzes the demethylation of m^{1}A in both ssDNA and ssRNA by producing an unstable hemiaminal intermediate. This hm^{1}A is readily fragmented to produce adenosine and formaldehyde.

the 5′ UTR [4]. Due to its localization in both nucleus and cytoplasm, ALKBH3 potentially influences RNA metabolism by regulating m^1A demethylation in tRNA. The demethylated tRNAs are reportedly more susceptible to angiogenin-induced cleavage and subsequently produce tRNA-derived small RNAs (tDRs) [4]. These tDRs are responsible for promoting ribosome assembly and impeding cell apoptosis, thereby playing a role in cancer progression [4]. Similarly, ALKBH3-catalyzed demethylation of m^1A in mRNA is known to regulate gene transcription and is implicated in the onset of various cancers [5–8]. Overexpression of ALKBH3 has been implicated in the survival of NSCLC cells [9] and progression of pancreatic cancer [6, 7, 10], urothelial [11], and colorectal cancer [12]. These findings collectively highlight the emerging roles of ALKBH3 as an m^1A RNA demethylase as opposed to its previously recognized functions as a DNA repair enzyme. ALKBH3 has previously been structurally characterized giving insights into the catalytic site of the enzyme.

7.11.2 ALKBH3 Crystal Structure

The crystal structure of human ALKBH3 in a complex with Fe(II) and 2OG was first determined in 2006 (PDB ID: 2IUW) [13]. The general structure of ALKBH3 consists of 14 β strands and 2 α-helices. The central DSBH fold is composed of eight β strands divided into two β sheets. The active site Fe(II) (catalytically inactive due to aerobic growth conditions) is chelated to His191, Asp193, and His257 from ALKBH3 along with bidentate chelation of 2OG [13]. In comparison to the bacterial AlkB crystal structure, the substrate binding pocket is constituted by polar residues and lacks a corresponding substrate stacking residue rationalizing the narrow substrate specificity of ALKBH3 relative to AlkB [13]. Interestingly, the ALKBH3 crystal structure reveals the entrance of the substrate (DNA/RNA) binding cleft is flexible and lined with negatively charged Glu123, Asp189, and Asp194 residues from the β4–β5 loop which differentiates between single-stranded and double-stranded substrates. Notably, the residue Leu177 undergoes self-hydroxylation and is crucial for substrate binding and demethylation activity [13].

7.11.3 ALKBH3 Inhibition

Several small molecule inhibitors including the broad spectrum 2OG competitors are commonly shared among FTO, ALKBH5, and ALKBH3 [14–17]. These non-selective compounds and their mode of inhibition against FTO and ALKBH5 have been described in the previous sections. As the inhibition of ALKBH3 by these common inhibitors has been reported and discussed extensively elsewhere [14–18], this section will summarize small molecule compounds that have been reported to selectively target ALKBH3.

High-throughput screening of a library of compounds identified compound (**57**) and related analogues from the benzimidazole family as potent and selective PCA-1/ALKBH3 inhibitors with therapeutic potential in pancreatic cancer [19, 20]. These compounds significantly enhanced enzyme inhibition as revealed by cell-based assays. Notably, animal studies indicated that HUHS015 (**58**, IC_{50} 0.67 μM) demonstrated relatively good bioavailability (7.2%) in rats after

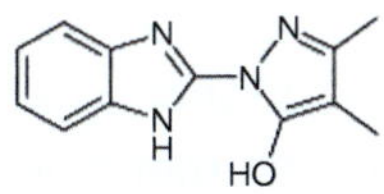

57

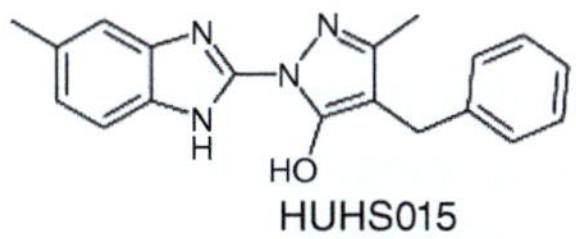

HUHS015
58

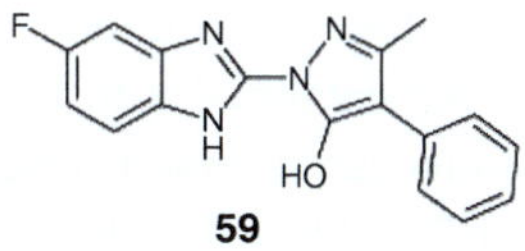

59

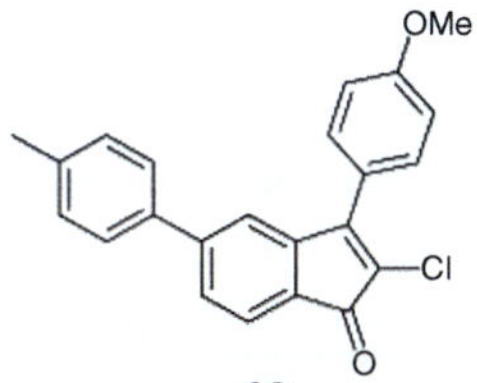

60

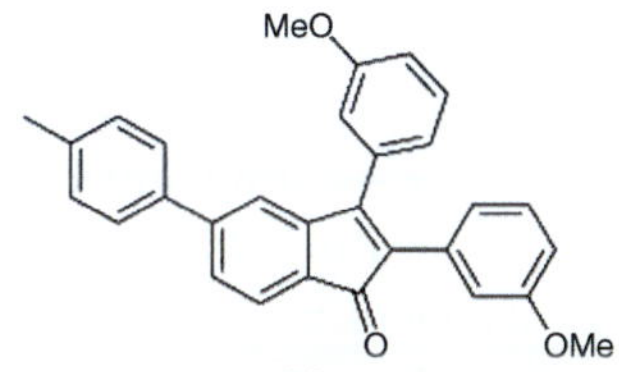

61

Figure 7.13 Reported chemical structures of ALKBH3 inhibitors.

administration and remarkably suppressed the DU145 tumor growth in mice without the appearance of any side effects [19, 20]. However, *in vivo* decomposition of HUHS015 by metabolic enzymes diminished the drug efficacy within one week of administration. To overcome this limitation, compounds with substituted benzimidazole rings were evaluated by S9 mixture stability assays to identify metabolically stable inhibitors [20]. Interestingly, compound **59** significantly improved the *in vivo* inhibition of DU145 tumors in xenograft mice models but displayed weaker inhibition *in vitro* (IC_{50} 2.9 μM). Both HUHS015 and 59 have varied membrane permeability, which explains the contrasting inhibitory effects *in vitro* versus *in vivo* [20]. Moreover, unlike HUHS015, **59** demonstrated enhanced stability in S9 mixture and elevated concentrations in serum (1.02 μg/ml) after administration at 10 mg/kg [20]. Another study reported indenone-based compounds could also selectively inhibit ALKBH3 [21]. Among the tested compounds, compounds **60** and **61**, with IC_{50} values of 9.8 μM and 13.1 μM, respectively were determined as the most potent inhibitors [21]. Results from biochemical studies confirmed that **60** demonstrated enhanced selectivity for ALKBH3 as compared to AlkB and ALKBH2 [21]. While the listed compounds are promising candidates for ALKBH3 inhibition, thorough investigations are required to understand their inhibitory effects against other related AlkB oxygenases such as ALKBH5 and FTO. Moreover, selective inhibition of ALKBH3 by all these compounds is speculated to be driven by their competitive binding to the substrate binding site, but the precise mode of inhibition is not yet understood. In this regard, crystallographic models of the ALKBH3-inhibitor complexes could provide detailed information into their respective recognition mode Figure 7.13.

7.12 Zn^{2+}-Dependent RNA Editing Enzymes

7.12.1 Adenosine Deaminases Acting on RNAs (ADARs)

7.12.1.1 Biological Functions of ADARs

The ADAR family of enzymes are Zn(II) metalloenzymes and specifically catalyze the formation of inosine (I) via hydrolytic deamination of adenosine (A) in double-stranded RNA (dsRNA) substrates [22–24]. The non-canonical inosine resembles guanine due to their similar base-pairing properties [24]. As a result, ADAR-catalyzed A-to-I editing is often misinterpreted as A-to-G substitution which influences reverse transcription, splicing, pre-mRNA processing, and translation [25–27]. For example, editing of the coding regions of RNA can alter the amino acid sequence of the translated protein. This recoding of mRNAs may significantly impact protein function, as evidenced in neural pathways [25]. Reports have also suggested the potential roles of ADARs in the innate immune response, RNA interference mechanisms, and in regulating miRNA processing [25, 28–30].

The human genome encodes for three ADAR proteins, ADAR1–3. However, the deamination at C6 position of adenosine in dsRNA is catalyzed by two active forms namely: ADAR1 and ADAR2 while ADAR3 was reported to be catalytically inactive [31]. ADAR1 is ubiquitously expressed in various tissues and exists in two isoforms: p110 and p150 [24, 28]. ADAR1-catalyzed editing is prevalent in non-coding regions of transcripts derived from repetitive elements such as Alu repeats [32, 33]. This consequently regulates the mRNA export by retaining the RNAs with embedded inverted Alu repeats within the nucleus [34]. ADAR2, on the other hand, is primarily associated with the editing of the non-repeated coding regions [31].

The human ADAR proteins and their editing activity are tightly regulated and affect various downstream signaling pathways. Aberrant expression of ADARs has been implicated in several diseases including cancer progression, viral infections, and neurological disorders [35, 36]. Evidence suggests strong links between ADARs and autoimmune disorders such as Aicardi-Goutières syndrome (AGS) [37, 38], and Bilateral Striatal Dystonia (BSD) [39]. ADAR1 plays roles in differentiating between self and non-self RNA [40] and has been recognized for its crucial roles in breast cancer [41, 42], lung cancer [43], melanoma [44–46], and chronic myeloid leukemia [47]. In these instances, ADAR1-catalyzed editing of RNA derived from oncogenes, tumor suppressor genes, miRNAs, and endogenous dsRNAs assists tumor cells to evade innate anti-tumor responses which subsequently contribute to tumor progression. Similarly, ADAR2-mediated RNA editing has contributed to psychiatric disorders such as schizophrenia [48], depression [49], and autism [50], while demonstrating conflicting roles in several cancers. In cancers such as glioblastoma, ADAR2-catalyzed miRNA editing promotes tumorigenesis and migration of tumor cells [30, 51]. On the contrary, transcript editing by this deaminase is correlated with suppression of oncogenic miRNA in hepatocellular carcinoma (HCC) [52, 53]. These extensive contributions by the ADAR family of enzymes make them attractive therapeutic targets for anticancer drug discovery.

All members of the ADAR family comprise a nuclear localization signal (NLS), indicating that they predominantly localize in the nucleus [54, 55], a dsRNA binding domain (dsRBD), and a catalytic deaminase domain (CDD) [28]. In addition, both isoforms of ADAR1 (p110 and p150) harbor a Zβ domain [28]. Furthermore, ADAR1p150 consists of an extra Zα domain for selective binding of Z-RNA substrates [28]. The presence of a nuclear export signal (NES) within this isoform enables it to oscillate between the nucleus and cytoplasm for dsRNA sensing [56]. *in vitro* studies have reported that ADAR3 harbors an arginine-rich

R domain which allows it to bind to ssRNA [37]. These structural features rely on substrate length, shape, and localization to govern the substrate specificity.

Mechanistically, the human ADAR enzymes share a concerted mechanism as previously observed with cytidine deaminases [57]. The base to be edited is flipped into the active site and the catalytically conserved glutamic acid residue (Glu396 in ADAR2) in the active site deprotonates the Zn(II) metal by activating a nucleophilic water molecule. This is followed by a nucleophilic attack by the Zn(II)-bound hydroxide at the electrophilic *C6* carbon of adenosine. The tetrahedral reaction intermediate, generated upon simultaneous protonation of *N1,* then undergoes proton transfer to release ammonia and generate inosine as the product (Figure 7.14) [57].

7.12.1.2 Crystal Structure of Human ADARs

The different domains of ADAR deaminases have been structurally characterized giving insights into the editing mechanism employed by these enzymes. In 2005, a crystal structure of the catalytic deaminase domain (CDD) of ADAR2 bound to dsRNA was solved, which revealed Zn(II) as the metal ion center. This metal ion was coordinated by conserved residues: His394, Glu396, Cys451, and Cys516 (PDB ID: 1ZY7) [58]. These residues are crucial for its deamination activity and are conserved across species [59, 60]. Additionally, the negatively charged inositol hexakisphosphatase (IP6) in the CDD binds within a cavity lined by basic/positively charged residues [58]. Loss of IP6 led to a significant decline in the activity, implying that it is a critical determinant in regulating ADAR deaminases. This further opened potential pathways toward targeting the IP6 binding domain for rational design of novel small molecule inhibitors. However, interestingly, ADAR3 lacks the editing activity despite possessing the corresponding residues for IP6 recognition and binding, suggesting that IP6 does not play any role in influencing the deaminase activity of ADAR3 [58].

Based on the structural information obtained from the four complexes of ADAR2 with dsRNA substrates containing the hydrated 8-azaN (reaction intermediate mimic), a base-flipping mechanism and neighboring sequence preferences for deaminases was proposed (Figure 7.15) [61, 62]. The residues from the base-flipping loop assist the adenosine to be pushed out of the duplex RNA toward the active site where deamination occurs. Reports have suggested that the isolated CDD of only

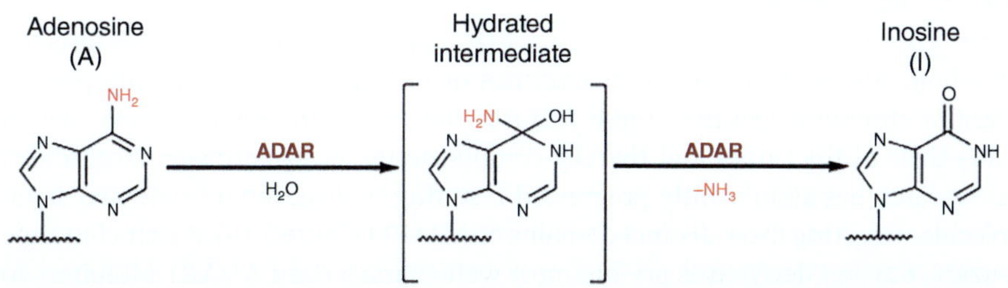

Figure 7.14 Reaction scheme for ADAR-catalyzed A-to-I editing. Adenosine deamination by ADAR proceeds via a hydrolytic step to form a tetrahedral-hydrated intermediate which undergoes proton transfer to produce inosine as the reaction product with the release of ammonia. *Source:* [57] / American Chemical Society.

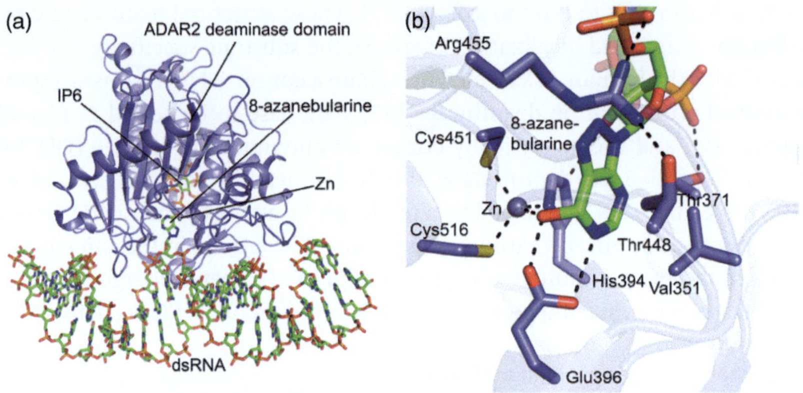

Figure 7.15 Crystal structure of human ADARs. (a) Overall crystal structure of human ADAR2 deaminase domain (colored in violet) bound to Zn(II) (purple sphere), IP6 (shown as green sticks), and 8-azaN containing dsRNA (green sticks) (PDB ID: 5HP2). Note: The modified 8-azaN nucleobase is flipped into the active site for editing. The negatively charged IP6 is critical for deamination activity. (b) Close-up view of the active site of ADAR2 shows octahedral Zn(II) coordination to conserved residues. The interacting residues are shown as sticks and dashed lines representing interactions between the substrate and these residues. *Source:* Adapted from [61].

ADAR1 and ADAR2 are capable of catalyzing deamination [63]. Moreover, structural investigations have concluded that the RNA-binding loop, located in the CDD of the deaminases determines the substrate selectivity between ADAR1 and ADAR2 [61, 63]. The varying amino acid sequences in the RBD of the two deaminases are potentially what drives the specificity. Crystallographic analyses on dsRBD of ADAR1 and ADAR2 complexed to dsRNA (PDB ID: 2B7T, 2B7V, and 2MDR) showed that the dsRBD can recognize and bind duplex RNA [64, 65]. Emerging evidence also suggests the involvement of dsRBD in subcellular localization of ADARs which is regulated by the binding of duplex RNA substrates to the conserved lysine residues within the dsRBD [66]. Insights into the structural knowledge and biological roles of human ADARs have necessitated the efforts to develop novel small molecule inhibitors targeting these enzymes for therapeutic applications.

7.12.1.3 ADAR Inhibition

To our knowledge, to date, there are no FDA-approved drugs for ADAR-targeted inhibition. Although the different enzymes of the human ADAR family possess common structural features, these features are unique to each enzyme, which define their distinct roles and thereby complicate the design strategy. Regardless, this research has significantly progressed resulting in discovery of potential small molecules targeting these distinct domains of ADARs (Figure 7.16). 8-azaneburaline (**8-azaN, 62**) and derivatives are the most well-characterized ADAR1 inhibitors to be identified to date. **62** is enzymatically hydrated by ADAR to generate a product resembling the reaction intermediate of ADAR. This hydrated product was proposed to abort the catalytic turnover of the ADAR1 [67]. A recent study by Mendoza *et al.* investigated the inhibition of **8-azaN** in different structural contexts such as

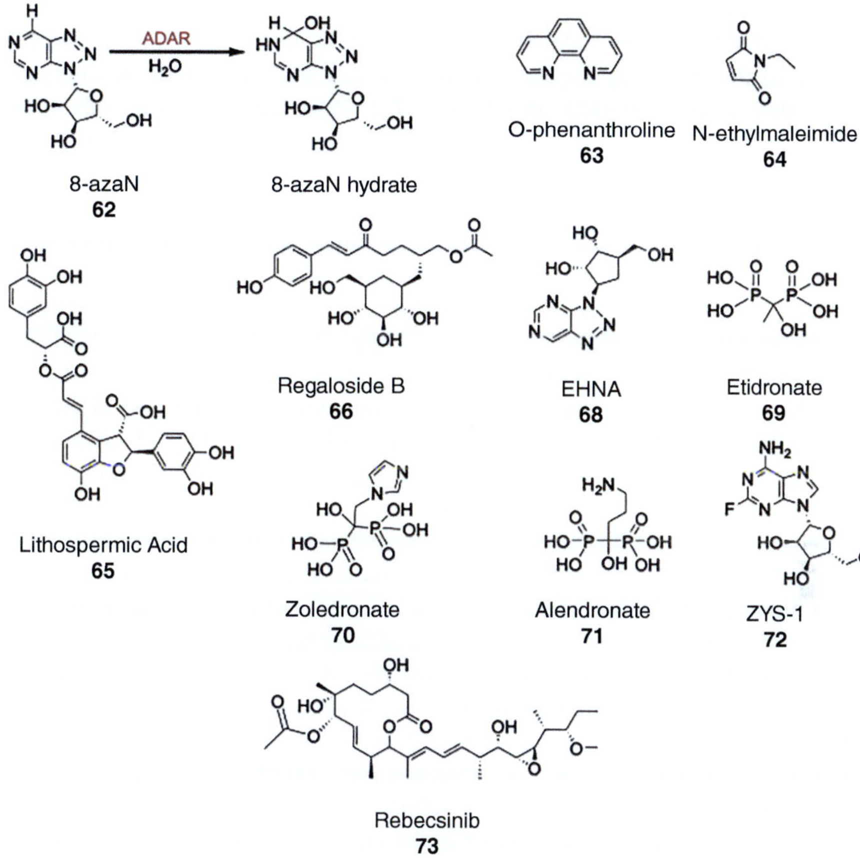

Figure 7.16 Chemical structures of known ADAR inhibitors.

free nucleoside, ssRNA, and dsRNA [67]. Results from gel shift assays and *in vitro* deamination assays suggested that only short RNA duplexes of a minimum 14 bp containing 8-azaN are capable of being recognized and edited by ADAR1 [67]. The same study also suggested that these 8-azaN-modified dsRNAs selectively inhibit ADAR1 (both isoforms) over ADAR2, with IC_{50} values in the lower nanomolar range [67].

In another study, a metal ion chelating compound O-phenanthroline (**63**) and N-ethylmaleimide (**64**) were shown to partially inhibit the ADAR1 activity [68]. However, detailed biochemical and functional assays are needed to validate these findings and to describe the distinct phenotypes resulting from these compounds.

The Zα domain of ADAR1p150 isoform has been a potential target for site-selective inhibition. Independent studies using *in silico* screening and high-throughput approaches have led to the identification of several small molecule inhibitors targeting the Zα domain. These include lithospermic acid (**65**) [69] and regaloside B (**66**) [69], AVA-ADR-001 (**67**; chemical structure not available) [70], erythro-9-(2-hydroxy-3-nonyl) adenine hydrochloride (EHNA **68**) [71], etidronate (**69**), zoledronate (**70**), and alendronate (**71**) [72]. MD simulations predicted that compounds **69–71** occupy the Zα domain's binding site and reportedly interacted with Lys169, Lys170, Asn173, and Tyr178 [72]. ZYS1 (**72**), a halogen-substituted derivative of 8-azaN has been investigated for therapeutic use in prostate cancer [73]. ADAR1 is a critical oncogene in the majority of prostate cancer cases and is highly expressed in PCSCs. ZYS1 has been shown to effectively inhibit ADAR1, which subsequently retards metastasis and inhibits tumor growth [73]. A pre-mRNA splicing modulator, rebecsinib (**73**), has been reported as a promising ADAR1p150 inhibitor for treatment of hematological malignancies [74]. ADAR1p150 mRNA and proteins are overexpressed in hematopoietic progenitor cells (HPCs) obtained from patients suffering from myeloproliferative neoplasms (MPNs) [74]. Preliminary data indicates that **73** is likely to inhibit the expression of ADAR1p150 in diseased HPCs by regulating the post-transcriptional processing of ADAR1p150 mRNA [74]. Contrary to ADAR1, the inhibition studies on ADAR2 are relatively limited. While 8-azaN has also been shown to target ADAR2 (IC_{50} 15 μM) [75], majority of the reported inhibitors of ADAR2 have been identified using virtual screening and validated by MD studies. A study by Broni *et al.* predicted three potential binding sites within human ADAR2 to virtual screen a library of traditional Chinese medicine compounds [76]. Nine lead compounds specifically targeting the IP6 binding site displayed favorable binding to the human ADAR2. Most of these compounds harbored either benzofuran, naphthoquinone, furanocoumarin, or indole scaffolds in their chemical structures. The results from their ADMET profiles indicated that these compounds showed negligible toxicity [76]. Moreover, the same group also targeted the RNA-binding loop of ADAR2 and obtained five hits from TCM compound virtual screening and MD simulations [48]. Though promising, further biochemical, structural, and cell-based investigations are needed to validate these observations and evaluate the inhibition profiles of these compounds. Nonetheless, the findings from these *in silico* studies provide substantial insights into the molecular behavior of ADAR2 with small molecules, stirring interest in developing better and selective ADAR2 inhibitors.

7.12.2 Zn^{2+}-Dependent Endonuclease: Human Cleavage and Polyadenylation Specificity Factor (CPSF73)

7.12.2.1 Pre-mRNA 3′-End Processing

The 3′ end of the eukaryotic pre-mRNAs undergo endonucleolytic cleavage and subsequent polyadenylation as a part of their post-transcriptional maturation [77, 78]. The replication-dependent histone pre-mRNAs, however, are an exception as they are only cleaved but not polyadenylated. Instead, these pre-mRNAs are processed by the U7 snRNP machinery [79, 80]. Alternatively, majority of the pre-mRNAs are polyadenylated by poly(A) polymerases (PAPs) at their 3′ end [77, 78]. This is a critical step in mRNA biogenesis and it impacts mRNA stability, nuclear to cytoplasmic export, and translation, implying that mRNA polyadenylation plays regulatory roles in gene expression [81–83]. Moreover, the pre-mRNAs can also be subjected to alternative polyadenylation by altering the position of the cleavage sites, commonly referred to as the poly(A) site (PAS). As a result, mRNA and proteins with different isoforms and varying 3′ UTRs are generated, which impact their interactions with several 3′-UTR-interacting factors and miRNAs [84–86].

In mammals, a cis-acting PAS hexamer motif A(A/U)UAAA is responsible for defining the cleavage and polyadenylation site [77, 87]. This sequence motif is generally positioned roughly 10–30 nucleotides upstream of the endonucleolytic site of cleavage and is specifically recognized by the cleavage and polyadenylation specificity factor (CPSF) [88–90]. CPSF is a multisubunit protein complex and a critical component of the 3′-end processing machinery. Structural and biochemical characterization of CPSF initially revealed a complex core consisting of four subunits: CPSF160, CPSF100, CPSF73, and CPSF30 [91, 92]. Later studies identified Fip1 and WDR33 as the additional CPSF domains mainly responsible for PAS selection [93, 94]. The focus of this review, however, is on the zinc-dependent metalloenzyme CPSF73 (or CPSF3).

7.12.2.2 Processing Roles of CPSF73 and Link to Human Diseases

CPSF73, a member of the metallo-β-lactamase (MBL) family of nucleases primarily catalyzes the zinc-dependent endonucleolytic cleavage of pre-mRNAs (Figure 7.17) [93] and is sequentially and functionally conserved across species [94]. Notably, CPSF73 is the critical cleavage component in both the canonical machinery [97, 98] as well as the replication-dependent histone pre-mRNA cleavage complex (HCC) [99, 100]. In addition to its role as an endonuclease, reports have also suggested exonucleolytic functions for CPSF73 in histone pre-mRNA processing [101]. For the

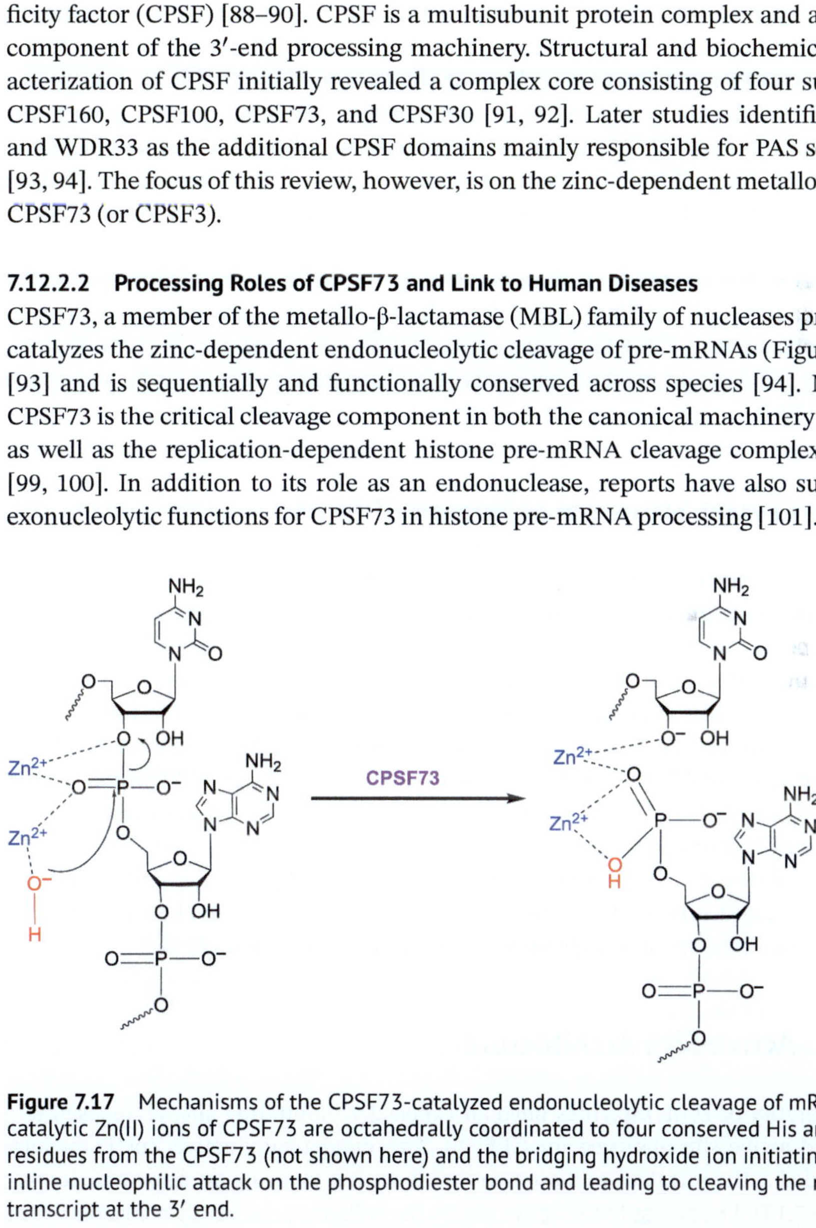

Figure 7.17 Mechanisms of the CPSF73-catalyzed endonucleolytic cleavage of mRNA. The catalytic Zn(II) ions of CPSF73 are octahedrally coordinated to four conserved His and Asp residues from the CPSF73 (not shown here) and the bridging hydroxide ion initiating an inline nucleophilic attack on the phosphodiester bond and leading to cleaving the mRNA transcript at the 3′ end.

mRNA transcripts to be polyadenylated, it directs the recruitment of PAP to the polyadenylation site and facilitates the release of mature transcripts for nuclear export [89, 90, 96]. CPSF73-catalyzed pre-mRNA cleavage also aids in transcription termination, thus, controlling the transcriptional interference of the downstream genes [96]. Given the critical roles played by CPSF73 in mRNA biogenesis, dysregulation of CPSF73 at mRNA and protein levels severely impacts gene expression with implications in several human diseases including cancer. Overexpression of CPSF73 mRNA in bladder cancer cells is linked to high expression of an immune checkpoint molecule CD276 resulting in immune invasion and poor prognosis. In prostate cancer, downregulation and methylation of cellular response 1 (CSR1) leads to cancer metastasis [102]. Both *in vivo* and *in vitro* studies have suggested that CSR1 interacts with CPSF73 to function as a tumor-suppressor gene [102]. The inactivation of CPSF73 is induced upon binding of the C-terminal of CSR1 to the former [102]. This shifts the translocation of the CPSF73 from the nucleus to the cytoplasm, which impedes the polyadenylation process and therefore causes cancer cell death [102]. Elevated expressions of CPSF73 in HCC altered the pre-mRNA cleavage products from circRNA to linear RNA, thereby promoting the cell migration and proliferation of HCC [103]. Similarly, evidence also suggests the involvement of CPSF73 in lung cancer [104], colorectal cancer [105], Ewing's sarcoma [105], acute myeloid leukemia [106], pancreatic cancer [107], and breast cancer [108].

7.13 Crystal Structure of Human CPSF73

Structural characterization of CPSF73 and other enzymes of the canonical 3′-end processing machinery has provided great insights into their respective roles in mRNA processing [84, 85, 95, 97, 109, 110]. The overall three-dimensional structure of human CPSF73 (PDB ID: 2I7T) reveals two distinct domains similar to canonical MBL nucleases: the MBL domain formed by NTD residues (1–208) and the β-CASP domain (residues 209–394) [95]. One distinct feature of the MBD domain of CPSF73 is the presence of CTD residues 395–460 that contribute three additional β strands to the central MBL fold. A similar feature has also been observed in the related MBL nucleases CPSF100 and RNaseZ and is critical for enzymatic activity [95]. On the other hand, the β-CASP domain consists of six parallel β sheet strands forming a central core and surrounded by five α helices on either side [95]. The entire domain constitutes a cassette and is positioned within the MBL domain [95].

7.14 Active Site Architecture

The majority of MBL enzymes have an exposed zinc-binding site as opposed to a shielded active site observed for CPSF73. Two catalytically active Zn(II) ions are embedded at the interface of these two core domains, favoring nuclease activity [95] (Figure 7.18). The access to the active site by the substrate is severely restricted by the

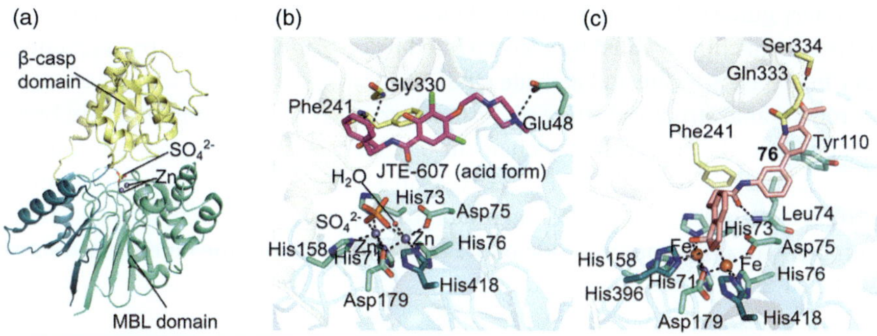

Figure 7.18 Crystallographic structures of human CPSF73 endonuclease. (a) Overall crystal structure of human CPSF73 (PDB ID: 2I7T). *Source:* Adapted from [95]. The protein is represented as cartoons and consists of two major domains: the MBL domain (green) and the β-CASP domain (yellow). The bound Zn(II) (gray spheres) and sulfate ions from the crystallization buffer (shown as orange sticks) are also shown. (b) The complex of CPSF73 bound to an inhibitor JTE-607 (**75**) (PDB ID: 6M8Q, magenta sticks) shows that it binds in the wide interfacial cavity of the enzyme but does not contact Zn(II) ions. *Source:* Adapted from [106]. (c) Complex of CPSF73 bound to inhibitor **76** (PDB ID: 8T1Q, salmon sticks). Notably, the metal coordination of 76 is distinct as compared to JTE607 and it does coordinate directly with the Zn(II) ion. *Source:* Adapted from [111].

β-CASP domain implying that CPSF73 undergoes potential conformational changes during binding and catalysis. Both the Zn(II) ions are octahedrally coordinated to four conserved His and Asp residues from the CPSF73 and one hydroxide ion as the bridging ligand, which also acts as a nucleophile in canonical MBL enzymes [95, 112]. Furthermore, in the crystal structure of human CPSF73 (PDB ID: 2I7T, 2I7V), the Zn(II) ion is also shown to be coordinated to the oxygen from a sulfate ion (from the crystallization buffer) at the sixth vacant site. The positioning of the sulfate ion in the active site suggests that it imitates the phosphate group of the pre-mRNA substrate at the site of cleavage [95]. Additionally, the hydroxide is correctly positioned with respect to the sulfate ion to facilitate an inline nucleophilic attack. This binding mode of zinc present in CPSF73 is reminiscent of RNase Z but differs from other MBL proteins.

7.15 Assembly of the 3′ Processing Machinery Activates the CPSF73 Endonuclease

Biochemical studies have reported that CPSF73 alone exhibits weak cleavage demonstrating that assembly of CPSF73 with its binding partners at the cleavage site is crucial for proper functioning of the processing machinery [95]. This weak activity is the result of closed conformation of CPSF73, which restricts the access of mRNA substrate to the active site. This finding has also been validated by structural studies on CPSF73 in both humans [95] and yeast [113]. Moreover, CPSF73 is unable to interact with its cognate RNA substrate in the absence of its accessory RNA-recognition components [96]. These recognition elements of the processing machinery guide CPSF73 to the desired cleavage site. The complete assembly of the processing machinery must be accompanied by conformational rearrangements in order to precisely locate and activate CPSF73.

A remarkable structural study on histone pre-mRNA processing provided breakthroughs into the molecular mechanism of CPSF73 activation [99]. The findings from this study revealed how CPSF73 exists in a closed conformation prior to incorporation into the HCC complex and undergoes extensive structural changes during assembly. This open conformation of the enzymes facilitates the binding and subsequent cleavage of mRNA substrate [99].

7.16 CPSF73 Inhibition in Cancer

CPSF73 is an established endonuclease involved in the 3′-end pre-mRNA processing and has been linked to several human diseases, fuelling interest in its inhibition. In a compelling study using phenotypic screening and chemical genetics, JTE-607 (**74**), an anti-inflammatory drug was identified as the direct inhibitor of CPSF73 (K_d = 370 nM) for therapeutic intervention in AML and Ewing's sarcoma (ES) [106]. Cell-based assays found that JTE-607 alters the cell differentiation and gene expression in both cancer cell lines by modulating pre-mRNA processing [106]. In cells, the ester prodrug of **74** is rapidly converted to its corresponding acid (**75**), which then binds to CPSF73, subsequently blocking the engagement of pre-mRNAs with the endonuclease [106]. As a result, the cleavage and export of these mRNAs are inhibited, which results in read-through transcription and generation of DNA–RNA hybrid R-loop structures. In both AML and ES, CPSF73 inhibition affects the expression of associated downstream effectors and promotes apoptosis [106]. A cocrystallized structure of CPSF73 bound to the acid form of JTE-607 (**74**) (PDB ID:6M8Q) revealed that the compound occupies the large interfacial cavity of the metalloenzyme (Figure 7.18b) [106]. The inhibitor does not directly chelate to zinc ions in the active site as evidenced by the distance between them (7 Å) but mirrors the binding mode of the native mRNA substrate [106]. Moreover, the binding of the inhibitor induces a conformational change with the β-CASP domain rotating 7.3° relative to the MBL domain [106]. The side chain of Phe241 undergoes a major conformational change to avoid steric clashes and accommodate the inhibitor. Further rearrangements are also observed in the loops critical for accessing the mRNA substrate suggesting that compound **80** potentially occupies the same binding sites as two phosphate groups of the corresponding mRNA substrate [106]. Besides AML and ES, the inhibition activity of JTE-607 against CPSF73 has also been demonstrated in pancreatic ductal adenocarcinoma (PDAC) [107]. Downregulation of CPSF3 in PDAC blocks cell proliferation *in vitro* and suppresses tumor growth *in vivo*. JTE-607 blocks the endonuclease activity of CPSF73 via transcriptional read-through transcription of histone mRNAs [107]. As a result, the tumor cells are arrested in S-phase due to repressed expression of histone mRNAs, which disrupts the structure of chromatin [107].

Following this, molecular modeling studies based on the CPSF73-JTE-607 structure led to the identification of several benzoxaboroles-containing compounds as promising drug candidates targeting CPSF73 in ovarian cancer cells [114]. The hit compound (**76**) with substituted biphenyl ring and 7-propanamide group was obtained and the overall predicted binding mode was similar to that observed for JTE-607 [114]. In particular, the 3-acetylphenyl group of **76** was speculated to be exposed to the solvent, which may potentially affect the solubility and bioavailability of the compound [114]. Interestingly, a recent X-ray crystal structure of CPSF73 in complex with compound **76** (PDB ID: 8T1Q) was determined. The structure revealed that CPSF73, when bound to **76**, was in a closed inactive conformation [111]. Contrary to the modeled structure, compound **76** was indeed shielded from the solvent, while the hydrated benzoxaborole's boronnic monoester group chelated the active site metal ion via oxygen atoms. While the overall binding mode of **76** was similar to active form of **75** [95] with both inhibitors preferring the large cavity of the active site, the major difference was observed in the metal coordination by these inhibitors (Figure 7.18c). This highlights the flexibility of the active site pocket of the enzyme, which can be exploited to fit diverse chemical inhibitors. Additionally, this binding mode and inhibitor-development strategy also resemble those of FTO inhibitors that occupy two different binding pockets, one of which allows for metal chelation.

Relying on the predicted structure of **76** with CPSF73, the 3-acetylphenyl group of **76** was substituted for hydrophilic groups to generate three structural analogues namely, HQY426 (**77**), HQY436 (**78**), and XHJ1049 (**79**) [114]. Cellular thermal shift assays and modeling studies confirmed that all these compounds directly interacted with CPSF73 and exhibited a similar binding mode as previously observed for the lead compound **76**. Furthermore, the median inhibitory concentration data of these compounds as determined by fluorescence-based binding assays indicated that compounds **77–79** were more potent than JTE-607 [114]. Mechanistically, inhibition of the endonuclease CPSF73 by benzoxaboroles minimized the DNA damage response while allowing CPSF73-induced transcription termination in tumor cells [114]. This suggested a novel phenomenon for targeting CPSF73 as previously seen with JTE-607, which exerts inhibitory effect via APA and read-through transcription [106, 115, 116].

7.17 CPSF73 Inhibition in Parasitic Infections

Besides cancer, targeting protozoan CPSF73 by benzoxaboroles and other small molecules has sparked interest in the development of effective therapeutic strategies against parasitic infections [117–120]. The prevailing treatment options pose a risk among young children and immunocompromised patients, are toxic, and are mostly ineffective [120]. In this regard, the notable inhibitors identified are AN3661 (**80**) and AN11736 (**81**), which selectively inhibit the protozoan CPSF73 over mammalian CPSF73 [120]. Structural studies on *Cryptosporidium* CPSF73 complexed to AN3661 (PDB ID: 6Q55) shed light on the inhibition mechanism which involves the binding of the oxaborole moiety at the metal-dependent catalytic site [120]. This effectively impairs the mRNA-processing activity of CPSF73. Although the overall structure is similar to the previously discussed structures of complexes with

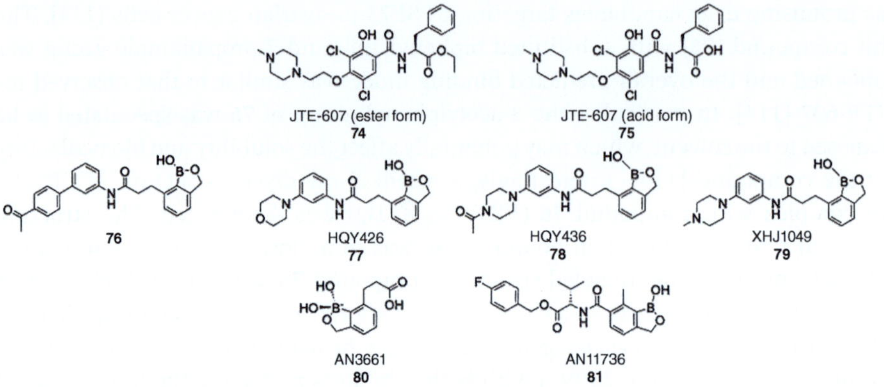

Figure 7.19 Chemical structures of reported CPSF73 inhibitors.

75 [95] and **76** [114], the propionate group of **80** is positioned opposite relative to the corresponding amide of **76** displaying a varied binding mode from that of human CPSF73 [120]. These structural findings of benzoxaboroles with CPSF73 have provided great insights into the inhibition mechanism of these compounds paving the way for development of inhibitors with improved selectivity and bioavailability. The structures of the discussed inhibitors are shown in Figure 7.19.

7.18 Conclusion and Perspectives

Metalloenzymes targeting RNA are emerging as attractive targets for drug discovery. This chapter attempts to group different families of RNA-modifying/processing metalloenzymes for a bird's eye view of their association with different types of diseases and strategies in developing inhibitors. Several prominent features include utilization of metal chelation and other binding pockets for inhibitor design. Notably, structure-based rational design by combining inhibitor fragments that simultaneously bind the metal binding pocket and extended substrate binding pocket can result in improved potency and selectivity. Subsequent challenges include cellular activity and "drug likeness", however, in the case of FTO inhibition, there were examples of modifications that could result in cell and *in vivo* activities [95]. With regard to ADAR inhibition, inhibition studies are still generally quite limited. The active site of ADAR has an additional disadvantage in that the zinc ion is tetrahedrally coordinated with three sites being occupied by amino acid residues, leaving one vacant site for monodentate chelation by potential inhibitors [58]. In the case of 8-azanebularine as inhibitor, this strategy involves the use of a transition state analogue [67]. Whether this could be a potential strategy for other metalloenzymes modifying RNA remains to be explored. Likewise, lessons learned from inhibition of CPSF73 by JTE-607 [106] and FTO by MA [75], in which inhibition of metalloenzymes does not always need metal chelation, may be a useful inhibition strategy for the ADARs.

References

1 Duncan, T., Trewick, S.C., Koivisto, P. et al. (2002). *Reversal of DNA alkylation damage by two human dioxygenases. Proceedings of the National Academy of Sciences* 99 (26): 16660–16665.

2 Aas, P.A., Otterlei, M., Falnes, P.O. et al. (2003). *Human and bacterial oxidative demethylases repair alkylation damage in both RNA and DNA. Nature* 421 (6925): 859–863.

3 Monsen, V.T., Sundheim, O., Aas, P.A. et al. (2010). *Divergent β-hairpins determine double-strand versus single-strand substrate recognition of human AlkB-homologues 2 and 3. Nucleic Acids Research* 38 (19): 6447–6455.

4 Chen, Z., Qi, M., Shen, B. et al. (2018). *Transfer RNA demethylase ALKBH3 promotes cancer progression via induction of tRNA-derived small RNAs. Nucleic Acids Research* 47 (5): 2533–2545.

5 Woo, H.-H. and Chambers, S.K. (2019). *Human ALKBH3-induced m1A demethylation increases the CSF-1 mRNA stability in breast and ovarian cancer cells. Biochimica et Biophysica Acta (BBA) - Gene Regulatory Mechanisms* 1862 (1): 35–46.

6 Hotta, K., Sho, M., Fujimoto, K. et al. (2015). *Clinical significance and therapeutic potential of prostate cancer antigen-1/ALKBH3 in human renal cell carcinoma. Oncology Reports* 34 (2): 648–654.

7 Yamato, I., Sho, M., Shimada, K. et al. (2012). *PCA-1/ALKBH3 contributes to pancreatic cancer by supporting apoptotic resistance and angiogenesis. Cancer Research* 72 (18): 4829–4839.

8 Kuang, W., Jin, H., Yang, F. et al. (2022). *ALKBH3-dependent m1A demethylation of Aurora A mRNA inhibits ciliogenesis. Cell Discovery* 8 (1): 25.

9 Tasaki, M., Shimada, K., Kimura, H. et al. (2011). ALKBH3, a human AlkB homologue, contributes to cell survival in human non-small-cell lung cancer. *British Journal of Cancer* 104 (4): 700–706.

10 Konishi, N., Nakamura, M., Ishida, E. et al. (2005). *High expression of a new marker PCA-1 in human prostate carcinoma. Clinical Cancer Research* 11 (14): 5090–5097.

11 Shimada, K., Fujii, T., Tsujikawa, K. et al. (2012). *ALKBH3 contributes to survival and angiogenesis of human urothelial carcinoma cells through NADPH oxidase and tweak/Fn14/VEGF signals. Clinical Cancer Research* 18 (19): 5247–5255.

12 Luo, J., Emanuele, M.J., Li, D. et al. (2009). *A genome-wide RNAi screen identifies multiple synthetic lethal interactions with the Ras oncogene. Cell* 137 (5): 835–848.

13 Sundheim, O., Vågbø, C.B., Bjørås, M. et al. (2006). *Human ABH3 structure and key residues for oxidative demethylation to reverse DNA/RNA damage. The EMBO Journal* 25 (14): 3389–3397.

14 Das, M., Yang, T., Dong, J. et al. (2018). *Multiprotein dynamic combinatorial chemistry: a strategy for the simultaneous discovery of subfamily-selective* *inhibitors for nucleic acid demethylases FTO and ALKBH3. Chemistry – An Asian Journal* 13 (19): 2854–2867.

15 Li, Q., Huang, Y., Liu, X. et al. (2016). Rhein inhibits AlkB repair enzymes and sensitizes cells to methylated DNA damage. The Journal of Biological Chemistry 291 (21): 11083–11093.

16 Huang, Y., Yan, J., Li, Q. et al. (2015). Meclofenamic acid selectively inhibits FTO demethylation of m6A over ALKBH5. Nucleic Acids Research 43 (1): 373–384.

17 Toh, J.D.W., Sun, L., Lau, L.Z.M. et al. (2015). A strategy based on nucleotide specificity leads to a subfamily-selective and cell-active inhibitor of N6-methyladenosine demethylase FTO. Chemical Science 6 (1): 112–122.

18 Perry, G.S., Das, M., and Woon, E.C.Y. (2021). Inhibition of AlkB nucleic acid demethylases: promising new epigenetic targets. Journal of Medicinal Chemistry 64 (23): 16974–17003.

19 Nakao, S., Mabuchi, M., Shimizu, T. et al. (2014). *Design and synthesis of prostate cancer antigen-1 (PCA-1/ALKBH3) inhibitors as anti-prostate cancer drugs. Bioorganic & Medicinal Chemistry Letters* 24 (4): 1071–1074.

20 Ueda, M., Shimizu, T., Mabuchi, M. et al. (2018). *Novel metabolically stable PCA-1/ALKBH3 inhibitor has potent antiproliferative effects on DU145 cells in vivo. Anticancer Research* 38 (1): 211–218.

21 Nigam, R., Babu, K.R., Ghosh, T. et al. (2018). *Indenone derivatives as inhibitor of human DNA dealkylation repair enzyme AlkBH3. Bioorganic & Medicinal Chemistry* 26 (14): 4100–4112.

22 Bass, B.L. (2000). *Double-stranded RNA as a template for gene silencing. Cell* 101 (3): 235–238.

23 Samuel, C.E. (2019). *Adenosine deaminase acting on RNA (ADAR1), a suppressor of double-stranded RNA–triggered innate immune responses. Journal of Biological Chemistry* 294 (5): 1710–1720.

24 Wang, Y., Zheng, Y., and Beal, P.A. (2017). *Adenosine deaminases that act on RNA (ADARs). Enzymes* 41: 215–268.

25 Nishikura, K. (2010). Functions and regulation of RNA editing by ADAR deaminases. *Annual Review of Biochemistry* 79: 321–349.

26 Bass, B.L. (2002). *RNA editing by adenosine deaminases that act on RNA. Annual Review of Biochemistry* 71: 817–846.

27 Fritzell, K., Xu, L.D., Lagergren, J. et al. (2018). *ADARs and editing: the role of A-to-I RNA modification in cancer progression.* In: *Seminars in Cell & Developmental Biology*. Elsevier.

28 Nishikura, K. (2016). *A-to-I editing of coding and non-coding RNAs by ADARs. Nature Reviews. Molecular Cell Biology* 17 (2): 83–96.

29 Tassinari, V., Cerboni, C., and Soriani, A. (2022). *Self or non-self? It Is also a matter of RNA recognition and editing by ADAR1. Biology* 11 (4): 568.

30 Alon, S., Mor, E., Vigneault, F. et al. (2012). *Systematic identification of edited microRNAs in the human brain. Genome Research* 22 (8): 1533–1540.

31 Tan, M.H., Li, Q., Shanmugam, R. et al. (2017). *Dynamic landscape and regulation of RNA editing in mammals. Nature* 550 (7675): 249–254.

32 Schaffer, A.A. and Levanon, E.Y. (2021). *ALU A-to-I RNA editing: millions of sites and many open questions*, 149–162. RNA Editing: Methods and Protocols.

33 Eisenberg, E. and Levanon, E.Y. (2018). *A-to-I RNA editing — immune protector and transcriptome diversifier. Nature Reviews Genetics* 19 (8): 473–490.

34 Chen, L.L., DeCerbo, J.N., and Carmichael, G.G. (2008). *Alu element-mediated gene silencing. The EMBO Journal* 27 (12): 1694–1705.

35 Slotkin, W. and Nishikura, K. (2013). *Adenosine-to-inosine RNA editing and human disease. Genome Medicine* 5: 1–13.

36 Gallo, A., Vukic, D., Michalík, D. et al. (2017). *ADAR RNA editing in human disease; more to it than meets the I. Human Genetics* 136: 1265–1278.

37 Chen, C.X., Cho, D.S., Wang, Q. et al. (2000). *A third member of the RNA-specific adenosine deaminase gene family, ADAR3, contains both single- and double-stranded RNA binding domains. RNA* 6 (5): 755–767.

38 Rice, G.I., Kasher, P.R., Forte, G.M. et al. (2012). *Mutations in ADAR1 cause Aicardi-Goutières syndrome associated with a type I interferon signature. Nature Genetics* 44 (11): 1243–1248.

39 Livingston, J.H., Lin, J.P., Dale, R.C. et al. (2014). *A type I interferon signature identifies bilateral striatal necrosis due to mutations in ADAR1. Journal of Medical Genetics* 51 (2): 76–82.

40 Liddicoat, B.J., Piskol, R., Chalk, A.M. et al. (2015). *RNA editing by ADAR1 prevents MDA5 sensing of endogenous dsRNA as nonself. Science* 349 (6252): 1115–1120.

41 Nakano, M., Fukami, T., Gotoh, S. et al. (2017). *A-to-I RNA editing p-regulates human dihydrofolate reductase in breast cancer *. Journal of Biological Chemistry* 292 (12): 4873–4884.

42 Kung, C.-P., Cottrell, K.A., Ryu, S. et al. (2021). *Evaluating the therapeutic potential of ADAR1 inhibition for triple-negative breast cancer. Oncogene* 40 (1): 189–202.

43 Amin, E.M., Liu, Y., Deng, S. et al. (2017). *The RNA-editing enzyme ADAR promotes lung adenocarcinoma migration and invasion by stabilizing. Science Signaling* 10 (497): eaah3941.

44 Galore-Haskel, G., Nemlich, Y., Greenberg, E. et al. (2015). *A novel immune resistance mechanism of melanoma cells controlled by the ADAR1 enzyme. Oncotarget* 6 (30).

45 Nemlich, Y., Greenberg, E., Ortenberg, R. et al. (2013). *MicroRNA-mediated loss of ADAR1 in metastatic melanoma promotes tumor growth. The Journal of Clinical Investigation* 123 (6): 2703–2718.

46 Shoshan, E., Mobley, A.K., Braeuer, R.R. et al. (2015). *Reduced adenosine-to-inosine miR-455-5p editing promotes melanoma growth and metastasis. Nature Cell Biology* 17 (3): 311–321.

47 Zipeto, M.A., Court, A.C., Sadarangani, A. et al. (2016). *ADAR1 activation drives leukemia stem cell self-renewal by impairing let-7 biogenesis. Cell Stem Cell* 19 (2): 177–191.

48 Broni, E., Ashley, C., Velazquez, M. et al. (2023). *In silico discovery of potential inhibitors targeting the RNA binding loop of ADAR2 and 5-HT2CR from traditional chinese natural compounds. International Journal of Molecular Sciences* 24 (16): 12612.

49 Mombereau, C., Kawahara, Y., Gundersen, B.B. et al. (2010). *Functional relevance of serotonin 2C receptor mRNA editing in antidepressant- and anxiety-like behaviors. Neuropharmacology* 59 (6): 468–473.

50 Eran, A., Li, J.B., Vatalaro, K. et al. (2013). *Comparative RNA editing in autistic and neurotypical cerebella. Molecular Psychiatry* 18 (9): 1041–1048.

51 Tomaselli, S., Galeano, F., Alon, S. et al. (2015). *Modulation of microRNA editing, expression and processing by ADAR2 deaminase in glioblastoma. Genome Biology* 16 (1): 5.

52 Liu, W.-H., Chen, C.H., Yeh, K.H. et al. (2013). *ADAR2-mediated editing of miR-214 and miR-122 precursor and antisense RNA transcripts in liver cancers. PLOS ONE* 8 (12): e81922.

53 Chan, T.H.M., Lin, C.H., Qi, L. et al. (2014). *A disrupted RNA editing balance mediated by ADARs (Adenosine DeAminases that act on RNA) in human hepatocellular carcinoma. Gut* 63 (5): 832.

54 Patterson, J.B. and Samuel, C.E. (1995). *Expression and regulation by interferon of a double-stranded-RNA-specific adenosine deaminase from human cells: evidence for two forms of the deaminase. Molecular and Cellular Biology* 15 (10): 5376–5388.

55 Desterro, J.M.P., Keegan, L.P., Lafarga, M. et al. (2003). *Dynamic association of RNA-editing enzymes with the nucleolus. Journal of Cell Science* 116 (9): 1805–1818.

56 Rehwinkel, J. and Mehdipour, P. (2024). *ADAR1: from basic mechanisms to inhibitors. Trends in Cell Biology.*

57 Haudenschild, B.L., Maydanovych, O., Véliz, E.A. et al. (2004). *A transition state analogue for an RNA-editing reaction. Journal of the American Chemical Society* 126 (36): 11213–11219.

58 Macbeth, M.R., Schubert, H.L., Vandemark, A.P. et al. (2005). *Inositol hexakisphosphate Is bound in the ADAR2 core and required for RNA editing. Science* 309 (5740): 1534–1539.

59 Kim, U., Wang, Y., Sanford, T. et al. (1994). *Molecular cloning of cDNA for double-stranded RNA adenosine deaminase, a candidate enzyme for nuclear RNA editing. Proceedings of the National Academy of Sciences of the United States of America* 91 (24): 11457–11461.

60 Gerber, A.P. and Keller, W. (2001). *RNA editing by base deamination: more enzymes, more targets, new mysteries. Trends in Biochemical Sciences* 26 (6): 376–384.

61 Matthews, M.M., Thomas, J.M., Zheng, Y. et al. (2016). *Structures of human ADAR2 bound to dsRNA reveal base-flipping mechanism and basis for site selectivity. Nature Structural & Molecular Biology* 23 (5): 426–433.

62 Hong, S. and Cheng, X. (2016). *DNA base flipping: a general mechanism for writing, reading, and erasing DNA modifications. Advances in Experimental Medicine and Biology* 945: 321–341.

63 Ashley, C.N., Broni, E., and Miller, W.A. 3rd, (2024). *ADAR family proteins: a structural review. Current Issues in Molecular Biology* 46 (5): 3919–3945.

64 Stefl, R., Xu, M., Skrisovska, L. et al. (2006). *Structure and specific RNA binding of ADAR2 double-stranded RNA binding motifs. Structure* 14 (2): 345–355.

65 Barraud, P., Banerjee, S., Mohamed, W.I. et al. (2014). *A bimodular nuclear localization signal assembled via an extended double-stranded RNA-binding domain acts as an RNA-sensing signal for transportin 1. Proceedings of the National Academy of Sciences* 111 (18): E1852–E1861.

66 Sansam, C.L., Wells, K.S., and Emeson, R.B. (2003). *Modulation of RNA editing by functional nucleolar sequestration of ADAR2. Proceedings of the National Academy of Sciences* 100 (24): 14018–14023.

67 Mendoza, H.G., Matos, V.J., Park, S. et al. (2023). *Selective inhibition of ADAR1 using 8-azanebularine-modified RNA duplexes. Biochemistry* 62 (8): 1376–1387.

68 O'Connell, M.A., Gerber, A., and Keller, W. (1997). *Purification of human double-stranded RNA-specific editase 1 (hRED1) involved in editing of brain glutamate receptor B pre-mRNA *. Journal of Biological Chemistry* 272 (1): 473–478.

69 Hong, X., Wei, Z., He, L. et al. (2024). *High-throughput virtual screening to identify potential small molecule inhibitors of the Zα domain of the adenosine deaminases acting on RNA 1(ADAR1). European Journal of Pharmaceutical Sciences* 193: 106672.

70 Goswami, A., Deb, B., Goyal, S. et al. (2023). *1041 Discovery of a potential first-in-class small molecule inhibitor of ADAR1 p150 which demonstrates strong anti-tumor efficacy in B16F10 syngeneic melanoma model. Journal for ImmunoTherapy of Cancer* 11 (Suppl 1): A1148.

71 Pham, N.T., Tohda, M., Tezuka, Y. et al. (2010). *Influence of an adenosine deaminase inhibitor, erythro-9-(2-hydroxy-3-nonyl) adenine hydrochloride, on 5-HT2CR mRNA editing in primary cultured cortical cells. Biological & Pharmaceutical Bulletin* 33 (3): 527–529.

72 Choudhry, H. (2021). *High-throughput screening to identify potential inhibitors of the Zα domain of the adenosine deaminase 1 (ADAR1). Saudi Journal of Biological Sciences* 28 (11): 6297–6304.

73 Wang, X., Li, J., Zhu, Y. et al., *Targeting ADAR1 with a Novel Small-Molecule for the Treatment of Prostate Cancer*. 2021.

74 Crews, L.A., Ma, W., Ladel, L. et al. (2023). *Reversal of malignant ADAR1 splice isoform switching with rebecsinib. Cell Stem Cell* 30 (3): 250–263.e6.

75 Véliz, E.A., Easterwood, L.M., and Beal, P.A. (2003). *Substrate analogues for an RNA-editing adenosine deaminase: mechanistic investigation and inhibitor design. Journal of the American Chemical Society* 125 (36): 10867–10876.

76 Broni, E., Striegel, A., Ashley, C. et al. (2023). *Molecular docking and dynamics simulation studies predict potential anti-ADAR2 inhibitors: implications for* *the treatment of cancer, neurological, immunological and infectious diseases. International Journal of Molecular Sciences* 24 (7): 6795.

77 Chan, S., Choi, E.-A., and Shi, Y. (2011). Pre-mRNA 3'-end processing complex assembly and function. *WIREs RNA* 2 (3): 321–335.

78 Shi, Y. and Manley, J.L. (2015). The end of the message: multiple protein-RNA interactions define the mRNA polyadenylation site. *Genes & Development* 29 (9): 889–897.

79 Dominski, Z. and Marzluff, W.F. (2007). *Formation of the 3′ end of histone mRNA: getting closer to the end. Gene* 396 (2): 373–390.

80 Romeo, V. and Schümperli, D. (2016). *Cycling in the nucleus: regulation of RNA 3′ processing and nuclear organization of replication-dependent histone genes. Current Opinion in Cell Biology* 40: 23–31.

81 Sandberg, R., Neilson, J.R., Sarma, A. et al. (2008). *Proliferating cells express mRNAs with shortened 3′ untranslated regions and fewer microRNA target sites. Science* 320 (5883): 1643–1647.

82 Shepard, P.J., Choi, E.A., Lu, J. et al. (2011). *Complex and dynamic landscape of RNA polyadenylation revealed by PAS-Seq. RNA* 17 (4): 761–772.

83 Graber, J.H., Nazeer, F. I, Yeh, P.C. et al. (2013). *DNA damage induces targeted, genome-wide variation of poly(A) sites in budding yeast. Genome Research* 23 (10): 1690–1703.

84 Gruber, A.J. and Zavolan, M. (2019). *Alternative cleavage and polyadenylation in health and disease. Nature Reviews Genetics* 20 (10): 599–614.

85 Tian, B. and Manley, J.L. (2017). *Alternative polyadenylation of mRNA precursors. Nature Reviews Molecular Cell Biology* 18 (1): 18–30.

86 Ren, F., Zhang, N., Zhang, L. et al. (2020). *Alternative polyadenylation: a new frontier in post transcriptional regulation. Biomarker Research* 8 (1): 67.

87 Proudfoot, N.J. and Brownlee, G.G. (1976). *3′ Non-coding region sequences in eukaryotic messenger RNA. Nature* 263 (5574): 211–214.

88 Sheets, M.D., Ogg, S.C., and Wickens, M.P. (1990). Point mutations in AAUAAA and the poly (A) addition site: effects on the accuracy and efficiency of cleavage and polyadenylation in vitro. *Nucleic Acids Research* 18 (19): 5799–5805.

89 Takagaki, Y., Ryner, L.C., and Manley, J.L. (1988). Separation and characterization of a poly(A) polymerase and a cleavage/specificity factor required for pre-mRNA polyadenylation. *Cell* 52 (5): 731–742.

90 Keller, W., Bienroth, S., Lang, K.M. et al. (1991). Cleavage and polyadenylation factor CPF specifically interacts with the pre-mRNA 3' processing signal AAUAAA. *The EMBO Journal* 10 (13): 4241–4249.

91 Bienroth, S., Wahle, E., Suter-Crazzolara, C. et al. (1991). *Purification of the cleavage and polyadenylation factor involved in the 3′-processing of messenger RNA precursors. The Journal of Biological Chemistry* 266 (29): 19768–19776.

92 Murthy, K.G. and Manley, J.L. (1992). *Characterization of the multisubunit cleavage-polyadenylation specificity factor from calf thymus. The Journal of Biological Chemistry* 267 (21): 14804–14811.

93 Shi, Y., Di Giammartino, D.C., Taylor, D. et al. (2009). *Molecular architecture of the human pre-mRNA 3&#x2032. Processing Complex. Molecular Cell* 33 (3): 365–376.

94 Kaufmann, I., Martin, G., Friedlein, A. et al. (2004). *Human Fip1 is a subunit of CPSF that binds to U-rich RNA elements and stimulates poly(A) polymerase. The EMBO Journal* 23 (3): 616–626.

95 Mandel, C.R., Kaneko, S., Zhang, H. et al. (2006). *Polyadenylation factor CPSF-73 is the pre-mRNA 3′-end-processing endonuclease. Nature* 444 (7121): 953–956.

96 Liu, H. and Moore, C.L. (2021). *On the cutting edge: regulation and therapeutic potential of the mRNA 3′ end nuclease. Trends in Biochemical Sciences* 46 (9): 772–784.

97 Sun, Y., Hamilton, K., and Tong, L. (2020). *Recent molecular insights into canonical pre-mRNA 3′-end processing. Transcription* 11 (2): 83–96.

98 Zhang, Y., Sun, Y., Shi, Y. et al. (2020). *Structural insights into the human pre-mRNA 3′-end processing machinery. Molecular Cell* 77 (4): 800–809.e6.

99 Sun, Y., Zhang, Y., Aik, W.S. et al. (2020). *Structure of an active human histone pre-mRNA 3′-end processing machinery. Science* 367 (6478): 700–703.

100 Sullivan, K.D., Steiniger, M., and Marzluff, W.F. (2009). *A core complex of CPSF73, CPSF100, and symplekin may form two different cleavage factors for processing of poly(A) and histone mRNAs. Molecular Cell* 34 (3): 322–332.

101 Dominski, Z., Yang, X.C., and Marzluff, W.F. (2005). *The polyadenylation factor CPSF-73 is involved in histone-pre-mRNA processing. Cell* 123 (1): 37–48.

102 Zhu, Z.H., Yu, Y., Shi, Y.-K. et al. (2009). *CSR1 induces cell death through inactivation of CPSF3. Oncogene* 28 (1): 41–51.

103 Huang, Y., Ji, H., Dong, J. et al. (2023). *CPSF3 promotes pre-mRNA splicing and prevents circRNA cyclization in hepatocellular carcinoma. Cancers* 15 (16): 4057.

104 Ning, Y., Liu, W., Guan, X. et al. (2019). *CPSF3 is a promising prognostic biomarker and predicts recurrence of non-small cell lung cancer. Oncology Letters* 18 (3): 2835–2844.

105 Luo, K., Geng, J., Zhang, Q. et al. (2019). *LncRNA CASC9 interacts with CPSF3 to regulate TGF-β signaling in colorectal cancer. Journal of Experimental & Clinical Cancer Research* 38: 1–16.

106 Ross, N.T., Lohmann, F., Carbonneau, S. et al. (2020). *CPSF3-dependent pre-mRNA processing as a druggable node in AML and Ewing's sarcoma. Nature Chemical Biology* 16 (1): 50–59.

107 Alahmari, A.A., Chaubey, A.H., Jonnakuti, V.S. et al. (2024). *CPSF3 inhibition blocks pancreatic cancer cell proliferation through disruption of core histone mRNA processing. RNA* 30 (3): 281–297.

108 Liu, H., Heller-Trulli, D., and Moore, C.L. (2022). *Targeting the mRNA endonuclease CPSF73 inhibits breast cancer cell migration, invasion, and self-renewal. iScience* 25 (8): 104804.

109 Clerici, M., Faini, M., Aebersold, R. et al. (2017). *Structural insights into the assembly and polyA signal recognition mechanism of the human CPSF complex. eLife* 6.

110 Xiang, K., Tong, L., and Manley, J.L. (2014). *Delineating the structural blueprint of the pre-mRNA 3′-end processing machinery. Mol Cell Biol* 34 (11): 1894–1910.

111 Tao, Y., Budhipramono, A., Huang, J. et al. (2024). *Anticancer benzoxaboroles block pre-mRNA processing by directly inhibiting CPSF3. Cell Chemical Biology* 31 (1): 139–149.e14.

112 Baillat, D., Hakimi, M.A., Näär, A.M. et al. (2005). *Integrator, a multiprotein mediator of small nuclear RNA processing, associates with the C-terminal repeat of RNA polymerase II. Cell* 123 (2): 265–276.

113 Hill, C.H., Boreikaitė, V., Kumar, A. et al. (2019). *Activation of the endonuclease that defines mRNA 3′ ends requires incorporation into an 8-subunit core cleavage and polyadenylation factor complex. Molecular Cell* 73 (6): 1217–1231.e11.

114 Shen, P., Ye, K., Xiang, H. et al. (2023). *Therapeutic targeting of CPSF3-dependent transcriptional termination in ovarian cancer. Science Advances* 9 (47): eadj0123.

115 Eaton, J.D., Davidson, L., Bauer, D.L.V. et al. (2018). *Xrn2 accelerates termination by RNA polymerase II, which is underpinned by CPSF73 activity. Genes & Development* 32 (2): 127–139.

116 Cui, Y., Wang, L., Ding, Q. et al. (2023). *Elevated pre-mRNA 3′ end processing activity in cancer cells renders vulnerability to inhibition of cleavage and polyadenylation. Nature Communications* 14 (1): 4480.

117 Sonoiki, E., Ng, C.L., Lee, M.C. et al. (2017). *A potent antimalarial benzoxaborole targets a Plasmodium falciparum cleavage and polyadenylation specificity factor homologue. Nature Communications* 8: 14574.

118 Palencia, A., Bougdour, A., Brenier-Pinchart, M.P. et al. (2017). *Targeting toxoplasma gondii CPSF3 as a new approach to control toxoplasmosis. EMBO Molecular Medicine* 9 (3): 385–394.

119 Wall, R.J., Rico, E., Lukac, I. et al. (2018). *Clinical and veterinary trypanocidal benzoxaboroles target CPSF3. Proceedings of the National Academy of Sciences* 115 (38): 9616–9621.

120 Swale, C., Bougdour, A., Gnahoui-David, A. et al. (2019). *Metal-captured inhibition of pre-mRNA processing activity by CPSF3 controls Cryptosporidium infection. Science Translational Medicine* 517.

8

Cyclic Nucleotide Phosphodiesterases: Important Therapeutic Targets

Deyan Wu, Shuheng Huang, and Hai-Bin Luo

Hainan University, Key Laboratory of Tropical Biological Resources of Ministry of Education, School of Pharmaceutical Sciences, No.58 Renmin Avenue, Haikou, 570228, P.R. China

8.1 Introduction

The cyclic adenosine monophosphate (cAMP) and cyclic guanosine monophosphate (cGMP) signaling pathways are crucial regulators of numerous physiological processes, including visual transduction, cell proliferation and differentiation, gene expression, inflammation, apoptosis, cell-cycle control, and metabolic function [1–3]. The intracellular levels of cAMP and cGMP are tightly controlled by cyclic nucleotide phosphodiesterases (PDEs). As illustrated in Figure 8.1, cAMP and cGMP are synthesized by adenylyl cyclase and guanylyl cyclase, respectively, which are activated by G-protein-coupled receptors and signaling molecules such as natriuretic peptides or nitric oxide. cAMP, in turn, activates protein kinase A (PKA) and exchange protein directly activated by cAMP (EPAC). PKA plays a pivotal role in metabolic regulation, cell growth, differentiation, and proliferation, while EPAC is involved in various cellular processes, including integrin-mediated adhesion, cell–cell junction formation, exocytosis, and insulin secretion [4–8]. cGMP activates protein kinase G (PKG), which mediates the phosphorylation of target proteins involved in apoptosis, inflammation, smooth muscle contractility, visual transduction, and platelet aggregation [9]. PDEs regulate the intracellular concentrations of cAMP and cGMP by catalyzing their hydrolysis, thereby modulating their wide-ranging biological effects.

8.2 Phosphodiesterases (PDEs)

8.2.1 Classification

PDEs are a family of enzymes responsible for hydrolyzing the second messengers cAMP and cGMP. The PDE superfamily comprises 21 genes and is categorized into 11 subtypes (PDE1–11). Among these, PDEs 4, 7, and 8 specifically hydrolyze cAMP, while PDEs 5, 6, and 9 target cGMP. The remaining PDE subtypes are capable of

Drug Discovery Targeting Metalloenzymes: Strategies and Applications, First Edition. Edited by Guo-Bo Li.

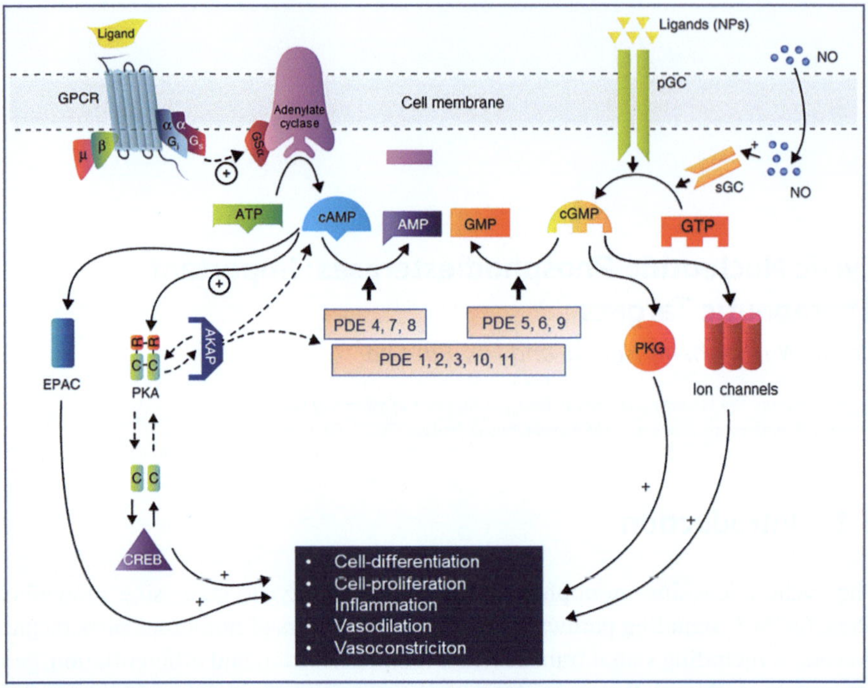

Figure 8.1 Summary of cyclic nucleotide signaling pathways. *Source:* Ref. [4] / with permission of Elsevier.

hydrolyzing both cAMP and cGMP [2, 10–13]. As depicted in Figure 8.2, many PDE families contain amino-terminal subdomains – such as GAF, transmembrane, targeting domains, upstream conserved regions (UCRs), poly(A) site (PAS), and REC domains – as well as hydrophobic N-terminal regions. These structural features are critical for subcellular localization, incorporation into compartmentalized signalosomes, interactions with signaling molecules and molecular scaffolds, and regulation of PDE activity [2, 14–16]. The conserved catalytic domain (highlighted in red) is located in the carboxy-terminal region of PDEs. Notably, the catalytic domain of PDE3 contains a unique 44-amino-acid insertion (indicated in black). Additionally, the GAF domains regulate the allosteric binding of cGMP (in PDE2, PDE5, PDE6, and PDE11), the binding of cAMP (in PDE10), and the modulation of catalytic activity (in PDE2, PDE5, and PDE6).

8.2.2 PDE Structures and Catalytic Mechanisms

Cyclic nucleotide PDEs are crucial for regulating the intracellular levels of the second messengers cAMP and cGMP. The hydrolysis of these cyclic nucleotides occurs within the substrate-binding pocket of the PDE catalytic domain, facilitated by two metal ions that occupy the adjacent metal-binding site [17, 18]. X-ray crystallographic studies of PDEs have revealed the presence of a unique binuclear metal-binding site in the catalytic pocket, which is thought to be integral to the

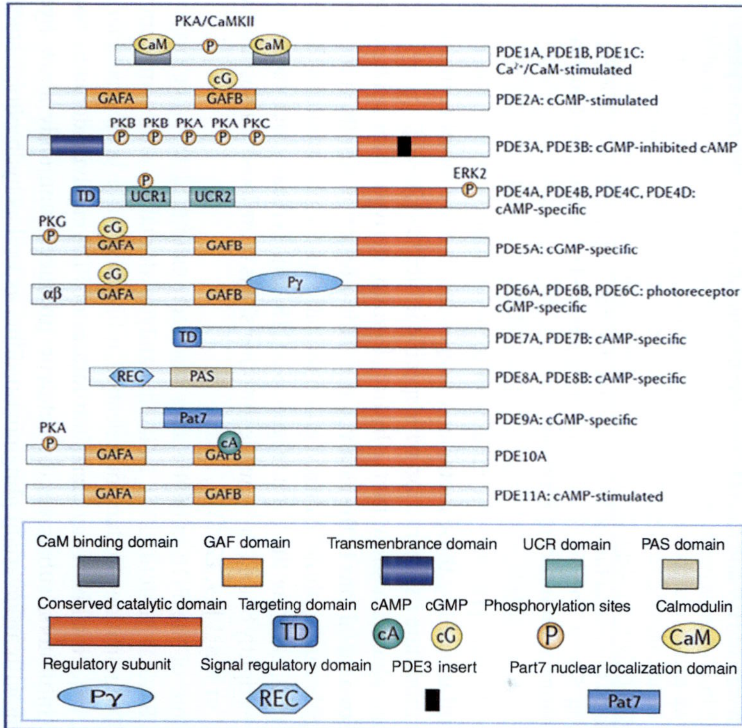

PDE family	Subfamily (number of splice variants)	Substrate
PDE1	A(4), B(1), C(5)	cAMP/cGMP
PDE2	A(3)	cAMP/cGMP
PDE3	A(1), B(1)	cAMP/cGMP
PDE4	A(8), B(3), C(4), D(5)	cAMP
PDE5	A(3)	cGMP
PDE6	A(1), B(1), C(1)	cGMP
PDE7	A(3), B(1)	cAMP
PDE8	A(5), B(1)	cAMP
PDE9	A(6)	cGMP
PDE10	A(2)	cAMP/cGMP
PDE11	A(4)	cAMP/cGMP

Figure 8.2 Structure and domain organization of 11 mammalian PDE families.

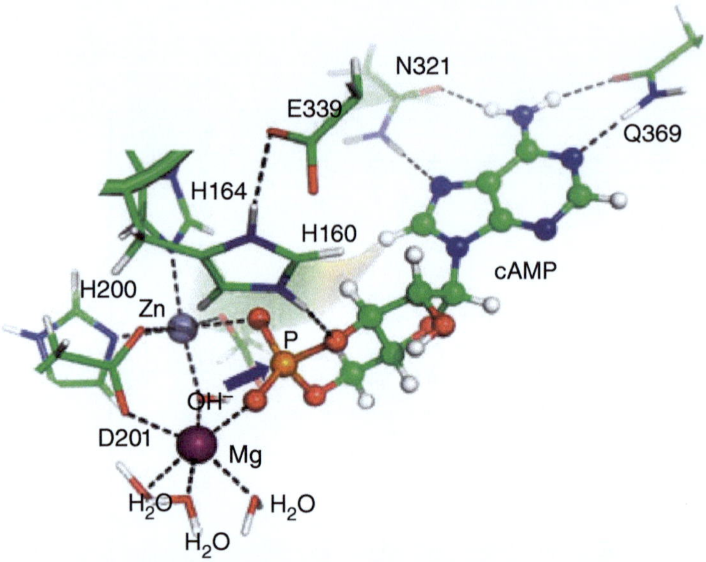

Figure 8.3 Proposed mechanism for the hydrolysis of cAMP by PDE4. The adenine moiety (highlighted in green and blue at the upper right) is stabilized through hydrogen bonding (dashed lines) with Gln369 and Asn321. The phosphorus atom within the cyclic phosphate ring (depicted in orange) is positioned for nucleophilic attack by a hydroxyl ion, which bridges the two metal cofactors, Zn^{2+} (gray) and Mg^{2+} (purple). The blue arrow indicates the nucleophilic attack, leading to cleavage of the cyclic phosphate ring. Residues involved in metal ion coordination are depicted, along with the Glu339/His160 hydrogen-bond relay, which facilitates the interaction of His160 with one of the oxygen atoms (red) in the cyclic phosphate ring. *Source:* This figure was generously provided by Prof. Chang-Guo Zhan, College of Pharmacy, University of Kentucky.

catalytic mechanism [18, 19]. The binding of certain inhibitors to the PDE catalytic site can be influenced by these metal ions, suggesting that the metal-bound form of a PDE may modulate its interaction with specific inhibitors [20–25].

Crystallographic data show that a hydroxyl group, derived from solvent water, bridges the two metal ions in the catalytic site. This interaction results in the formation of a highly nucleophilic hydroxyl group that attacks the phosphate in the cyclic nucleotide ring, cleaving the bond (Figure 8.3) [18, 26]. Typically, one metal site is occupied by a tightly bound Zn^{2+}, while the other site is more loosely associated with either Mg^{2+} or Mn^{2+} [19, 22, 23].

The volume of the PDE catalytic sites has been estimated to range from 330 to 450 Å^3. Several structures of isolated catalytic domains, either in complex with the 50-nucleotide product or selective inhibitors, have been characterized [19, 22, 27, 28]. Notably, X-ray crystal structures of PDE catalytic domains bound to various inhibitors, substrates, or catalytic products commonly show hydrogen bonding with an invariant glutamine residue, as well as hydrophobic stacking interactions between the substrate/product/inhibitor ring structure and a conserved phenylalanine (present in most PDEs) (Figure 8.3) [19, 22, 27, 28].

For instance, the PDE4–cAMP complex (Figure 8.4) reveals that the catalytic pocket contains a unique binuclear metal-binding site, which is believed to be

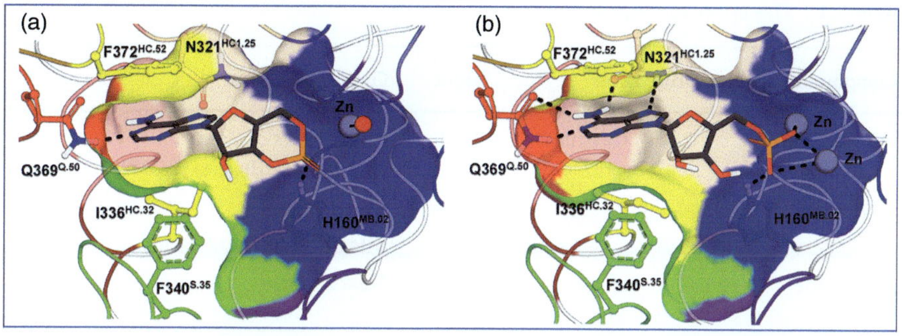

Figure 8.4 Binding modes of: (a) the substrate cAMP (PDB: 2PW3 *Source:* Adapted from [29]) and (b) the product AMP (PDB: 1PTW *Source:* Adapted from [30]) bound to PDE4D. The key interacting residues are shown colored by the pocket region.

essential for the catalytic mechanism. One of the metal ions is required to be Zn^{2+} to sustain enzyme activity, while the second metal ion is typically Mg^{2+} [15, 19, 26]. X-ray co-crystal structures of both the substrate and product provide valuable insights into the hydrolysis mechanism.

As mentioned, while PDE catalytic sites share strong structural similarities, distinct PDE subtypes exhibit varying substrate specificities. PDEs 4, 7, and 8 are highly selective for cAMP hydrolysis, while PDEs 5, 6, and 9 specifically hydrolyze cGMP. Other PDEs (1, 2, 3, 10, and 11) can hydrolyze both cyclic nucleotides. Despite having high sequence identity, closely related PDEs can exhibit significantly different functional characteristics, providing opportunities for the development of selective inhibitors [18].

For instance, PDE1A, PDE1B, and PDE1C, though products of separate genes with catalytic domains sharing approximately 75% sequence homology, demonstrate distinct selectivities for cGMP: PDE1C has a K_m of 1 μM, PDE1B has a K_m of 3 μM, and PDE1A has a K_m of 5 μM for cGMP, compared to K_m values of 1 μM, 24 μM, and 113 μM for cAMP, respectively. In another example, although PDE5 and PDE6 catalytic domains share about 42% sequence identity, PDE6 has a much weaker affinity for cGMP ($K_m \sim 14$ μM) compared to PDE5 ($K_m \sim 2$ μM), and its catalytic rate (~2000 mmol/min/mg) is approximately 1000 times greater than that of PDE5 [31, 32]. Notably, the potent PDE5 inhibitors sildenafil and tadalafil exhibit differing selectivity for PDE6, with selectivity ratios of 5-fold and 110-fold, respectively [33]. These findings suggest that subtle differences in the topology and chemical properties of the active site can significantly influence substrate specificity, catalytic efficiency, and inhibitor potency [31, 32].

8.3 PDEs Inhibitor Discovery

cAMP and cGMP play critical roles in cellular signaling and function, and PDE inhibitors are employed to modulate various biological processes by elevating cellular levels of these cyclic nucleotides. To date, several PDE inhibitors have been

Table 8.1 The approved PDE inhibitors.

Compounds	Drug name	Target	Clinical use
Vinpocetine	Calan, Cavinton	PDE1	Parkinson's disease; Alzheimer's disease
Cilostazol	Pletal, Pletaal	PDE3	Antiplatelet; Intermittent claudication
Amrinone lactate	Inocor	PDE3	Heart failure
Milrinone lactate	Primacor	PDE3	Congestive heart failure
Roflumilast	Daxas, Daliresp	PDE4	Chronic obstructive pulmonary disease
Apremilast	Otezla	PDE4	Psoriasis and psoriatic arthritis
Crisaborole	Eucrisa	PDE4	Allergic dermatitis
Sildenafil citrate	Viagra	PDE5	Erectile dysfunction; Pulmonary arterial hypertension
Tadalafil	Cialis	PDE5	Erectile dysfunction; Pulmonary arterial hypertension
Vardenafil hydrochloride	Vivanza	PDE5	Erectile dysfunction
Avanafil	Zepeed, Stendra	PDE5	Erectile dysfunction

approved as therapies for conditions such as erectile dysfunction (ED), pulmonary hypertension, chronic obstructive pulmonary disease (COPD), psoriasis, allergic dermatitis, and heart failure (Table 8.1) [11, 12]. Additionally, numerous studies have been conducted to identify potent and selective PDE inhibitors.

8.3.1 PDE1 Inhibitors

PDE1 is widely expressed across various cell types, with its isoforms exhibiting distinct distributions and functional roles in the heart, brain, lungs, and smooth muscle [10]. A distinctive feature of this PDE family is its regulation by two Ca^{2+}/calmodulin (CaM) binding domains and two phosphorylation sites in the N-terminus [34]. The specific expression of PDE1 in the brain, combined with its regulation by intracellular calcium and calmodulin, makes it a promising target for addressing cognitive impairments in neurodegenerative diseases such as Alzheimer's disease (AD), schizophrenia, and Parkinson's disease [35]. Research indicates that PDE1B and PDE1C are the predominant isoforms in humans, with PDE1A being expressed at relatively low levels. Moreover, each isoform is expressed in a tissue-specific manner [12]. Recently, several novel PDE1 inhibitors have been reported (Figure 8.5).

Vinpocetine (**1**), a derivative of the alkaloid vincamine, exhibits weak inhibition of PDE1 (IC_{50} = 30 μM) and has been widely used in the treatment of cognitive

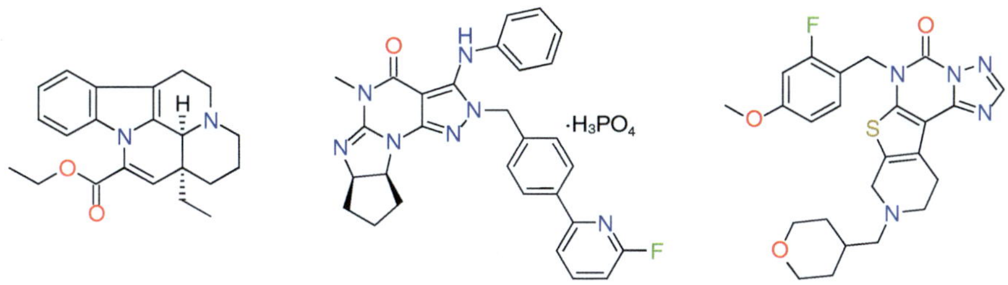

1, Vinpocetine   2, ITI-214   3, DNS-0056

Figure 8.5 Reported PDE1 inhibitors.

dysfunction (Figure 8.5) [36, 37]. ITI-214 (**2**), a PDE1 inhibitor developed by Intra-Cellular Therapies in 2012, shows a potent IC_{50} value of 0.058 nM against PDE1 and demonstrates exceptional selectivity (>1000-fold) over other PDEs (Figure 8.5) [38]. The favorable pharmacokinetic properties of ITI-214 make it an ideal candidate for central nervous system (CNS) applications. To date, ITI-214 has completed four Phase I clinical trials, including a single rising dose study in healthy volunteers and a multiple rising dose study administered once daily [38]. More recently, the thienotriazolopyrimidinone PDE1 inhibitor DNS-0056 (**3**) has been developed, showing good pharmacokinetics and effective brain penetration (Figure 8.5) [39].

For instance, systematic optimization of pyrazolo[3,4-*d*]pyrimidinones, a scaffold structurally similar to cAMP, led to the identification of the clinical candidate **2** (Figure 8.6) [38]. Initially, these compounds were developed as dual inhibitors of PDE1 and PDE5, exhibiting nanomolar to micromolar inhibitory activities [38]. Li and colleagues demonstrated that shifting the nitrogen atom from position 3 to position 2 of the pyrazole ring disrupted the hydrogen bond network. This insight led to the design of the polycyclic 3-aminopyrazolo[3,4-*d*]pyrimidinone scaffold, which was intended to form a critical hydrogen bond through amino group substitution at carbon-3 of the pyrazole ring (Figure 8.6). Subsequent structure–activity relationship (SAR) studies of this polycyclic scaffold resulted in the discovery of ITI-214 as a novel PDE1 inhibitor, which showed picomolar inhibitory potency, excellent selectivity against other PDE families, and strong *in vivo* efficacy. Currently, ITI-214 is in Phase I clinical trials and is being explored for the treatment of various conditions, including cognitive deficits in schizophrenia and Alzheimer's disease, movement disorders, attention deficit hyperactivity disorder (ADHD), and other CNS and non-CNS disorders [38].

In this study, the X-ray crystal structure of the catalytic domain of human recombinant PDE1B, complexed with compound **3**, was determined to investigate the interactions between PDE1 and the inhibitor, as well as to explore the SAR of this compound. As shown in Figure 8.7, the pyrazolo[3,4-*d*]pyrimidinone core is securely anchored by a "hydrophobic clamp"formed primarily by F424, L388, and F392, which are located above and below the aromatic core of compound **3**. The π–π stacking interactions and hydrophobic contacts between these residues and the planar core significantly contribute to the picomolar binding affinity of **3**.

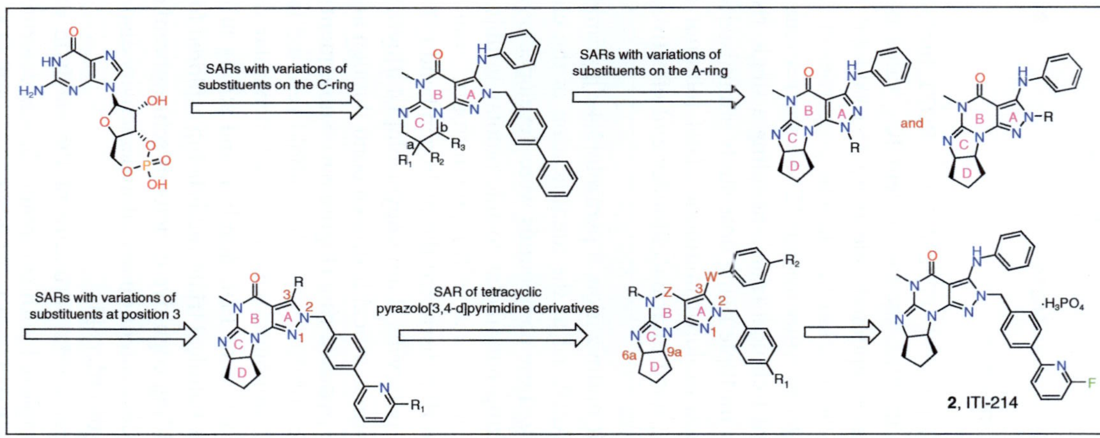

Figure 8.6 systematic optimizations of pyrazolo[3,4-*d*]pyrimidinones culminated in the identification of the clinical candidate ITI-214.

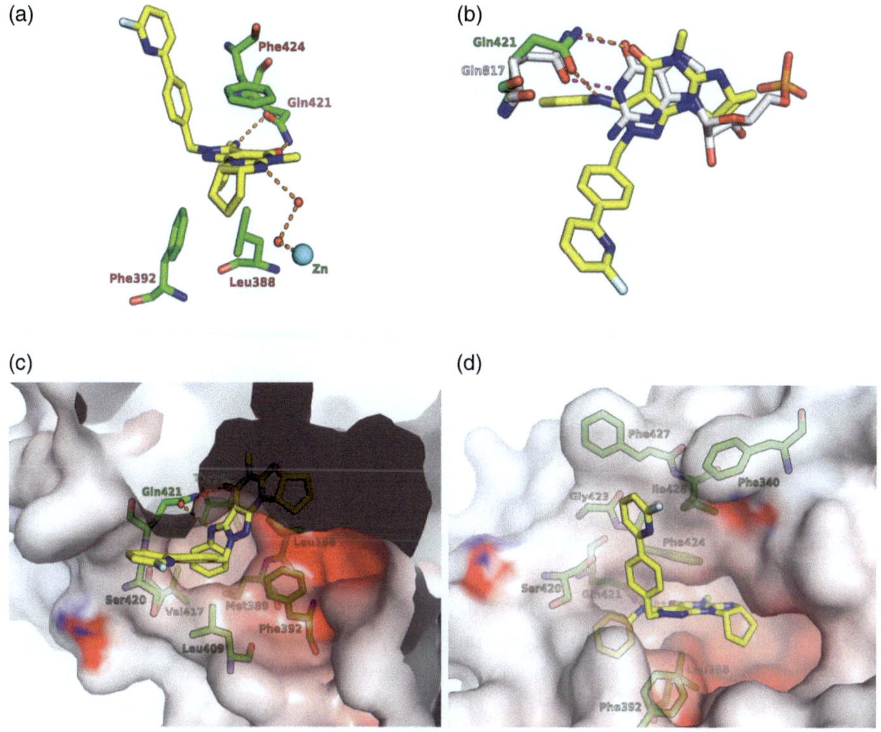

Figure 8.7 Binding interactions of compound **3** within the active site of human recombinant PDE1B. (a) Interactions of the pyrazolo[3,4-*d*]pyrimidinone core with key residues F424, L388, F392, Q421, and the coordinated Zn^{2+}. (b) Superposition of the PDE5A–cGMP complex (carbon atoms shown in white, PDB ID: 1T9S) onto the PDE1B–ITI-214 complex (carbon atoms shown in yellow), highlighting structural similarities and differences. (c) Interactions of the phenylamino group at position three of the pyrazole ring of compound 3 with hydrophobic pocket residues F392, L388, M389, V417, S420, T385, and L409. (d) Interactions of the 4-(6-fluoropyridin-2-yl)benzyl moiety of **3** with residues F424, F427, G423, S420, F340, and I428. Hydrogen bonds are depicted as dashed lines *Source:* Adapted from [38].

Additionally, the exocyclic carbonyl group of the pyrimidone and the amino group at position 3 form bidentate hydrogen bonds with the γ-carboxamide of the conserved Q421 (Figure 8.7). A water-mediated hydrogen bond is also observed between the guanidyl nitrogen on the B-ring and the bound Zn^{2+}.

8.3.2 PDE2 Inhibitors

PDE2 is activated by cGMP and hydrolyzes both cGMP and cAMP, with K_m values of approximately 10 μM and 30 μM, respectively [4, 40]. In the presence of cGMP, the hydrolysis of cAMP by PDE2 is notably enhanced by sixfold, leading to its designation as cGMP-stimulated PDE [4, 40]. It is encoded by the single gene PDE2A, which produces three isoforms: PDE2A1, PDE2A2, and PDE2A3 [4, 41]. PDE2A is predominantly expressed in various brain regions, including the caudate, nucleus

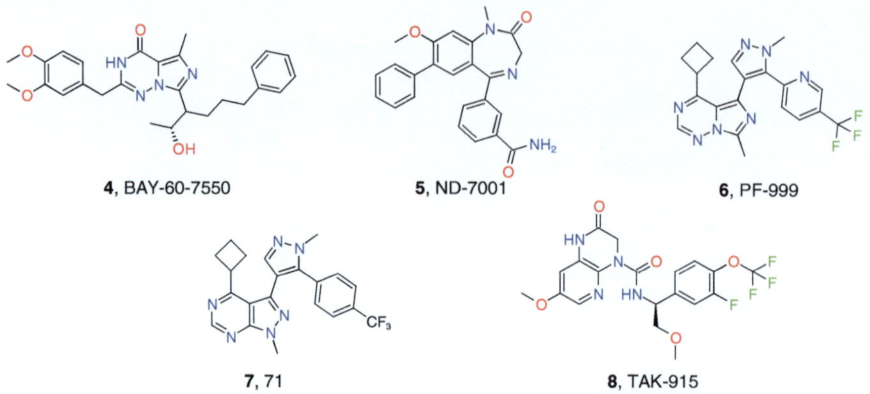

Figure 8.8 Reported PDE2 inhibitors.

accumbens, cortex, and hippocampus [13]. In most peripheral tissues, excluding the spleen, PDE2 expression is relatively low. This specific distribution suggests that PDE2 inhibitors may be effective in treating cognitive disorders with fewer cardiovascular and other side effects commonly associated with other PDE inhibitors [40].

Several selective PDE2 inhibitors have been developed, including BAY-60-7550 (**4**), a highly selective compound from Bayer with an IC_{50} of 4.7 nM and up to 100-fold selectivity over other PDEs (Figure 8.8) [40]. However, pharmacokinetic studies in rats showed poor brain penetration of BAY-60-7550. Administration of a 10 mg/kg dose resulted in a brain concentration of only 3.6 ng/g [42]. These suboptimal pharmacokinetic properties have limited its clinical applications, and as a result, BAY-60-7550 is primarily used as a research tool to explore the potential therapeutic benefits of PDE2 inhibitors.

ND-7001 (**5**), developed by Neuro3d, exhibited an IC_{50} of 50 nM against PDE2 with good selectivity over PDE3 and PDE4 (Figure 8.8) [43]. Phase I trials assessed its safety, tolerability, and pharmacokinetics, showing that it was well tolerated at high doses without causing sedation, memory impairment, or withdrawal symptoms [44]. However, no further development of ND-7001 has been reported since 2010.

PF-999 (**6**, also known as PF-05180999), developed by Pfizer, demonstrated significant inhibitory activity against PDE2 (IC_{50} = 2.3 nM) and high selectivity for PDE2 over other PDEs, along with a favorable brain/plasma ratio in rats (Figure 8.8) [45]. PF-999 was shown to elevate cGMP levels in the cerebrospinal fluid of rats, alleviate ketamine-induced memory deficits, and improve spatial learning and memory in scopolamine-induced models [44]. Two Phase I clinical trials have been completed: one assessing its safety, tolerability, and pharmacokinetics in healthy volunteers, and the other evaluating the relative bioavailability of modified-release formulations (30 mg and 120 mg) in patients with schizophrenia [46–48]. However, no further developments have been reported since 2012.

Recently, compound 71 (**7**), developed by Pfizer, exhibited an IC_{50} of 2 nM against PDE2 and demonstrated selectivity up to 4000-fold over other PDE isoforms (Figure 8.8) [49]. Compound **7** elevated cGMP levels in rodent brain regions with the highest expression of the PDE2A enzyme. In the radial arm maze, **7** notably reduced memory deficits induced by ketamine in rats.

TAK-915 (**8**), developed by Takeda, completed two Phase I clinical trials in healthy volunteers in 2015. One trial assessed the degree and duration of brain PDE2A enzyme occupancy and target engagement following administration, providing critical data for dose optimization and future clinical trial planning for schizophrenia [50].

8.3.3 PDE3 Inhibitors

PDE3 hydrolyzes both cAMP and cGMP, with a higher affinity for cGMP than for cAMP [1]. As a result, cGMP serves as a strong competitive inhibitor of cAMP hydrolysis. The PDE3 family consists of two genes, PDE3A and PDE3B. Three splice variants of PDE3A are expressed: PDE3A1 (136 kDa), PDE3A2 (118 kDa), and PDE3A3 (94 kDa), whereas no splice variants of PDE3B have been identified [51]. PDE3 is predominantly expressed in cardiac and vascular myocytes, brain, liver, adipose tissue, pancreatic β-cells, endothelium, epithelium, oocytes, and platelets [52]. PDE3A is the main subtype involved in cardiac contractility, platelet aggregation, vascular smooth muscle contraction, oocyte maturation, and renin release, whereas PDE3B is primarily associated with insulin signaling and cell cycle/proliferation [3, 53, 54]. Several potent and selective PDE3 inhibitors have been developed, including milrinone (**9**), amrinone (**10**), cilostamide (**11**), and cilostazol (**12**) (Figure 8.9).

8.3.4 PDE4 Inhibitors

PDE4 comprises four isoforms, i.e. PDE4A, PDE4B, PDE4C, and PDE4D. It is the largest and one of the earliest identified PDE families, specifically hydrolyzing cAMP with a K_m in the range of 2–4 μM [55]. PDE4 is expressed across various human tissues, including the brain, olfactory system, liver, heart, smooth muscle,

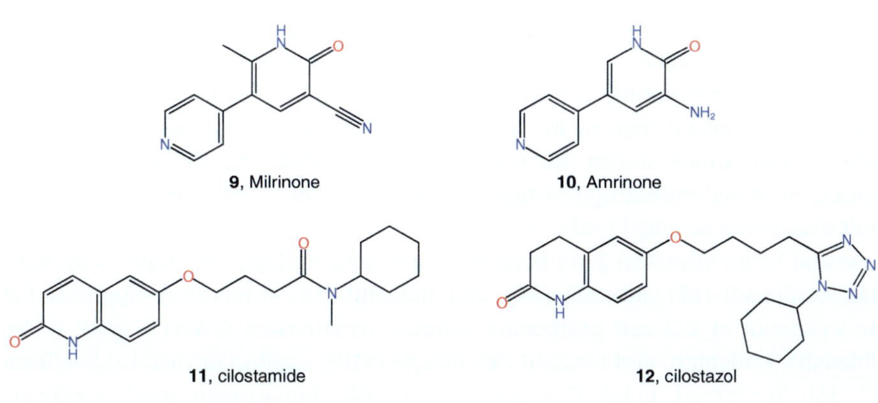

Figure 8.9 Reported PDE3 inhibitors.

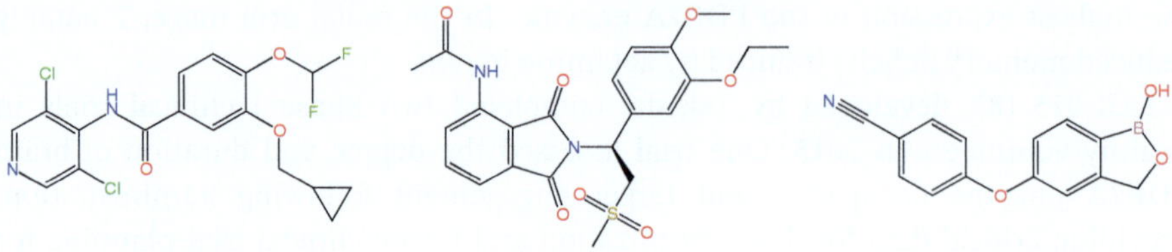

13, Roflumilast **14**, Apremilast **15**, Crisaborole

Figure 8.10 Reported PDE4 inhibitors.

lung, endothelial cells, and immune cells. As one of the most extensively studied PDE families, PDE4 plays a significant role in numerous physiological processes, including brain function, activation of monocytes and macrophages, neutrophil infiltration, vascular smooth muscle proliferation, fertility, vasodilation, and cardiac contractility [3, 56].

Several PDE4 inhibitors have been developed and studied, with three, namely roflumilast (**13**), apremilast (**14**), and crisaborole (**15**), having received approval for treating COPD, atopic dermatitis, psoriatic arthritis, and Alzheimer's disease (Figure 8.10) [57].

8.3.5 PDE5 Inhibitors

PDE5 specifically hydrolyzes cGMP and is encoded by the single PDE5A gene, which produces three N-terminal variants in humans: PDE5A1, PDE5A2, and PDE5A3 [58]. It is predominantly expressed in platelets, vascular smooth muscle, brain, lung, heart, kidney, and skeletal muscle [59]. While PDE5A1 and PDE5A2 are broadly distributed across various tissues, PDE5A3 is specific to vascular smooth muscle. PDE5 is a well-characterized regulator of vascular smooth muscle contraction, particularly in the penis and lungs, and plays a role in NO-cGMP signaling in platelets, modulating aggregation. It may also influence cGMP signaling in the brain [60].

Overexpression of PDE5 has been observed in several carcinomas, including urinary bladder, prostate, breast, brain cancers, colonic adenocarcinomas, chronic lymphocytic leukemia, oral squamous cell carcinoma, and non-small cell lung cancer [60, 61]. Notably, PDE5 inhibitors may enhance the efficacy of anticancer treatments by promoting endocytosis-mediated cellular drug uptake, offering potential as adjuvant therapy for certain cancers, such as lung cancer [62]. Additionally, studies have shown that sildenafil and vardenafil can reverse ABCB1- or ABCG2-mediated multidrug resistance (MDR) in cancer cells by directly inhibiting their drug efflux activity [3, 63].

Several PDE5 inhibitors have been developed and studied, with four – sildenafil (**16**), vardenafil (**17**), avanafil (**18**), and tadalafil (**19**) – receiving approval for the treatment of ED and pulmonary arterial hypertension (PAH) (Figure 8.11). Sildenafil, vardenafil, and avanafil can inhibit PDE6, leading to visual side effects [13, 33]. In contrast, tadalafil is selective for PDE5 but strongly inhibits PDE11, which can cause back and muscle pain [33, 64].

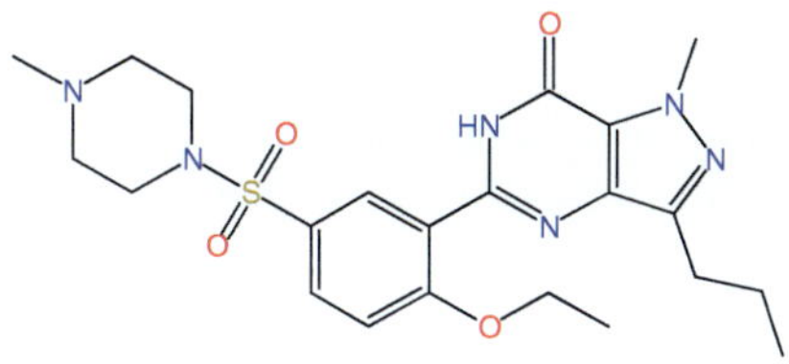

16, Sildenafil

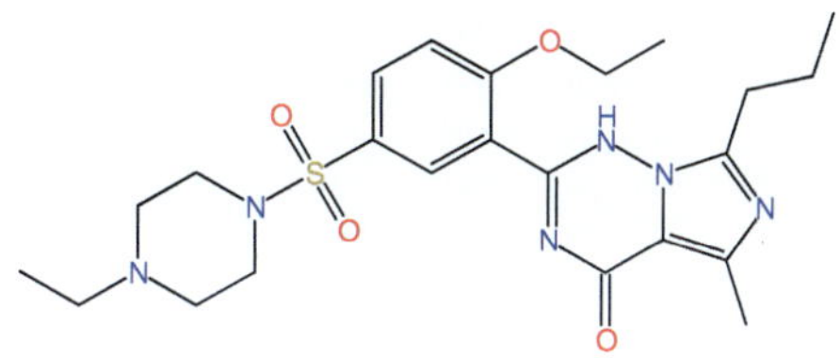

17, vardenafil

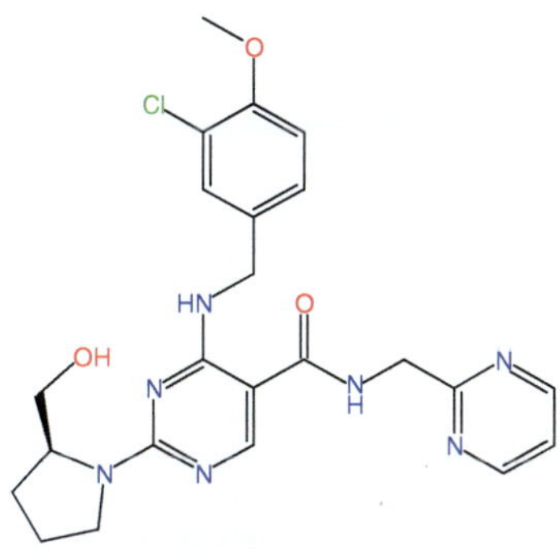

18, Avanafil

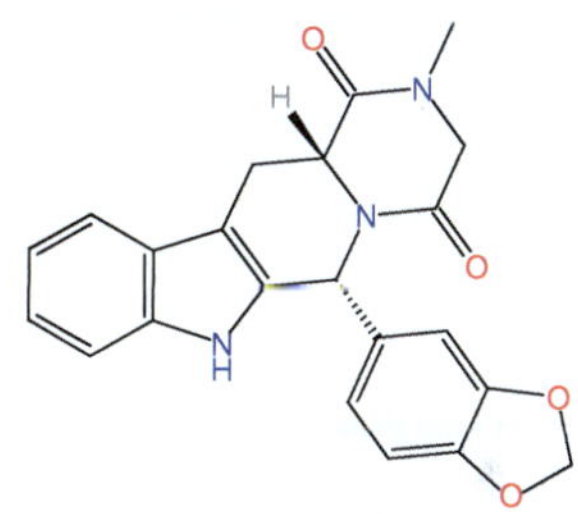

19, Tadalafil

Figure 8.11 Reported PDE5 inhibitors.

8.3.6 PDE7 Inhibitors

PDE7 is a cAMP-specific subfamily consisting of two isoforms, PDE7A and PDE7B. PDE7A expresses two variants (PDE7A1 and PDE7A2), while PDE7B has four variants. Research has shown that PDE7B1 is activated through the cAMP/PKA/CREB pathway in striatal neurons and may be linked to memory function, suggesting it as a potential therapeutic target for Parkinson's and Huntington's diseases [65]. Additionally, studies have demonstrated that overexpression of PDE7A in EC cells enhances cancer cell migration and invasion by downregulating the miR-1/133a cluster [66]. Despite these findings, only a limited number of selective PDE7 inhibitors have been reported to date, and these compounds have primarily been used in *in vitro* pharmacological studies [3].

8.3.7 PDE8 Inhibitors

PDE8 specifically hydrolyzes cAMP with the highest affinity among all PDEs and is composed of two highly homologous genes, PDE8A and PDE8B [3, 67]. It is expressed in various tissues, with the highest expression levels in the testis and T-cells, while PDE8B is predominantly found in the brain and thyroid [68]. PDE8 is believed to play a role in T-cell activation, sperm and Leydig cell functions, the production of T4 and T3, and cardiac function [69]. However, limited efforts have been made to identify selective PDE8A inhibitors. In our previous study, clofarabine demonstrated an IC_{50} of 3.1 μM for PDE2A [70] and an IC_{50} of 0.12 μM against PDE8A [71]. Research has identified Tyr748 as a key residue for developing highly

(a)

PDE8A	Y555	M670	V727	N729	I744	**Y748**	F767	S777	Q778	F781	F785
PDE1B	Y222	M336	I371	H373	L388	**F392**	C410	S420	Q421	F424	I428
PDE2A	Y655	L770	L809	D811	I826	**F830**	M848	L858	Q859	F862	I866
PDE3A	Y751	L930	I951	G953	I968	**F972**	M990	L1000	Q1001	F1004	I1008
PDE4B	Y233	M346	L393	N395	I410	**F414**	C432	S442	Q443	F446	I450
PDE5A	Y612	L725	L765	A767	V782	**F786**	N806	M816	Q817	F820	I824
PDE6A	Y558	L671	L721	A723	V738	**F742**	D762	L772	Q773	F776	V780
PDE7A	Y211	I323	I363	N365	V380	**F384**	C402	I412	Q413	F416	L420
PDE9A	F251	M365	I403	N405	L420	**Y424**	M442	A452	Q453	F456	V460
PDE10A	Y524	L635	L675	S677	I692	**F696**	M714	G725	Q726	F729	V733
PDE11A	Y413	L517	L567	A569	V584	**F588**	D608	L618	Q619	W622	I626

(b)

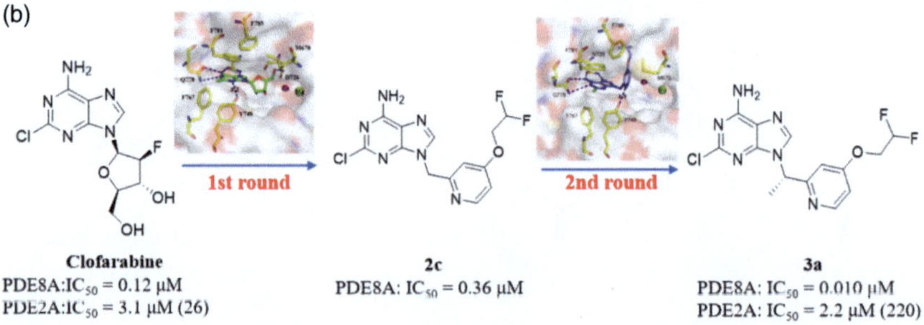

Figure 8.12 Structure-based optimization of 2-chloroadenine derivatives as novel PDE8A inhibitors with enhanced potency and selectivity through targeting Tyr748. (a) Sequence alignment of active site residues across different PDE families. (b) Two iterative rounds of structure-based optimization using clofarabine as a template led to the development of the highly potent PDE8A inhibitor 3a. The crystal structures of the PDE8A–clofarabine and PDE8A–2c complexes are available under PDB IDs 7CWA and 7CWF, respectively. *Source:* Ref. [71] / Elsevier.

selective PDE8A inhibitors. Medicinal chemistry optimizations targeting Tyr748 (Figures 8.12 and 8.13) were conducted based on the hit compound clofarabine. As a result, lead compound 3a (IC_{50} = 0.010 μM) exhibited high selectivity and a favorable drug-like profile [71]. Notably, the X-ray crystal structure of the PDE8A–3a complex revealed the binding pattern between the selective inhibitor and PDE8A, which could facilitate the discovery of novel PDE8A inhibitors. Furthermore, oral administration of 3a resulted in improved spatial learning and memory in a vascular dementia (VaD) mouse model, suggesting that PDE8 inhibitors could be potential therapeutic agents for VaD [71].

8.3.8 PDE9 Inhibitors

PDE9 is a cGMP-specific enzyme family with the lowest K_m among cGMP-specific PDE families [10, 14, 22]. It is primarily expressed in the spleen, intestine, and brain, with the highest expression levels found in Purkinje neurons and the cerebellum. Selective PDE9 inhibitors have been explored as potential treatments for diabetes and CNS diseases, including Alzheimer's disease [72–75]. The crystal structures of the PDE9A catalytic domain in complex with inhibitors and the substrate cGMP have provided valuable insights into the enzyme's catalytic mechanism and served

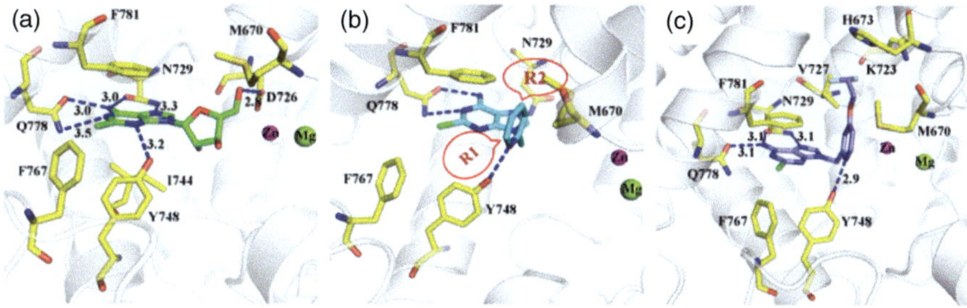

Figure 8.13 Structure-based optimization of selective PDE8A inhibitors. (a) Cartoon representation of clofarabine binding to the active site of PDE8A, with clofarabine shown as green sticks (PDB ID: 7CWA). (b) Rational design of a scaffold predicted to form a hydrogen bond with Tyr748 and achieve a tight fit within the PDE8A binding pocket. (c) Cartoon representation of the binding mode of compound 2c within the PDE8A pocket, with 2c depicted as purple sticks (PDB ID: 7CWF). *Source:* Ref. [71] / Elsevier.

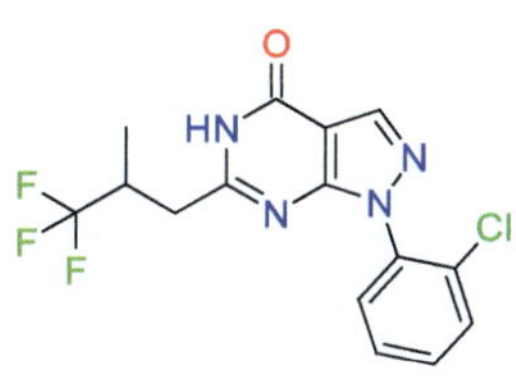

20, BAY 73-6691

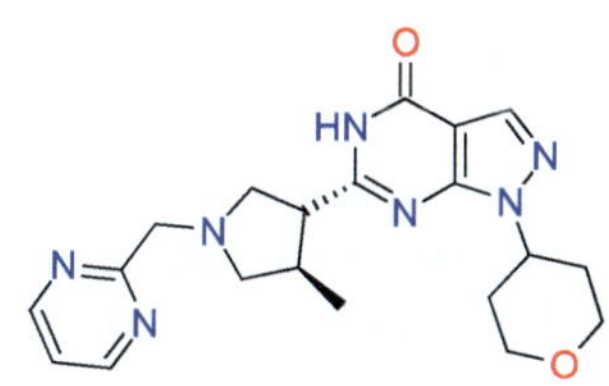

21, PF-04447943

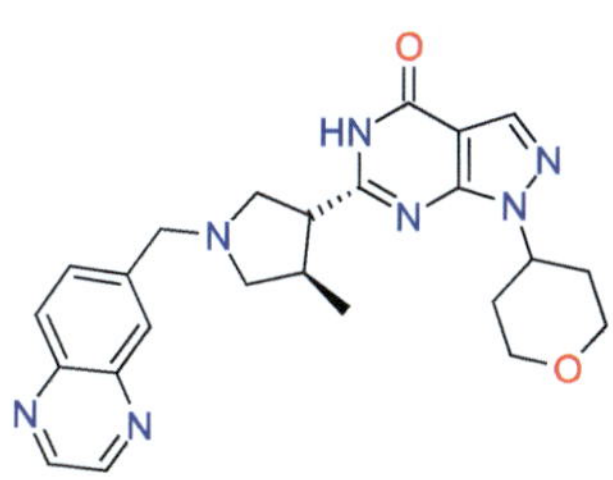

22, PF-4181366

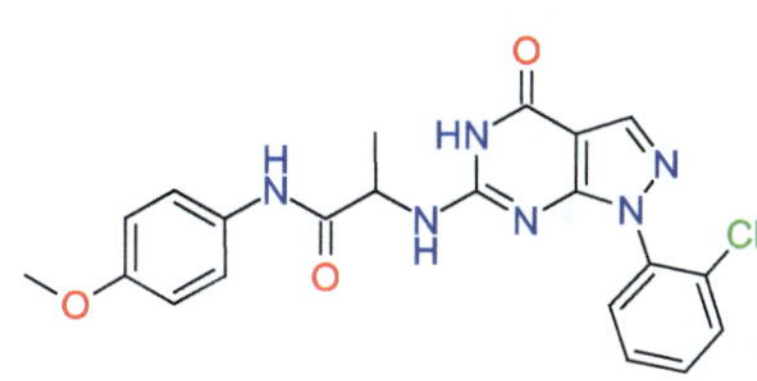

23, 28 (*R*-28 and *S*-28)

Figure 8.14 Reported PDE9 inhibitors.

as templates for the development of high-affinity PDE9 inhibitors [73–75]. Following the publication of the first selective PDE9 inhibitor, BAY73-6691 (**20**) [76], highly potent PDE9A inhibitors, such as PF-04447943 (**21**) [74], PF-4181366 (**22**) [75], and 28 (**23**) [77], have been reported (Figure 8.14).

8.3.9 PDE10 Inhibitors

PDE10A is a dual-specificity enzyme that hydrolyzes both cAMP (K_m = 0.05 μM) and cGMP (K_m = 3 μM) [78]. It is predominantly expressed in the brain, thyroid, and pituitary gland, with the highest expression observed in the striatal region. PDE10A is considered a key regulator of cGMP signaling in the brain and may play a role in learning and memory [79]. Several PDE10A inhibitors are currently in clinical

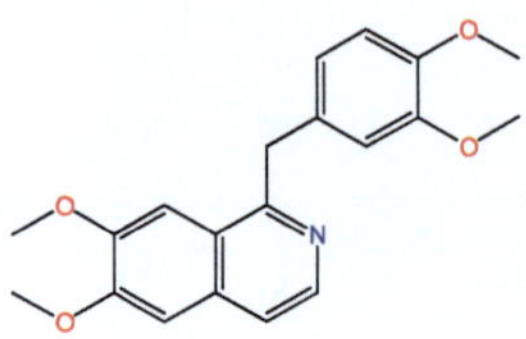

24, papaverine

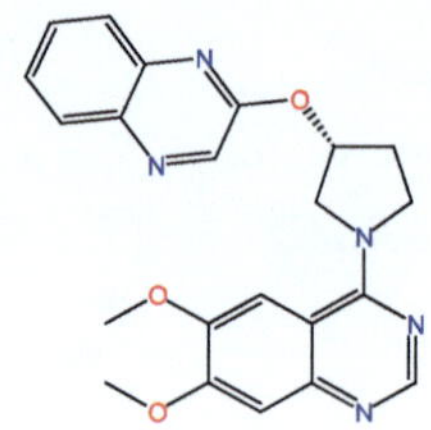

25, PQ-10

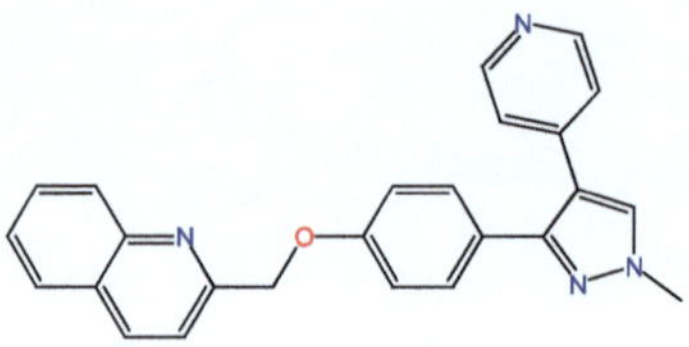

26, PF-2545920/MP-10

Figure 8.15 Reported PDE10 inhibitors.

development, including papaverine (**24**) (IC_{50} = 36 nM), PQ-10 (**25**) (IC_{50} = 6.0 nM), and PF-2545920/MP-10 (**26**) (IC_{50} = 0.18 nM) (Figure 8.15) [80–82]. Most research on these inhibitors has focused on their potential for treating CNS disorders.

8.4 Concluding Remarks and Future Perspectives

Over the past three decades, significant efforts have been devoted to understanding the roles of PDEs and discovering effective inhibitors for the treatment of conditions such as ED, PAH, acute refractory cardiac failure, psoriasis, psoriatic arthritis, allergic dermatitis, intermittent claudication, and COPD. However, greater attention is still required in the discovery of inhibitors with enhanced selectivity for specific PDE isozymes, which could result in drugs with improved safety profiles. Moving forward, integrating co-crystal structures from across the PDE superfamily with ligand scaffolds may offer new opportunities for developing novel PDE inhibitors with better selectivity and potency.

References

1 Beavo, J.A. (1995). Cyclic nucleotide phosphodiesterases: functional implications of multiple isoforms. *Physiological Reviews* 75: 725–748.

2 Maurice, D.H., Ke, H., Ahmad, F. et al. (2014). Advances in targeting cyclic nucleotide phosphodiesterases. *Nature Reviews Drug Discovery* 13: 290–314.

3 Peng, T., Gong, J., Jin, Y. et al. (2018). Inhibitors of phosphodiesterase as cancer therapeutics. *European Journal of Medicinal Chemistry* 150: 742–756.

4 Levy, I., Horvath, A., Azevedo, M. et al. (2011). Phosphodiesterase function and endocrine cells: links to human disease and roles in tumor development and treatment. *Current Opinion in Pharmacology* 11: 689–697.

5 Bos, J.L. (2006). Epac proteins: multi-purpose cAMP targets. *Trends in Biochemical Sciences* 31: 680–686.

6 Kaneko, M. and Takahashi, T. (2004). Presynaptic mechanism underlying cAMP-dependent synaptic potentiation. *Journal of Neuroscience* 24: 5202–5208.

7 Sakaba, T. and Neher, E. (2003). Direct modulation of synaptic vesicle priming by GABA(B) receptor activation at a glutamatergic synapse. *Nature* 424: 775–778.

8 Zhong, N. and Zucker, R.S. (2005). cAMP acts on exchange protein activated by cAMP/cAMP regulated guanine nucleotide exchange protein to regulate transmitter release at the crayfish neuromuscular junction. *Journal of Neuroscience* 25: 208–214.

9 Lincoln, T.M., Dey, N., and Sellak, H. (2001). Invited review: cGMP-dependent protein kinase signaling mechanisms in smooth muscle: from the regulation of tone to gene expression. *Journal of Applied Physiology* 91: 1421–1430.

10 Bender, A.T. and Beavo, J.A. (2006). Cyclic nucleotide phosphodiesterases: molecular regulation to clinical use. *Pharmacological Review* 58: 488–520.

11 Azevedo, M.F., Faucz, F.R., Bimpaki, E. et al. (2014). Clinical and molecular genetics of the phosphodiesterases (PDEs). *Endocrine Reviews* 35: 195–233.

12 Wu, Y., Li, Z., Huang, Y.-Y. et al. (2018). Novel phosphodiesterase inhibitors for cognitive improvement in Alzheimer's Disease. *Journal of Medicinal Chemistry* 61: 5467–5483.

13 Lakics, V., Karran, E.H., and Boess, F.G. (2010). Quantitative comparison of phosphodiesterase mRNA distribution in human brain and peripheral tissues. *Neuropharmacology* 59: 367–374.

14 Conti, M. and Beavo, J. (2007). Biochemistry and physiology of cyclic nucleotide phosphodiesterases: essential components in cyclic nucleotide signaling. *Annual Review of Biochemistry* 76: 481–511.

15 Francis, S., Blount, M., and Corbin, J. (2011). Mammalian cyclic nucleotide phosphodiesterases: molecular mechanisms and physiological functions. *Physiological Reviews* 91: 651–690.

16 Keravis, T. and Lugnier, C. (2012). Cyclic nucleotide phosphodiesterase (PDE) isozymes as targets of the intracellular signalling network: benefits of PDE inhibitors in various diseases and perspectives for future therapeutic developments. *British Journal of Pharmacology* 165: 1288–1305.

17 Jansen, C., Kooistra, A.J., Kanev, G.K. et al. (2016). PDEStrIAn: a phosphodiesterase structure and ligand interaction annotated database as a tool for structure-based drug design. *Journal of Medicinal Chemistry* 59: 7029–7065.

18 Francis, S.H., Conti, M., and Houslay, M.D. (ed.) (2011). Phosphodiesterases as drug targets. In: *Handbook of Experimental Pharmacology*, vol. 204. Springer Science & Business Media.

19 Xu, R.X., Hassell, A.M., Vanderwall, D. et al. (2000). Atomic structure of PDE4: insights into phosphodiesterase mechanism and specificity. *Science* 288: 1822–1825.

20 Chen, G., Wang, H., Robinson, H. et al. (2008). An insight into the pharmacophores of phosphodiesterase-5 inhibitors from synthetic and crystal structural studies. *Biochemical Pharmacology* 75: 1717–1728.

21 Corbin, J.D., Blount, M.A., Weeks, J.L. et al. (2003). [3H]sildenafil binding to phosphodiesterase-5 is specific, kinetically heterogeneous, and stimulated by cGMP. *Molecular Pharmacology* 63: 1364–1372.

22 Ke, H. and Wang, H. (2007). Crystal structures of phosphodiesterases and implications on substrate specificity and inhibitor selectivity. *Current Topics in Medicinal Chemistry* 7: 391–403.

23 Sung, B.J., Hwang, K.Y., Jeon, Y.H. et al. (2003). Structure of the catalytic domain of human phosphodiesterase 5 with bound drug molecules. *Nature* 425: 98–102.

24 Wang, H., Yan, Z., Yang, S. et al. (2008). Kinetic and structural studies of phosphodiesterase-8A and implication on the inhibitor selectivity. *Biochemistry* 47: 12760–12768.

25 Wang, H., Ye, M., Robinson, H. et al. (2008). Conformational variations of both phosphodiesterase-5 and inhibitors provide the structural basis for the physiological effects of vardenafil and sildenafil. *Molecular Pharmacology* 73: 104–110.

26 Liu, S., Mansour, M.N., Dillman, K.S. et al. (2008). Structural basis for the catalytic mechanism of human phosphodiesterase 9. *Proceedings of the National Academy of Sciences of the United States of America* 105: 13309–13314.

27 Wang, H., Peng, M.S., Chen, Y. et al. (2007). Structures of the four subfamilies of phosphodiesterase-4 provide insight into the selectivity of their inhibitors. *Biochemical Journal* 408: 193–201.

28 Xu, R.X., Rocque, W.J., Lambert, M.H. et al. (2004). Crystal structures of the catalytic domain of phosphodiesterase 4B complexed with AMP, 8-Br-AMP, and rolipram. *Journal of Molecular Biology* 337: 355–365.

29 Wang, H., Robinson, H., and Ke, H. (2007). The molecular basis for different recognition of substrates by phosphodiesterase families 4 and 10. *Journal of Molecular Biology* 371: 302–307.

30 Huai, Q., Colicelli, J., and Ke, H. (2003). The crystal structure of Amp-bound PDE4 suggests a mechanism for phosphodiesterase catalysis. *Biochemistry* 42: 13220–13226.

31 Cote, R.H. (2006). Photoreceptorphosphodiesterase (PDE6): a G-protein-activated PDE regulating visual excitation in rod and cone photoreceptor cells. In: *Cyclic Nucleotide Phosphodiesterases in Health and Disease* (ed. J. Beavo, S.H. Francis, and M.D. Houslay), 165–193. Boca Raton: CRC Press.

32 Francis, S.H., Zoraghi, R., Kotera, J. et al. (2006). Phosphodiesterase-5: molecular characteristics relating to structure, function, and regulation. In: *Cyclic Nucleotide Phosphodiesterases in Health and Disease* (ed. S.H.F.J.A. Beavo and M.D. Houslay), 131–164. Boca Raton: CRC Press.

33 Pissarnitski, D. (2006). Phosphodiesterase 5 (PDE 5) inhibitors for thetreatment of male erectile disorder: attaining selectivity versus PDE6. *Medicinal Research Reviews* 26: 369–395.

34 Goraya, T.A. and Cooper, D.M.F. (2005). Ca^{2+}-calmodulin-dependent phosphodiesterase (PDE1): current perspectives. *Cell Signaling* 17: 789–797.

35 Wennogle, L., Hoxie, H., Peng, Y., and Hendrick, J.P. (2017). Phosphodiesterase 1: a unique therapeutic target with multiple potential indications. *Chinese Journal of Pharmacology and Toxicology* 31: 452.

36 Bonoczk, P., Gulyas, B., Adam-Vizi, V. et al. (2000). Role of sodium channel inhibition in neuroprotection: effect of vinpocetine. *Brain Research Bulletin* 53: 245–254.

37 Vas, A. and Gulyas, B. (2005). Eburnamine derivatives and the brain. *Medicinal Research Reviews* 25: 737–757.

38 Li, P., Zheng, H., Zhao, J. et al. (2016). Discovery of potent and selective inhibitors of phosphodiesterase 1 for the treatment of cognitive impairment associated with neurodegenerative and neuropsychiatric diseases. *Journal of Medicinal Chemistry* 59: 1149–1164.

39 Dyck, B., Branstetter, B., Gharbaoui, T. et al. (2017). Discovery of selective phosphodiesterase 1 inhibitors with memory enhancing properties. *Journal of Medicinal Chemistry* 60: 3472–3483.

40 Boss, F. G., Hendrix, M., Konig, G. et al. (2002). Selective Phosphodiesterase 2 Inhibitors Used as Medicaments for Improving Cognition. *WO2002009713 A2.*

41 Rosman, G.J., Martins, T.J., Sonnenburg, W.K. et al. (1997). Isolation and characterization of human cDNAs encoding a cGMP-stimulated 3′,5′-cyclic nucleotide phosphodiesterase. *Gene* 191: 89–95.

42 Reneerkens, O.A., Rutten, K., Bollen, E. et al. (2013). Inhibition of phoshodiesterase type 2 or type 10 reverses object memory deficits induced by scopolamine or MK-801. *Behavioural Brain Research* 236: 16–22.

43 Abarghaz, M., Biondi, S., Duranton, J. et al. (2005). Benzo-1,4-diazepin-2-one Derivatives as Phosphodiesterase 2 Inhibitors, Preparation and Therapeutic Use Thereof. *WO2005063723.*

44 Gomez, L. and Breitenbucher, J.G. (2013). PDE2 inhibition: potential for the treatment of cognitive disorders. *Bioorganic and Medicinal Chemistry Letters* 23: 6522–6527.

45 Helal, C. J.; Chappie, T. A.; Humphrey, J. M. et al. (2012). Imidazo[5,1-f][1,2,4] triazines for the Treatment of Neurological Disorders. *US 20120214791.*

46 Helal, C. J. (2012). Identification of a brain penetrant, highly selective phosphodiesterase 2A inhibitor for the treatment of cognitive impairment associated with schizophrenia (CIAS). Abstracts of Papers, 244th National Meeting & Exposition of the American Chemical Society, Philadelphia, PA, U.S., August 19–23, 2012; American Chemical Society: Washington, DC.

47 National Center for Biotechnology Information (2012). Clinical trial study found in clinical trials for PF-05180999: NCT01429740. https://clinicaltrials.gov/ct2/show/NCT01429740?term=PF-05180999&rank=2 (accessed 24 July 2017).

48 National Center for Biotechnology Information (2012). Clinical trial study found in clinical trials for PF-05180999: NCT01530529. https://clinicaltrials.gov/ct2/show/NCT01530529?term=PF-05180999&rank=3 (accessed 24 July 2017).

49 Helal, C.J., Arnold, E.P., Boyden, T.L. et al. (2017). Application of structure-based design and parallel chemistry to identify a potent, selective, and brain penetrant phosphodiesterase 2A inhibitor. *Journal of Medicinal Chemistry* 60: 5673–5698.

50 National Center for Biotechnology Information (2016). Clinical trial study found in clinical trials for TAK-915: NCT02584569. https://clinicaltrials.gov/ct2/show/NCT02584569?term=TAK-915&rank=1 (accessed 24 July 2017).

51 Wechsler, J., Choi, Y.H., Krall, J. et al. (2002). Isoforms of cyclic nucleotide phosphodiesterase PDE3A in cardiac myocytes. *Journal of Biological Chemistry* 277: 38072–38078.

52 Shakur, Y., Holst, L.S., Landstrom, T.R. et al. (2001). Regulation and function of the cyclic nucleotide phosphodiesterase (PDE3) gene family. *Progress in Nucleic Acid Research and Molecular Biology* 66: 241–277.

53 Beca, S., Ahmad, F., Shen, W. et al. (2013). Phosphodiesterase type 3A regulates basal myocardial contractility through interacting with sarcoplasmic reticulum calcium ATPase type 2a signaling complexes in mouse heart. *Circulation Research* 112: 289–297.

54 Ahmad, F., Degerman, E., and Manganiello, V.C. (2012). Cyclic nucleotide phosphodiesterase 3 signaling complexes. *Hormone and Metabolic Research* 44: 776–785.

55 Bolger, G., Michaeli, T., Martins, T. et al. (1993). A family of human phosphodiesterases homologous to the dunce learning and memory gene product of Drosophila melanogaster are potential targets for antidepressant drugs. *Molecular and Cellular Biology* 13: 6558–6571.

56 Eskandari, N., Mirmosayyeb, O., Bordbari, G. et al. (2015). A short review on structure and role of cyclic-3′,5′-adenosine monophosphate-specific phosphodiesterase 4 as a treatment tool. *Journal of Research in Pharmacy Practice* 4: 175–181.

57 Spina, D. (2008). PDE4 inhibitors: current status. *British Journal of Pharmacology* 155: 308–315.

58 Kotera, J., Fujishige, K., Imai, Y. et al. (1999). Genomic origin and transcriptional regulation of two variants of cGMP-binding cGMP-specific phosphodiesterases. *European Journal of Biochemistry* 262: 866–873.

59 Giordano, D., De Stefano, M.E., Citro, G. et al. (2001). Expression of cGMP-binding cGMP-specific phosphodiesterase (PDE5) in mouse tissues and cell lines using an antibody against the enzyme amino-terminal domain. *Biochimica et Biophysica Acta* 1539: 16–27.

60 Barone, I., Giordano, C., Bonofiglio, D. et al. (2015). Phosphodiesterase type 5 as a candidate therapeutic target in cancers. *Current Pathobiology Reports* 3: 193–201.

61 Cesarini, V., Martini, M., Vitiani, L.R. et al. (2017). Type 5 phosphodiesterase regulates glioblastoma multiforme aggressiveness and clinical outcome. *Oncotarget* 8: 13223–13239.

62 Li, Q. and Shu, Y. (2014). Pharmacological modulation of cytotoxicity and cellular uptake of anti-cancer drugs by PDE5 inhibitors in lung cancer cells. *Pharmaceutical Research* 31: 86–96.

63 Shi, Z., Tiwari, A.K., Patel, A.S. et al. (2011). Roles of sildenafil in enhancing drug sensitivity in cancer. *Cancer Research* 71: 3735–3738.

64 Yamazaki, A., Moskvin, O., and Yamazaki, R.K. (2002). Phosphorylation by cyclin-dependent protein kinase 5 of the regulatory subunit (Pγ) of retinal cGMP phosphodiesterase (PDE6): its implications in phototransduction. *Advances in Experimental Medicine and Biology* 514: 131–153.

65 Morales-Garcia, J.A., Aguilar-Morante, D., Hernandez-Encinas, E. et al. (2015). Silencing phosphodiesterase 7B gene by lentiviral-shRNA interference attenuates neurodegeneration and motor deficits in hemiparkinsonian mice. *Neurobiology of Aging* 36: 1160–1173.

66 Yamamoto, N., Nishikawa, R., Chiyomaru, T. et al. (2015). The tumor suppressive microRNA-1/133a cluster targets PDE7A and inhibits cancer cell migration and invasion in endometrial cancer. *International Journal of Oncology* 47: 325–334.

67 Gamanuma, M., Yuasa, K., Sasaki, T. et al. (2003). Comparison of enzymatic characterization and gene organization of cyclic nucleotide phosphodiesterase 8 family in humans. *Cellular Signalling* 15: 565–574.

68 Jorde, R., Schirmer, H., Wilsgaard, T. et al. (2014). The phosphodiesterase 8B gene rs4704397 is associated with thyroid function, risk of myocardial infarction, and body height: the Tromso study. *Thyroid* 24: 215–222.

69 Patrucco, E., Albergine, M.S., Santana, L.F., and Beavo, J.A. (2010). Phosphodiesterase 8A (PDE8A) regulates excitation-contraction coupling in ventricular myocytes. *Journal of Molecular and Cellular Cardiology* 49: 330–333.

70 Qiu, X., Huang, Y., Wu, D. et al. (2018). Discovery of novel purine nucleoside derivatives as phosphodiesterase 2 (PDE2) inhibitors: structure-based virtual screening, optimization and biological evaluation. *Bioorganic and Medicinal Chemistry* 26: 119–133.

71 Huang, Y., Wu, X.-N., Zhou, Q. et al. (2020). Rational design of 2-chloroadenine derivatives as highly selective phosphodiesterase 8A inhibitors. *Journal of Medicinal Chemistry* 63 (24): 15852–15863.

72 van der Staay, F.J., Rutten, K., Barfacker, L. et al. (2008). The novel selective PDE9 inhibitor BAY 73-6691 improves learning and memory in rodents. *Neuropharmacology* 55: 908–918.

73 Verhoest, P.R., Proulx-Lafrance, C., Corman, M. et al. (2009). Identification of a brain penetrant PDE9A inhibitor utilizing prospective design and chemical enablement as a rapid lead optimization strategy. *Journal of Medicinal Chemistry* 52: 7946–7949.

74 Hutson, P.H., Finger, E.N., Magliaro, B.C. et al. (2011). The selective phosphodiesterase 9 (PDE9) inhibitor PF-04447943(6-[(3S,4S)-4-methyl-1-(pyrimidin-2-ylmethyl)pyrrolidin-3-yl]-1-(tetrahydro-2H-pyran-4-yl)-1,5-dihydro-4H-pyrazolo [3,4-d]pyrimidin-4-one) enhances synaptic plasticity and cognitive function in rodents. *Neuropharmacology* 61: 665–676.

75 Vardigan, J.D., Converso, A., Hutson, P.H., and Uslaner, J.M. (2011). The selective phosphodiesterase 9 (PDE9) inhibitor PF-04447943 attenuates a scopolamine-induced deficit in a novel rodent attention task. *Journal of Neurogenetics* 25: 120–126.

76 Deninno, M.P., Andrews, M., Bell, A.S. et al. (2009). The discovery of potent, selective, and orally bioavailable PDE9 inhibitors as potential hypoglycemic agents. *Bioorganic and Medicinal Chemistry Letters* 19: 2537–2541.

77 Meng, F., Hou, J., Shao, Y.-X. et al. (2012). Structure-based discovery of highly selective phosphodiesterase-9A inhibitors and implications for inhibitor design. *Journal of Medicinal Chemistry* 55: 8549–8558.

78 Soderling, S.H., Bayuga, S.J., and Beavo, J.A. (1999). Isolation and characterization of a dual-substrate phosphodiesterase gene family: PDE10A. *Proceedings of the National Academy of Sciences of the United States of America* 96: 7071–7076.

79 Hebb, A.L., Robertson, H.A., and Denovan-Wright, E.M. (2004). Striatal phosphodiesterase mRNA and protein levels are reduced in Huntington's disease transgenic mice prior to the onset of motor symptoms. *Neuroscience* 123: 967–981.

80 Siuciak, J.A., Chapin, D.S., Harms, J.F. et al. (2006). Inhibition of the striatumenriched phosphodiesterase PDE10A: a novel approach to the treatment of psychosis. *Neuropharmacology* 51: 386–396.

81 Verhoest, P.R., Chapin, D.S., Corman, M. et al. (2009). Discovery of a novel class of phosphodiesterase 10A inhibitors and identification of clinical candidate 2-[4-(1-Methyl-4-pyridin-4-yl-1H-pyrazol-3-yl)-phenoxymethyl]-quinoline (PF-2545920) for the treatment of schizophrenia. *Journal of Medicinal Chemistry* 52: 5188–5196.

82 Funke, U., Deuther-Conrad, W., Schwan, G. et al. (2012). Radiosynthesis and radiotracer properties of a 7-(2-18F fluoroethoxy)-6-methoxypyrrolidinylquinazoline for imaging of phosphodiesterase 10A with PET. *Pharmaceuticals* 5: 169–188.

9

HDAC: A Rising Star in Cancer Therapy

Tao Liang[1], *Hao Fang*[2], *and Xuben Hou*[2]

[1] *Shandong First Medical University and Shandong Academy of Medical Sciences, Department of Pharmacy, Shandong Cancer Hospital and Institute, 440, Jiyan Road, Jinan 250117, China*
[2] *School of Pharmaceutical Sciences, Cheeloo College of Medicine, Shandong University, Shandong Key Laboratory of Druggability Optimization and Evaluation for Lead Compounds, 44, West Wenhua Road, Jinan, 250012, China*

9.1 Introduction

Epigenetics regulates gene expression in a reversible and heritable manner while preserving the DNA sequence unchanged. The essential epigenetic processes or mechanisms comprise DNA/RNA methylation, histone modification, histone variants, RNA editing, and noncoding chromatin remodeling [1–3]. In aforementioned mechanisms, histone modification, particularly deacetylation and acetylation catalyzed by histone deacetylases (HDACs) and histone acetyltransferases (HATs), plays a central role [4, 5]. The nucleosome, a fundamental unit of eukaryotic chromatin, comprises DNA coiled around the histone core. As epigenetic erasers, HDACs in conjunction with HATs, modify the nucleosome's structure and regulate gene transcription [6]. Specifically, HDACs remove acetyl groups from lysine residues in histones, strengthening the interaction between histone tails and DNA. This prevents transcription cofactors from accessing DNA, leading to gene repression. In contrast, HATs promote gene transcription by acetylating the ε-NH2 group, which allows transcription cofactors to access DNA more readily and promotes gene transcription (Figure 9.1) [7, 8].

9.2 HDACs

9.2.1 Classifications of HDACs

Cofactors and primary homologous structures show that 18 HDAC members are phylogenetically classified as NAD^+-dependent and Zn^{2+}-dependent HDACs. Zn^{2+}-dependent HDACs, mainly consisting of classes I, II, and IV, catalyze histone

Drug Discovery Targeting Metalloenzymes: Strategies and Applications, First Edition. Edited by Guo-Bo Li.

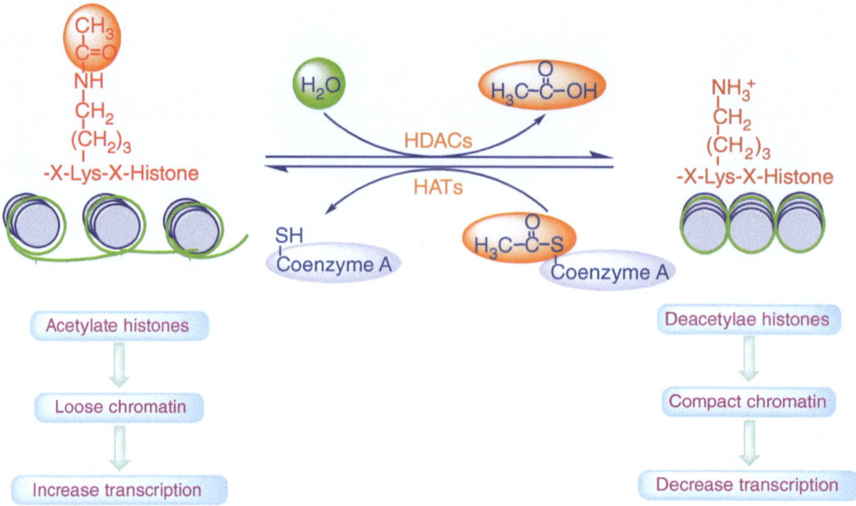

Figure 9.1 Gene transcription regulated by HDACs/HATs.

deacetylation by means of zinc cation (Figure 9.2). In contrast, class III HDACs comprise Sirtuins (Sirt1–7), and they are identified as NAD^+-dependent enzymes utilizing NAD^+ as a cofactor for catalysis [9, 10]. Notably, the term "HDACs" typically refers to classical HDACs, and it is important to recognize that Sirt1–7 are distinct from classical HDACs in both structure and evolutionary origin.

9.2.2 The Catalytic Features of HDACs

Class I HDACs, excluding HDAC8, exhibit significant sequence homology (45–94%) and play a dominant role in intracellular deacetylation due to their high enzymatic activity [9, 11–13]. These HDACs are ubiquitously present, mainly localized in the nucleus, and participate in numerous biological processes, either through enzymatic activity or by forming corepressor complexes [8]. Research has also linked class I HDACs to cancer development, with their overexpression frequently observed in various malignancies [14–16]. In contrast, HDAC8 displays weaker deacetylation activity compared to other class I members but demonstrates unique efficiency in hydrolyzing long-chain fatty acyl groups from H3K9 peptides [17–19].

Class II HDACs are grouped into subclasses IIa and IIb, with sequence identities of 48%–57% and 55%, respectively. However, the overall homology within class II is low (23–81%) due to the additional catalytic domain in HDAC6 [12]. Despite sharing catalytic domain similarities with class I HDACs, class II enzymes exhibit significantly reduced catalytic activity (approximately 1/1000-fold) [9, 20]. These HDACs are unique in their capacity to shuttle between the nucleus and cytoplasm, enabling them to target nuclear and cytosolic proteins for deacetylation [10].

As the sole member of class IV HDACs, HDAC11 was discovered in 2002, and it is the smallest HDAC. It shares a more distant evolutionary relationship with other HDAC family members [21]. Notably, HDAC11 excels as a fatty acid deacetylase,

HDACs			Gene	Size (aa)	Structure	Localization	Substrate
Zn^{2+}–dependent HDACs	Class I	HDAC1	1p34	482		Nuclear	Histones, YY1, p53, SHP, DNMT1, E2F-1, ER, AR, ATM, STAT3, pRb, GATA, MeCP2, MEF2, MyoD, NF-κB
		HDAC2	6q21	488		Nuclear	Histones, YY1, STAT3, BRCA1, pRb, GATA2, NF-κB, Bcl-6, HOP
		HDAC3	5q31	428		Nuclear/cytoplasmatic	Histones, pRb, SHP, MEF2D, YY-1, STAT3, NF-κB, GATA1, RelA
		HDAC8	Xq13	377		Nuclear/cytoplasmatic	Histones, SMC3, p53, ERRα, HSP70
	Class IIa	HDAC4	2q37.3	1084		Nuclear/cytoplasmatic	Histones, p21, HP1, p53, HIF-1α, FOXO, GATA1, SRF, Runx2, SUV39H1, GCMa,
		HDAC5	17q21	1122		Nuclear/cytoplasmatic	CaM, YY1, HP1, MEF2, GCMa, Runx2, Smad7
		HDAC7	12q13.1	952		Nuclear/cytoplasmatic	FLAG1, FLAG2
		HDAC9	7p21.1	1011		Nuclear/cytoplasmatic	Histones, CaM, MEF2, HIF-1α, PML, Runx2
	Class IIb	HDAC6	Xp11.23	1215		cytoplasmatic	α-Tubulin, Tau, SHP, Hsp90, HSF-1, Runx2, Smad7, cortactin
		HDAC10	22q13.31	669		cytoplasmatic	HSP90, LcoR
	Class IV	HDAC11	3p25.1	347		Nuclear/cytoplasmatic	Histones (longer chain acyllysine residues), Cdt1
NAD^+–dependent HDACs	Class III	Stir1	10q21.3	747		Nuclear/cytoplasmatic	HIF-1α, HIF-2α, MYC
		Stir2	19q13.2	389		Nuclear/cytoplasmatic	Tubulin, Foxo3a, EIF5A, P53, G6PD, MYC
		Stir3	11p15.5	399		Mitochondrial	SOD2, PDMC1a, IDH2, GOT2, FoxO3a
		Stir4	12q24.31	314		Mitochondrial	GDH, PDH
		Stir5	6p23	310		Mitochondrial	CPS1
		Stir6	19p13.3	355		Nuclear	
		Stir7	17q25.3	400		Nuclear	HIF-1α, HIF-2α

Figure 9.2 Depiction of HDACs' characteristics. The catalytic domains are represented by yellow bars (HDAC1–11) and purple bars (Stir1–7).

with its defatty-acylase activity outstripping its deacetylase activity by a staggering 10,000-fold [22].

9.2.3 Structure of HDACs

As shown in Figure 9.3, HDACs share a highly conserved structure, and the rim (region around the catalytic cavity), wall (an internal tubular cavity adjacent to the catalytic site), and bottom regions (an 11 Å catalytic site using a Zn^{2+} as a cofactor) comprise the conserved tube-like binding channel of HDACs [23]. Beyond these common structural elements, several HDAC isoforms possess additional configurations, including foot pocket, side pocket, lower pocket, and potential pockets. The design of an isoform-selective HDAC inhibitor will be significantly aided by these secondary pockets.

HDAC1, HDAC2, and HDAC3 are distinguished by narrow as well as deep catalytic channels in relation to other isoforms. Additionally, they feature a unique secondary internal cavity, termed the foot pocket, located at the underside region, presumed to facilitate water entry and acetic acid removal [24, 25]. Targeting the foot pocket by incorporating specific groups to the zinc-binding group (ZBG) can enhance binding capacity and isoform specificity/selectivity (Figure 9.3a). Notably, HDAC1/2 possess a larger foot pocket attributed to the small Ser113 residues, while the larger Tyr96 residue endows HDAC3 with a smaller foot pocket [26].

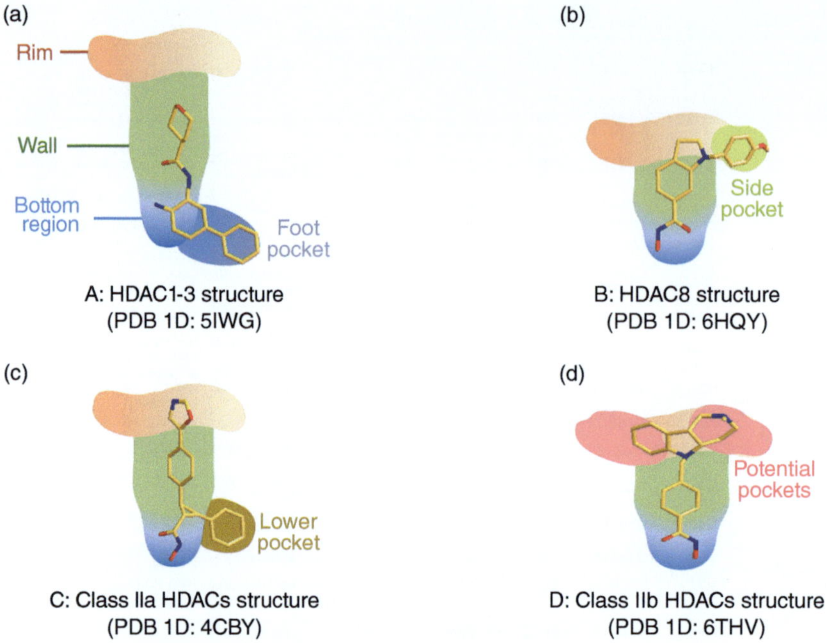

Figure 9.3 Structure of different HDAC isoforms with inhibitor.

HDAC8, unlike other class I isoforms, features a side pocket formed by L1 and L6 loops at the rim of its binding channel. This side pocket accommodates the potent and selective L-shaped inhibitor PCI-34051 (Figure 9.3b) [27, 28]. In contrast, class IIa HDACs lack foot and side pockets but possess a lower pocket, which can be exploited by linker-aside fragments to develop potent U-shaped inhibitors (Figure 9.3c) [29, 30].

Class IIb HDACs, characterized by a broad as well as shallow channel, favor inhibitors with short, bulky linkers. Additionally, their rim region contains potential pockets (Figure 9.3d), which can be targeted with large, extended, rigid cap groups to achieve high affinity and selectivity [31].

The structural details of HDAC11 remain largely elusive, attributed to the unavailability of the crystal structure. Functionally, HDAC11 operates more as a defatty-acylase than a deacetylase, given its low deacetylase activity and high defatty-acylation efficiency [22]. Consequently, activity-driven design strategies have been employed to develop HDAC11-selective inhibitors, incorporating long-chain fatty acyl groups to align with its physiological role [32].

9.2.4 Biological Functions of HDACs

HDACs extensively participate in diverse biological events through their deacetylase activities or by complexing with partners. As depicted in Figure 9.4, HDACs are engaged in the following key processes.

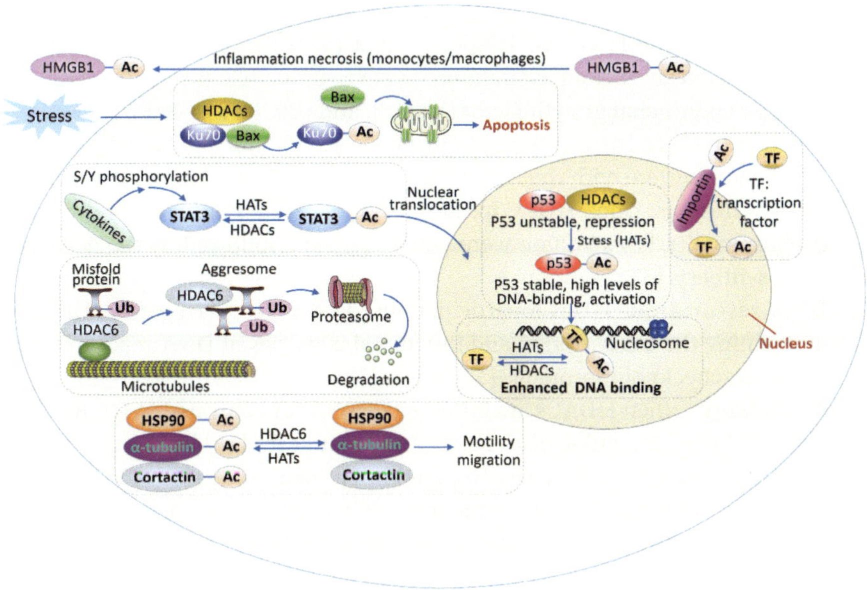

Figure 9.4 Illustration of HDACs' biological cascades.

(1) **Protein transport**: HDACs and HATs collaboratively govern the acetylation of importin proteins, influencing the nuclear entry and exit of transcription factors or HMGB1 [33].

(2) **Protein translocation**: Acetylation or knockdown of Ku70 disrupts the "Ku70-Bax" complex, enabling Bax to translocate to mitochondria [34]. Additionally, HDACs/HATs modulate the subcellular localization of STAT3 through reversible acetylation [35].

(3) **Apoptosis regulation**: By regulating the intrinsic or extrinsic apoptosis pathway, HDACs prolong cell life and prevent apoptosis [36, 37].

(4) **Misfolded protein degradation**: Misfolded protein can be attracted to the aggresome by HDAC6, followed by its degradation [38].

(5) **Cell migration and motility**: HDAC6 eliminates the acetyl group from its substrates, including cortactin, HSP90, as well as α-tubulin. Low acetylation promotes the migration and motility of cells [39, 40]. Furthermore, HDACs also upregulate matrix metalloproteinases (MMPs), which decompose the cellular physical barrier, facilitating cell invasion [41, 42].

(6) **Gene transcription**: HDACs manage gene expression by modifying nucleosome structure or modulating the access of transcription factors to DNA [43–46].

(7) **Protein stability**: By controlling the acetylation and ubiquitylation of lysine residues, HDACs together with HATs influence the stability of proteins like p53 and CDT1 [47, 48].

(8) **Immune regulation**: HDACs regulate natural immunity by modulating inflammatory cytokine production, while class IIa HDACs affect antigen presentation, contributing to adaptive immunity [36].

(9) **Angiogenesis**: HDACs promote the growth of angiogenesis by downregulating p53 as well as von Hippel–Lindau (VHL) protein, or upregulating pro-angiogenesis factors containing hypoxia-inducible factor 1α (HIF-1α), vascular endothelial growth factor (VEGF), and CXCR4 [49–52].

(10) **Protein–protein interaction**: For instance, acetylation regulated by HDACs/HATs can interfere with the interaction between p53 and MDM2 [53, 54].

(11) **DNA synthesis**: Upon HDAC inhibition, thymidylate synthetase and cytidine triphosphate (CTP) synthase were downregulated, followed by the decreased DNA synthesis [55].

(12) **DNA restoration**: HDACs participate in DNA damage response (DDR) by modulating the transcription and functional activities of DNA repair proteins as well as checkpoint proteins. [56–60].

(13) **Autophagy**: When HDACs are inhibited, mTOR is inactivated. ATG, Beclin-1, and LC370 are upregulated, and autophagy is triggered [61].

(14) **Cell cycle**: HDACs influence cell cycle progression by altering the transcription or function of cell cycle regulators (CCRs) within the crosstalk network [62, 63].

9.2.5 The Disease Involved in HDACs

Under physiological conditions, HDACs maintain cellular homeostasis and ontogeny through their intrinsic enzymatic activities or formation of functional protein complexes. However, dysregulation of HDAC expression or activity can disrupt these homeostatic mechanisms, leading to the pathogenesis of various diseases, with cancer being particularly prominent. As systematically summarized in Table 9.1, numerous disease states have been associated with aberrant HDAC, highlighting the clinical values of HDACs as promising therapeutic targets.

9.2.6 Observations/Phenotypes of HDAC Knockouts

In addition to exploring the structural characteristics and biology of HDACs, investigating their knockout phenotypes is indispensable for the rational design of isoform-specific inhibitors. In mouse models, HDAC knockout observations and phenotypes are summarized (Table 9.2). Complete HDAC1 knockout leads to embryonic death prior to E10.5 due to proliferation defects and developmental retardation. Notably, the upregulation of HDAC2/3 cannot offset the loss of HDAC1 [65]. Mice lacking HDAC2 remain alive until birth but fall prey to various cardiac abnormalities, including bradycardia, cardiomyocyte apoptosis, as well as right ventricular lumen obliteration [66]. Moreover, HDAC1/HDAC2 double knockouts exhibit exacerbated phenotypes, comprising augmented apoptosis and cell cycle stalling, in relation to individual knockouts of HDAC1 or HDAC2 [67]. In addition, accumulating evidences reveal the necessity of HDAC3 in early embryonic development, and its deletion leads to embryonic death between E9.5 and E10.5 because of gastrulation failure. HDAC3-deficient mouse embryonic fibroblasts (MEFs) display

Table 9.1 Diseases related to aberrant HDACs.

HDACs	Related diseases
HDAC1	Immunological disorders (allergic diseases and allergic rhinitis), Neoplastic conditions (various carcinomas), Cardiovascular pathologies, Neurological diseases (neurodegenerative diseases, memory and learning disorders), Infectious diseases (viral infections), and Musculoskeletal disorders (osteoarthritis).
HDAC2	Respiratory disorders (airway illness and chronic obstructive pulmonary disease), Cardiovascular conditions (cardiomegaly), Oncological manifestations (various cancers), Metabolic disorders (diabetes mellitus), Hepatic pathologies (liver diseases), Neurological diseases (cognitive deficits, memory and learning disorders and neurodegenerative diseases), Infectious diseases (viral infections), and Musculoskeletal disorders (osteoarthritis)
HDAC3	Immunological disorders (allergic rhinitis and rheumatoid arthritis), Neoplastic conditions (various cancers), Cardiovascular pathologies, Metabolic disorders (diabetes mellitus and obesity), Inflammatory conditions, Organ-specific diseases (lung and kidney diseases), Neurological diseases (cognitive deficits, memory and learning disorders, and neurodegenerative diseases), and Musculoskeletal disorders (osteoarthritis).
HDAC4	Cognitive disorders, Neurodegenerative disorders
HDAC5	Diabetes mellitus, Neurological diseases, Neurodegenerative disorders, Schizophrenia, and Vascular hypertrophy
HDAC6	Autoimmune diseases, Cancers, Cardiovascular diseases, Cognitive deficits, Inflammatory diseases, Neurodegenerative disorders, and Viral infections
HDAC7	Pulmonary disorders (acute lung injury, cystic fibrosis, and respiratory diseases), Autoimmune conditions (autoimmune diseases and systemic sclerosis), Neoplastic transformations (various cancers), Metabolic disorders (hepatic steatosis and diabetes), Neurodegenerative disorders (Huntington's disease), Gastrointestinal inflammation (inflammatory bowel diseases), Connective tissue disorders (Peyronie's disease and osteoarthritis), and Hepatic pathologies (hepatic fibrosis and cholangitis)
HDAC8	Cardiovascular diseases, Neoplastic conditions (various carcinomas), Genetic disorders (Cornelia de Lange syndrome, Duchenne muscular dystrophy, X-linked disorders), Cardiovascular diseases, Infectious diseases, Hepatic diseases (Hepatic diseases, Liver fibrosis), Myopathy, neuroinflammation-mediated diseases, Pulmonary diseases, and Renal fibrosis
HDAC9	Autoimmune diseases, carcinomas, Cerebrovascular diseases, Liver fibrosis, Obesity, and osteoporosis
HDAC10	Cancers, HIV infection, Immunoglobulin A nephropathy, Intracerebral Hemorrhage, and Schizophrenia
HDAC11	Age-related macular degeneration, Allergic rhinitis, Cancers, Metabolic disorders, Neurological and mental disorders

Source: [64]/with permission of Elsevier/CC BY-NC-ND 4.0.

Table 9.2 Observations/phenotypes of HDAC knockouts.

HDAC knockout	Observation/phenotype
HDAC1	Embryonic lethality caused by defects in embryonic stem cell proliferation, increased apoptosis, and delayed cell cycle progression
HDAC2	Perinatal lethality resulting from cardiac abnormalities, delayed cell cycle transition, and apoptosis
HDAC3	Embryonic lethality attributed to gastrulation failure, cell cycle dysregulation, DNA lesions, and apoptosis
HDAC4	Induces mitotic segregation defects in p53-deficient human tumor cells with no observable impact on normal cells.
HDAC5	Cardiomegaly
HDAC6	Normal development with a slight influence on bone density
HDAC7	Embryonic lethality caused by blood vessel dilation and rupture
HDAC8	Perinatal lethality ascribed to craniofacial malformations
HDAC9	Cardiac hypertrophy
HDAC10	Viable without any detectable abnormalities
HDAC11	Show no influence on stem cell proliferation or differentiation

Source: [64]/with permission of Elsevier/CC BY-NC-ND 4.0.

signs of apoptosis, DNA damage, and delayed cell cycle [68]. Collectively, these findings highlight the critical roles of HDAC1, HDAC2, and HDAC3 in regulating cell proliferation and survival.

Interestingly, the inactivation of HDAC4 produces distinct results. In tumor cells, HDAC4 knockout induces chromosome segregation defects, mitotic arrest, and caspase-dependent apoptosis. However, these effects are not observed in normal human dermal fibroblasts, myelopoietic progenitors, or embryonic fibroblasts [69]. Notably, HDAC4 inactivation impacts the proliferation of both p53 wild-type and p53-deficient malignancy cells, whereas only p53-deficient cells exhibit chromosome segregation defects [69]. These findings suggest that HDAC4-selective inhibitors may serve as a more effective and less toxic therapeutic strategy for p53-deficient tumors.

HDAC5 and HDAC9 act as repressors of cardiomegaly and redundantly govern cardiac development by regulating a cluster of cardiac stress signaling pathways [70]. While mice deficient in either HDAC5 or HDAC9 are viable at birth but develop severe cardiac enlargement, double knockouts of HDAC5/HDAC9 result in embryonic or perinatal lethality because of thin ventricular walls as well as ventricular septal defects [70, 71].

In contrast to other HDAC isoforms, the disruption of HDAC6 has no fatal or teratogenic outcomes. Mice with HDAC6 silencing exhibit normal growth and development, showing only minor alterations in immune response and bone density [72]. Notably, the inhibition or silencing of HDAC6 was proven to effectively reduce the proliferation of carcinoma cells, and this finding has prompted the exploration of HDAC6-selective inhibitors which demonstrated significant antiproliferative activity with minimal side effects in cancer treatment [73–75]. Several of these inhibitors, including Purinostat, Ricolinostat, and Citarinostat, are currently undergoing clinical trials. These compounds exhibit promising anticancer efficacy and attenuated adverse effects, both as monotherapies and in combination therapies (www.clinicaltrials.gov). Collectively, the aforementioned findings indicate that isozyme-specific/isoform-selective inhibitors toward HDAC6 show advantages of minimizing on-target adverse effects.

HDAC7 is necessary for the formation of blood vessels. Its interaction with myocyte enhancer factor-2 suppresses MMP-10 gene transcription, thereby sustaining vascular integrity. Consequently, the silencing of HDAC7 results in impaired endothelial cell–cell adhesion, leading to vascular dilation, rupture, and ultimately embryonic lethality [76].

Similarly, HDAC8 is responsible for the management of transcription factors associated with cranial morphogenesis. Complete HDAC8 inactivation contributes to cranial instability and perinatal lethality [77].

Recent studies by Edward Seto and colleagues have revealed that HDAC10 may act as a potential tumor repressor. Moreover, their studies indicated that HDAC10-deficient cells acquire tumorigenic and stem-like characteristics [78]. Moreover, mice lacking HDAC10 are healthy, displaying no developmental abnormalities.

Furthermore, the disruption of HDAC11 demonstrates no significant effect on the proliferation or differentiation of neural stem/precursor cells [79]. Interestingly, additional research showed that HDAC11 disruption selectively affects carcinoma cells while sparing normal cells [80].

9.3 The Roles of HDACs in Cancer

Extensive research has established a significant association between overexpression of HDACs and tumorigenesis. Elevated levels of HDACs have been consistently observed in a broad spectrum of cancers, including lymphoma, leukemia, neuroblastoma, medulloblastoma, ovarian malignancies, pancreatic malignancies, prostate malignancies, gastric malignancies, liver malignancies, kidney malignancies, lung malignancies, colon malignancies, and breast malignancies [44, 45, 81–84]. As more data comes to light, it has been validated that HDACs are concerned with multiple tumor-associated cascades, including apoptosis, autophagy, cell cycle progression, cellular proliferation and growth, cell maturation and differentiation, cellular metastasis, angiogenesis, and drug resistance (Figure 9.5) [7, 85–88].

9.3.1 Apoptosis

Through both extrinsic apoptosis pathways (death receptor-mediated pathways) and intrinsic apoptosis pathways (mitochondrial pathways), HDACs are capable of modulating apoptosis. In the extrinsic apoptosis pathway, HDAC inhibition makes

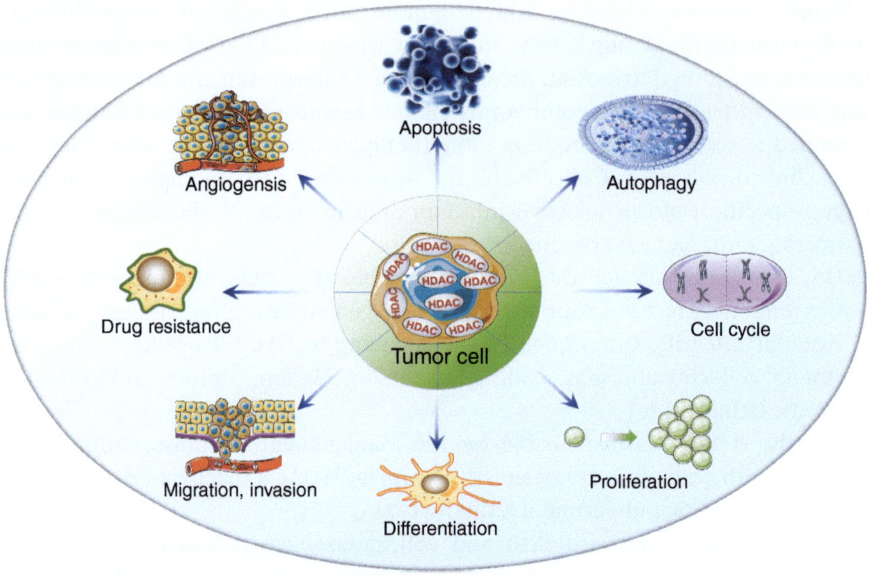

Figure 9.5 The roles of HDACs in cancer.

malignancies more susceptible to tumor necrosis factor-related apoptosis-inducing ligand (TRAIL)-induced apoptosis through multiple mechanisms: upregulation of cell surface death receptors, downregulation of cellular-FLICE inhibitory protein (c-FLIP), and promotion of death-inducing signaling complex (DISC) formation [45, 89]. Additionally, HDAC inhibition directly triggers the TNF superfamily member 10 (TNFS10) gene promoter, bringing about TRAIL upregulation as well as subsequent apoptosis.

Regarding the intrinsic apoptotic pathway, HDACs primarily regulate apoptosis by modulating the balance between proapoptotic and antiapoptotic proteins (Figure 9.6) [90, 91]. For instance, HDAC1 inhibition increases the Bax/Bcl-2 ratio, thereby enhancing carcinoma cell susceptibility to apoptosis [92], while HDAC2 knockdown reduces Bcl-2 expression and upregulates proapoptotic proteins (AIF, Apaf-1, and Bax) [93]. Notably, HDAC3 inhibition promotes p53 binding to the p53 upregulated modulator of apoptosis (PUMA) promoter, resulting in increased expression of this pro-apoptotic protein [81].

HDAC8 and HDAC1 demonstrate unique regulatory functions through their interaction with the Bcl-2-modifying factor (BMF) gene, where they downregulate BMF to create a pro-survival scenario [94]. Importantly, HDAC8 ablation was shown to effectively elevate BMF expression and trigger BMF-mediated apoptosis [94]. HDAC6 exhibits a distinct mechanism of apoptosis regulation by modulating the Bax-Ku70 interaction. HDAC inhibition leads to cAMP response element-binding protein (CREB)-binding protein-mediated acetylation of Ku70, resulting in Bax release from the "Bax-Ku70" complex and subsequent Bax conformation activation, ultimately initiating apoptosis [34].

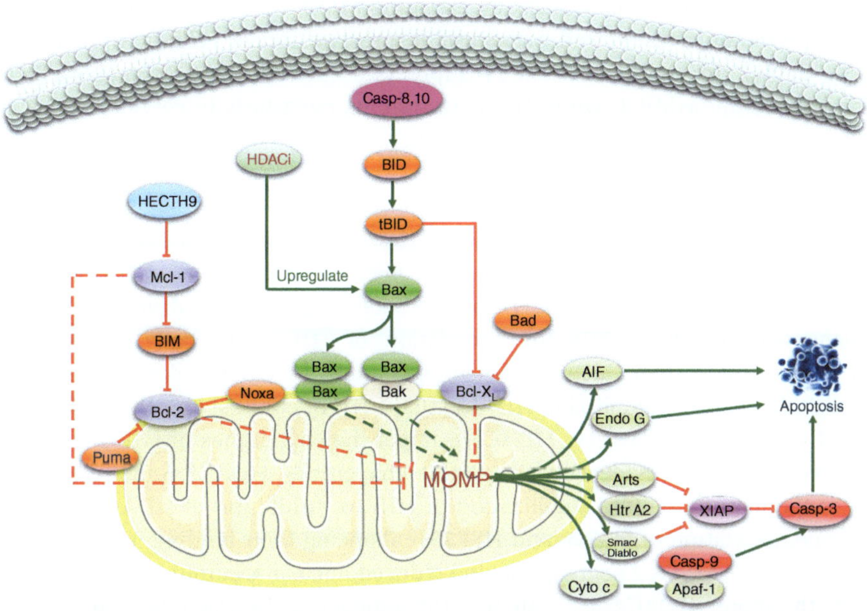

Figure 9.6 The intrinsic (mitochondrial) apoptosis pathway regulated by HDACs.

9.3.2 Cell Cycle Transition

Cyclins, cyclin-dependent kinases (CDKs), and cyclin-dependent kinase inhibitors (CDKIs) constitute key components of the CCR network, which orchestrates the precisely controlled cell cycle transition, a sophisticated and well-coordinated biological process. Within this regulatory network, cyclins act as positive regulators of CDK activity, whereas CDKIs function as negative modulators. Specifically, HDAC1 and HDAC2 repress the transcription of CDKIs such as p21, p27, and p57, thereby accelerating cell cycle progression and promoting uncontrolled proliferation [37, 95–97]. The regulation of cyclin A stability represents another critical mechanism mediated by HDAC3. Inhibition of HDAC3 triggers PCAF/GCN5-mediated acetylation of cyclin A, marking it for proteasomal degradation and subsequently triggering cell cycle stalling at the G2/M and S phases [98]. Furthermore, genetic depletion of HDAC5 induces G1 phase arrest through a dual mechanism involving upregulation of p21 and concurrent downregulation of CDK2/4/6 and cyclin D1 [99]. Additionally, HDAC10 has been identified as a regulator of the G2/M transition, exerting its effects through the let-7/HMGA2/cyclin A2 pathway [100].

9.3.3 Cell Metastasis and Invasion

The extracellular matrix and intact basement membrane act as physical barriers that restrict the spread of carcinoma cells. However, HDAC-mediated upregulation of MMPs can degrade these barriers, enabling carcinoma cells to infiltrate surrounding tissues. As an example in breast malignancies, overexpression of HDAC1, HDAC6, and HDAC8 enhances metastasis by elevating MMP-9 expression [42]. Similarly, Sirt-1 promotes invasion and metastasis in prostate cancer cells by upregulating MMP-2 [41]. In contrast, HDAC11 suppresses colorectal cancer metastasis by downregulating MMP-3, while HDAC10 inhibits metastasis in cervical cancer by reducing MMP-2 and MMP-9 expression [101, 102].

9.3.4 Angiogenesis

A prominent characteristic of the tumor microenvironment (TME) is hypoxia, which enables malignant cells to promote angiogenesis through multiple mechanisms involving HIF-1α. Acetylation of HIF-1α typically attributes to its ubiquitin-dependent degradation, but HDAC1/4-mediated deacetylation can abolish this process, stabilizing HIF-1α [103, 104]. In contrast to HDAC1/4, which directly deacetylates HIF-1α, HDAC5/6 target the chaperones of HIF-1α, namely HSP90 and HSP70. By deacetylating these chaperones, HDAC5/6 indirectly facilitates the maturation and stabilization of HIF-1α. Inhibition of HDAC5/6 results in hyperacetylation of HSP90 and HSP70, enhancing their binding to HIF-1α and leading to its expedited degradation and reduced nuclear accumulation [105].

Furthermore, HDAC4/5/7 enhance the interaction between HIF-1α and the transcriptional coactivators CBP/p300, thereby boosting HIF-1α-mediated transcription [103, 106, 107]. Beyond HIF-1α, overexpression of HDAC9 suppresses the antiangiogenic microRNA-17-92 cluster, causing endothelial cell germination and angiogenesis [108].

9.3.5 Cell Proliferation and Chemoresistance

Extensive research has established that HDACs are necessary for cell cycle progression and cellular proliferation, with their inhibition or depletion consistently resulting in either apoptotic cell death or delayed cell cycle. A prominent example is class I HDACs, which enhance cell cycle progression and proliferation in smooth muscle cells, while their elimination significantly inhibits growth and induces G1/S phase arrest [109].

The regulatory functions of HDAC isoforms have been extensively characterized in various cancer models. In glioma cells, HDAC4 promotes tumor progression or chemoresistance *via* dual mechanisms: suppression of CDKIs (p21 and p27) and downregulation of proapoptotic genes (PMAIP1 and Bcl2-interacting killer [BIK]), with HDAC4 depletion resulting in G0/G1 arrest and apoptosis induction [110, 111]. Similarly, HDAC5 exerts oncogenic effects in human hepatoma cells by upregulating Six1 expression, and its knockdown markedly suppresses hepatocellular carcinoma proliferation [112]. The proliferative functions of HDACs extend to other malignancies, as evidenced by HDAC7-mediated acceleration of cell division in HeLa cells and HDAC9-driven cell cycle progression in retinoblastoma cells [113, 114]. Among class IIb HDACs, HDAC6 overexpression has been implicated in glioblastoma pathogenesis, conferring temozolomide resistance and promoting tumor growth [115].

9.3.6 Cell Differentiation

HDACs are particularly important for ontogeny and are instrumental in the differentiation processes of various cell types, including normal cells (neuronal cells, myocytes), stem cells (glioblastoma stem cells), and malignancies (colorectal carcinoma cells) [116–122].

9.4 HDAC Inhibitors

9.4.1 General Concept of HDAC Inhibitors

Classical HDACs are characterized by a highly conserved catalytic domain that features three common structural components: a zinc cation at the active site, a catalytic channel, and several secondary pockets surrounding the channel. To accommodate the unique structures of classical HDACs, researchers have developed diverse HDAC inhibitors, which typically consist of four distinct pharmacophoric elements: (i) a cap group for protein surface recognition, (ii) a connecting unit, (iii) a linker region, and (iv) a ZBG. However, some inhibitors may contain only two or three of these functional pharmacophores [123].

By interacting with the peripheral pockets of the HDAC catalytic channel, the cap group can enhance the binding capacity of the HDAC inhibitor and block substrate access. The linker is tasked with delivering ZBG to bind with zinc $^{2+}$, and HDAC inhibitor can achieve strong inhibitory activity with the aid of an appropriate linker. However, insufficient linker length may prevent effective zinc chelation, while excessive length may impair the cap group's interaction with the protein surface, reducing binding affinity. The ZBG represents the core functional component that directly inhibits HDAC activity through zinc ion chelation. Among the various ZBG types, hydroxamic acid and anilinobenzamide are commonly used strong chelating agents, while thiocarbonate, hydrazide, carboxylic acid, boric acid, mercaptoacetamide, and trifluoromethyl ketone are weak chelating agents [124].

9.4.2 Evaluation Assay of HDAC Inhibitors

With the development of various HDAC inhibitors, a fluorescence assay was employed to assess their HDAC inhibitory potency. The procedure is briefly outlined as follows: (i) Incubate the HDAC enzyme with a series of diluted test compounds for 10 minutes at 37 °C; (ii) Add the fluorogenic substrate and incubate the mixture for the indicated time at 37 °C; (iii) Quench the reaction by adding a developer solution comprising trypsin and trichostatin A (TSA), followed by a 30-minute incubation; (iv) Measure the fluorescence intensity at 390/460 nm. Notably, some measurement parameters in the evaluation of HDAC inhibitory activity (HDAC enzyme dosage, types of fluorescent substrate, fluorescent substrate concentration, and coincubation time of substrate with HDAC enzyme) were illustrated in Table 9.3. Readers interested in HDAC inhibitory activity evaluation can refer to the above data.

Table 9.3 The measurement parameters of HDAC inhibitory activity evaluation.

HDAC	Fluorescent substrate	Enzyme dosage (ng)[a]	Substrate concentration (μM)[b]	Incubation time (h)[c]
HDAC1	Ac-Leu-Gly- Lys(Ac)-AMC	7	20	1
HDAC2	Ac-Leu-Gly- Lys(Ac)-AMC	3	20	1
HDAC3	Ac-Leu-Gly- Lys(Ac)-AMC	10	20	1
HDAC4	Ac-Leu-Gly-Lys(tfa)-AMC	2	20	1
HDAC5	Ac-Leu-Gly-Lys(tfa)-AMC	50	120	1
HDAC6	Ac-Leu-Gly- Lys(Ac)-AMC	25	40	2
HDAC7	Ac-Leu-Gly-Lys(tfa)-AMC	2	40	1
HDAC8	Ac-Leu-Gly-Lys(tfa)-AMC	5	80	1
HDAC9	Ac-Leu-Gly-Lys(tfa)-AMC	40	80	1
HDAC10	Ac-Arg-His-Lys(Ac)-Lys(Ac)-AMC	500	50	1
HDAC11	Ac-Leu-Gly- Lys(Ac)-AMC	500	40	1

a) The dosage of different HDAC enzymes.
b) The final concentration of the fluorescent substrate.
c) The coincubation time of substrate with HDAC enzyme.
Source: Adapted from [125].

9.4.3 Approved HDAC Inhibitors

Currently, five HDAC inhibitors are marketed for oncological applications. Among these, chidamide (CS055) was authorized by the China Food and Drug Administration (CFDA) for the treatment of peripheral T-cell lymphoma (PTCL) and advanced breast cancer (metastatic or locally recurrent, inoperable cases). The remaining four inhibitors, vorinostat (SAHA), romidepsin (FK228), belinostat (PXD101), and panobinostat (LBH589) were approved by either the US Food and Drug Administration (FDA) or the European Medicines Agency (EMA) for multiple myeloma (MM), cutaneous T-cell lymphoma (CTCL), PTCL and breast cancer (Figure 9.7) [124].

The available data revealed that the aforementioned approved HDAC inhibitors are nonspecific HDAC inhibitors, and they demonstrate strong inhibition against almost all HDAC isoforms (as depicted in Table 9.4). Although chidamide demonstrates a preference for inhibiting class I HDACs, its potent inhibitory effects on HDAC10/11 indicate that it is not an isoform-selective inhibitor.

9.4.4 Adverse Effects of Approved HDAC Inhibitors

Currently approved HDAC inhibitors, although demonstrating efficacy in specific indications, are associated with significant adverse effects owing to their limited isoform selectivity, off-target toxicities, and the use of hydroxamate as ZBG [126].

Vorinostat (SAHA), a broad-spectrum HDAC inhibitor (pan-HDAC inhibitor) using hydroxamate as ZBG, was first approved for use in CTCL therapy in 2006.

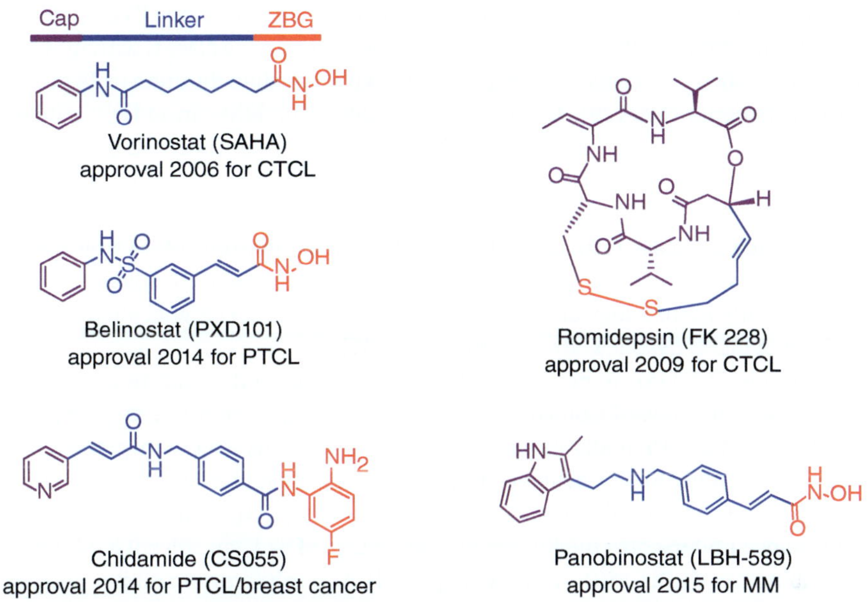

Figure 9.7 Approved HDAC inhibitors.

Table 9.4 The inhibitory activities of approved HDAC inhibitors.

HDAC isoform	IC_{50} (nM)				
	Vorinostat	Romidepsin	Belinostat	Chidamide	Panobinostat
HDAC1	60	1	26	100	3
HDAC2	42	1	22	200	2
HDAC3	36	1	19	100	2
HDAC4	20	647	15	> 10,000	1
HDAC5	36	> 1000	25	> 10,000	1
HDAC6	29	226	10	> 10,000	1
HDAC7	129	> 1000	51	> 10,000	2
HDAC8	173	> 1000	22	700	22
HDAC9	49	> 1000	24	> 10,000	1
HDAC10	60	1	59	100	31
HDAC11	31	0.3	27	400	4

Source: Adapted from [124].

Although showing promising activity against hematological malignancies (24–30% overall response rate at 400 mg/day in refractory CTCL) [127], its efficacy in solid tumors remains limited. The therapeutic profile of vorinostat is marred by frequent adverse events, ranging from mild (thrombocytopenia, anorexia, diarrhea, nausea, fatigue) to severe (thrombosis) [127, 128].

Romidepsin (FK-228), approved in 2009 for relapsed/refractory PTCL, demonstrates preferential inhibition of class I HDACs with moderate class II activity. Clinical trials revealed a 25% objective response rate with a median duration of 28 months in PTCL patients [52, 129]. Despite its favorable tolerability in elderly patients, common adverse effects include hematological toxicities (anemia, leukopenia, thrombocytopenia) and constitutional symptoms (fever, fatigue) [130].

Belinostat (PXD-101), another pan-HDAC inhibitor approved for PTCL, demonstrated a 25.8% response rate with a median duration of 13.6 months in phase II trials [131]. However, 96.9% of patients experienced adverse events, predominantly hematological and gastrointestinal toxicities (fatigue, anemia, fever, vomiting, nausea, dyspnea, and pneumonia) [131].

Chidamide (CS055), a benzamide-based HDAC inhibitor approved in 2014, represents a shift toward isoform-selective inhibition, preferentially targeting class I and IIb HDACs with moderate class IV activity [132]. This selectivity profile correlates with improved safety, evidenced by a 28% response rate in PTCL with reduced adverse events (primarily hematological toxicities) [133]. Chidamide's clinical performance underscores the therapeutic advantage of isoform-selective inhibition.

Panobinostat (LBH-589), a potent pan-HDAC inhibitor, exhibits excellent inhibition against all HDAC enzymes. Although panobinostat has notable side effects and clinical toxicity, it was authorized in 2015 as part of a combination regimen with bortezomib and dexamethasone for relapsed multiple myeloma. In the phase II clinical trial involving 35 patients, adverse events were observed in all participants. Among them, four patients reported grade 4 toxicity, while the majority (71.4%) experienced ≥ grade 3 adverse event [134]. The frequent adverse effects were thrombocytopenia (45.7%), nausea (51.4%), and fatigue (62.9%) [135].

Research revealed that there are three main mechanisms for the side effects of the aforementioned pan-HDAC inhibitors: (i) Pan-HDAC inhibitors lack isoform selectivity and are likely to interfere with other HDAC isoforms or unrelated signaling pathways [24]; (ii) Most pan-HDAC inhibitors employ hydroxamate as ZBG, which potentially transform into an isocyanate susceptible to nucleophilic attack by DNA residues, leading to genotoxicity [126]; (iii) As a strong zinc ion chelating group, in addition to HDAC binding, hydroxamate also causes off-target effects *via* hERG channel inhibition and nonspecific chelation [126, 136]. Severe side effects of HDAC inhibitors may result in early termination of drug development or severe prescribing restrictions. Therefore, developing next-generation HDAC inhibitors with high efficiency and attenuated toxicity is a new trend in medicinal chemistry. Given aforementioned mechanisms, targeting appropriate HDAC isoform to develop non-hydroxamate HDAC selective inhibitors can effectively attenuate the undesirable interference toward irrelevant HDAC isoforms and eliminate the toxicity of hydroxamate.

9.4.5 Limited Efficiency of Approved HDAC Inhibitors in Solid Malignancies

In addition to the severe adverse effects, another challenge to be addressed is the limited therapeutic potential in solid malignancies when used as monotherapy. As

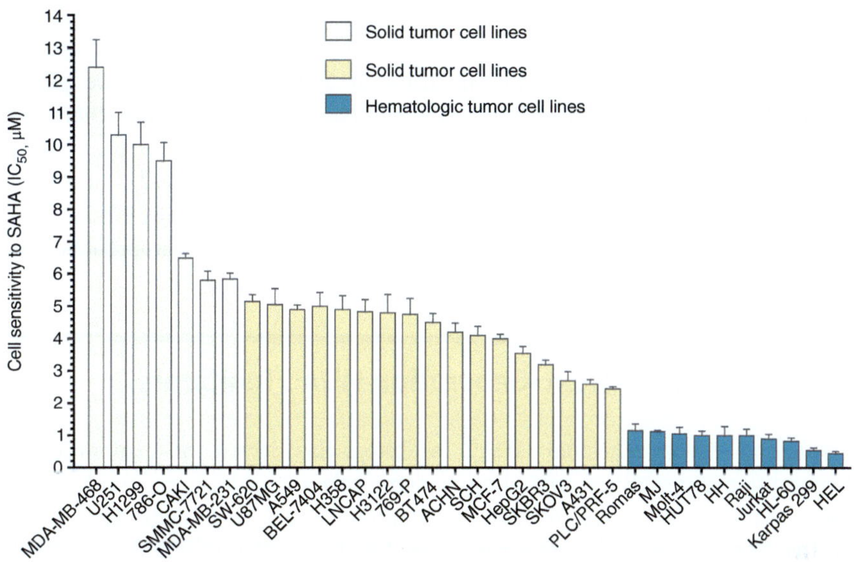

Figure 9.8 Cell sensitivity to vorinostat.

shown in Figure 9.8, vorinostat demonstrated restricted therapeutic effect over solid malignancies, though it shows exceptional clinical benefits in defined groups of hematological malignancies [137]. Despite the identification of a few more potent HDAC inhibitors, including panobinostat, belinostat, chidamide, and romidepsin, the effectiveness of HDAC inhibitors against solid malignancies is still insufficient, probably due to their ineffective low concentrations or increased Treg cells [138]. Furthermore, available data showed that few HDAC inhibitors are effective in the treatment of practically all solid malignancies, including breast cancer, prostate cancer, and renal cancer [139].

Several mechanisms may explain the modest therapeutic effects of HDAC inhibitors in solid malignancies. Geng et al. investigated this issue using a breast cancer model. In their study, upon HDAC inhibition, the gene promoter of LIFR was acetylated, the BRD4-mediated transcription of LIFR was activated, and the expression level of leukemia inhibitor factor receptor (LIFR) was increased, resulting in the activation of JAK1-STAT3 signaling and insensitivity to HDAC inhibition [137]. Additionally, their study revealed that inhibition of BRD4 or JAK1 overcomes HDAC inhibitor resistance, and simultaneously inhibiting HDAC, BRD4, and JAK1 can achieve a breakthrough in therapeutic efficacy [137]. Furthermore, Tan et al. employ a tandem mass tag (TMT)-based quantitative proteomic technology to analyze HDAC inhibitor–induced changes in protein and phosphoprotein profiles in both HDAC inhibitor–sensitive and resistant cells. They revealed that nucleolar protein 16 (NOP16), Pescadillo1 (PES1), WD repeat-containing protein 74 (WDR74) and mRNA turnover protein 4 homolog (MRTO4) may be associated with HDAC inhibitor resistance, while the rho-associated kinase and pyruvate dehydrogenase kinase 1 were identified as potential HDAC inhibitor–resistant signatures [140].

On the other hand, published data suggested that combining HDAC inhibitors with other anticancer drugs can lead to significant advancements in therapeutic outcomes or expansion of applications through additive or synergistic effects [141]. Combination therapy or multitarget agent–based HDAC inhibitor, therefore, provides an avenue for the effective treatment of solid tumors. Currently, some combination regimens involving HDAC inhibitors [142–145] and multitarget agent–based HDAC inhibitors [146–148] show promising anticancer efficacy and favorable safety properties, highlighting that they can be useful approaches for sensitizing solid malignancies.

9.5 The Trends of Next-Generation HDAC Inhibitors

The deficiency of conventional HDAC inhibitors has driven the exploration of next-generation alternatives, including isozyme-selective inhibitors, combination regimens, multitarget drugs (hybrid compounds), and HDAC degraders. These innovative approaches aim to overcome the drawbacks of traditional pan-HDAC inhibitors. The following sections provide a concise perspective of the trends and challenges for next-generation HDAC inhibitors.

9.5.1 HDAC Isozyme-Selective Inhibitors

The key topic surrounding the HDAC inhibitor is isozyme-selective or lack thereof, as pan-HDAC inhibitors can negatively affect other HDAC isoforms or signaling pathways, resulting in a cascade of harmful effects. Consequently, developing HDAC isoform-selective inhibitors has become the predominant trend in the evolution of next-generation HDAC inhibitors.

9.5.1.1 Advantages of Isozyme-selective HDAC Inhibitors

There is general consensus that compounds with good isozyme selectivity offer improved therapeutic potency and a superior safety profile, particularly in chronic diseases, specifically neurodegenerative disorders, fibrosis, obesity, and inflammation [124]. Additionally, HDAC isozyme-selective inhibitors hold promise as more effective anticancer agents and valuable tools for understanding the biology and cellular distribution of specific isoforms in both physiological and pathological settings, compared to pan-HDAC inhibitors [25]. As a result, HDAC isozyme-selective inhibitors are emerging as a viable and compelling alternative to pan-HDAC inhibitors, representing a significant trend in the field.

9.5.1.2 Challenges of Isozyme-Selective HDAC Inhibitors

Despite the identification of potent HDAC isozyme-selective inhibitors, several significant challenges impede their development: (i) The high degree of structural conservation among HDAC isoforms, particularly in their catalytic domains, presents substantial obstacles for achieving selective inhibition; (ii) The absence of crystal structures for several HDAC isoforms limits structure-based drug design approaches; (iii) Incomplete understanding of the enzymatic mechanisms and biological functions of certain isoforms, notably HDAC10 and HDAC11, restricts targeted inhibitor development. These fundamental limitations have resulted in the current early-stage development status of isozyme-specific HDAC inhibitors.

9.5.2 Combination Regimens with HDAC Inhibitors

Accumulating evidence revealed that HDAC inhibitors demonstrate significant results as individual treatments in a specific group of hematological malignancies, but their effects toward solid tumors are quite minimal [139]. Consequently, the limited therapeutic outcomes of current HDAC inhibitors toward solid malignancies facilitate the development of combined therapies [149].

9.5.2.1 Advantages of Combination Regimens

HDACs participate extensively in numerous biological processes through their enzymic functions or complexing with collaborators. This property of HDACs enables the synergy of the HDAC inhibitor with multiple anticancer drugs. When an HDAC inhibitor is used in conjunction with an anticancer drug, it can lead to advancements in therapeutic outcomes and expansion of applications through synergistic or additive effects while decreasing toxicity as well as chemoresistance by enabling dose reduction [141]. To guide the development of effective combination regimens, we propose the following practical principles: (i) Both agents should exhibit the same biological effect; (ii) They should generate synergistic responses; (iii) Each ingredient should have distinct modes of action or nonoverlapping resistance patterns; (iv) The combination should be well-tolerated so that dose reduction is possible.

9.5.2.2 Challenges of Combination Regimens

Given the adaptable dosing regimens, enhanced efficacy profiles, diminished drug resistance, and expanded indications, various combination treatments have become mainstream in the treatment of a number of serious diseases, particularly in acquired immunodeficiency syndrome and challenging-to-conquer solid malignancies, which currently seldom yield a successful cure [150–152]. Nevertheless, there are several challenges to tackle, including insufficient patient adherence, intricate trial designs for clinical studies, and drug–drug interactions. Furthermore, the distinct metabolism rates of individual drugs in combination therapy result in erratic relationships between pharmacokinetics (PK) and pharmacodynamics (PD), which in turn require costly and time-consuming clinical studies [153, 154]. Despite the use of cocktails or multicomponent agents that combine several agents into a single tablet to increase patient compliance, there are still unresolved issues. Additionally, experiences suggested that combinations may cause more toxicities or negative effects because several agents would be administered rather than one agent [154].

Considering the above key factors, multitarget agents – a single entity with several desirable properties – may represent a more alluring and affordable alternative option to combination therapy [155, 156].

9.5.2.3 Known Combination Regimens with HDAC Inhibitors

Given the insufficient treatment provided by monotherapy, researchers have extensively explored various combination regimens, yielding positive clinical results in the treatment of deadly disorders. A notable example comes from advanced breast cancer management, where the HDAC inhibitor chidamide combined with exemestane demonstrated superior progression-free survival outcomes relative to exemestane monotherapy in the phase III trial (NCT02482753) [145]. Emerging clinical data further validate the therapeutic potential of HDAC inhibitor-based combinations in oncology: the vorinostat–pembrolizumab combination exhibited enhanced antitumor activity with favorable safety in advanced/metastatic non-small cell lung cancer (NSCLC) [157]; chidamide demonstrated synergistic effects with carboplatin–paclitaxel chemotherapy in advanced NSCLC (NCT01836679) [144]; citarinostat combinations showed promise both with paclitaxel in solid tumors [143] and with nivolumab in NSCLC [158]. Current research has systematically identified multiple synergistic partners for HDAC inhibitors, including antimetabolites, targeted therapies (kinase/protease inhibitors), immune checkpoint modulators (PD-1/PD-L1, cytotoxic T-lymphocyte-associated antigen [CTLA-4]), biologics (monoclonal antibodies), and various chemotherapeutic agents (Figure 9.9) [143–145, 157–164].

In addition, the agents in combination with approved HDAC inhibitors are summarized in Table 9.5, and readers who are interested in these drug combination schedules can visit www.clinicaltrials.gov for more details.

Aforementioned evidences make one believe that combination therapy holds great promise for treating those solid tumors challenging to treat, and it provides access to effective solid tumor therapy.

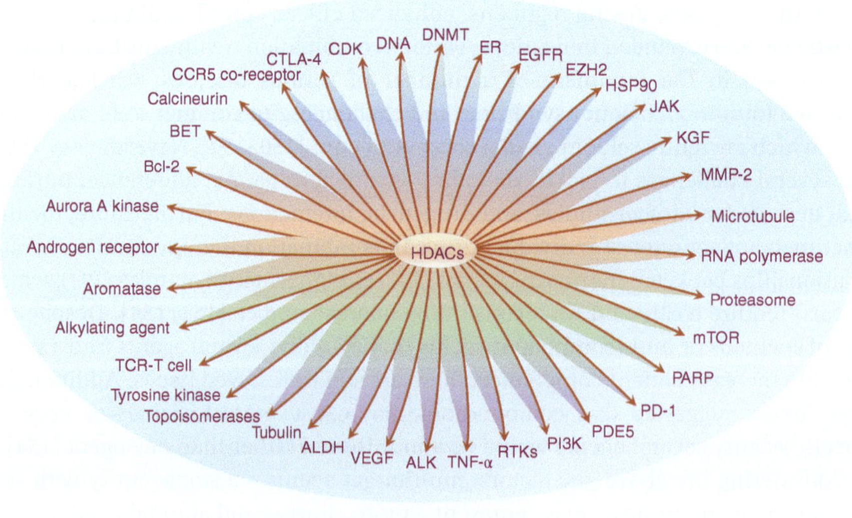

Figure 9.9 Promising synergistic targets with HDACs.

Table 9.5 Clinically investigated combination partners for approved HDAC inhibitors.

HDAC inhibitor	Combination drug[a)]
Vorinostat	Alisertib, Alvocidib, Anastrozole, Azacytidine, Bevacizumab, Bortezomib, Busulfan, Capecitabine, Carboplatin, Carfilzomib, Carmustine, Ceritinib, Cisplatin, Clofarabine, Cobomarsen, Curcumin, Cyclophosphamide, Cytarabine, Cyclosporine, Dasatinib, Decitabine, Dexamethasone, Disulfiram, Docetaxel, Doxil, Doxorubicin, Eltrombopag, Erlotinib, Etoposide, Everolimus, Filgrastim, Fludarabine, Fluorouracil, Gefitinib, Gemcitabine, Gemtuzumab, Hydroxychloroquine, Idarubicin, Ifosfamide, Irinotecan, Ixabepilone, Isotretinoin, Lenalidomide, Letrozole, Leucovorin calcium, Liposomal Lapatinib, Maraviroc, Marizomib, Melphalan, Methotrexate, Mitoxantrone, Mycophenolate, Niacinamide, Olaparib, Oxaliplatin, Ozogamicin, Paclitaxel, Pazopanib, Pegylated, Pembrolizumab, Pemetrexed, Radiation Therapy, Prednisone, Regorafenib, Rituximab, Sirolimus, Sorafenib, Tacrolimus, Tamoxifen, Temsirolimus Ch14.18 Monoclonal Antibody, Temozolomide, Topotecan, Trastuzumab, Ustekinumab, Vinorelbine, Vincristine, Zolinza.
Romidepsin	5-azacitidine, Abraxane, Alisertib, Alvocidib, Antiretrovirals, Bortezomib, Brentuximab, Busulfan, Carfilzomib, Chidamide, Cisplatin, Copanlisib, Decitabine, Dexamethasone, Doxil, Doxorubicin, Durvalumab, Duvelisib, Etoposide, Fludarabine, Gemcitabine, Ifosfamide, Ketoconazole, Lenalidomide, Nivolumab, Oxaliplatin, Parsaclisib, Pomalidomide, Pralatrexate, Rifampin, Sintilimab, Xazomib, Tenalisib, Volasertib, Venetoclax.
Belinostat	Azacitidine, Azacytidine, Atazanavir, Bevacizumab, Bortezomib, Busulfan, Caphosol, Carfilzomib, Carboplatin, Dexamethasone, Doxorubicin, Epoetin, Erlotinib, Etoposide, Glutamine, Idarubicin, Ifosfamide, Interferon-Alfa-2b, Ipilimumab, Isotretinoin, Mesna, Nivolumab, Paclitaxel, Pevonedistat, Ribociclib, Rituximab, Romidepsin, Sirolimus, Talazoparib, Tanespimycin, Volasertib, Warfarin, Zidovudine.
Panobinostat	Abemaciclib, Abiraterone, Afatinib, Bevacizumab, Bicalutamide, Bortezomib, Carfilzomib, Capecitabine, Carboplatin, Cisplatin, Cytarabine, Daratumumab, Daunorubicin, Decitabine, Dexamethasone, Epirubicin, Etoposide, Everolimus, Fluorouracil, Gemcitabine, Ifosfamide, Ipilimumab, Lapatinib, Lenalidomide, Letrozole, Marizomib, Melphalan, Methylprednisolone, Palifermin, Pemetrexed, Rituximab, Ruxolitinib, Sorafenib, Temozolomide, Thalidomide, Trastuzumab, Velcade.
Chidamide	Adriacin, Afatinib, Anti-PD-1 antibody+Peg-Asparaginase, Azacitidine, Camrelizumab, TCR-T cell, Carboplatin, Chiauranib, Cisplatin, Crizotinib, Cyclophosphamide, Cyclosporine A, Dasatinib, Decitabine, Dexamethasone, Doxorubicin, Envafolimab, Epirubicin, Etoposide, Exemestane, Fulvestrant, Gemcitabine, Lenalidomide, Oxaliplatin, Paclitaxel, Prednisone, Rituximab, Sintilimab, Tislelizumab, Tofacitinib, Vincristine, Vinorelbine.

a) The data *was extracted from the* www.clinicaltrials.gov.

9.5.3 HDAC Inhibitor–Based Multitarget Agents

9.5.3.1 Advantages, Challenges, and Design of Multitarget Agents

Multitarget agents present distinct advantages over combination therapies, particularly in terms of enhanced patient adherence, simplified clinical trial protocols, and more predictable PK/PD profiles [165]. Although multitarget agents have the aforementioned advantages, it can be difficult to rationalize multitarget agents because a single chemical entity must match the desired profiles at two distinct targets. The rational design of multitarget agents requires careful consideration of several critical factors, including the structural characteristics of the intended targets, the structure–activity relationships of ligands at each target, and the activity level ratio of the compound across different targets.

Luckily, research has established two principal strategies for the systematic development of multitarget ligands [166]. Knowledge-based approaches: Utilizing existing information from scientific literature, established drug molecules, and clinical trial data. Screening-based approaches: Employing computational chemistry techniques for systematic molecular evaluation.

9.5.3.2 Development of HDAC Inhibitor–Based Multitarget Agents

Cumulative research efforts have developed a variety of HDAC inhibitor–derived multitarget agents whose targets contain DNA, enzymes, kinases, receptors, apoptosis regulators, transcription factors, and other regulatory proteins. Empirical evidence shows that multitarget agents usually possess better qualities in terms of safety/tolerability, anti-proliferation/growth suppression, anti-invasion/anti-metastasis, or anti-angiogenesis in relation to individual drugs. For further information about these multitarget agents (chemical structures, targets, biological activities, etc.), readers can consult the relevant literature [64].

Although combination therapy has historically attracted more attention than multitarget agents, both approaches have advantages over monotherapy and have the potential to achieve increased safety, improved efficacy, and attenuated drug resistance. Aforementioned approaches are expected to provide valuable frameworks for the effective management of various diseases, particularly solid tumors. When developing combination regimens or multitarget agents, the key to success lies in choosing rational targets or associated signaling pathways that achieve synergistic effects. Consequently, adequate preclinical research is a major requisite for the exploration of combination regimens or multitarget agents.

9.5.4 PROTAC

9.5.4.1 General Concept of PROTAC

The proteolysis-targeting chimera (PROTAC) represents a groundbreaking technology in drug discovery by harnessing the ubiquitin–proteasome system (UPS) for the targeted degradation of specific proteins. PROTACs are heterobifunctional molecules comprising three key components: a ligand interacting with the intended target, a ligand binding to E3 ligases, and a linker connecting these two ligands [167]. What sets PROTACs apart is their unique catalytic mechanism of action, which enables the degradation of target proteins and the elimination of both their enzymatic and nonenzymatic functions at low concentrations [168, 169]. This contrasts with traditional inhibitors, which typically require higher concentrations to merely inhibit enzyme activity or partially block the functions of target proteins. Given these distinctive properties, PROTACs have emerged as a compelling strategy in drug development, particularly for challenging undruggable targets.

9.5.4.2 Advantages and Challenges of PROTAC

PROTACs are a cutting-edge strategy that has garnered great interest due to their benefits: (i) target undruggable protein; (ii) substoichiometric catalytic; (iii) reversible and rapid protein knockdown; (iv) removal of nonenzymatic functions; (v) surmount drug resistance; and (vi) good safety profiles [170]. A plethora of benefits makes PROTACs effective tools or agents for the management of neurodegenerative illnesses, inflammatory/immune diseases, and cancer [169, 171].

Besides the above advantages, there are a few challenges and limitations as well: (i) Limited availability of E3 ligase ligands suitable for PROTAC design; (ii) screening target protein ligands compatible with PROTACs is challenging; (iii) rational design of PROTAC is demanding; (iv) there have been few successes with undruggable targets; (v) assessment of degradation activity is complicated; (vi) potential for off-target protein degradation with unpredictable consequences; and (vii) poor druggability or variable PK/PD properties [169, 172]. We must therefore focus more on PROTACs owing to the difficulties.

9.6 Concluding Remarks and Future Perspectives

As essential modulators, HDACs preserve homeostasis and ontogeny *via* their enzymatic activity or the formation of complexes with partners. Regardless, extant data have demonstrated that HDAC overexpression has been identified as a biomarker for oncogenesis, and that the application of inhibitors to treat aberrant HDACs can yield favorable antitumor outcomes. Such diverse biological roles of HDACs underscore their potential as viable targets for effective cancer therapy. Over the past two decades, extensive research and development efforts have culminated in five approved HDAC inhibitors. While these agents have demonstrated efficacy in their approved indications, their clinical utility is limited by their restricted effectiveness against solid tumors and significant adverse effects and off-target toxicities. Therefore, it is imperative to develop novel HDAC inhibitors, such as isozyme-selective inhibitors, combination regimens, hybrid/multitarget agents, and HDAC degraders. As the successor of pan-HDAC inhibitors, isozyme-selective inhibitors have proven to be a highly valuable agent owing to their dual applications (as potent, safe anticancer agents or as probes for individual HDAC isoform functional study). However, their development is hindered by challenges such as the conserved active site architecture, limited availability of crystal structures, and incomplete understanding of isoform-specific functions. On the other hand, combination regimens and multitarget agents leverage synergistic or additive effects to effectively combat chemoresistance and improve therapeutic outcomes in solid malignancies, making them favorable approaches for difficult-to-treat cancers. Additionally, PROTAC shows some advantages but also presents some difficulties and problems, and therefore still has a long way to go.

In the future, the trends for next-generation HDAC inhibitors are likely to focus on isozyme-specific/isoform-selective inhibitors, combination regimens, multitarget/hybrid agents, and HDAC degraders, and more sustained research efforts are required to address challenges and unlock the full therapeutic potential of HDAC-targeted strategies.

Glossary

NAD Nicotinamide adenine dinucleotide, an essential and necessary cofactor for the activity of enzymes and fundamental biological processes.

Sirt Sirtuin, class III HDACs with NAD^+ as a cofactor.

Foot pocket Secondary internal cavity domain at the bottom region of HDAC1–3.

Side pocket Secondary pocket on the channel rim made up of L1 and L6 loops.

Lower pocket Secondary pocket in the cavity channel of class IIa HDACs.

Potential pockets Secondary pocket in HDAC6 isoform.

HMGB1 High mobility group box protein 1, an evolutionary ancient nuclear protein that exerts divergent biological functions inside and outside of cells.

Ku70 A protein involved in DNA repair *via* the nonhomologous end joining pathway.

HSP90 A predominant member among heat shock proteins involved in myriad cellular processes.

CDT1 Chromatin licensing and DNA replication factor 1, a protein modulating the onset of DNA replication during the cell cycle.

VHL Von Hippel–Lindau protein, a tumor suppressor involved in cellular oxygen sensing.

VEGF Vascular endothelial growth factor, an angiogenesis regulator.

CXCR4 C-X-C chemokine receptor type 4, a G-protein-coupled seven-span transmembrane receptor participating in immune response, cell migration, and cancer progression.

MDM2 Mouse double minute 2, a repressor of the p53 tumor suppressor.

CTP Cytidine triphosphate, a nucleotide associated with DNA, RNA, and phospholipid biosynthesis.

mTOR Mammalian target of rapamycin, a key kinase that controls cell growth and metabolism.

ATG Autophagy-related, a eukaryotic factor associated with autophagy.

Beclin-1 An important protein for autophagy.

LC3 Microtubule-associated protein 1A/1B-LC3, a protein associated with autophagy.

c-FLIP A master anti-apoptotic modulator.

TNFS10 Tumor necrosis factor ligand superfamily member 10, an apoptosis regulator.
Bax Bcl-2-associated X protein, a pro-apoptotic protein.
Bcl-2 B-cell lymphoma 2, an anti-apoptotic protein.
AIF Apoptosis-inducing factor, a mitochondrial flavoprotein in the intrinsic apoptotic pathway.
Apaf-1 Apoptotic protease activating factor-1, an adaptor in response to cytochrome c release.
PUMA p53 upregulated modulator of apoptosis, a BH3-only protein involved in apoptosis initiation.
CBP CREB-binding protein, a transcriptional coactivator.
PCAF p300/CBP-associated factor, a histone acetyltransferase.
GCN5 General control non-repressed protein 5, a histone acetyltransferase.

References

1. Cheng, Y., He, C., Wang, M.-N. et al. (2019). Targeting epigenetic regulators for cancer therapy: mechanisms and advances in clinical trials. *Signal Transduction and Targeted Therapy* 4: 62.
2. Smith, Z.D., Hetzel, S., and Meissner, A. (2025). DNA methylation in mammalian development and disease. *Nature Reviews Genetics* 26: 7–30.
3. Wang, D., Zhang, Y., Li, Q.-B. et al. (2024). Epigenetics: mechanisms, potential roles, and therapeutic strategies in cancer progression. *Genes & Diseases* 11: 101020.
4. Millán-Zambrano, G., Burton, A., Bannister, A.J., and Schneider, R. (2022). Histone post-translational modifications-cause and consequence of genome function. *Nature Reviews Genetics* 23: 563–580.
5. Yu, X.-Y., Zhao, H., Wang, R.-Q. et al. (2024). Cancer epigenetics: from laboratory studies and clinical trials to precision medicine. *Cell Death Discovery* 10: 28.
6. Tsunaka, Y., Furukawa, A., and Nishimura, Y. (2022). Histone tail network and modulation in a nucleosome. *Current Opinion in Structural Biology* 75: 102436.
7. Karagiannis, D. and Rampias, T. (2021). HDAC inhibitors: dissecting mechanisms of action to counter tumor heterogeneity. *Cancers* 13: 3575.
8. Milazzo, G., Mercatelli, D., Di Muzio, G. et al. (2020). Histone deacetylases (HDACs): evolution, specificity, role in transcriptional complexes, and pharmacological actionability. *Genes* 11: 556.
9. Park, S.Y. and Kim, J.S. (2020). A short guide to histone deacetylases including recent progress on class II enzymes. *Experimental and Molecular Medicine* 52: 204–212.
10. Shanmugam, G., Rakshit, S., and Sarkar, K. (2022). HDAC inhibitors: targets for tumor therapy, immune modulation and lung diseases. *Translational Oncology* 16: 101312.

11 Schultz, B.E., Misialek, S., Wu, J. et al. (2004). Kinetics and comparative reactivity of human class I and class IIb histone. *Biochemistry* 43: 11083–11091.

12 Seto, E. and Yoshida, M. (2014). Erasers of histone acetylation: the histone deacetylase enzymes. *Cold Spring Harbor Perspectives in Biology* 6: a018713.

13 Wei, W., Liu, X.-G., Chen, J.-W. et al. (2017). Class I histone deacetylases are major histone decrotonylases: evidence for critical and broad function of histone crotonylation in transcription. *Cell Research* 27: 898–915.

14 Hai, R.-H., Yang, D.-Y., Zheng, F.-F. et al. (2022). The emerging roles of HDACs and their therapeutic implications in cancer. *European Journal of Pharmacology* 931: 175216.

15 Liang, G.-Y., Oh, T.G., Hah, N. et al. (2023). Inhibiting stromal class I HDACs curbs pancreatic cancer progression. *Nature Communications* 14: 7791.

16 Shinke, G., Yamada, D., Eguchi, H. et al. (2018). Role of histone deacetylase 1 in distant metastasis of pancreatic ductal cancer. *Cancer Science* 109: 2520–2531.

17 Aramsangtienchai, P., Spiegelman, N.A., He, B. et al. (2016). HDAC8 catalyzes the hydrolysis of long chain fatty acyl lysine. *ACS Chemical Biology* 11: 2685–2692.

18 Fontana, A., Cursaro, I., Carullo, G. et al. (2022). A therapeutic perspective of HDAC8 in different diseases: an overview of selective inhibitors. *International Journal of Molecular Sciences* 23: 10014.

19 Kim, J.Y., Cho, H., Yoo, J. et al. (2022). Pathological role of HDAC8: cancer and beyond. *Cells* 11: 3161.

20 Asfaha, Y., Schrenk, C., Alves Avelar, L.A. et al. (2019). Recent advances in class IIa histone deacetylases research. *Bioorganic & Medicinal Chemistry* 27: 115087.

21 Gao, L., Cueto, M.A., Asselbergs, F., and Atadja, P. (2002). Cloning and functional characterization of HDAC11, a novel member of the human histone deacetylase family. *Journal of Biological Chemistry* 277: 25748–25755.

22 Liu, S.-S., Wu, F., Jin, Y.-M. et al. (2020). HDAC11: a rising star in epigenetics. *Biomedicine and Pharmacotherapy* 131: 110607.

23 Drakontaeidi, A. and Pontiki, E. (2023). A review on molecular docking on HDAC isoforms: novel tool for designing selective inhibitors. *Pharmaceuticals* 16: 1639.

24 Melesina, J., Simoben, C.V., Praetorius, L. et al. (2021). Strategies to design selective histone deacetylase inhibitors. *ChemMedChem* 16: 1336–1359.

25 Roche, J. and Bertrand, P. (2016). Inside HDACs with more selective HDAC inhibitors. *European Journal of Medicinal Chemistry* 121: 451–483.

26 Luo, Y.-X. and Li, H.-L. (2020). Structure-based inhibitor discovery of class I histone deacetylases (HDACs). *International Journal of Molecular Sciences* 21: 8828.

27 Cheshmazar, N., Hamzeh-Mivehroud, M., Nozad Charoudeh, H. et al. (2022). Current trends in development of HDAC-based chemotherapeutics. *Life Sciences* 308: 120946.

28 Marek, M., Shaik, T.B., Heimburg, T. et al. (2018). Characterization of histone deacetylase 8 (HDAC8) selective inhibition reveals specific active site structural and functional determinants. *Journal of Medicinal Chemistry* 61: 10000–10016.
29 Burli, R.W., Luckhurst, C.A., Aziz, O. et al. (2013). Design, synthesis, and biological evaluation of potent and selective class IIa histone deacetylase (HDAC) inhibitors as a potential therapy for Huntington's disease. *Journal of Medicinal Chemistry* 56: 9934–9954.
30 Mak, J.Y.W., Wu, K.C., Gupta, P.K. et al. (2021). HDAC7 inhibition by phenacetyl and phenylbenzoyl hydroxamates. *Journal of Medicinal Chemistry* 64: 2186–2204.
31 Liang, T., Hou, X.-B., Zhou, Y. et al. (2019). Design, synthesis, and biological evaluation of 2,4-imidazolinedione derivatives as HDAC6 isoform-selective inhibitors. *ACS Medicinal Chemistry Letters* 10: 1122–1127.
32 Son, S.I., Cao, J., Zhu, C.-L. et al. (2019). Activity-guided design of HDAC11-specific inhibitors. *ACS Chemical Biology* 14: 1393–1397.
33 Andersson, U. and Yang, H. (2022). HMGB1 is a critical molecule in the pathogenesis of Gram-negative sepsis. *Journal of Intensive Care* 2: 156–166.
34 Gong, P., Wang, Y.-T., and Jing, Y.-K. (2019). Apoptosis induction by histone deacetylase inhibitors in cancer cells: role of ku70. *International Journal of Molecular Sciences* 20: 1601.
35 Zhuang, S.-G. (2013). Regulation of STAT signaling by acetylation. *Cellular Signalling* 25: 1924–1931.
36 Falkenberg, K.J. and Johnstone, R.W. (2014). Histone deacetylases and their inhibitors in cancer, neurological diseases and immune disorders. *Nature Reviews: Drug Discovery* 13: 673–691.
37 Ramaiah, M.J., Tangutur, A.D., and Manyam, R.R. (2021). Epigenetic modulation and understanding of HDAC inhibitors in cancer therapy. *Life Sciences* 277: 119504.
38 Zhu, Y.-Z., Feng, M.-K., Wang, B. et al. (2023). New insights into the non-enzymatic function of HDAC6. *Biomedicine and Pharmacotherapy* 161: 114438.
39 Kaur, S., Rajoria, P., and Chopra, M. (2022). HDAC6: a unique HDAC family member as a cancer target. *Cellular Oncology (Dordrecht)* 45: 779–829.
40 Pham, T.Q., Robinson, K., Xu, L. et al. (2021). HDAC6 promotes growth, migration/invasion, and self-renewal of rhabdomyosarcoma. *Oncogene* 40: 578–591.
41 Lovaas, J.D., Zhu, L., Chiao, C.Y. et al. (2013). SIRT1 enhances matrix metalloproteinase-2 expression and tumor cell invasion in prostate cancer cells. *Prostate* 73: 522–530.
42 Park, S.Y., Jun, J.A., Jeong, K.J. et al. (2011). Histone deacetylases 1, 6 and 8 are critical for invasion in breast cancer. *Oncology Reports* 25: 1677–1681.
43 Chen, H.-P., Zhao, Y.-T., and Zhao, T.-C. (2015). Histone deacetylases and mechanisms of regulation of gene expression. *Critical Reviews in Oncology/Hematology* 20: 35–47.
44 Chun, P. (2015). Histone deacetylase inhibitors in hematological malignancies and solid tumors. *Archives of Pharmacal Research* 38: 933–949.

45 Li, Y.-X. and Seto, E. (2016). HDACs and HDAC inhibitors in cancer development and therapy. *Cold Spring Harbor Perspectives in Medicine* 6: a026831.

46 Pahl, M.C., Erdman, R., Kuivaniemi, H. et al. (2015). Transcriptional (Chip-Chip) analysis of Elf1, Ets2, Runx1 and Stat5 in human abdominal aortic aneurysm. *International Journal of Molecular Sciences* 16: 11229–11258.

47 Caron, C., Boyault, C., and Khochbin, S. (2005). Regulatory cross-talk between lysine acetylation and ubiquitination: role in the control of protein stability. *Bioessays* 27: 408–415.

48 Glozak, M.A. and Seto, E. (2009). Acetylation/deacetylation modulates the stability of DNA replication licensing factor Cdt1. *Journal of Biological Chemistry* 284: 11446–11453.

49 Deng, B., Luo, Q., Halim, A. et al. (2020). The antiangiogenesis role of histone deacetylase inhibitors: their potential application to tumor therapy and tissue repair. *DNA and Cell Biology* 39: 167–176.

50 Ellis, L., Hammers, H., and Pili, R. (2009). Targeting tumor angiogenesis with histone deacetylase inhibitors. *Cancer Letters* 280: 145–153.

51 Kim, M.S., Kwon, H.J., Lee, Y.M. et al. (2001). Histone deacetylases induce angiogenesis by negative regulation of tumor suppressor genes. *Nature Medicine* 7: 437–443.

52 Turtoi, A., Peixoto, P., Castronovo, V., and Bellahcène, A. (2015). Histone deacetylases and cancer-associated angiogenesis: current understanding of the biology and clinical perspectives. *Critical Reviews in Oncology/Hematology* 20: 119–137.

53 Bode, A.M. and Dong, Z. (2004). Post-translational modification of p53 in tumorigenesis. *Nature Reviews: Cancer* 4: 793–805.

54 Yu, S.-Y., Cai, X.-X., Wu, C.-X. et al. (2017). Targeting HSP90-HDAC6 regulating network implicates precision treatment of breast cancer. *International Journal of Biological Sciences* 13: 505–517.

55 Adhikari, N., Jha, T., and Ghosh, B. (2021). Dissecting histone deacetylase 3 in multiple disease conditions: selective inhibition as a promising therapeutic strategy. *Journal of Medicinal Chemistry* 64: 8827–8869.

56 Gkotzamanidou, M., Terpou, E., Kentepozidis, N., and Terpos, E. (2021). Targeting the interplay between HDACs and DNA damage repair for myeloma therapy. *International Journal of Molecular Sciences* 22: 10406.

57 Al Emam, A., Arbon, D., Jeeves, M., and Kysela, B. (2018). Ku70 N-terminal lysines acetylation/deacetylation is required for radiation-induced DNA-double strand breaks repair. *Neoplasma* 65: 708–719.

58 Bhaskara, S. (2015). Histone deacetylases 1 and 2 regulate DNA replication and DNA repair: potential targets for genome stability-mechanism-based therapeutics for a subset of cancers. *Cell Cycle* 14: 1779–1785.

59 Chao, O.S. and Goodman, O.B. Jr., (2014). Synergistic loss of prostate cancer cell viability by coinhibition of HDAC and PARP. *Molecular Cancer Research* 12: 1755–1766.

60 Munshi, A., Kurland, J.F., Nishikawa, T. et al. (2005). Histone deacetylase inhibitors radiosensitize human melanoma cells by suppressing DNA repair activity. *Clinical Cancer Research* 11: 4912–4922.

61 Mrakovcic, M., Kleinheinz, J., and Frohlich, L.F. (2017). Histone deacetylase inhibitor-induced autophagy in tumor cells: implications for p53. *International Journal of Molecular Sciences* 18: 1883.

62 Manal, M., Chandrasekar, M.J., Gomathi Priya, J., and Nanjan, M.J. (2016). Inhibitors of histone deacetylase as antitumor agents: a critical review. *Bioorganic Chemistry* 67: 18–42.

63 Lee, K.W., Whedon, S.D., Wang, Z.A., and Cole, P.A. (2022). Distinct biochemical properties of the class I histone deacetylase complexes. *Current Opinion in Chemical Biology* 70: 102179.

64 Liang, T., Wang, F.-L., Elhassan, R.M. et al. (2023). Targeting histone deacetylases for cancer therapy: trends and challenges. *Acta Pharmaceutica Sinica B* 13: 2425–2463.

65 Lagger, G., Rembold, M., Tischler, J. et al. (2002). Essential function of histone deacetylase 1 in proliferation control and CDK inhibitor repression. *EMBO Journal* 21: 2672–2681.

66 Montgomery, R.L., Davis, C.A., Potthoff, M.J. et al. (2007). Histone deacetylases 1 and 2 redundantly regulate cardiac morphogenesis, growth, and contractility. *Genes and Development* 21: 1790–1802.

67 Lin, C.-L., Tsai, M.-L., Lin, C.-Y. et al. (2019). HDAC1 and HDAC2 double knockout triggers cell apoptosis in advanced thyroid cancer. *International Journal of Molecular Sciences* 20: 454.

68 Bhaskara, S., Chyla, B.J., Amann, J.M. et al. (2008). Deletion of histone deacetylase 3 reveals critical roles in S phase progression and DNA damage control. *Molecular Cell* 30: 61–72.

69 Cadot, B., Brunetti, M., Coppari, S. et al. (2009). Loss of histone deacetylase 4 causes segregation defects during mitosis of p53-deficient human tumor cells. *Cancer Research* 69: 6074–6082.

70 Chang, S., McKinsey, T.A., Zhang, C.-L. et al. (2004). Histone deacetylases 5 and 9 govern responsiveness of the heart to a subset of stress signals and play redundant roles in heart development. *Molecular and Cellular Biology* 24: 8467–8476.

71 Zhang, C.-L., Mckinsey, T.A., Chang, S. et al. (2002). Class II histone deacetylases act as signal-responsive repressors of cardiac hypertrophy. *Cell* 110: 479–488.

72 Zhang, Y., Kwon, S., Yamaguchi, T. et al. (2008). Mice lacking histone deacetylase 6 have hyperacetylated tubulin but are viable and develop normally. *Molecular and Cellular Biology* 28: 1688–1701.

73 Lee, H.Y., Nepali, K., Huang, F.-I. et al. (2018). (*N*-Hydroxycarbonylbenylamino) quinolines as selective histone deacetylase 6 inhibitors suppress growth of multiple myeloma in vitro and in vivo. *Journal of Medicinal Chemistry* 61: 905–917.

74 Santo, L., Cirstea, D., Wang, B. et al. (2012). Role of selective HDAC6 inhibition on multiple myeloma bone disease. *Blood* 120: 328–328.

75 Yang, Z., Wang, T.-J., Wang, F. et al. (2016). Discovery of selective histone deacetylase 6 inhibitors using the quinazoline as the cap for the treatment of cancer. *Journal of Medicinal Chemistry* 59: 1455–1470.

76 Chang, S.-R., Young, B.D., Li, S.-J. et al. (2006). Histone deacetylase 7 maintains vascular integrity by repressing matrix metalloproteinase 10. *Cell* 126: 321–334.

77 Haberland, M., Mokalled, M.H., Montgomery, R.L., and Olson, E.N. (2009). Epigenetic control of skull morphogenesis by histone deacetylase 8. *Genes & Development* 23: 1625–1630.

78 Li, Y.-X., Zhang, X.-Y., Zhu, S.-Q. et al. (2020). HDAC10 regulates cancer stem-like cell properties in KRAS-driven lung adenocarcinoma. *Cancer Research* 80: 3265–3278.

79 Bryant, D.T., Landles, C., Papadopoulou, A.S. et al. (2017). Disruption to schizophrenia-associated gene Fez1 in the hippocampus of HDAC11 knockout mice. *Scientific Reports* 7: 11900.

80 Deubzer, H.E., Schier, M.C., Oehme, I. et al. (2013). HDAC11 is a novel drug target in carcinomas. *International Journal of Cancer* 132: 2200–2208.

81 Feng, L.-F., Pan, M.-P., Sun, J. et al. (2013). Histone deacetylase 3 inhibits expression of PUMA in gastric cancer cells. *Journal of Molecular Medicine (Berlin, Germany)* 91: 49–58.

82 Fritzsche, F.R., Weichert, W., Roske, A. et al. (2008). Class I histone deacetylases 1, 2 and 3 are highly expressed in renal cell cancer. *BMC Cancer* 8: 381.

83 Poyet, C., Jentsch, B., Hermanns, T. et al. (2014). Expression of histone deacetylases 1,2 and 3 in urothelial bladder cancer. *BMC Clinical Pathology* 14: 10.

84 Rettig, I., Koeneke, E., Trippel, F. et al. (2015). Selective inhibition of HDAC8 decreases neuroblastoma growth in vitro and in vivo and enhances retinoic acid-mediated differentiation. *Cell Death & Disease* 6: e1657.

85 Draney, C., Austin, M.C., Leifer, A.H. et al. (2018). HDAC1 overexpression enhances beta-cell proliferation by down-regulating Cdkn1b/p27. *Biochemical Journal* 475: 3997–4010.

86 Hassell, K.N. (2019). Histone deacetylases and their inhibitors in cancer epigenetics. *Diseases* 7: 57.

87 Hayashi, A., Horiuchi, A., Kikuchi, N. et al. (2010). Type-specific roles of histone deacetylase (HDAC) overexpression in ovarian carcinoma: HDAC1 enhances cell proliferation and HDAC3 stimulates cell migration with downregulation of E-cadherin. *International Journal of Cancer* 127: 1332–1346.

88 Zhao, H.-S., Yu, Z.-J., Zhao, L. et al. (2016). HDAC2 overexpression is a poor prognostic factor of breast cancer patients with increased multidrug resistance-associated protein expression who received anthracyclines therapy. *Japanese Journal of Clinical Oncology* 46: 893–902.

89 Zhang, J. and Zhong, Q. (2014). Histone deacetylase inhibitors and cell death. *Cellular and Molecular Life Sciences* 71: 3885–3901.

90 Liang, T., Zhou, Y., Elhassan, R.M. et al. (2020). HDAC-Bax multiple ligands enhance bax-dependent apoptosis in hela cells. *Journal of Medicinal Chemistry* 63: 12083–12099.

91 Schneller, A., Zojer, N., Bolomsky, A., and Ludwig, H. (2021). Synergistic interaction between HDAC and MCL-1 inhibitors through downregulation of BCL-XL in multiple myeloma. *Haematologica* 106: 2516–2521.

92 Kim, J.K., Noh, J.H., Eun, J.W. et al. (2013). Targeted inactivation of HDAC2 restores p16INK4a activity and exerts antitumor effects on human gastric cancer. *Molecular Cancer Research* 11: 62–73.

93 Zhao, B. and He, T.-H. (2015). Chidamide, a histone deacetylase inhibitor, functions as a tumor inhibitor by modulating the ratio of Bax/Bcl-2 and P21 in pancreatic cancer. *Oncology Reports* 33: 304–310.

94 Kang, Y., Nian, H., Rajendran, P. et al. (2014). HDAC8 and STAT3 repress BMF gene activity in colon cancer cells. *Cell Death & Disease* 5: e1476.

95 Telles, E. and Seto, E. (2012). Modulation of cell cycle regulators by HDACs. *Frontiers in Bioscience-Scholar* 4: 831–839.

96 Yamaguchi, T., Cubizolles, F., Zhang, Y. et al. (2010). Histone deacetylases 1 and 2 act in concert to promote the G1-to-S progression. *Genes & Development* 24: 455–469.

97 Zupkovitz, G., Grausenburger, R., Brunmeir, R. et al. (2010). The cyclin-dependent kinase inhibitor p21 is a crucial target for histone deacetylase 1 as a regulator of cellular proliferation. *Molecular and Cellular Biology* 30: 1171–1181.

98 Vidal-Laliena, M., Gallastegui, E., Mateo, F. et al. (2013). Histone deacetylase 3 regulates cyclin A stability. *Journal of Biological Chemistry* 288: 21096–21104.

99 Fan, J., Lou, B., Chen, W. et al. (2014). Down-regulation of HDAC5 inhibits growth of human hepatocellular carcinoma by induction of apoptosis and cell cycle arrest. *Tumour Biology* 35: 11523–11532.

100 Li, Y.-X., Peng, L.-R., and Seto, E. (2015). Histone deacetylase 10 regulates the cell cycle g2/m phase transition via a novel Let-7-HMGA2-Cyclin A2 pathway. *Molecular and Cellular Biology* 35: 3547–3565.

101 Song, C.-L., Zhu, S.-C., Wu, C.-Y., and Kang, J.-H. (2013). Histone deacetylase (HDAC) 10 suppresses cervical cancer metastasis through inhibition of matrix metalloproteinase (MMP) 2 and 9 expression. *Journal of Biological Chemistry* 288: 28021–28033.

102 Wen, Y.-Q., Zhang, X.-M., Li, X.-Y. et al. (2022). Histone deacetylase (HDAC) 11 inhibits matrix metalloproteinase (MMP) 3 expression to suppress colorectal cancer metastasis. *Journal of Cancer* 13: 1923–1932.

103 Geng, H., Harvey, C.T., Pittsenbarger, J. et al. (2011). HDAC4 protein regulates HIF1alpha protein lysine acetylation and cancer cell response to hypoxia. *Journal of Biological Chemistry* 286: 38095–38102.

104 Yoo, Y.G., Kong, G., and Lee, M.O. (2006). Metastasis-associated protein 1 enhances stability of hypoxia-inducible factor-1alpha protein by recruiting histone deacetylase 1. *EMBO Journal* 25: 1231–1241.

105 Chen, S.-Y., Yin, C.-Q., Lao, T.-T. et al. (2015). AMPK-HDAC5 pathway facilitates nuclear accumulation of HIF-1alpha and functional activation of HIF-1 by deacetylating Hsp70 in the cytosol. *Cell Cycle* 14: 2520–2536.

106 Kato, H., Tamamizu-Kato, S., and Shibasaki, F. (2004). Histone deacetylase 7 associates with hypoxia-inducible factor 1alpha and increases transcriptional activity. *Journal of Biological Chemistry* 279: 41966–41974.

107 Seo, H.W., Kim, E.J., Na, H., and Lee, M.O. (2009). Transcriptional activation of hypoxia-inducible factor-1alpha by HDAC4 and HDAC5 involves differential recruitment of p300 and FIH-1. *FEBS Letters* 583: 55–60.

108 Kaluza, D., Kroll, J., Gesierich, S. et al. (2013). Histone deacetylase 9 promotes angiogenesis by targeting the antiangiogenic microRNA-17-92 cluster in endothelial cells. *Arteriosclerosis, Thrombosis, and Vascular Biology* 33: 533–543.

109 Reichert, N., Choukrallah, M.A., and Matthias, P. (2012). Multiple roles of class I HDACs in proliferation, differentiation, and development. *Cellular and Molecular Life Sciences* 69: 2173–2187.

110 Cai, J.-Y., Xu, T.-T., Wang, Y. et al. (2018). Histone deacetylase HDAC4 promotes the proliferation and invasion of glioma cells. *International Journal of Oncology* 53: 2758–2768.

111 Spaety, M.E., Gries, A., Badie, A. et al. (2019). HDAC4 levels control sensibility toward cisplatin in gastric cancer via the p53-p73/bik pathway. *Cancers* 11: 1747.

112 Feng, G.-W., Dong, L.-D., Shang, W.-J. et al. (2014). HDAC5 promotes cell proliferation in human hepatocellular carcinoma by up-regulating Six1 expression. *European Review for Medical and Pharmacological Sciences* 18: 811–816.

113 Zhang, Y.T., Wu, D., Xia, F.-J. et al. (2016). Downregulation of HDAC9 inhibits cell proliferation and tumor formation by inducing cell cycle arrest in retinoblastoma. *Biochemical and Biophysical Research Communications* 473: 600–606.

114 Zhu, C.-H., Chen, Q., Xie, Z.-Q. et al. (2011). The role of histone deacetylase 7 (HDAC7) in cancer cell proliferation: regulation on c-Myc. *Journal of Molecular Medicine (Berlin, Germany)* 89: 279–289.

115 Wang, Z.-H., Hu, P.-C., Tang, F. et al. (2016). HDAC6 promotes cell proliferation and confers resistance to temozolomide in glioblastoma. *Cancer Letters* 379: 134–142.

116 Blixt, N.C., Faulkner, B.K., Astleford, K. et al. (2017). Class II and IV HDACs function as inhibitors of osteoclast differentiation. *PLoS One* 12: e0185441.

117 Dressel, U., Bailey, P.J., Wang, S.C. et al. (2001). A dynamic role for HDAC7 in MEF2-mediated muscle differentiation. *Journal of Biological Chemistry* 276: 17007–17013.

118 Ferrari, L., Bragato, C., Brioschi, L. et al. (2019). HDAC8 regulates canonical Wnt pathway to promote differentiation in skeletal muscles. *Journal of Cellular Physiology* 234: 6067–6076.

119 Li, H., Xie, H., Liu, W. et al. (2009). A novel microRNA targeting HDAC5 regulates osteoblast differentiation in mice and contributes to primary osteoporosis in humans. *Journal of Clinical Investigation* 119: 3666–3677.

120 Spurling, C.C., Godman, C.A., Noonan, E.J. et al. (2008). HDAC3 overexpression and colon cancer cell proliferation and differentiation. *Molecular Carcinogenesis* 47: 137–147.

121 Yang, W., Liu, Y.-Y., Gao, R.-L. et al. (2018). HDAC6 inhibition induces glioma stem cells differentiation and enhances cellular radiation sensitivity through the SHH/Gli1 signaling pathway. *Cancer Letters* 415: 164–176.

122 Ye, F., Chen, Y., Hoang, T. et al. (2009). HDAC1 and HDAC2 regulate oligodendrocyte differentiation by disrupting the beta-catenin-TCF interaction. *Nature Neuroscience* 12: 829–838.

123 Daśko, M., de Pascual-Teresa, B., Ortín, I., and Ramos, A. (2022). HDAC inhibitors: innovative strategies for their design and applications. *Molecules* 27: 715.

124 Ho, T.C.S., Chan, A.H.Y., and Ganesan, A. (2020). Thirty Years of HDAC Inhibitors: 2020 Insight and Hindsight. *Journal of Medicinal Chemistry* 63: 12460–12484.

125 Villadsen, J.S., Stephansen, H.M., Maolanon, A.R. et al. (2013). Total synthesis and full histone deacetylase inhibitory profiling of Azumamides A-E as well as β^2- epi-Azumamide E and β^3-epi-Azumamide E. *Journal of Medicinal Chemistry* 56: 6512–6520.

126 Geurs, S., Clarisse, D., De Bosscher, K., and D'Hooghe, M. (2023). The zinc-binding group effect: lessons from non-hydroxamic acid vorinostat analogs. *Journal of Medicinal Chemistry* 66: 7698–7729.

127 Duvic, M. and Vu, J. (2007). Vorinostat: a new oral histone deacetylase inhibitor approved for cutaneous T-cell lymphoma. *Expert Opinion on Investigational Drugs* 16: 1111–1120.

128 Mann, B.S., Johnson, J.R., He, K. et al. (2007). Vorinostat for treatment of cutaneous manifestations of advanced primary cutaneous T-cell lymphoma. *Clinical Cancer Research* 13: 2318–2322.

129 Shustov, A., Coiffier, B., Horwitz, S. et al. (2017). Romidepsin is effective and well tolerated in older patients with peripheral T-cell lymphoma: analysis of two phase II trials. *Leukemia & Lymphoma* 58: 2335–2341.

130 Whittaker, S.J., Demierre, M.F., Kim, E.J. et al. (2010). Final results from a multicenter, international, pivotal study of romidepsin in refractory cutaneous T-cell lymphoma. *Journal of Clinical Oncology* 28: 4485–4491.

131 O'Connor, O.A., Horwitz, S., Masszi, T. et al. (2015). Belinostat in patients with relapsed or refractory peripheral t-cell lymphoma: results of the pivotal phase ii belief (Cln-19) study. *Journal of Clinical Oncology* 33: 2492–2499.

132 Ning, Z.-Q., Li, Z.-B., Newman, M.J. et al. (2012). Chidamide (CS055/HBI-8000): a new histone deacetylase inhibitor of the benzamide class with antitumor activity and the ability to enhance immune cell-mediated tumor cell cytotoxicity. *Cancer Chemotherapy and Pharmacology* 69: 901–909.

133 Shi, Y., Dong, M., Hong, X. et al. (2015). Results from a multicenter, open-label, pivotal phase II study of chidamide in relapsed or refractory peripheral T-cell lymphoma. *Annals of Oncology* 26: 1766–1771.

134 Rathkopf, D.E., Picus, J., Hussain, A. et al. (2013). A phase 2 study of intravenous panobinostat in patients with castration-resistant prostate cancer. *Cancer Chemotherapy and Pharmacology* 72: 537–544.

135 San-Miguel, J.F., Hungria, V.T.M., Yoon, S.-S. et al. (2014). Panobinostat plus bortezomib and dexamethasone versus placebo plus bortezomib and dexamethasone in patients with relapsed or relapsed and refractory multiple myeloma: a multicentre, randomised, double-blind phase 3 trial. *Lancet Oncology* 15: 1195–1206.

136 Lechner, S., Malgapo, M.I.P., Grätz, C. et al. (2022). Target deconvolution of HDAC pharmacopoeia reveals MBLAC2 as common off-target. *Nature Chemical Biology* 18: 812–820.

137 Zeng, H.-L., Qu, J., Jin, N. et al. (2016). Feedback activation of leukemia inhibitory factor receptor limits response to histone deacetylase inhibitors in breast cancer. *Cancer Cell* 30: 459–473.

138 Gryder, B.E., Sodji, Q.H., and Oyelere, A.K. (2012). Targeted cancer therapy: giving histone deacetylase inhibitors all they need to succeed. *Future Medicinal Chemistry* 4: 505–524.

139 Huang, Z., Zhou, W., Li, Y.-T. et al. (2018). Novel hybrid molecule overcomes the limited response of solid tumours to HDAC inhibitors via suppressing JAK1-STAT3-BCL2 signalling. *Theranostics* 8: 4995–5011.

140 Hao, B.-B., Ma, K., Xu, J.-Y. et al. (2024). Proteomics analysis of histone deacetylase inhibitor-resistant solid tumors reveals resistant signatures and potential drug combinations. *Acta Pharmacologica Sinica* 45: 1305–1315.

141 Shah, R.R. (2019). Safety and tolerability of histone deacetylase (HDAC) inhibitors in oncology. *Drug Safety* 42: 235–245.

142 Awad, M.M., Le Bruchec, Y., Lu, B. et al. (2022). Corrigendum: selective histone deacetylase inhibitor acy-241 (citarinostat) plus nivolumab in advanced non-small cell lung cancer: results from a phase IB study. *Frontiers in Oncology* 12: 889996.

143 Gordon, M.S., Shapiro, G., Sarantopoulos, J. et al. (2018). A phase 1b study of the safety, pharmacokinetics, and preliminary antitumor activity of citarinostat (ACY-241) in combination with paclitaxel (Pac) in patients (pts) with advanced solid tumors (AST). *Journal of Clinical Oncology* 36: 2547.

144 Hu, X.-S., Wang, L., Lin, L. et al. (2016). A phase I trial of an oral subtype-selective histone deacetylase inhibitor, chidamide, in combination with paclitaxel and carboplatin in patients with advanced non-small cell lung cancer. *Chinese Journal of Cancer Research* 28: 444–451.

145 Jiang, Z.-F., Li, W., Hu, X.-C. et al. (2019). Tucidinostat plus exemestane for postmenopausal patients with advanced, hormone receptor-positive breast cancer (ACE): a randomised, double-blind, placebo-controlled, phase 3 trial. *Lancet Oncology* 20: 806–815.

146 Cai, X., Zhai, H.-X., Wang, J. et al. (2010). Discovery of 7-(4-(3-ethynylphenylamino)-7-methoxyquinazolin-6-yloxy)-N-hydroxyheptanamide (CUDc-101) as a potent multi-acting HDAC, EGFR, and HER2 inhibitor for the treatment of cancer. *Journal of Medicinal Chemistry* 53: 2000–2009.

147 Liu, C., Ding, H.-Y., Li, X. et al. (2015). A DNA/HDAC dual-targeting drug CY190602 with significantly enhanced anticancer potency. *EMBO Molecular Medicine* 7: 438–449.

148 Qian, C., Lai, C.-J., Bao, R. et al. (2012). Cancer network disruption by a single molecule inhibitor targeting both histone deacetylase activity and phosphatidylinositol 3-kinase signaling. *Clinical Cancer Research* 18: 4104–4113.

149 Arrighetti, N., Corno, C., and Gatti, L. (2015). Drug combinations with HDAC inhibitors in antitumor therapy. *Critical Reviews in Oncogenesis* 20: 83–117.

150 Tonekaboni, S.A.M., Ghoraie, L.S., Manem, V.S.K., and Haibe-Kains, B. (2018). Predictive approaches for drug combination discovery in cancer. *Brief Bioinformatics* 19: 263–276.

151 Yuan, S.-Q., Wang, F., Chen, G. et al. (2013). Effective elimination of cancer stem cells by a novel drug combination strategy. *Stem Cells* 31: 23–34.

152 Zahedi, P., De Souza, R., Huynh, L. et al. (2011). Combination drug delivery strategy for the treatment of multidrug resistant ovarian cancer. *Molecular Pharmaceutics* 8: 260–269.

153 Al-Lazikani, B., Banerji, U., and Workman, P. (2012). Combinatorial drug therapy for cancer in the post-genomic era. *Nature Biotechnology* 30: 679–692.

154 Anighoro, A., Bajorath, J., and Rastelli, G. (2014). Polypharmacology: challenges and opportunities in drug discovery. *Journal of Medicinal Chemistry* 57: 7874–7887.

155 Fortin, S. and Bérubé, G. (2013). Advances in the development of hybrid anticancer drugs. *Expert Opinion on Drug Discovery* 8: 1029–1047.

156 Morphy, R. and Rankovic, Z. (2005). Designed multiple ligands. An emerging drug discovery paradigm. *Journal of Medicinal Chemistry* 48: 6523–6543.

157 Gray, J.E., Saltos, A., Tanvetyanon, T. et al. (2019). Phase I/Ib study of pembrolizumab plus vorinostat in advanced/metastatic non-small cell lung cancer. *Clinical Cancer Research* 25: 6623–6632.

158 Awad, M.M., Le Bruchec, Y., Lu, B. et al. (2021). Selective histone deacetylase inhibitor acy-241 (citarinostat) plus nivolumab in advanced non-small cell lung cancer: results from a phase Ib study. *Frontiers in Oncology* 11: 696512.

159 Chao, M.-W., Chang, L.-H., Tu, H.-J. et al. (2019). Combination treatment strategy for pancreatic cancer involving the novel HDAC inhibitor MPT0E028 with a MEK inhibitor beyond K-Ras status. *Clinical Epigenetics* 11: 85.

160 Kyaw, M.T.H., Yamaguchi, Y., Choijookhuu, N. et al. (2019). The HDAC inhibitor, saha, combined with cisplatin synergistically induces apoptosis in alpha-fetoprotein-producing hepatoid adenocarcinoma cells. *Acta Histochemica et Cytochemica* 52: 1–8.

161 Ngamphaiboon, N., Dy, G.K., Ma, W.W. et al. (2015). A phase I study of the histone deacetylase (HDAC) inhibitor entinostat, in combination with sorafenib in patients with advanced solid tumors. *Investigational New Drugs* 33: 225–232.

162 Novotny-Diermayr, V., Hart, S., Goh, K.C. et al. (2012). The oral HDAC inhibitor pracinostat (SB939) is efficacious and synergistic with the JAK2 inhibitor pacritinib (SB1518) in preclinical models of AML. *Blood Cancer Journal* 2: e69.

163 Que, Y., Zhang, X.-L., Liu, Z.-X. et al. (2021). Frequent amplification of HDAC genes and efficacy of HDAC inhibitor chidamide and PD-1 blockade combination in soft tissue sarcoma. *Journal for Immunotherapy of Cancer* 9: e001696.

164 Santo, L., Hideshima, T., Kung, A.L. et al. (2012). Preclinical activity, pharmacodynamic, and pharmacokinetic properties of a selective HDAC6 inhibitor, ACY-1215, in combination with bortezomib in multiple myeloma. *Blood* 119: 2579–2589.

165 Roy, R., Ria, T., RoyMahaPatra, D., and Sk, U.H. (2023). Single inhibitors versus dual inhibitors: role of HDAC in cancer. *ACS Omega* 8: 16532–16544.

166 Shaker, B., Ahmad, S., Lee, J. et al. (2021). In silico methods and tools for drug discovery. *Computers in Biology and Medicine* 137: 104851.

167 Garber, K. (2022). The PROTAC gold rush. *Nature Biotechnology* 40: 12–16.

168 Békés, M., Langley, D.R., and Crews, C.M. (2022). PROTAC targeted protein degraders: the past is prologue. *Nature Reviews Drug Discovery* 21: 181–200.

169 Gao, H.-Y., Sun, X.-Y., and Rao, Y. (2020). PROTAC technology: opportunities and challenges. *ACS Medicinal Chemistry Letters* 11: 237–240.

170 Wang, Y., Jiang, X.-Y., Feng, F. et al. (2020). Degradation of proteins by PROTACs and other strategies. *Acta Pharmaceutica Sinica B* 10: 207–238.

171 Rodrigues, D.A., Roe, A., Griffith, D., and Chonghaile, T.N. (2022). Advances in the design and development of protac-mediated HDAC degradation. *Current Topics in Medicinal Chemistry* 22: 408–424.

172 Rutherford, K.A. and McManus, K.J. (2024). PROTACs: current and future potential as a precision medicine strategy to combat cancer. *Molecular Cancer Therapeutics* 23: 454–463.